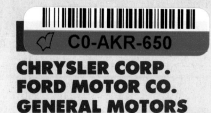

CHRYSLER CORP.
FORD MOTOR CO.
GENERAL MOTORS

SUPPLEMENT

1993 MITCHELL® DOMESTIC CARS SERVICE & REPAIR

The Leader in Professional Estimating and Repair Information.

Mitchell International

ACKNOWLEDGMENT

Mitchell International thanks the domestic manufacturers, distributors and dealers for their generous cooperation and assistance which make this manual possible.

Chrysler Corporation
Ford Motor Company
General Motors Corporation

MARKETING

Director
David R. Koontz

EDITORIAL

Senior Vice President
& Editor-in-Chief
Larry Laumann

Manager, Annual Data Editorial
Thomas L. Landis

Manager, Special Product Editorial
Ronald E. Garrett

Senior Editors
Chuck Vedra
Ramiro Gutierrez
John M. Fisher
Tom L. Hall
James A. Hawes
Serge G. Pirino

Technical Editors
Scott A. Olsen
Bob Reel
David W. Himes
Alex A. Solis
Donald T. Pellettera
David C. Rust
Michael C. May
Scott A. Tiner
James R. Warren
James D. Boxberger
David M. Finley

Technical Editors (Cont.)
Bobby R. Gifford
Linda M. Murphy
Tim P. Lockwood
Dave L. Skora
Donald Lawler
Wayne D. Charbonneau
Sal Caloca
Charles "Bud" Gardner
Dan Hankins
Robert L. Eller

WIRING DIAGRAMS

Manager
Matthew M. Krimple
Senior Editor
Lloyd Adams
Electrical Editors
Leonard McVicker
Santiago Llano
Harry Piper
Richard B. Speake
Brian Durbin
Grant B. Larsen

QUALITY ASSURANCE

Manager
Daryl F. Visser
Sr. QA Specialist
Nick DiVerde
QA Specialists
Trang Nguyen
Brian W. Hutchins
Julia A. Kinneer

TECHNICAL LIBRARIAN

Charlotte Norris

PRODUCT SUPPORT

Manager
Eddie Santangelo

Senior Product Specialist
Robert L. Rothgery

Product Specialists
William E. Bond
James A. Wafford

Diagnostic Support Specialist
Jeffrey H. Lenzkes

GRAPHICS

Manager
Judie LaPierre
Supervisor
Ann Klimetz

Published By

MITCHELL INTERNATIONAL
9889 Willow Creek Road
P.O. Box 26260
San Diego, CA 92196-0260

Customer Service Numbers:
Subscription/Billing Information:
1-800-648-8010 or 619-578-6550
Technical Information:
1-800-854-7030 or 619-578-6550
Or Write: P.O. Box 26260, San Diego, CA 92196-0260

INTRODUCTION

This supplement is to be used in conjunction with the 1993 Mitchell ® Domestic Cars Service & Repair manual (ADD). The information contained in this manual compliments the ADD information.

The information in this supplement is presented by manufacturer. The Chrysler and Ford portions contain Accessories & Equipment (section 4) information that was not included in the 1993 ADD.

The General Motors portion contains Wiring Diagrams (section 3) information and Accessories & Equipment (section 4) information. The Wiring Diagrams section contains 1993 Saturn diagrams that were not available for the publication of the ADD. These include Engine Performance, Electrical (Charging and Starting Diagrams), Cooling Fan, Anti-Lock Brake, Traction Control and Variable Assist Steering diagrams.

The Accessories & Equipment section (section 4) covers all General Motors (including Saturn). The information in this section is in addition to the information contained in the 1993 ADD.

Use the Contents Page in this supplement in conjunction with the Contents Page of Book 1 and Book 2 of the ADD to locate any necessary information.

CHRYSLER CORP.

FORD MOTOR CO.

GENERAL MOTORS

WIRING DIAGRAMS

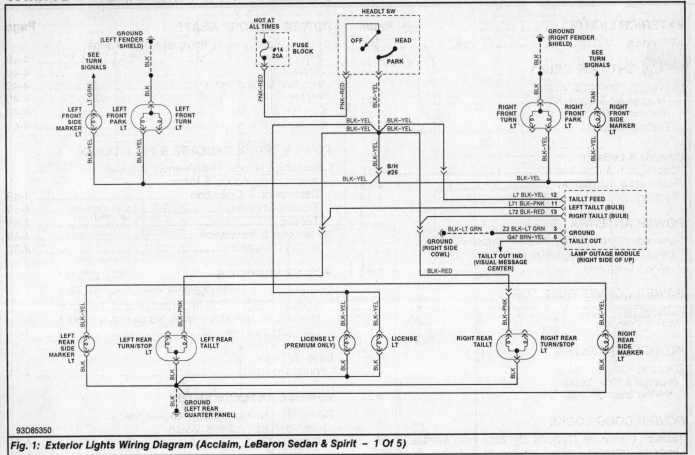

Fig. 1: Exterior Lights Wiring Diagram (Acclaim, LeBaron Sedan & Spirit – 1 Of 5)

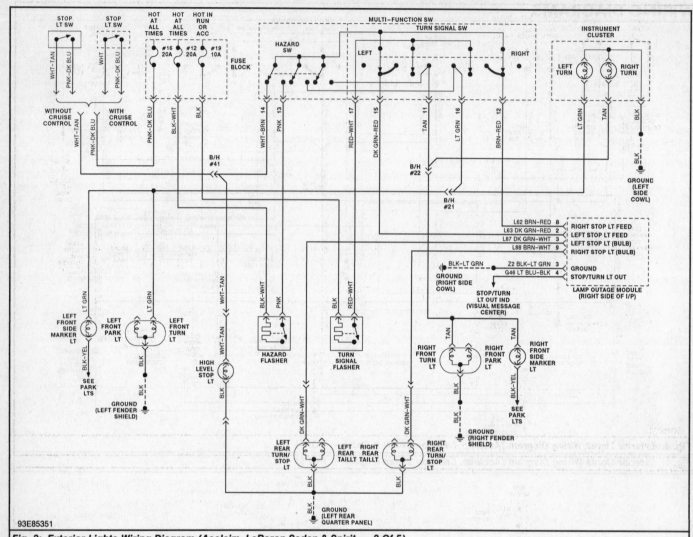

Fig. 2: *Exterior Lights Wiring Diagram (Acclaim, LeBaron Sedan & Spirit — 2 Of 5)*

93E85351

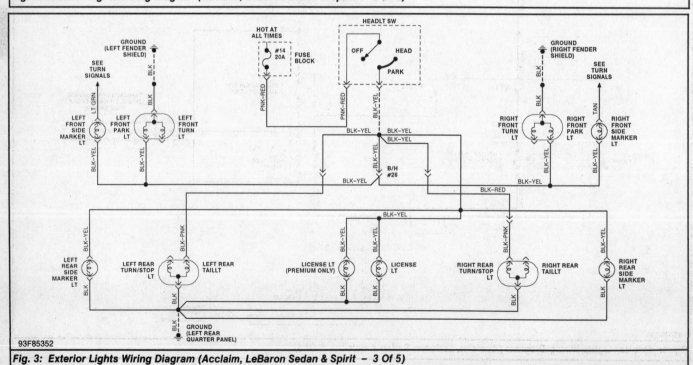

Fig. 3: *Exterior Lights Wiring Diagram (Acclaim, LeBaron Sedan & Spirit — 3 Of 5)*

93F85352

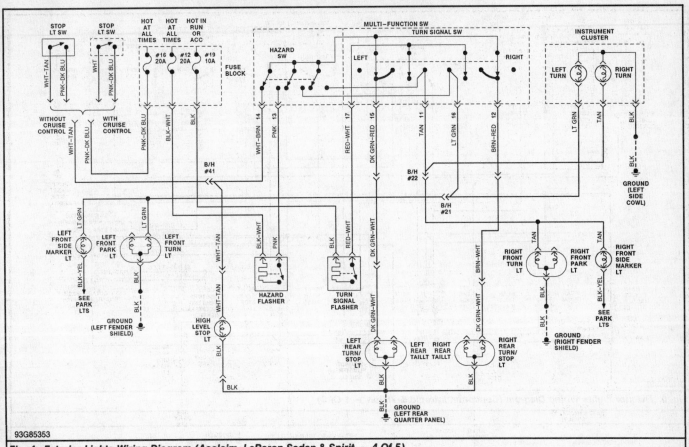

Fig. 4: Exterior Lights Wiring Diagram (Acclaim, LeBaron Sedan & Spirit – 4 Of 5)

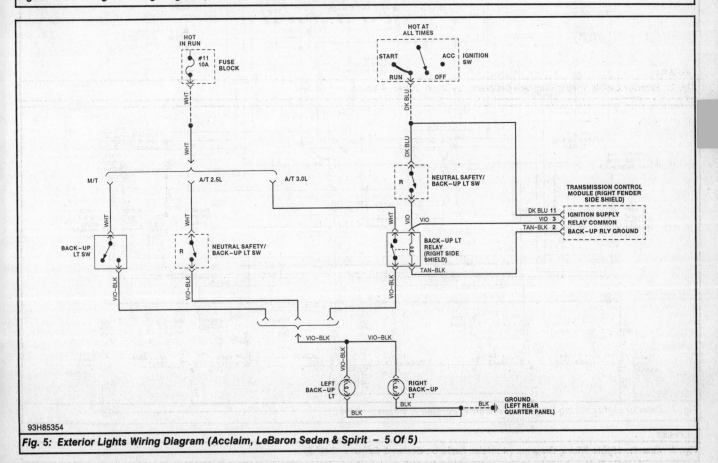

Fig. 5: Exterior Lights Wiring Diagram (Acclaim, LeBaron Sedan & Spirit – 5 Of 5)

1993 ACCESSORIES & EQUIPMENT
Exterior Lights (Cont.)

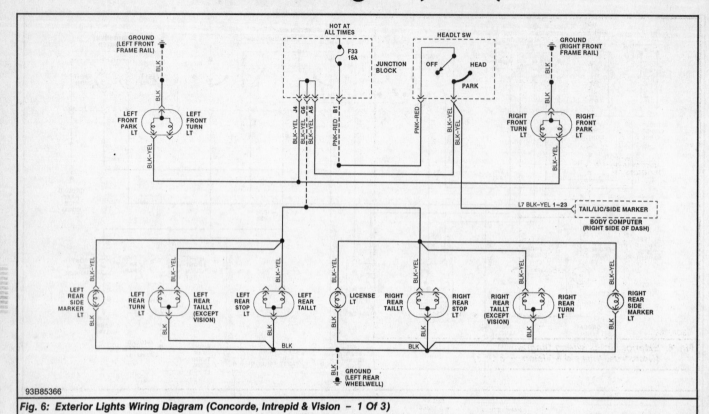

Fig. 6: Exterior Lights Wiring Diagram (Concorde, Intrepid & Vision – 1 Of 3)

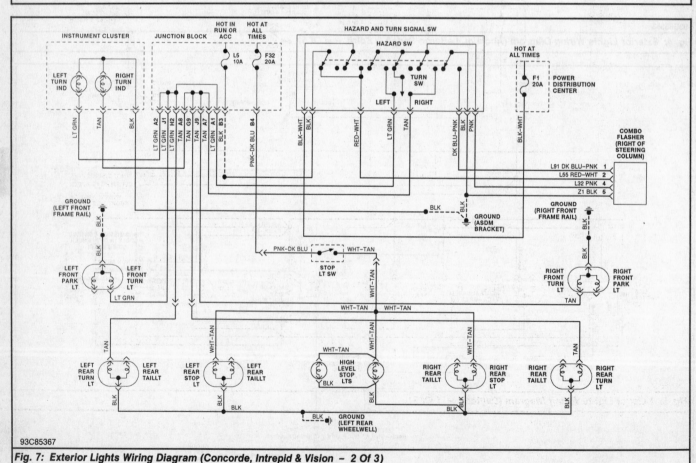

Fig. 7: Exterior Lights Wiring Diagram (Concorde, Intrepid & Vision – 2 Of 3)

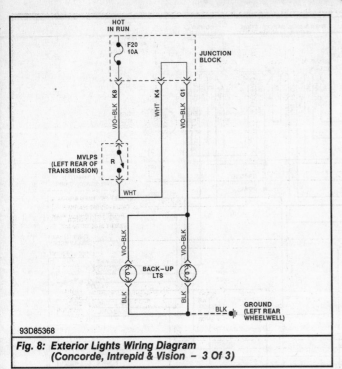

93D85368

Fig. 8: Exterior Lights Wiring Diagram
(Concorde, Intrepid & Vision – 3 Of 3)

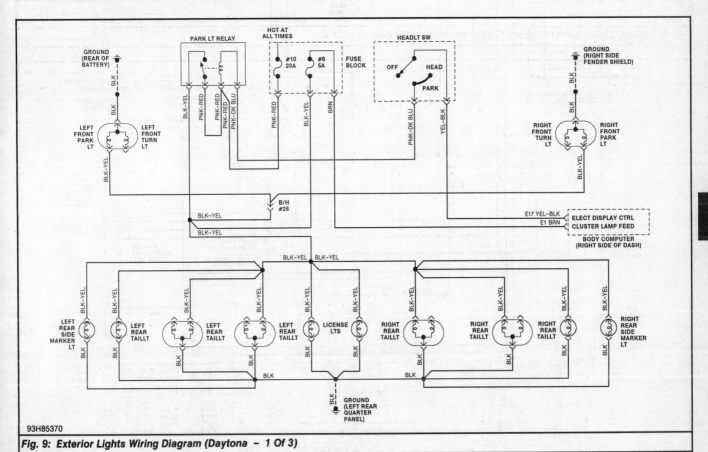

93H85370

Fig. 9: Exterior Lights Wiring Diagram (Daytona – 1 Of 3)

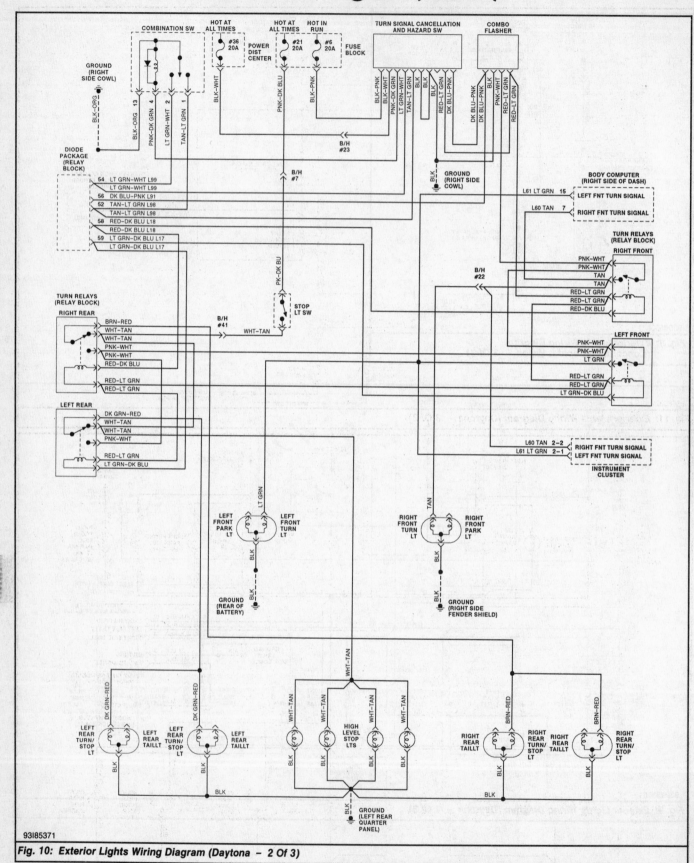

Fig. 10: Exterior Lights Wiring Diagram (Daytona – 2 Of 3)

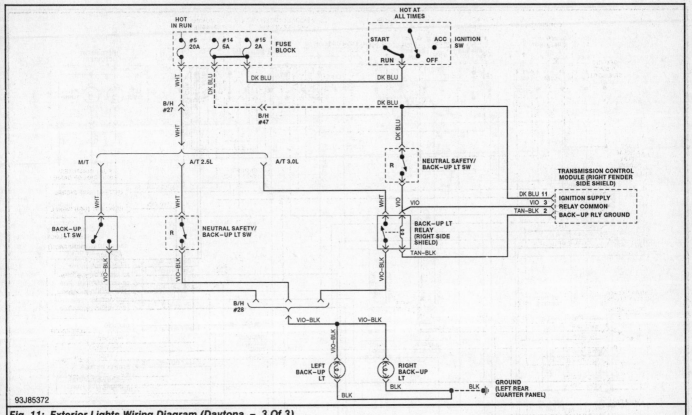

Fig. 11: Exterior Lights Wiring Diagram (Daytona – 3 Of 3)

93J85372

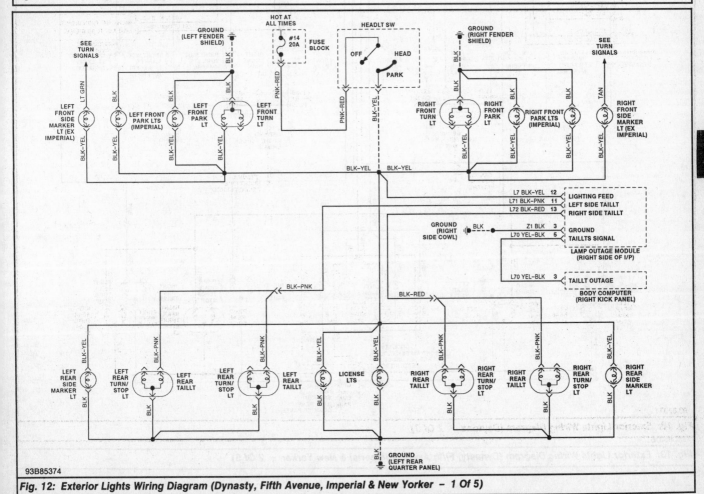

Fig. 12: Exterior Lights Wiring Diagram (Dynasty, Fifth Avenue, Imperial & New Yorker – 1 Of 5)

93B85374

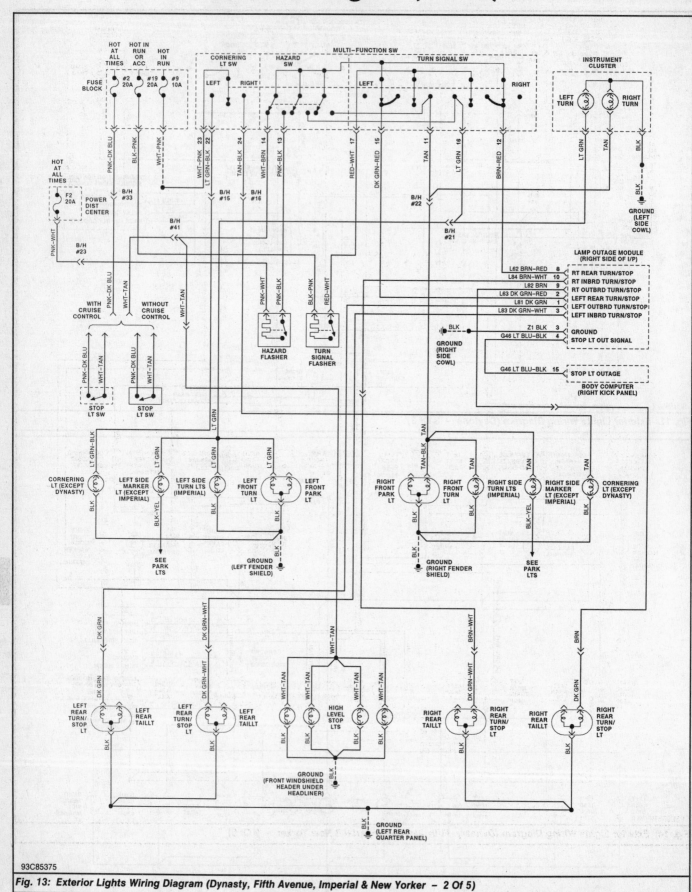

Fig. 13: *Exterior Lights Wiring Diagram (Dynasty, Fifth Avenue, Imperial & New Yorker - 2 Of 5)*

93C85375

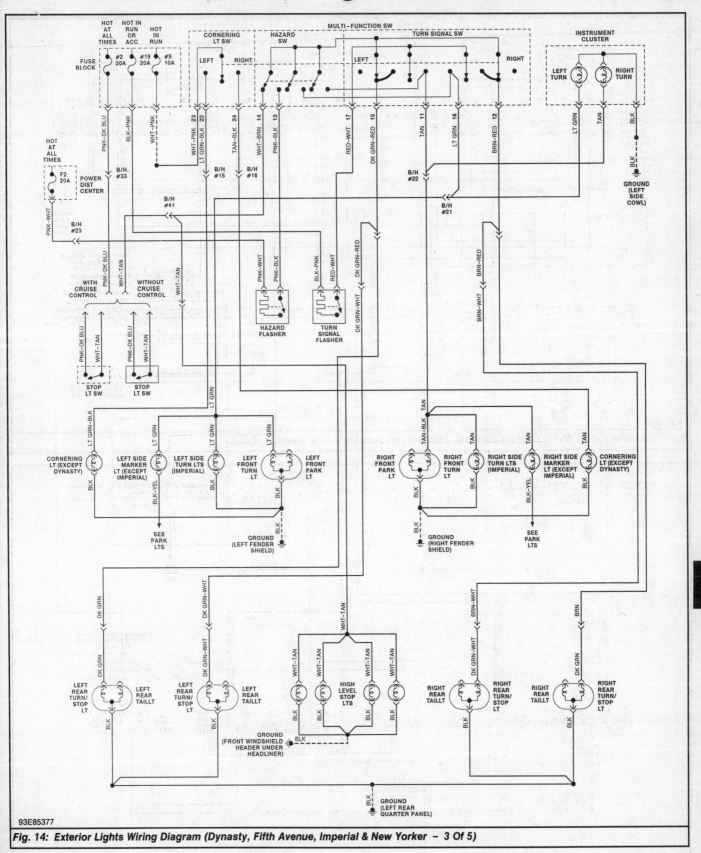

Fig. 14: Exterior Lights Wiring Diagram (Dynasty, Fifth Avenue, Imperial & New Yorker – 3 Of 5)

93E85377

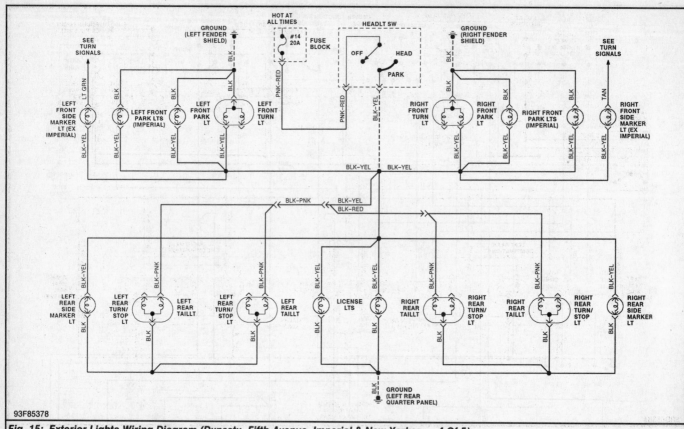

93F85378

Fig. 15: Exterior Lights Wiring Diagram (Dynasty, Fifth Avenue, Imperial & New Yorker – 4 Of 5)

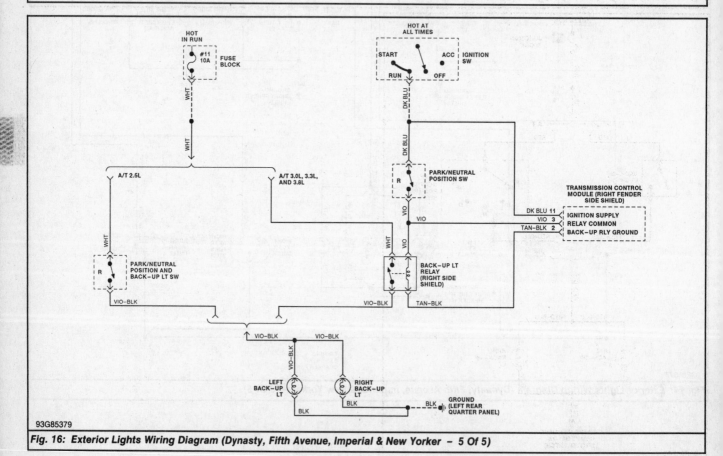

93G85379

Fig. 16: Exterior Lights Wiring Diagram (Dynasty, Fifth Avenue, Imperial & New Yorker – 5 Of 5)

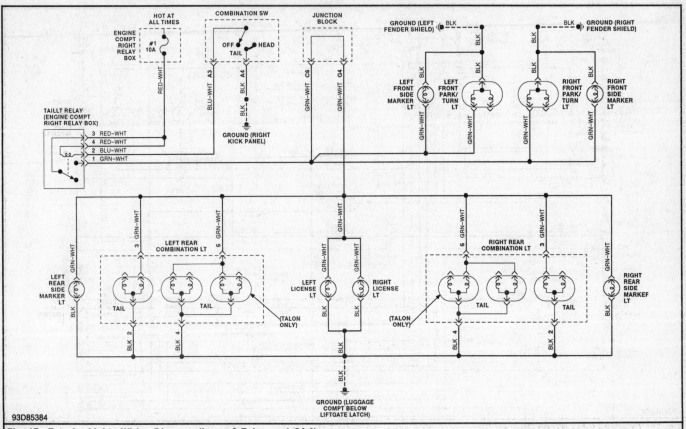

93D85384

Fig. 17: Exterior Lights Wiring Diagram (Laser & Talon – 1 Of 4)

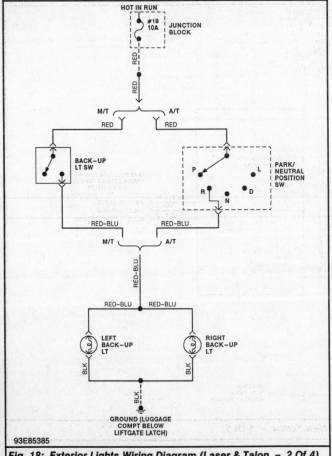

93E85385

Fig. 18: Exterior Lights Wiring Diagram (Laser & Talon – 2 Of 4)

1993 ACCESSORIES & EQUIPMENT
Exterior Lights (Cont.)

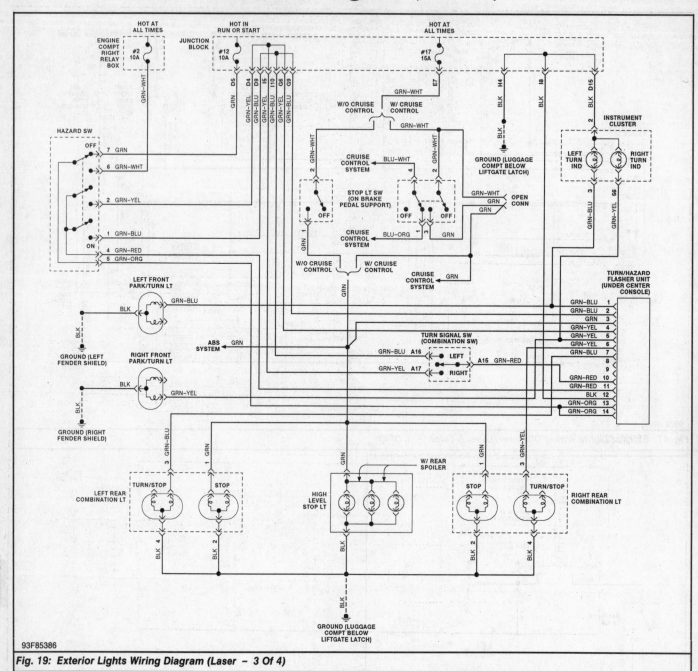

Fig. 19: Exterior Lights Wiring Diagram (Laser – 3 Of 4)

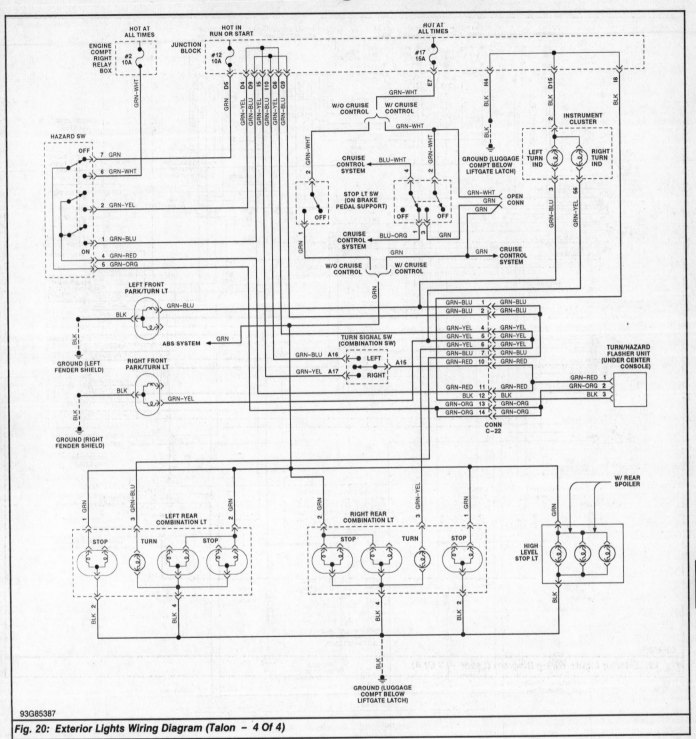

93G85387

Fig. 20: Exterior Lights Wiring Diagram (Talon – 4 Of 4)

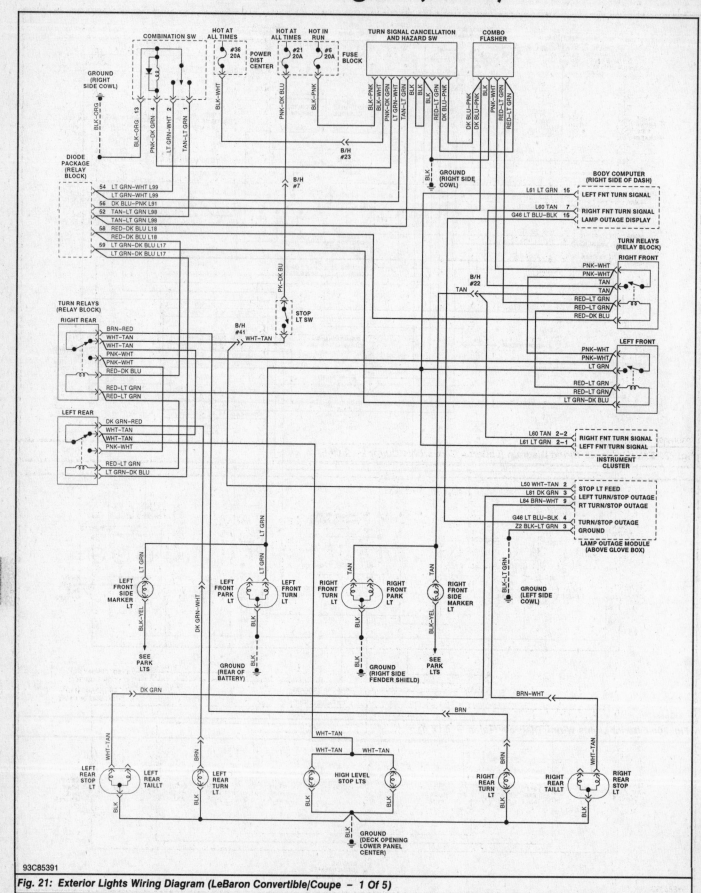

Fig. 21: Exterior Lights Wiring Diagram (LeBaron Convertible/Coupe – 1 Of 5)

93C85391

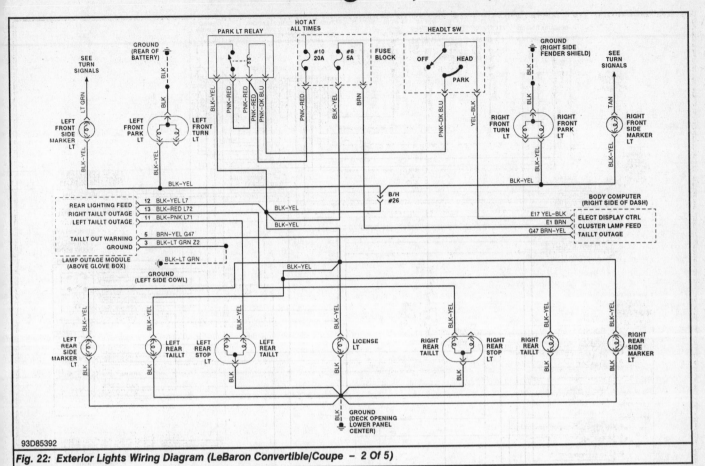

Fig. 22: Exterior Lights Wiring Diagram (LeBaron Convertible/Coupe – 2 Of 5)

93D85392

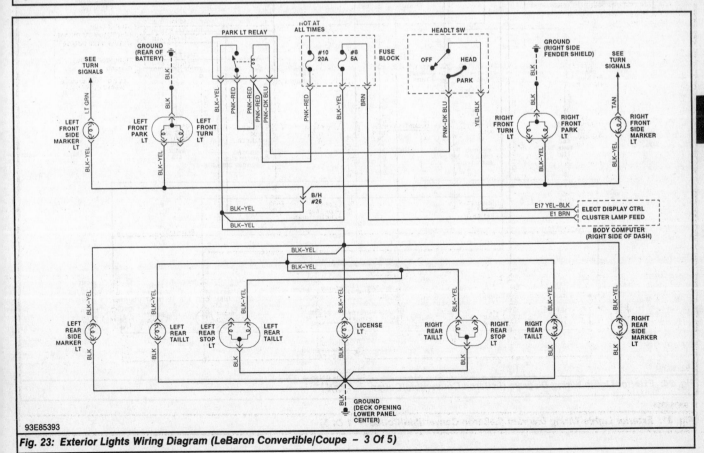

Fig. 23: Exterior Lights Wiring Diagram (LeBaron Convertible/Coupe – 3 Of 5)

93E85393

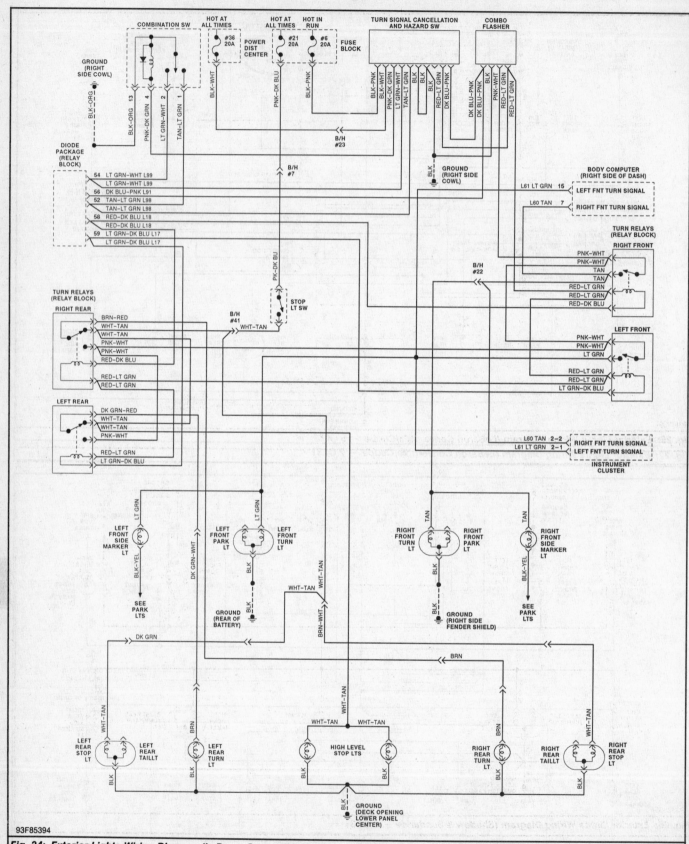

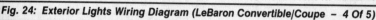

93F85394

Fig. 24: Exterior Lights Wiring Diagram (LeBaron Convertible/Coupe – 4 Of 5)

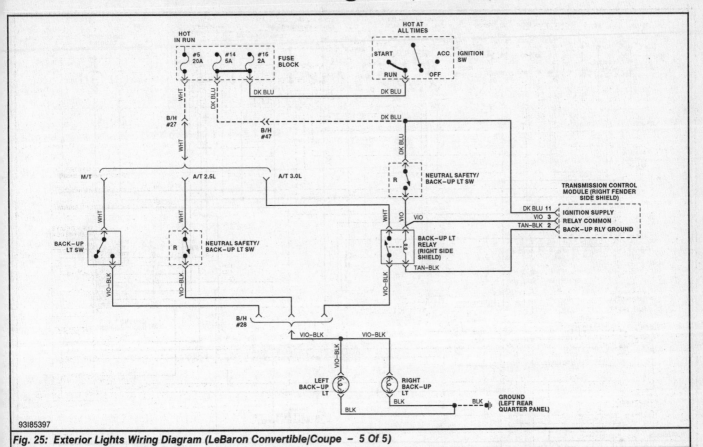

Fig. 25: Exterior Lights Wiring Diagram (LeBaron Convertible/Coupe – 5 Of 5)

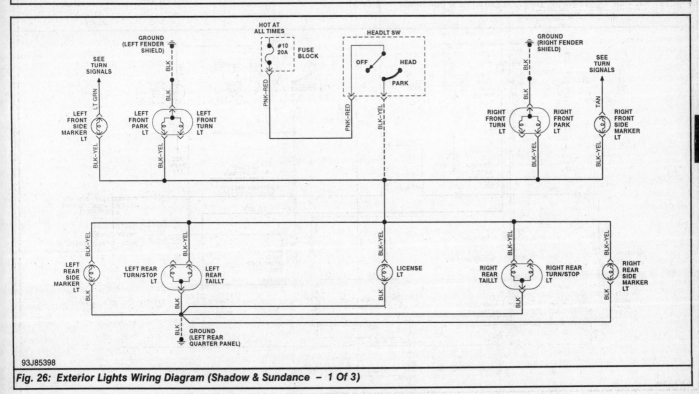

Fig. 26: Exterior Lights Wiring Diagram (Shadow & Sundance – 1 Of 3)

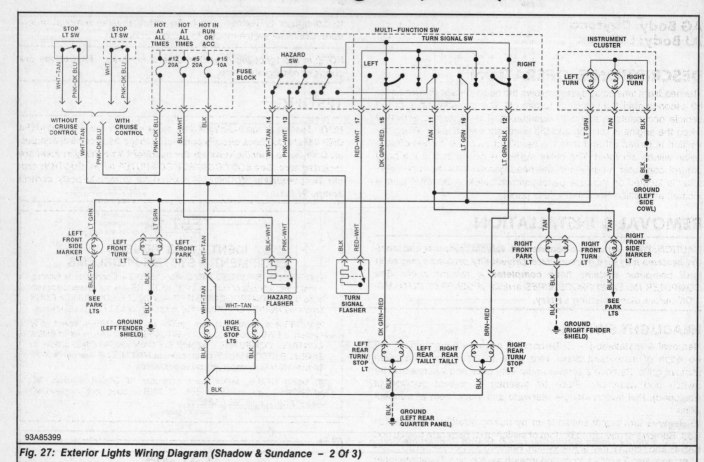

93A85399

Fig. 27: Exterior Lights Wiring Diagram (Shadow & Sundance – 2 Of 3)

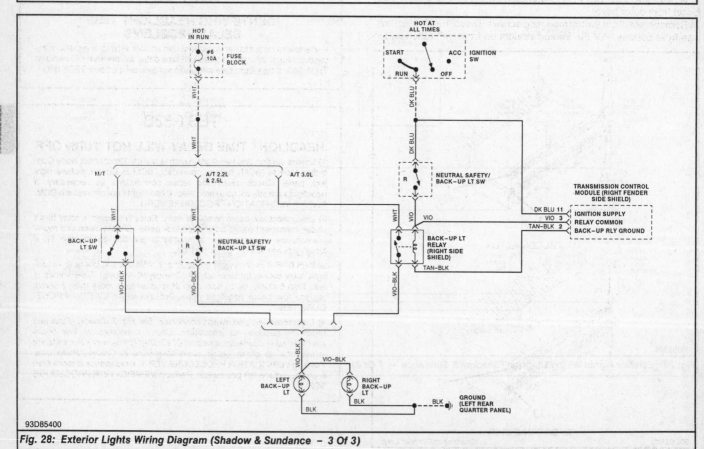

93D85400

Fig. 28: Exterior Lights Wiring Diagram (Shadow & Sundance – 3 Of 3)

AG Body: Daytona
AJ Body: LeBaron

DESCRIPTION & OPERATION

The headlight time delay system allows the headlights to remain on for 60 seconds after the vehicle is turned off. This provides time for the vehicle occupants to exit with illumination. The system is activated when the engine is running and the headlight switch is on. When the ignition is turned off and then the headlight switch is turned off, the delay will be activated. The delay system is connected to the body control computer module and the headlight switch. The time delay relay is located on the fuse panel junction block. A 30 amp. fuse is located at position No. 5 in the fuse panel.

REMOVAL & INSTALLATION

CAUTION: When battery is disconnected, vehicle computer and memory systems may lose memory data. Driveability problems may exist until computer systems have completed a relearn cycle. See COMPUTER RELEARN PROCEDURES article in GENERAL INFORMATION before disconnecting battery.

HEADLIGHT SWITCH

Removal & Installation – 1) Disconnect negative battery cable. Pry up edge of instrument panel vent grille to disengage clips, then remove grille. Remove 2 screws under vent grille and 2 screws under switch pod assembly. Place tilt steering to lowest position (if equipped). Pull switch module rearward and disconnect all connections.

2) Remove turn signal switch lever by pulling straight out of switch pod. Remove screws from bottom of switch pod. Separate switch pod halves and remove turn signal switch. Remove 5 inner switch pod panel screws and 3 screws from underneath switch pod. Separate inner bezel from outer bezel.

3) Remove headlight switch mounting screws. Disconnect switch linkage from buttons. Pull the linkage straight up from the switch button

NATURAL CONNECTOR

BLACK CONNECTOR

93D85343   Courtesy of Chrysler Corp.

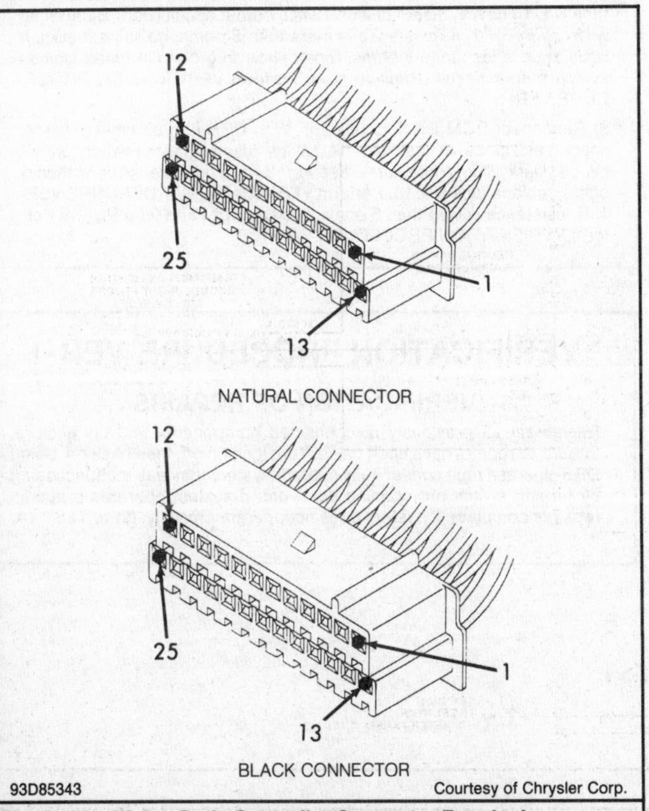

Fig. 1: Identifying Body Controller Connector Terminals

to disengage it. Remove switch. To install, reverse removal procedure. Check all switch modes for proper operation.

NOTE: In the following headlight time delay tests, illustrations are courtesy of Chrysler Corp.

TESTING

NOTE: Testing of the headlight time delay system requires using the DRB-II tester to check circuits connected to the body control computer. Only those specific tests for the headlight time delay system are included here. See BODY CONTROL COMPUTER INTRODUCTION article in appropriate MITCHELL® manual for complete body control computer tests.

TEST 1A

IDENTIFYING VEHICLE EQUIPMENT & SYSTEM PROBLEMS

1) Connect DRB-II to Data Link Connector (DLC). Connector is located under lower left side of instrument panel. If DRB-II is not operational, refer to BODY CONTROL COMPUTER – VEHICLE COMMUNICATIONS article in ENGINE PERFORMANCE in appropriate MITCHELL® manual.

2) If DRB-II is operational, turn ignition on. Using DRB-II, select body system. If DRB-II does not display BUS OPERATIONAL, refer to BODY CONTROL COMPUTER – VEHICLE COMMUNICATIONS article in ENGINE PERFORMANCE in appropriate MITCHELL® manual. If BUS OPERATIONAL is displayed, go to next step.

3) Using DRB-II, select body controller. If DRB-II displays NO RESPONSE, go to TEST 69A. If DRB-II does not display NO RESPONSE, go to TEST 58A.

TEST 58A

IDENTIFYING HEADLIGHT TIME DELAY PROBLEMS

Verify failure or customer complaint and ensure vehicle is experiencing the problem at this time. If headlight time delay will not turn off, perform TEST 58B. If headlight time delay will not turn on, perform TEST 58C.

TEST 58B

HEADLIGHT TIME DELAY WILL NOT TURN OFF

1) Ensure ignition and headlight switches are off. Disconnect Body Controller Module (BCM) Natural connector. BCM is located behind right kick panel. Check, clean and repair connections as necessary. If headlights are still on, go to next step. If headlights are off, replace BCM. Perform VERIFICATION PROCEDURE VER-1.

2) Disconnect low beam headlight relay. Relay is located in relay block under instrument panel, behind left kick panel. Check, clean and repair connections as necessary. If headlights are off, go to step **5)**. If headlights are still on, go to next step.

3) With DRB-II in ohmmeter mode, check resistance at low beam headlight relay connector terminal "C" (Orange/White wire). If resistance is less than 5 ohms, go to next step. If resistance is more than 5 ohms, replace low beam headlight relay. Perform VERIFICATION PROCEDURE VER-1.

4) Disconnect left pod switch connector. *See Fig. 2.* Check, clean and repair connections as necessary. Check resistance at low beam headlight relay connector terminal "C" (Orange/White wire). If resistance is less than 5 ohms, repair short to ground in Orange/White wire. Perform VERIFICATION PROCEDURE VER-1. If resistance is more than 5 ohms, replace left pod switch. Perform VERIFICATION PROCEDURE VER-1.

CHRY
4-20

1993 ACCESSORIES & EQUIPMENT
Headlight Time Delay – AG & AJ Bodies (Cont.)

TEST 58B (Cont.)

5) Remove fuse No. 17 and 18. If both headlights turn off, repair low beam headlight feed circuit for short to voltage. Perform VERIFICATION PROCEDURE VER-1. If only right headlight turns off, repair right low beam headlight output circuit between right headlight and low beam headlight relay for short to voltage. Perform VERIFICATION PROCEDURE VER-1. If only left headlight turns off, repair left low beam headlight output circuit between left headlight and low beam headlight relay for short to voltage. Perform VERIFICATION PROCEDURE VER-1.

93E85344

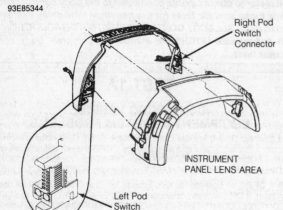

Fig. 2: Locating Pod Switch Connectors

TEST 58C

HEADLIGHT TIME DELAY WILL NOT TURN ON

1) Turn ignition on. Turn low beam headlights on. If low beam headlights operate properly, go to next step. If low beam headlights do not operate properly, see appropriate INSTRUMENT PANELS article in ACCESSORIES & EQUIPMENT.

2) Turn ignition off. Turn low beam headlights off. If headlights remain on for 60 seconds and then go off, headlight time delay circuit is functioning properly at this time. Perform VERIFICATION PROCEDURE VER-1. If headlights do not remain on for 60 seconds and then go off, go to next step.

3) Disconnect Body Controller Module (BCM) Natural connector. BCM is located behind right kick panel. Check, clean and repair connections as necessary. Connect a jumper wire between ground and terminal No. 15 (Orange/White wire) of BCM Natural connector. If headlights operate properly, repair open in Orange/White wire. Perform VERIFICATION PROCEDURE VER-1. If headlights do not operate properly, replace BCM. Perform VERIFICATION PROCEDURE VER-1.

TEST 69A

NO RESPONSE CONDITION

1) Turn ignition off. Disconnect Body Controller Module (BCM) Black connector. BCM is located behind right kick panel. Check, clean and repair connections as necessary. Turn ignition on. With DRB-II in voltmeter mode, check voltage on BCM Black connector terminal No. 12, fused ignition switch output circuit (Dark Blue/White wire). If voltage is less than 10 volts, go to step 6).

2) If voltage is more than 10 volts, check voltage on BCM Black connector terminal No. 16, fused battery (+) circuit (Pink wire). If voltage is more than 10 volts, go to next step. If voltage is less than 10 volts, repair open fused battery (+) circuit. Perform VERIFICATION PROCEDURE VER-1.

3) Turn ignition off. With DRB-II in ohmmeter mode, check resistance on BCM Black connector terminal No. 13, ground circuit (Blue/Light Green wire). If resistance is less than 15 ohms, go to next step. If resistance is more than 15 ohms, repair open ground circuit. Perform VERIFICATION PROCEDURE VER-1.

TEST 69A (Cont).

NOTE: DO NOT disconnect DRB-II from Data Link Connector (DLC) in the following steps. When instructed to check resistance at DLC, backprobe connector.

4) Using an external ohmmeter, check resistance of Violet/Brown wire (Chrysler Collision Detection (CCD) (+) circuit) between BCM Black connector terminal No. 14 and DLC terminal No. 4. If resistance is less than 5 ohms, go to next step. If resistance is more than 5 ohms, repair open in CCD (+) circuit. Perform VERIFICATION PROCEDURE VER-1.

5) Using an external ohmmeter, check resistance of White/Black wire (CCD (–) circuit) between BCM Black connector terminal No. 15 and DLC terminal No. 3. If resistance is less than 5 ohms, replace BCM. Perform VERIFICATION PROCEDURE VER-1. If resistance is more than 5 ohms, repair open in CCD (–) circuit. Perform VERIFICATION PROCEDURE VER-1.

6) Remove and inspect fuse No. 14. If fuse is okay, reinstall fuse and go to next step. If fuse is blown, go to step 8).

7) Ensure ignition switch is still in the ON position. With DRB-II in voltmeter mode, check voltage at fuse No. 14 cavity, ignition switch output circuit (Dark Blue wire). See Fig. 3. If voltage is more than 10 volts, repair open in fuse ignition switch output circuit between fuse block and BCM. Perform VERIFICATION PROCEDURE VER-1. If voltage is less than 10 volts, repair open in ignition switch output circuit between ignition switch and fuse block. Perform VERIFICATION PROCEDURE VER-1.

93F85345

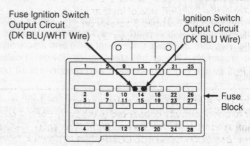

Fig. 2: Identifying Fuse No. 14 Circuits

8) Turn ignition off. With DRB-II in ohmmeter mode, check resistance at fuse No. 14 cavity, fused ignition switch output circuit (Dark Blue/White wire). See Fig. 3. If resistance is more than 5 ohms, go to next step. If resistance is less than 5 ohms, repair short to ground in fused ignition switch output circuit. Replace fuse. Perform VERIFICATION PROCEDURE VER-1.

9) Reconnect BCM Black connector. With DRB-II in ohmmeter mode, check resistance at fuse No. 14 cavity, fused ignition switch output circuit (Dark Blue/White wire). See Fig. 3. If resistance is more than 5 ohms, replace fuse No. 14. Perform VERIFICATION PROCEDURE VER-1. If resistance is less than 5 ohms, replace BCM and fuse No. 14. Perform VERIFICATION PROCEDURE VER-1.

VERIFICATION PROCEDURE VER-1

VERIFICATION OF REPAIRS

Reconnect all previously disconnected components and connectors. Ensure all repairs have been made. Turn ignition off, then back on. Using DRB-II, erase fault codes. Fully operate system that was malfunctioning by turning switch on, opening door, etc. If system operates properly, repair is complete. If system does not operate properly, go to TEST 1A.

Concorde, Intrepid, Vision

DESCRIPTION & OPERATION

The headlight time delay system allows the headlights to remain on for 60 seconds after the vehicle is turned off. This provides time for the vehicle occupants to exit with illumination. The system is activated when the engine is running and the headlight switch is on. When the ignition is turned off and then the headlight switch is turned off, the delay will be activated. The delay system is connected to the body control computer module and the headlight switch. The time delay relay is located on the fuse panel junction block. A 30 amp. fuse is located at position No. 5 in the fuse panel.

REMOVAL & INSTALLATION

CAUTION: When battery is disconnected, vehicle computer and memory systems may lose memory data. Driveability problems may exist until computer systems have completed a relearn cycle. See COMPUTER RELEARN PROCEDURES article in GENERAL INFORMATION before disconnecting battery.

HEADLIGHT SWITCH

Removal & Installation – Open driver's door and remove left end cover. Remove screw from left side of instrument panel and pull bezel rearward to remove clips. Remove 3 screws on switch and pull out to disconnect wiring connectors. Remove switch. To install, reverse removal procedure.

TESTING

NOTE: Testing of the headlight time delay system requires using the DRB-II tester to check circuits connected to the body control computer. Only those specific tests for the headlight time delay system are included here. See BODY CONTROL COMPUTER INTRODUCTION article in appropriate MITCHELL® manual for complete body control computer tests.

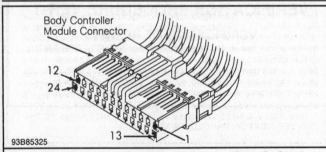

93B85325

Fig. 1: Identifying Body Controller Connector (Bone Or Gray) Terminals

TEST 1A

IDENTIFYING VEHICLE EQUIPMENT & SYSTEM PROBLEMS

1) Connect DRB-II to Data Link Connector (DLC). Connector is located under instrument cluster, next to center console. If DRB-II is not operational, refer to BODY CONTROL COMPUTER – VEHICLE COMMUNICATIONS article in ENGINE PERFORMANCE in appropriate MITCHELL® manual.

2) If DRB-II is operational, turn ignition on. Using DRB-II, select body system. If DRB-II does not display BUS OPERATIONAL, refer to BODY CONTROL COMPUTER – VEHICLE COMMUNICATIONS article in ENGINE PERFORMANCE in appropriate MITCHELL® manual. If BUS OPERATIONAL is displayed, go to next step.

3) Using DRB-II, select body controller. If DRB-II displays NO RESPONSE, go to TEST 53A. If DRB-II does not display NO RESPONSE, go to TEST 48A

TEST 48A

HEADLIGHTS WILL NOT TURN OFF

1) Ensure optical horn and headlight dimmer switch (multifunction control lever on steering column) is in low beam position and high/low switch in off position. If headlights do not stay on, go to TEST 49A. If headlights stay on, turn ignition off. Disconnect Body Controller Module (BCM). Module is located behind right kick panel. If headlights go off, replace BCM. Perform VERIFICATION PROCEDURE VER-1.

2) If headlights did not go off, disconnect headlight switch. If headlights go off, replace headlight switch. Perform VERIFICATION PROCEDURE VER-1. If headlights do not go off, go to next step.

3) Remove headlight time delay relay from fuse/relay block. Fuse/junction block is located behind end cover, on left side of instrument panel. If headlights do not go off, go to step **5)**. If headlights go off, go to next step.

4) With DRB-II in ohmmeter mode, check resistance of headlight time delay relay control circuit (Red/Dark Blue wire) on headlight time delay relay fuse/block connector. If resistance is less than 5 ohms, repair short to ground in Red/Dark Blue wire. Perform VERIFICATION PROCEDURE VER-1. If resistance is more than 5 ohms, replace headlight time delay relay. Perform VERIFICATION PROCEDURE VER-1.

5) Disconnect multifunction switch connector. Connector is located on upper part of steering column, behind trim cover. If headlights go off, go to step **7)**. If headlights do not go off, remove fuse No. 15 from fuse/junction block. If both headlights go off, repair short to battery in relay fused output circuit (Violet wire) between fuse No. 15 and left low beam. Perform VERIFICATION PROCEDURE VER-1.

6) If both headlights did not go off, install fuse No. 15. Remove fuse No. 16 from fuse/junction block. If right low beam headlight goes off, repair short to battery in relay fused output circuit (Violet wire) between fuse No. 16 and right low beam. Perform VERIFICATION PROCEDURE VER-1. If right low beam headlight does not go off, repair short to battery in headlight time delay relay switched output circuit (Light Green wire). Perform VERIFICATION PROCEDURE VER-1.

7) With DRB-II in voltmeter mode, check voltage on headlight time delay relay switched output circuit (Light Green wire) on headlight time delay relay fuse/relay block connector. If voltage is more than 10 volts, repair short to battery in Light Green wire. Perform VERIFICATION PROCEDURE VER-1. If voltage is less than 10 volts, replace multifunction switch. Perform VERIFICATION PROCEDURE VER-1.

TEST 49A

INOPERATIVE HEADLIGHT TIME DELAY RELAY CONTROL

1) Turn ignition on. Using DRB-II, actuate headlight time delay relay. If headlights do not toggle on and off, go to TEST 50A. If headlights toggle on and off, go to next step.

2) Using DRB-II, stop headlight time delay relay actuation test. Turn headlight switch on. If headlights do not come on, repair open headlight switch output circuit (Light Green wire). Perform VERIFICATION PROCEDURE VER-1.

3) If headlights come on, use DRB-II to read headlight switch status while turning headlight switch off then back on. If DRB-II reading corresponds with headlight switch position HEADLAMPS: OFF (switch off) then HEADLAMPS: ON (switch on), replace Body Controller Module (BCM). Module is located behind right kick panel. Perform VERIFICATION PROCEDURE VER-1.

4) If DRB-II reading does not correspond to headlight switch position, access fuse No. 5 on fuse/junction block. Fuse/junction block is located behind end cover, on left side of instrument panel. With DRB-II in voltmeter mode, check voltage on headlight switch output circuit (Light Green wire) on fuse/junction block connector of fuse No. 5. If voltage is less than 10 volts, repair open circuit in Light Green wire between headlight switch and fuse. Perform VERIFICATION PROCEDURE VER-1.

5) If voltage is more than 10 volts, turn headlight switch off. Inspect fuse No. 5. If fuse No. 5 is blown, go to TEST 49B. If fuse No. 5 is okay, turn ignition off. Disconnect BCM and turn headlight switch on. With DRB-II in voltmeter mode, check voltage on BCM Bone connector terminal No. 3, headlight switch fused output circuit (Red/Light Green wire). If voltage is less than 10 volts, repair open circuit in Red/Light Green wire between fuse No. 5 and BCM. Perform VERIFICATION PROCEDURE VER-1. If voltage is more than 10 volts, replace BCM. Perform VERIFICATION PROCEDURE VER-1.

TEST 49B

HEADLIGHT SWITCH
FUSED OUTPUT CIRCUIT SHORT

1) Disconnect Body Controller Module (BCM). Module is located behind right kick panel. With DRB-II in voltmeter mode, check voltage on BCM Bone connector terminal No. 3, headlight switch fused output circuit (Red/Light Green wire). If voltage is more than 10 volts, repair short to battery in Red/Light Green wire and replace fuse No. 5. Perform VERIFICATION PROCEDURE VER-1.

2) If voltage is less than 10 volts, use DRB-II in ohmmeter mode to check resistance on BCM Bone connector terminal No. 3, headlight switch fused output circuit (Red/Light Green wire). If resistance is less than 5 ohms, repair short to ground in Red/Light Green wire and replace fuse No. 5. Perform VERIFICATION PROCEDURE VER-1. If resistance is more than 5 ohms, replace BCM. Perform VERIFICATION PROCEDURE VER-1.

TEST 50A

INOPERATIVE HEADLIGHT
TIME DELAY RELAY OUTPUT

1) Using DRB-II, stop headlight relay actuation test. Turn ignition off and disconnect Body Controller Module (BCM). Module is located behind right kick panel. Connect jumper wire between chassis ground and BCM Gray connector terminal No. 2, headlight time delay relay control circuit (Red/Dark Blue wire). If headlights come on, replace BCM. Perform VERIFICATION PROCEDURE VER-1.

2) If headlights does not come on, disconnect jumper wire. Remove headlight time delay relay from fuse/junction block. Fuse/junction block is located behind end cover, on left side of instrument panel. With DRB-II in voltmeter mode, check voltage on battery feed circuit (Red/White wire) on headlight time delay relay fuse/junction block connector No. 23. If voltage is less than 10 volts, repair open circuit in Red/White wire between relay and fuse "E" of Power Distribution Center (PDC). Perform VERIFICATION PROCEDURE VER-1.

3) If voltage is more than 10 volts, check voltage on battery feed circuit (Red/White wire) on headlight time delay relay fuse/junction block connector No. 21 using DRB-II in voltmeter mode. If voltage is less than 10 volts, repair open circuit in Red/White wire between relay and fuse "E" of PDC. Perform VERIFICATION PROCEDURE VER-1.

4) If voltage is more than 10 volts, connect jumper wire between battery feed circuit (Red/White wire) and headlight switch output circuit (Light Green wire) on headlight time delay relay fuse/junction block connector No. 23 and connector No. 25. If headlights do not come, repair open circuit in Light Green wire between relay and optical horn switch. Perform VERIFICATION PROCEDURE VER-1.

TEST 50A (Cont.)

5) If headlights come on, disconnect jumper wire. Using an external ohmmeter, check resistance of headlight time delay relay control circuit (Red/Dark Blue wire) between terminal No. 2 of BCM Gray connector and fuse/junction block connector No. 22. If resistance is more than 5 ohms, repair open circuit in Red/Dark Blue wire between relay and BCM. Perform VERIFICATION PROCEDURE VER-1. If resistance is less than 5 ohms, replace headlight time delay relay. Perform VERIFICATION PROCEDURE VER-1.

TEST 53A

NO RESPONSE CONDITION

1) Turn ignition off. Disconnect Body Controller Module (BCM). Module is located behind right kick panel. With DRB-II in voltmeter mode, check voltage on BCM Bone connector terminal No. 19, fused battery feed circuit (Pink wire). If voltage is less than 10 volts, repair open circuit in Pink wire back to fuse/junction block. Perform VERIFICATION PROCEDURE VER-1.

2) If voltage is more than 10 volts, use DRB-II in ohmmeter mode to check resistance on BCM Bone connector terminal No. 21, ground circuit (Black wire). If resistance is more than 5 ohms, repair open circuit in Black (ground) wire. Perform VERIFICATION PROCEDURE VER-1.

3) If resistance is less than 5 ohms, check resistance on BCM Bone connector terminal No. 14, signal ground circuit (Black/Light Green wire). If resistance is more than 100 ohms, repair open circuit in Black/Light Green wire to BCM. Perform VERIFICATION PROCEDURE VER-1.

4) If resistance is more than 100 ohms, turn ignition on. With DRB-II in voltmeter mode, check voltage of Violet/Brown wire on BCM Bone connector terminal No. 8, Chrysler Collision Detection (CCD) bus (–) circuit. If voltage is less than one volt, repair open circuit in Violet/Brown wire to BCM. Perform VERIFICATION PROCEDURE VER-1.

5) If voltage is more than one volt, check voltage of White/Black wire on BCM Bone connector terminal No. 7, CCD bus (–) circuit. If voltage is less than one volt, repair open circuit in White/Black wire to BCM. Perform VERIFICATION PROCEDURE VER-1. If voltage is more than one volt, replace BCM. Perform VERIFICATION PROCEDURE VER-1.

VERIFICATION PROCEDURE VER-1

VERIFICATION OF REPAIRS

Reconnect all previously disconnected components and connectors. Ensure all repairs have been made. Turn ignition off, then back on. Using DRB-II, erase fault codes. Fully operate system that was malfunctioning by turning switch on, opening door, etc. If system operates properly, repair is complete. If system does not operate properly, go to TEST 1A.

WIRING DIAGRAMS

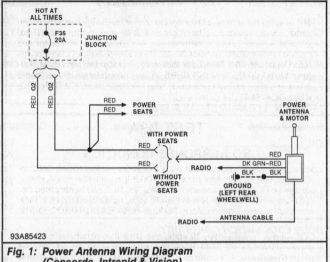

Fig. 1: Power Antenna Wiring Diagram (Concorde, Intrepid & Vision)

93A85423

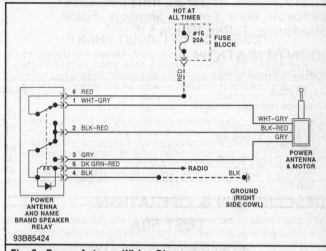

Fig. 2: Power Antenna Wiring Diagram (Dynasty, Fifth Avenue, Imperial & New Yorker)

93B85424

Power Convertible Tops & Sun Roofs

WIRING DIAGRAMS

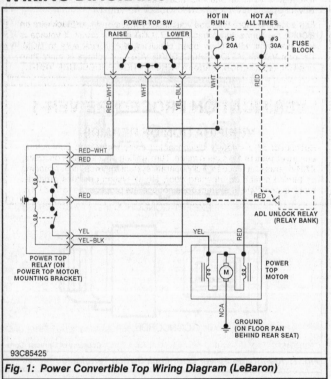

Fig. 1: Power Convertible Top Wiring Diagram (LeBaron)

93C85425

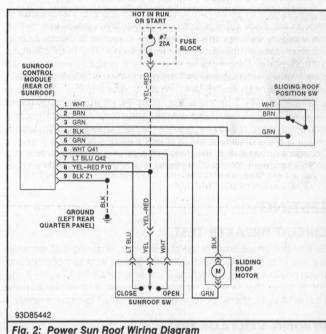

Fig. 2: Power Sun Roof Wiring Diagram (Dynasty, Fifth Avenue, Imperial & New Yorker)

93D85442

1993 ACCESSORIES & EQUIPMENT
Power Door Locks

Acclaim, Concorde, Daytona, Dynasty, Fifth Avenue, Imperial, Intrepid, Laser, LeBaron, New Yorker, Shadow, Spirit, Sundance, Talon, Vision

IDENTIFICATION

BODY IDENTIFICATION

Application	Body
Concorde, Intrepid, & Vision	LH
Daytona	AG
Dynasty & New Yorker	AC
Fifth Avenue & Imperial	AY
Laser & Talon	BD
LeBaron Convertible/Coupe	AJ
Shadow & Sundance	AP

DESCRIPTION & OPERATION

All doors can be locked or unlocked electrically using the switch on the front door panel or arm rest. All doors can also be locked or unlocked using the door locking knob. Front doors can be locked or unlocked from outside using the vehicle key. Driver's door can be unlocked from inside using the door handle. Passenger door on most models can also be unlocked from inside using the door handle. The power door lock inhibit system prevents power door lock operation when the key is in the ignition switch and any door is open, or when the key is in the ignition and the headlights are on. Some models use a remote keyless entry system in addition to power door locks. See REMOTE KEYLESS ENTRY article.

All models except Acclaim, Laser, Shadow, Spirit, Sundance and Talon are equipped with an automatic door lock function that is actuated through the Body Control Computer. When this system is activated the door locks will operate automatically. If system is disabled, locks will work through the door lock switches only. The body controller controls power door locks when door lock switch is activated. The controller will automatically lock the doors when all doors are closed, vehicle speed exceeds 15 MPH and the throttle position sensor tip-in is greater than 8-12 degrees. The controller will automatically relock the doors if same conditions are met and any of the doors become ajar. The controller does not operate the door unlock function. Unlock switch is wired directly to the door lock switches.

Concorde, Intrepid and Vision models also us a child protection lock on the rear doors. This disables the rear door inside handle when door is closed.

TESTING

CIRCUIT BREAKER TEST

Slightly pull circuit breaker out of fuse block, ensuring that terminals are still in contact. Connect voltmeter ground wire to good ground. Using positive probe, check both breaker terminals for 12 volts. If only one terminal checks okay, replace circuit breaker. If neither terminal shows 12 volts, check for open or shorted circuit to circuit breaker.

WIRING VOLTAGE TEST

Remove switch from driver's side trim panel. Separate multiple terminal block on wiring harness from switch body. Connect one lead of test light to ground terminal Black or Gray and touch other lead to Red wire terminal. If light comes on, wiring circuit is okay. If light does not come on, check circuit breaker or for an open wire.

DOOR SWITCH TEST

Remove switch from mounting location. Use an ohmmeter to check for correct continuity with switch in lock and unlock positions. If any continuity does not check as shown, replace switch.

DOOR LOCK SWITCH CONTINUITY (LASER & TALON)

Switch Position	Terminals	Continuity
Open	2 & 3	Yes
Closed	1 & 3	Yes

NOTE: On Laser and Talon, terminal No. 1 is top left pin of switch connector, terminal No. 2 is top right pin and terminal No. 3 is bottom pin.

DOOR LOCK SWITCH CONTINUITY (ACCLAIM, LEBARON SEDAN & SPIRIT)

Switch Position	Terminals	Continuity
Off	1 & 4	Yes
	2 & 5	Yes
Lock	2 & 3	Yes
	1 & 4	Yes
Unlock	3 & 4	Yes
	2 & 5	Yes

DOOR LOCK SWITCH CONTINUITY (CONCORDE, INTREPID & VISION)

Switch Position	Terminals	Continuity
Lock	1 & 4	Yes
Unlock	1 & 4	Yes

DOOR LOCK SWITCH CONTINUITY (ALL OTHER MODELS)

Switch Position	Terminals	Continuity
Off	1 & 4	Yes
	2 & 5	Yes
Lock	3 & 4	Yes
	2 & 5	Yes
Unlock	2 & 3	Yes
	1 & 4	Yes

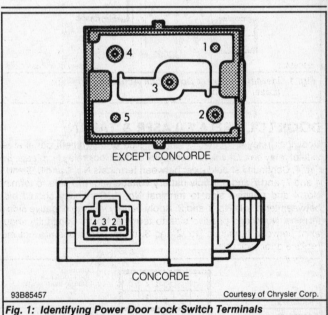

EXCEPT CONCORDE

CONCORDE

93B85457

Courtesy of Chrysler Corp.

Fig. 1: Identifying Power Door Lock Switch Terminals

DOOR LOCK MOTORS TEST

All Models – Ensure battery is fully charged. To determine which motor is faulty, check each motor individually. If none of the motors work, it may be a shorted motor or faulty switch. Disconnecting bad motor will allow others to work. If a motor does not work because of a broken wire, other motors will operate.

Door Lock Motor Test (All Models Exc. Laser & Talon) – To test an individual motor, disconnect connector at motor. *See Fig. 2.* To lock door, connect a 12-volt power source to positive pin of lock motor and a good ground to negative terminal. To unlock, reverse wire connections at terminals. If no voltage is present, repair wire(s). If motor still does not operate, replace motor.

Door Lock Actuator (Laser & Talon) – 1) Manually place actuator locking latch in LOCK position. *See Fig. 3.* Connect a 12-volt power source to terminal No. 1 for left door, or terminal No. 3 for right door. Ground terminal No. 3 for left door, or terminal No. 1 for right door, and ensure latch moves to UNLOCK position.

2) Manually place actuator locking latch in UNLOCK position. *See Fig. 3.* Connect a 12-volt power source to terminal No. 3 for left door, or terminal No. 1 for right door. Ground terminal No. 1 for left door, or terminal No. 3 for right door, and ensure latch moves to the LOCK position.

3) Check for continuity between terminals No. 2 and 4 with latch in UNLOCK position. Ensure there is no continuity.

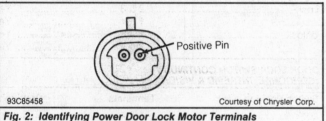

Fig. 2: Identifying Power Door Lock Motor Terminals (All Models Except Laser & Talon)

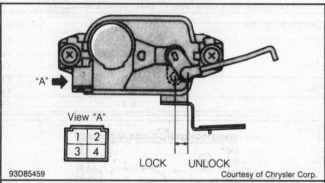

Fig. 3: Identifying Power Door Lock Actuator Terminals (Laser & Talon)

DOOR LOCK RELAY (LASER & TALON)

Door lock relay is located under left side of instrument panel at left side of relay box. Check for continuity of door lock relay terminals. *See Fig. 4.* Continuity should exist between terminals No. 1 and 5, 3 and 5, 4 and 7, and 7 and 8. Apply battery voltage negative side to terminal No. 4 and positive side to terminal No. 7. Continuity should exist between terminals No. 1 and 2. Apply battery voltage negative side to terminal No. 8 and positive side to terminal No. 7. Continuity should exist between terminals No. 2 and 3. If any conditions are not met, replace door lock relay.

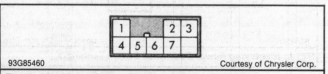

Fig. 4: Identifying Power Door Lock Relay Terminals (Laser & Talon)

REMOVAL & INSTALLATION

CAUTION: When battery is disconnected, vehicle computer and memory systems may lose memory data. Driveability problems may exist until computer systems have completed a relearn cycle. See COMPUTER RELEARN PROCEDURES article in GENERAL INFORMATION before disconnecting battery.

DOOR LOCK MOTORS

Removal & Installation – Remove inside door handle, window handle and door trim panel. Roll watershield away from lower rear corner of door. Reach through access hole and disconnect motor link. Disconnect wire connector from motor. Remove motor attaching screws and remove motor. To install, reverse removal procedure.

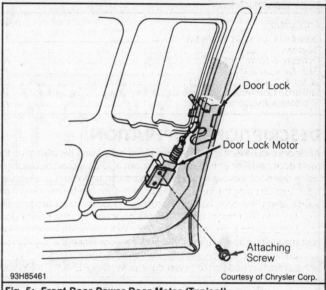

Fig. 5: Front Door Power Door Motor (Typical)

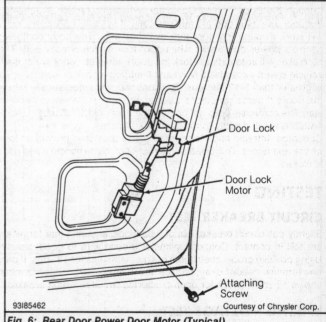

Fig. 6: Rear Door Power Door Motor (Typical)

DOOR LOCK SWITCHES

Removal & Installation – Move glass to down position. Disconnect negative battery cable. Pry upward at front of switch bezel and disengage from clip. Lift switch and disconnect wiring connector. Remove switch. To install, reverse removal procedure.

WIRING DIAGRAMS

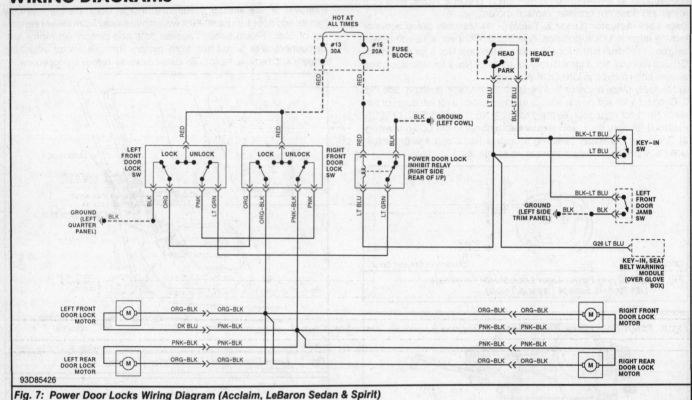

Fig. 7: Power Door Locks Wiring Diagram (Acclaim, LeBaron Sedan & Spirit)

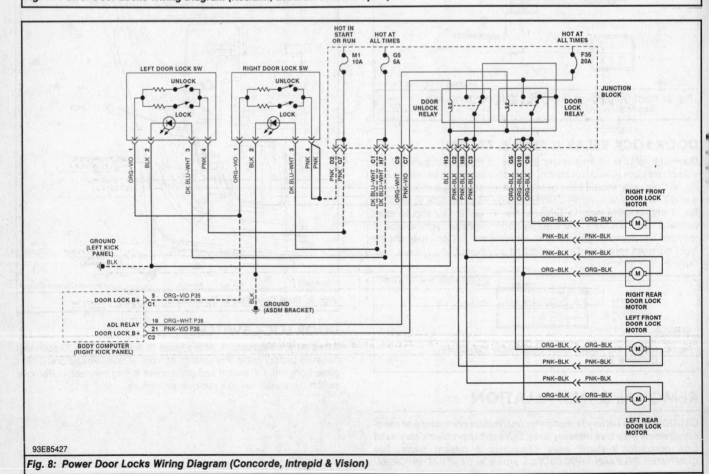

Fig. 8: Power Door Locks Wiring Diagram (Concorde, Intrepid & Vision)

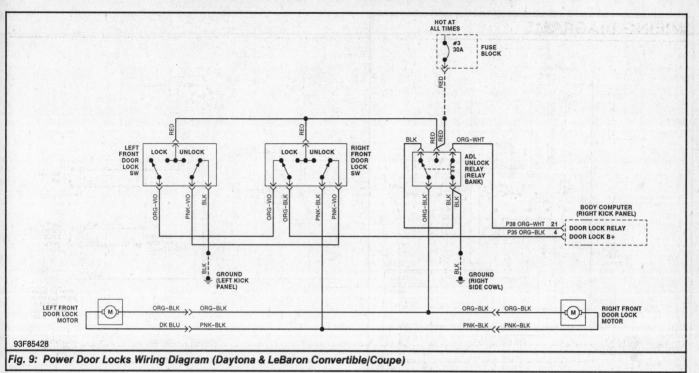

Fig. 9: Power Door Locks Wiring Diagram (Daytona & LeBaron Convertible/Coupe)

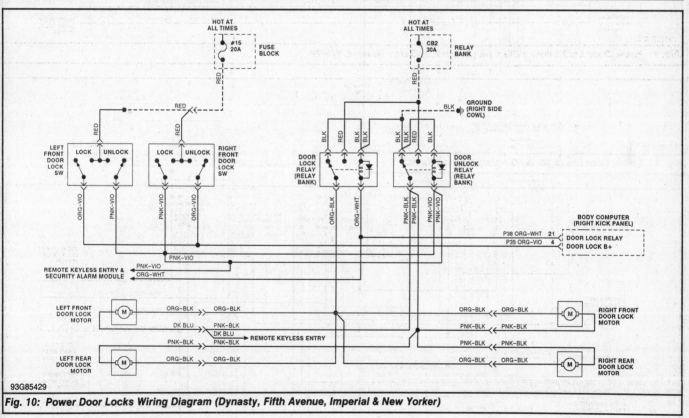

Fig. 10: Power Door Locks Wiring Diagram (Dynasty, Fifth Avenue, Imperial & New Yorker)

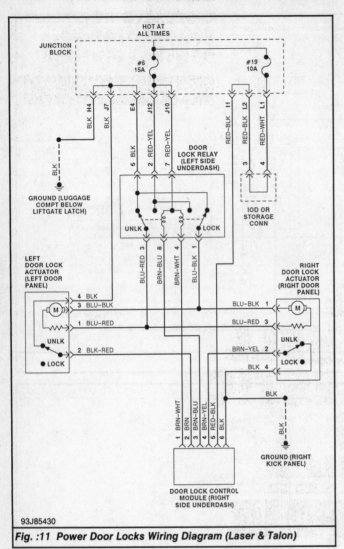

93J85430

Fig. :11 Power Door Locks Wiring Diagram (Laser & Talon)

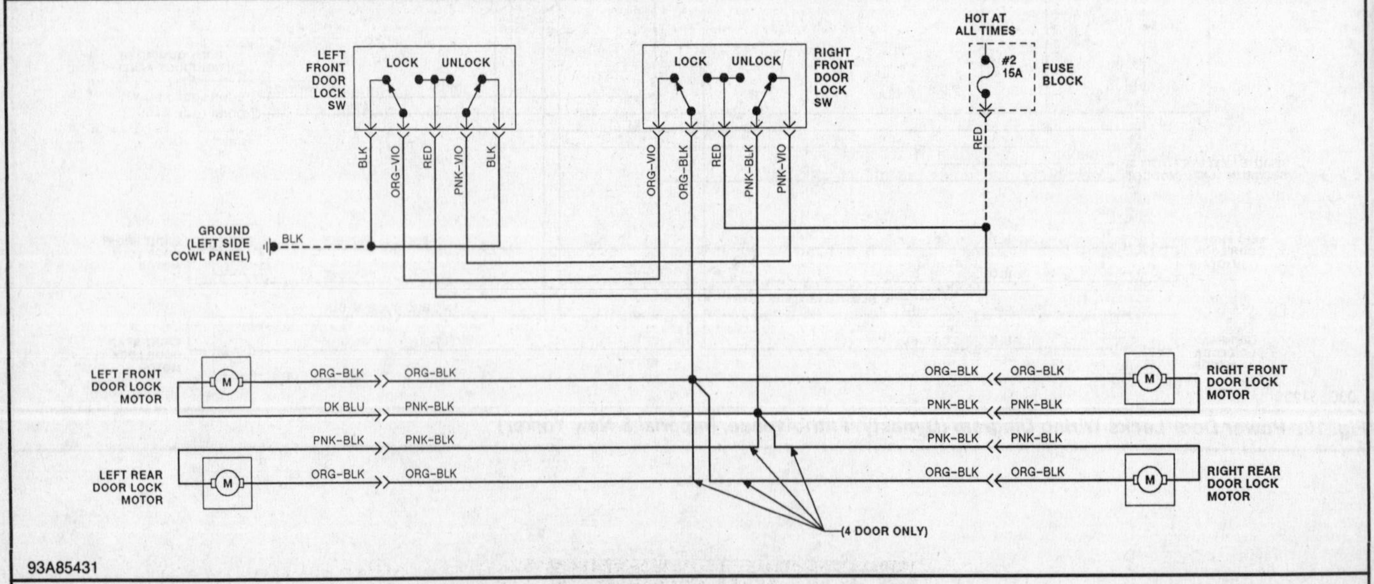

93A85431

Fig. 12: Power Door Locks Wiring Diagram (Shadow & Sundance)

DIAGNOSIS

NOTE: For complete Body Control Computer testing, see BODY CONTROL COMPUTER article in ENGINE PERFORMANCE. The following tests require the use of the DRB-II tester.

TEST 35A

AUTO DOOR LOCK PROBLEM
(LH BODY)

1) If vehicle is equipped with Remote Keyless Entry (RKE), go to TEST 36A of BODY CONTROL COMPUTER TESTS – LH BODY in ENGINE PERFORMANCE. If vehicle is not equipped with RKE, close all doors. Open driver's window and remove ignition key. Using DRB-II, actuate door UNLOCK test and then actuate door LOCK test. If any door locks, repair inoperative door lock motor(s) or wiring.

NOTE: The BCM must be connected while performing step 2). Failure to do so may lead to incorrect circuit/system diagnosis.

2) If doors do not lock, check if a door unlock problem exists. If an unlock problem exists, go to TEST 35B. If an unlock problem does not exist, access Body Controller Module (BCM). Module is located behind right kick panel. With DRB-II in voltmeter mode, backprobe BCM Gray connector terminal No. 18, door lock relay control circuit (Orange/White wire). *See Fig. 8.* If voltage is less than 10 volts, replace BCM. Perform VERIFICATION PROCEDURE VER-1.

3) If voltage is more than 10 volts, use DRB-II to stop door lock test. Press driver's side power door lock switch to the lock and then unlock position. If any door locks and unlocks, repair inoperative door lock motor(s) or wiring.

4) If doors do not lock and unlock, turn ignition off. Disconnect BCM Bone connector. With DRB-II in voltmeter mode, check voltage on BCM Bone connector terminal No. 9, power door lock switch circuit (Orange/Violet wire). Depress power door lock switch. If voltage is less than 10 volts, go to TEST 35C.

5) If voltage is more than 10 volts, reconnect BCM connector and turn ignition on. Remove door lock relay from fuse/junction block. Fuse/junction block is located behind end cover, on left side of instrument panel. Using DRB-II, actuate door locks. With DRB-II in voltmeter mode, check voltage on door lock relay control circuit (Orange/White wire) on door lock relay connector. If voltage is less than 10 volts, repair open circuit in Orange/White wire between door lock relay and BCM. Perform VERIFICATION PROCEDURE VER-1.

6) If voltage is more than 10 volts, use DRB-II in voltmeter mode to check voltage on door lock relay connector door lock circuit (Orange/Black wire). Using DRB-II, actuate door unlock test. If voltage is more than 10 volts, repair open circuit in Orange/Black wire. Perform VERIFICATION PROCEDURE VER-1.

7) If voltage is less than 10 volts, use DRB-II to stop door unlock test. Using DRB-II, check voltage on door lock relay connector fused battery feed circuit (Red wire). If voltage is less than 10 volts, repair open circuit in Red wire. Perform VERIFICATION PROCEDURE VER-1.

8) If voltage is more than 10 volts, use DRB-II in ohmmeter mode to check resistance on door lock relay connector ground circuit (Black wire). If resistance is more than 5 ohms, repair open circuit in Black wire. Perform VERIFICATION PROCEDURE VER-1. If resistance is less than 5 ohms, replace door lock relay. Perform VERIFICATION PROCEDURE VER-1.

TEST 35B

AUTO DOOR LOCK SWITCH SENSE
(LH BODY)

1) Using DRB-II, stop door lock test. Remove door unlock relay from fuse/junction block. Fuse/junction block is located behind end cover, on left side of instrument panel. Using DRB-II, actuate door unlock test. With DRB-II in voltmeter mode, check voltage on door unlock relay control circuit (Pink/Violet wire) on door unlock relay connector. If voltage is less than 10 volts, repair open circuit in Pink/Violet wire between relay and BCM. Perform VERIFICATION PROCEDURE VER-1.

2) If voltage is more than 10 volts, use DRB-II in voltmeter mode to check voltage on door unlock relay connector door unlock circuit (Pink/Black wire). Using DRB-II, actuate door lock test. If voltage is less than 10 volts, repair open circuit in Pink/Black wire. Perform VERIFICATION PROCEDURE VER-1.

TEST 35B (Cont.)

3) If voltage is more than 10 volts, use DRB-II to stop door unlock test. With DRB-II in voltmeter mode, check voltage on door unlock relay connector fused battery feed circuit (Red wire). If voltage is less than 10 volts, repair open circuit in Red wire. Perform VERIFICATION PROCEDURE VER-1.

4) If voltage is more than 10 volts, use DRB-II in ohmmeter mode to check resistance on door unlock relay connector ground circuit (Black wire). If resistance is more than 5 ohms, repair open circuit in Black wire. Perform VERIFICATION PROCEDURE VER-1. If resistance is less than 5 ohms, replace door unlock relay. Perform VERIFICATION PROCEDURE VER-1.

TEST 35C

AUTO DOOR LOCK CIRCUIT
(LH BODY)

1) Turn ignition off. Disconnect Body Controller Module (BCM) Bone connector. With DRB-II in voltmeter mode, check voltage on BCM Bone connector terminal No. 9, power door lock switch circuit (Orange/Violet wire). Depress opposite (passenger's) door switch to the lock position. If voltage is less than 10 volts, repair open door lock switch wire. Perform VERIFICATION PROCEDURE VER-1.

2) If voltage is more than 10 volts, turn ignition off and reconnect BCM Bone connector. Depress door lock switch to lock position. If doors do not lock, replace BCM. Perform VERIFICATION PROCEDURE VER-1. If doors lock, problem is in driver's door. Repair wiring.

93C40602 Courtesy of Chrysler Corp.

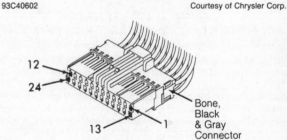

Fig. 8: Body Controller Connector Terminals (LH BODY)

TEST 2A

AUTO DOOR LOCK SYSTEM
(AC & AY BODIES)

1) Using DRB-II, read door lock status. If DRB-II does not display ENABLED, use DRB-II to enable door locks and perform VERIFICATION PROCEDURE VER-1.

2) If DRB-II displays ENABLED, lower left front window and close all doors. Remove key from ignition switch. Depress power door lock switch to LOCK position. If all doors lock, a faulty door ajar circuit is indicated.

3) If all door locks do not lock, turn ignition on (engine off). Using DRB-II, actuate door lock test. If all doors lock, go to TEST 2B. If some doors lock, check wiring and door lock motor in doors that do not lock. Repair as necessary. If no doors lock, put DRB-II in voltmeter mode.

4) While door lock actuation test is running, backprobe terminal No. 21 (Orange/White wire) of Body Control Module (BCM) Black connector. BCM is located behind right kick panel. If voltage pulsates between zero and 10 volts, go to TEST 2C. If voltage does not pulsate between zero and 10 volts, stop door lock actuation test using DRB-II.

5) Turn ignition off. Disconnect BCM Black connector. Check connector condition, and clean or repair connector as necessary. Put DRB-II in ohmmeter mode. Check resistance on terminal No. 21 (Orange/White wire) of BCM Black connector.

6) If resistance is less than 5 ohms, repair short to ground in Orange/White wire. Perform VERIFICATION PROCEDURE VER-1. If resistance is more than 5 ohms, replace BCM. Perform VERIFICATION PROCEDURE VER-1.

TEST 2B

DIAGNOSING LOCK SIGNAL
TO BODY CONTROL MODULE
(AC & AY BODIES)

1) Using DRB-II, stop door lock actuation test. Remove key from ignition switch. Using DRB-II, read key in ignition switch status. If DRB-II displays CIRCUIT CLOSED, go to TEST 47A of BODY CONTROL COMPUTER TESTS – AC & AY BODIES in ENGINE PERFORMANCE.

2) Turn ignition off. Disconnect Body Control Module (BCM) Black connector. BCM is located behind right kick panel. Check connector condition, and clean or repair connector as necessary.

3) Check voltage on terminal No. 4 (Orange/Violet wire) of BCM Black connector and observe DRB-II while locking doors using left door lock switch. If voltage is more than 10 volts, replace BCM. Perform VERIFICATION PROCEDURE VER-1. If voltage is less than 10 volts, check door lock wiring and/or door lock switch.

TEST 2C

AUTOMATIC DOOR LOCKS
WITHOUT REMOTE KEYLESS ENTRY
(AC & AY BODIES)

NOTE: Door lock/door unlock relay must remain in place when backprobing door lock/door unlock relay connector.

1) With DRB-II in voltmeter mode and door lock test still being actuated, gain access to door lock relay. Relay is located behind right side of glove box. Backprobe Orange/White wire at door lock relay connector. If voltage does not pulsate between zero and 12 volts, repair open Orange/White wire. Perform VERIFICATION PROCEDURE VER-1.

2) If voltage pulsates between zero and 12 volts, backprobe Orange/Black wire at door lock relay connector. If voltage does not pulsate between zero and 12 volts, go to step **5)**. If voltage pulsates between zero and 12 volts, backprobe Pink/Black wire at door unlock relay.

3) If voltage does not pulsate between zero and 12 volts, repair open in Pink/Black wire or Orange/Black wire. Perform VERIFICATION PROCEDURE VER-1. If voltage pulsates between zero and 12 volts, stop door lock actuation test using DRB-II. Turn ignition off. Put DRB-II in ohmmeter mode. Remove door lock and unlock relays. See Fig. 9.

4) Check condition of connectors, and clean or repair connectors as necessary. Check resistance of Black (ground) wire at door unlock relay connector. If resistance is more than 5 ohms, repair open Black wire. Perform VERIFICATION PROCEDURE VER-1. If resistance is less than 5 ohms, replace door unlock relay. Perform VERIFICATION PROCEDURE VER-1.

5) If voltage did not pulsate between zero and 12 volts in step **2)**, stop door lock actuation test using DRB-II. Backprobe Red wire at door lock relay. If voltage is less than 10 volts, repair open Red wire. Perform VERIFICATION PROCEDURE VER-1. If voltage is more than 10 volts, put DRB-II in ohmmeter mode. Remove door lock and unlock relays.

6) Check condition of connectors, and clean or repair connectors as necessary. Check resistance of Black (ground) wire at door lock relay connector. If resistance is more than 5 ohms, repair open Black wire. Perform VERIFICATION PROCEDURE VER-1. If resistance is less than 5 ohms, check resistance of Orange/Black wire at door lock relay connector.

7) If resistance is more than 5 ohms, replace door lock relay. Perform VERIFICATION PROCEDURE VER-1. If resistance is less than 5 ohms, repair short to ground in Orange/Black wire. Perform VERIFICATION PROCEDURE VER-1.

93B05753 Courtesy of Chrysler Corp.

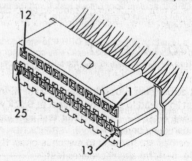

**Fig. 9: Body Controller Connector Terminals
(AC & AY BODIES)**

Daytona, Dynasty, Fifth Avenue, Imperial, LeBaron Convertible/Coupe, New Yorker

DESCRIPTION

The power seat system consists of a reversible motor with 3 armatures, a control switch assembly and a wiring harness. The circuit is protected by a 30-amp circuit breaker in the fuse panel. The driver's seat can be adjusted in 6 directions: up-and-down, forward-and-backward and tilt forward-and-tilt backward. The passenger seat can be adjusted in 4 directions. It cannot adjust tilt.

Daytona and LeBaron models have an optional sport seat package, which includes 6-way power seat, plus air adjustable lumbar and thigh support bags and adjustable seat cushion and back side wings. These mechanisms are controlled by lumbar control and seat wing switches.

The power bench seat system consists of a motor coupled through cables to worm gear box assemblies, a control switch assembly and a wiring harness. Daytona and LeBaron models also use a recliner feature which moves the back of the seat up and down.

Some models have an optional power memory seat system. See POWER MEMORY SEATS article.

OPERATION

The power seat control switch has 3 sections. The front section controls the up and down movement of the seat front. The rear section of the switch controls the seat rear. The center of the switch raises and lowers the entire seat. The center switch also moves the seat forward and backward. On models with recliner feature, the recliner switch moves the seat back up or down.

TESTING

NOTE: Before beginning any test procedure, ensure battery is fully charged. Clean and tighten all electrical connections and terminals to ensure proper continuity and ground.

POWER DRAW TEST

If power seat malfunctions, test for electrical or mechanical failure. With wiring connected and dome light on, operate switches. Watch dome light for evidence of power draw by seat motor. If dome light chimes, motor is jammed, indicating a mechanical problem. If there is no evidence of power draw, electrical problems are indicated.

HARNESS VOLTAGE TEST

This test will determine whether voltage is continuous through body harness to switch.
- Disconnect power seat 6-position switch from wiring harness.
- Connect test light lead to ground terminal at Black wire of harness connector. *See Figs. 1-2.* Touch other test light lead to Red wire terminal of harness connector.
- If test light comes on, harness to switch is okay. If test light does not come on, perform circuit breaker test.

CIRCUIT BREAKER TEST

Locate 30-amp circuit breaker in fuse box. With a voltmeter, check circuit breaker for battery voltage between each terminal and ground. If both terminals show battery voltage, circuit breaker is okay. If only one terminal shows battery voltage, circuit breaker is defective. If neither terminal shows battery voltage, check for open or shorted circuit to fuse box.

MOTOR TESTS

Disconnect power seat switch connector and attach covered jumper wires where indicated in following tests. If motor tests defective, replace motor assembly.
Front Motor Test (Daytona & LeBaron) – **1)** Disconnect power seat switch. Connect a jumper wire between Red wire terminal No. 2 and

Yellow/Light Blue wire terminals in center of switch connector. *See Fig. 1.*
2) Connect a second jumper wire between Black wire terminal and Red/Light Blue terminal. If motor does not operate, reverse jumpers Red to Red/Light Blue and Black to Yellow/Light Blue. If motor will not operate, inspect wiring harness. If wiring harness is okay, replace motor assembly.

Center Motor Test (Daytona & LeBaron) – **1)** Disconnect power seat switch. Connect a jumper wire between Red wire terminal No. 2 and Yellow/Light Green wire terminal in center of switch connector. *See Fig. 1.*
2) Connect second jumper between Black wire terminal and Red/Light Green wire terminal. If motor does not operate, reverse jumpers Red to Red/Light Green and Black to Yellow/Light Green. If motor will not operate, inspect wiring harness. If wiring harness is okay, replace motor assembly.

Rear Motor Test (Daytona & LeBaron) – **1)** Disconnect power seat switch. Connect a jumper wire between Red wire terminal No. 2 and Yellow/White wire terminal. *See Fig. 1.*
2) Connect second jumper wire between Black wire terminal and Red/White terminal. If motor does not operate, reverse jumper wires Red to Red/White and Black to Yellow/White. If motor will not operate, inspect wiring harness. If wiring is okay, replace motor assembly.

Recliner Motor (Daytona & LeBaron) – **1)** Disconnect power seat switch. Connect a jumper wire between Red wire terminal No. 2 and Gray/White wire terminal. *See Fig. 1.*
2) Connect second jumper wire between Black wire terminal and Green/Light Blue wire terminal. If motor does not operate, reverse jumper wires Red to Green/Light Blue and Black to Gray/White. If motor will not operate, inspect wiring harness. If wiring is okay, replace motor assembly.

Front Motor Test (Dynasty, Fifth Ave., Imperial & New Yorker) – **1)** Disconnect power seat switch. Connect a jumper wire between terminal No. 3 and terminal No. 8. *See Fig. 2.*
2) Connect a second jumper wire between terminal No. 6 and terminal No. 7. If motor does not operate, reverse jumpers No. 3 to 7 and No. 6 to 8. If motor will not operate, inspect wiring harness. If wiring harness is okay, replace motor assembly.

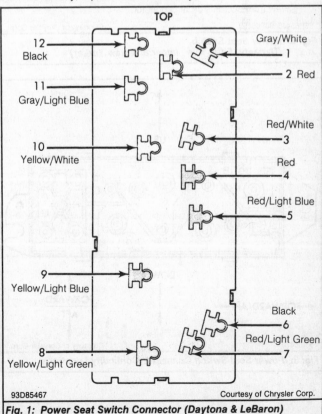

TOP

12 Black
11 Gray/Light Blue
10 Yellow/White
9 Yellow/Light Blue
8 Yellow/Light Green

Gray/White — 1
2 Red
Red/White — 3
Red — 4
Red/Light Blue — 5
Black — 6
Red/Light Green
7

93D85467
Courtesy of Chrysler Corp.

Fig. 1: Power Seat Switch Connector (Daytona & LeBaron)

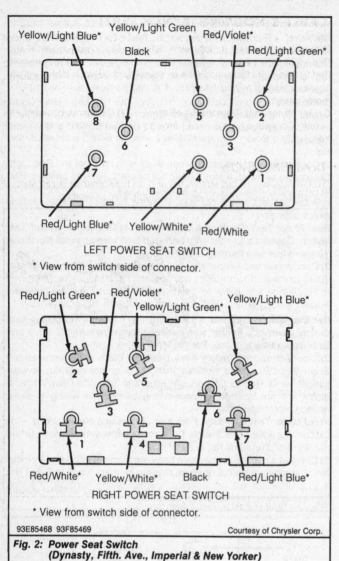

LEFT POWER SEAT SWITCH

* View from switch side of connector.

RIGHT POWER SEAT SWITCH

* View from switch side of connector.

93E85468 93F85469   Courtesy of Chrysler Corp.

**Fig. 2: Power Seat Switch
(Dynasty, Fifth. Ave., Imperial & New Yorker)**

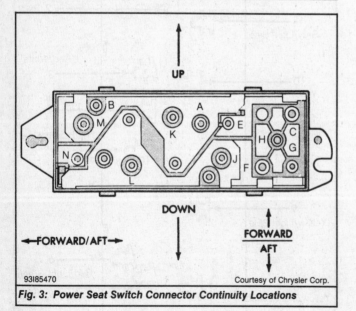

93I85470   Courtesy of Chrysler Corp.

Fig. 3: Power Seat Switch Connector Continuity Locations

Center Motor Test (Dynasty, Fifth Ave., Imperial & New Yorker) – 1)
Disconnect power seat switch. Connect a jumper wire between terminal No. 3 and terminal No. 5. See Fig. 2.
2) Connect second jumper between terminal No. 6 and terminal No. 2. If motor does not operate, reverse jumpers No. 3 to 2 and 6 to 5. If motor will not operate, inspect wiring harness. If wiring harness is okay, replace motor assembly.
Rear Motor Test (Dynasty, Fifth Ave., Imperial & New Yorker) – 1)
Disconnect power seat switch. Connect a jumper wire between terminal No. 3 and terminal No. 4. See Fig. 2.
2) Connect second jumper wire between terminal No. 6 and terminal No. 1. If motor does not operate, reverse jumper wires No. 3 to 1 and No. 6 to 4. If motor will not operate, inspect wiring harness. If wiring is okay, replace motor assembly.

POWER SEAT SWITCH CONTINUITY

If seat motors operate properly when switch is by-passed during continuity tests, the switch is defective. See Fig. 3 and POWER SEAT SWITCH CONTINUITY CHECK table in this article. Recliner continuity checks only for Daytona and LeBaron

POWER SEAT SWITCH CONTINUITY CHECK

Switch Position	Check Continuity Between
OFF	Pins B & N; Pins B & K
	Pins B & M; Pins B & K
	Pins B & E; Pins B & L
	Pins G & C (Recliner)
VERTICAL UP	Pins B & M; Pins B & E
	Pins A & N; Pins A & J
VERTICAL DOWN	Pins B & N; Pins B & J
	Pins A & M; Pins A & E
HORIZ. FORWARD	Pins B & K; Pins A & L
HORIZ. AFT	Pins B & L; Pins A & K
FRONT TILT-UP	Pins B & M; Pins A & N
FRONT TILT-DOWN	Pins B & N; Pins A & M
REAR TILT-UP	Pins B & E; Pins A & J
REAR TILT-DOWN	Pins B & J; Pins A & E
RECLINER FORWARD	Pins G & C; Pins H & F
RECLINER AFT	Pins G & F; Pins H & C

SPORT SEAT CONTROL SWITCHES

Daytona & LeBaron – 1) Remove each switch from its mounting position. Move switch to specified location and use an ohmmeter to check continuity between pins indicated in LUMBAR CONTROL SWITCH CONTINUITY and SEAT WING SWITCH CONTINUITY tables. If continuity is not proper, replace switch.

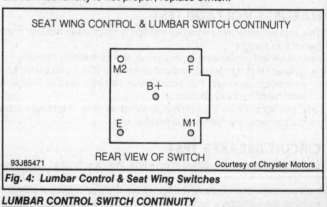

93J85471   Courtesy of Chrysler Motors

Fig. 4: Lumbar Control & Seat Wing Switches

LUMBAR CONTROL SWITCH CONTINUITY

Mode	Continuity Between
Off	Pins E & M1; Pins F & M2
Deflate	Pins F & M2; Pins M1 & B+
Inflate	Pins E & M1; Pins M2 & B+

SEAT WING SWITCH CONTINUITY

Mode	Continuity Between
Out	Pins E & M1; Pins F & M2
Off	Pins E & M1; Pins F & M2
In	Pins F & M2; Pins M1 & B+

REMOVAL & INSTALLATION

CAUTION: When battery is disconnected, vehicle computer and memory systems may lose memory data. Driveability problems may exist until computer systems have completed a relearn cycle. See COMPUTER RELEARN PROCEDURES article in GENERAL INFORMATION before disconnecting battery.

SEAT ASSEMBLY

Removal – Remove adjuster attaching bolts and nuts from floor pan. Move adjuster as needed for access. Disconnect negative battery cable. Disconnect wiring harness power lead at carpet. Remove assembly from vehicle.

Installation – Position seat assembly in vehicle. Connect wiring harness. Install and tighten mounting bolts and nuts. Connect negative battery cable.

ADJUSTER

Removal & Installation – Remove seat assembly. Lay seat on its back. Remove bolts attaching adjuster to seat assembly. Disconnect wiring at switch. Remove any tie straps holding cable housing to seat. To install, reverse removal procedure.

MOTOR

Removal – Remove seat assembly. Lay seat on its back. Remove motor mounting screws. Carefully disconnect housings and cables from motor. Remove motor.

Installation – Position motor onto support of seat assembly. Synchronize left side and right side adjuster positions. Connect housings and cables to motor. Install and tighten motor mounting screws and bolt securing motor to adjuster. Install seat assembly.

CABLE & HOUSING (BUCKET SEAT)

Removal – Remove motor assembly from seat. Disconnect cable from motor. Remove clamp from cable housing. Slide cable and housing out of connector. Check cable for kinks and wear.

Installation – Insert cable and housing into connector. Synchronize right and left side adjusters. Install motor assembly and seat assembly in vehicle.

CABLE & HOUSING (BENCH SEAT)

Removal – Remove seat assembly. See SEAT ASSEMBLY under REMOVAL & INSTALLATION in this article. Disconnect motor. Remove Corbin clamp from cable housing. Slide cable and housing out of bracket for seat adjuster. Remove 2 screws from bracket. Remove cables from motor.

Installation – Insert cable and housing into bracket. Install Corbin clamp. Synchronize left and right adjuster positions. With bracket in position, insert cables in motor. Install 2 bracket screws. Install motor assembly.

TRANSMISSION

Transmissions are not removable and no maintenance is required. If transmission fails, replace entire seat adjuster assembly.

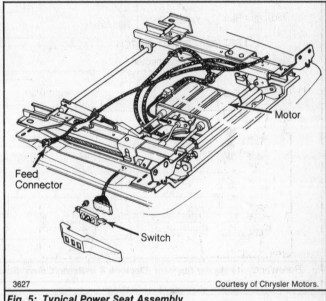

3627   Courtesy of Chrysler Motors.

Fig. 5: Typical Power Seat Assembly

1993 ACCESSORIES & EQUIPMENT
Power Seats (Cont.)

WIRING DIAGRAMS

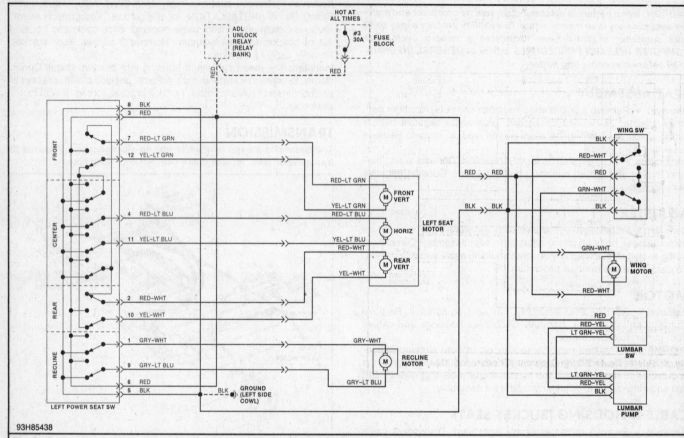

Fig. 6: Power Seats Wiring Diagram (Daytona & LeBaron Convertible/Coupe)

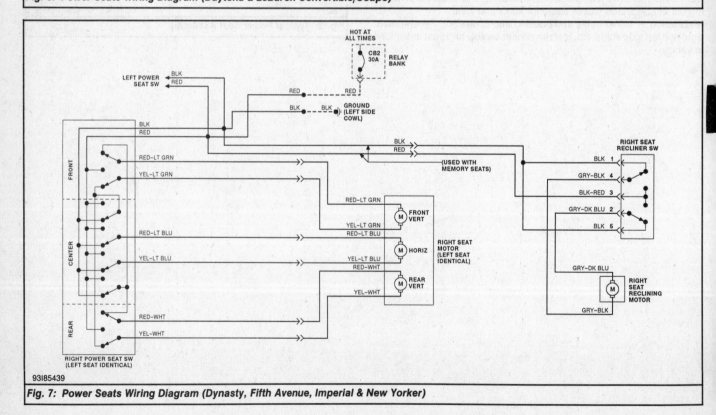

Fig. 7: Power Seats Wiring Diagram (Dynasty, Fifth Avenue, Imperial & New Yorker)

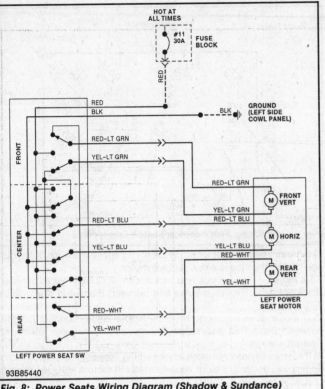

Fig. 8: Power Seats Wiring Diagram (Shadow & Sundance)

1993 ACCESSORIES & EQUIPMENT
Power Seats – AA & AJ Bodies

AA Body: Acclaim, Spirit
AJ Body: LeBaron Sedan

DESCRIPTION

The power seat system consists of a magnetic reversible motor with 3 armatures, a control switch assembly and a wiring harness. The circuit is protected by a 30-amp circuit breaker in the fuse panel. The power seats can be adjusted in 6 directions: up-and-down, forward-and-backward and tilt forward-and-tilt back.

OPERATION

The front control switch moves front of seat up-and-down. The rear switch controls rear of seat. The center switch raises and lowers entire seat and controls forward-and-backward movement.

TESTING

POWER DRAW TEST

1) Before beginning any test procedure, ensure battery is fully charged. Clean and tighten all electrical connections and terminals to ensure proper continuity and ground. Determine whether failure is mechanical or electrical.
2) With wiring connected and dome light on, operate switches. Watch dome light for evidence of power consumption by seat motor. If dome light dims, motor is jammed, indicating a power draw and a mechanical problem. Proceed to MOTOR TEST.
3) If there is no evidence of power draw, wiring and electrical problems are indicated. Proceed to CIRCUIT BREAKER TEST.

HARNESS VOLTAGE TEST

This test will determine whether voltage is continuous through body harness to switch.
- Remove power seat switch from mounting position. Disconnect seat position switch from wiring harness.
- Connect test light lead to ground terminal at Black wire of center section. Touch other test light lead to Red wire terminal.
- If test light comes on, harness voltage to switch is okay. If test light does not come on, perform circuit breaker test.

CIRCUIT BREAKER TEST

1) Locate 30-amp circuit breaker in fuse box. Move circuit breaker for access to terminals, while maintaining proper electrical connection. Connect negative voltmeter lead to ground. With positive lead, check each terminal of circuit breaker for voltage.
2) If both terminals show voltage, circuit breaker is okay. If only one terminal shows battery voltage, circuit breaker is defective. Replace circuit breaker. If neither terminal shows battery voltage, check for open or shorted circuit to fuse box.

MOTOR TESTS

These tests will by-pass switch to determine if switch or specified motor is at fault. Remove power seat position switch from mounting position and disconnect it from wiring harness. Connect jumper wires as indicated. *See Fig. 1.*

Center Motor – 1) To check center motor, connect jumper wires between Black/Red and Red/White wires and between Black and Yellow/White wires.
2) If motor does not work, reverse jumper leads. Connect jumpers between Black/Red and Yellow/White wires and between Black wire and Red/White wires.
3) If motor still does not work, check wiring between switch connector and motor. If wiring is okay, replace motor.

Front Motor – 1) To check front motor, connect jumper wires between Black/Red and Red/Green wires and between Black and Yellow/Green wires.
2) If motor does not work, reverse jumper leads. Connect jumpers between Black/Red and Yellow/Green wires and between Black and Red/Green wires.

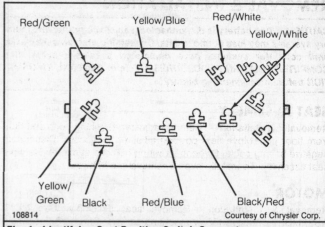

108814   Courtesy of Chrysler Corp.

Fig. 1: Identifying Seat Position Switch Connector

3) If motor still does not work, check wiring between switch connector and motor. If wiring is okay, replace motor.
Rear Motor – 1) To check rear motor, connect jumper wires between Black/Red and Red/Blue wires and between Black and Yellow/Blue wires.
2) If motor does not work, reverse jumper leads. Connect jumpers between Black/Red and Yellow/Blue wires and between Black and Red/Blue wires.
3) If motor still does not work, check wiring between switch connector and motor. If wiring is okay, replace motor. If motors and seat operate properly, proceed to SWITCH TEST.

SWITCH TEST

Remove power seat position switch from its mounting. Using an ohmmeter, perform continuity check between pins with switch set in specified position. See POWER SEAT SWITCH CONTINUITY CHECK table. *See Fig. 2.* If there is no continuity at any of the switch positions, replace switch.

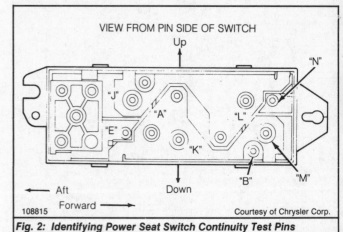

108815   Courtesy of Chrysler Corp.

Fig. 2: Identifying Power Seat Switch Continuity Test Pins

POWER SEAT SWITCH CONTINUITY CHECK

Switch Position	Check Continuity Between Pins
OFF	B & N; B & J
	B & M; B & E
	B & L; B & K
VERTICAL UP	A & E; A & M
	B & N; B & J
VERTICAL DOWN	A & J; A & N
	B & M; B & E
HORIZONTAL FORWARD	A & L; B & K
HORIZONTAL AFT	A & K; B & L
FRONT TILT UP	A & M; B & N
FRONT TILT DOWN	A & N; B & M
REAR TILT UP	A & E; B & J
REAR TILT DOWN	A & J; B & E

REMOVAL & INSTALLATION

CAUTION: When battery is disconnected, vehicle computer and memory systems may lose memory data. Driveability problems may exist until computer systems have completed a relearn cycle. See COMPUTER RELEARN PROCEDURES article in GENERAL INFORMATION before disconnecting battery.

SEAT ASSEMBLY

Removal & Installation – Remove adjuster attaching bolts and nuts from floor pan. Move seat position adjuster for access. Disconnect negative battery cable. Disconnect wiring harness at carpet. Remove seat assembly. To install, reverse removal procedure.

MOTOR

Removal & Installation – Remove seat assembly. See SEAT ASSEMBLY. Remove motor mounting screws. Carefully disconnect housing and cables from motor assembly. *See Fig. 3.* Remove bolt holding motor in position. To install, reverse removal procedure.

SEAT POSITION ADJUSTER TRACK

Removal & Installation – Remove seat assembly. See SEAT ASSEMBLY. Remove seat position adjuster-to-seat assembly bolts. Disconnect wiring harness at switch. To install, reverse removal procedure.

HORIZONTAL & VERTICAL TRANSMISSIONS

Removal & Installation – Transmissions are NOT removable or serviceable. If transmission fails, replace seat position adjuster.

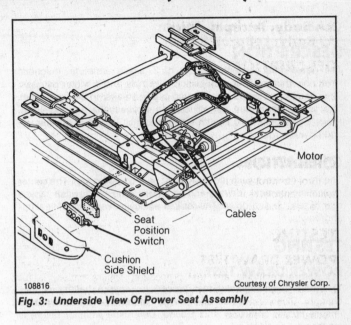

108816   Courtesy of Chrysler Corp.

Fig. 3: Underside View Of Power Seat Assembly

WIRING DIAGRAMS

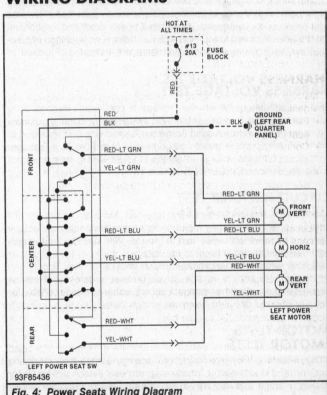

93F85436

Fig. 4: Power Seats Wiring Diagram (Acclaim, LeBaron Sedan & Spirit)

1993 ACCESSORIES & EQUIPMENT
Power Seats – LH Body

Concorde, Intrepid, Vision

DESCRIPTION

The power seat system consists of 2, single armature, magnetic reversible motors, a control switch assembly and a wiring harness. The circuit is protected by a 20-amp circuit breaker in the fuse panel. The power seats can be adjusted in 8 directions: up-and-down, forward-and-backward and tilt forward-and-tilt back and recliner up-and-down.

OPERATION

The front control switch moves front of seat up-and-down. The center switch moves seat forward-and-backward. The rear switch moves rear of seat up-and-down. The recliner switch moves back of seat up-and-down.

TESTING

POWER DRAW TEST

1) Before beginning any test procedure, ensure battery is fully charged. Clean and tighten all electrical connections and terminals to ensure proper continuity and ground. Determine whether failure is mechanical or electrical.

2) With wiring connected and dome light on, operate switches. Watch dome light for evidence of power consumption by seat motor. If dome light dims, motor is jammed, indicating a power draw and a mechanical problem. Proceed to MOTOR TEST. If there is no evidence of power draw, wiring and electrical problems are indicated. Proceed to CIRCUIT BREAKER TEST.

HARNESS VOLTAGE TEST

This test will determine whether voltage is continuous through body harness to switch. Remove power seat switch from mounting position. Disconnect switch from wiring harness. Connect one test light lead to pin No. 5 of ground terminal and other lead to pin No. 1. If test light comes on, harness voltage to switch is okay. If test light does not come on, perform CIRCUIT BREAKER TEST.

CIRCUIT BREAKER TEST

1) Locate 20-amp circuit breaker in fuse box. Move circuit breaker for access to terminals, while maintaining proper electrical connection. Connect negative voltmeter lead to ground. With positive lead, check each terminal of circuit breaker for voltage.

2) If both terminals show voltage, circuit breaker is okay. If only one terminal shows battery voltage, circuit breaker is defective. Replace circuit breaker. If neither terminal shows battery voltage, check for open or shorted circuit to fuse box.

MOTOR TESTS

These tests will by-pass switch to determine if switch or specified motor is at fault. Remove power seat position switch from mounting position and disconnect it from wiring harness. Check pin No. 5 for battery voltage and pin No. 1 for ground. Using 2 jumper wires, connect one wire to battery supply and ground. Connect other end of wires to pins as described below to check seat actions. See Fig. 1.

Center Motor – To check center motor, connect jumper wires between the following wire terminals:
- Positive lead to pin No. 6, negative lead to pin No. 3. Both seats should move forward.
- Positive lead to pin No. 3, negative lead to pin No. 6. Both seats should move backward.

If motor does not work, check wiring between switch connector and motor. If wiring is okay, replace motor.

Front Motor – To check front motor, connect jumper wires between the following wire terminals:
- Positive lead to pin No. 7, negative lead to pin No. 10. Front of driver seat should move up, front of passenger seat should move down.
- Positive lead to pin No. 10, negative lead to pin No. 7. Front of driver seat should move down, front of passenger seat should move up.

If motor does not work, check wiring between switch connector and motor. If wiring is okay, replace motor.

Rear Motor – To check rear motor, connect jumper wires between the following wire terminals:
- Positive lead to pin No. 8, negative lead to pin No. 9. Rear of driver seat should move up, rear of passenger seat should move down.
- Positive lead to pin No. 9, negative lead to pin No. 8. Rear of driver seat should move down, rear of passenger seat should move up.

If motor does not work, check wiring between switch connector and motor. If wiring is okay, replace motor.

Recliner Motor – To check recliner motor, connect jumper wires between the following wire terminals:
- Positive lead to pin No. 2, negative lead to pin No. 4. Driver seat recliner should move up, passenger seat recliner should move down.
- Positive lead to pin No. 4, negative lead to pin No. 2. Driver seat recliner should move down, passenger seat recliner should move up.

If motor still not work, check wiring between switch connector and motor. If wiring is okay, replace motor.

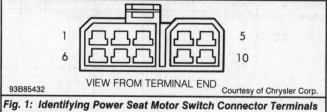

Fig. 1: Identifying Power Seat Motor Switch Connector Terminals

SWITCH TEST

Check seat operation. See MOTOR TESTS. If seats function properly, replace power seat motor switch.

REMOVAL & INSTALLATION

CAUTION: When battery is disconnected, vehicle computer and memory systems may lose memory data. Driveability problems may exist until computer systems have completed a relearn cycle. See COMPUTER RELEARN PROCEDURES article in GENERAL INFORMATION before disconnecting battery.

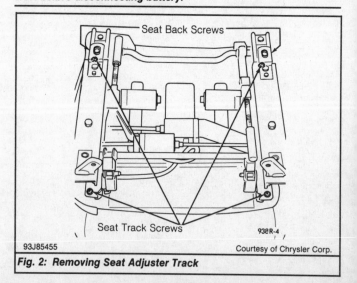

Fig. 2: Removing Seat Adjuster Track

SEAT ASSEMBLY

Removal & Installation – Remove adjuster attaching bolts and nuts from floor pan. Move seat position adjuster for access. Disconnect negative battery cable. Disconnect wiring harness at carpet. Remove seat assembly. To install, reverse removal procedure.

MOTOR

Removal & Installation – Remove seat assembly. See SEAT ASSEMBLY. Remove motor mounting screws. Carefully disconnect housing and cables from motor assembly. Remove bolt holding motor in position. To install, reverse removal procedure.

SEAT POSITION ADJUSTER TRACK

Removal & Installation – Remove seat assembly. See SEAT ASSEMBLY. Remove 2 seat back mounting screws and 4 seat track mounting screws. *See Fig. 2.* Remove track from seat. To install, reverse removal procedure.

HORIZONTAL & VERTICAL TRANSMISSIONS

Removal & Installation – Transmissions are not removable or serviceable. If transmission fails, replace seat position adjuster.

WIRING DIAGRAMS

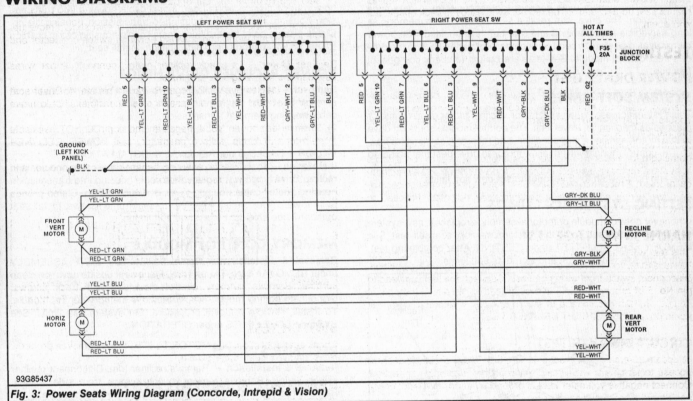

93G85437

Fig. 3: Power Seats Wiring Diagram (Concorde, Intrepid & Vision)

1993 ACCESSORIES & EQUIPMENT
Power Memory Seats

Dynasty, Fifth Avenue, Imperial, New Yorker

DESCRIPTION

The optional power memory seat system consists of a 2-position memory power seat, power recliner and memory power outside rear view mirror. The power recliner uses a motor and cable to allow driver to control angle of seat back. The system has a memory seat control module, 2 memory switches, a power mirror switch, an adjuster assembly switch, a power recliner motor, a recliner drive hinge, 3 seat motors and a motor in each mirror.

OPERATION

The memory seat allows driver to set and retain 2 seat and 2 recline positions. The system uses sensors (potentiometers) to determine seat position. The driver can recall a seat position from memory, as long as vehicle is not moving and seat belt is unbuckled. The power mirror uses rheostats to send positioning information back to the driver's seat control module. Self-tests are built-in to check component function.

SYSTEM SOFT LIMITS

This system activates when seat motor, recliner motor or mirror motor reaches its mechanical travel limit. The control module shuts off drive to that motor, sensing a stall condition, and records a soft limit for travel. The control module will not allow motor to drive past that point. To override soft limits, activate switch twice in proper direction. Reactivate and hold switch for 3 seconds to set new soft limits.

SETTING SYSTEM SOFT LIMITS

Whenever control module or motor assembly is replaced, new system soft limits must be set. To do this, perform memory seat self-test. See MEMORY SEAT SELF-TEST under TESTING. After completing test, control module will have set and stored its soft limits.

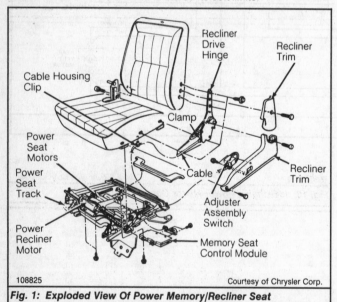

108825   Courtesy of Chrysler Corp.

Fig. 1: Exploded View Of Power Memory/Recliner Seat

REMOVAL & INSTALLATION

SEAT ASSEMBLY

Removal & Installation – Remove track adjuster bolts and nuts from floor pan. Disconnect negative battery cable. Disconnect wiring harness power lead at carpet. Remove seat. To install, reverse removal procedure.

POWER RECLINER MOTOR & CABLE

Removal – 1) Remove seat. See SEAT ASSEMBLY under REMOVAL & INSTALLATION. Remove recliner trim for access to recliner and recliner cable. *See Fig. 1.* Remove cable housing clip from cushion frame. Remove cable housing clamp from recliner transmission. Remove cable.

2) Place seat upside down on clean surface. Remove 4 track-to-cushion frame bolts. Remove 2 motor attachment screws from track cross strap. Disconnect recliner motor connectors. Remove recliner motor and cable.

Installation – 1) Install recliner motor and cable. Ensure cable is equipped with cable housing clip and clamp. Connect wiring. Install recliner motor-to-seat track front cross strap.

2) Align seat track with cushion frame. Route cable housing toward recliner through gap between cushion frame and track side strap. Install seat track to cushion frame.

3) Install cable. Ensure cable's square drive end connects with square hole in transmission worm gear. Install cable housing into transmission housing. Install cable housing-to-transmission housing clamp. Clamp prongs point toward floor. Install cable housing clip in cushion frame. Install seat outboard side shields. Install seat.

POWER RECLINER DRIVE HINGE

Removal – 1) Remove recliner trim. Remove 4 recliner-to-seat frame screws. Seat trim may cover screws on some models. Disconnect cable housing clamp at transmission.

2) Carefully disconnect cable from transmission. DO NOT pull cable from motor. If cable pulls from motor, see POWER RECLINER MOTOR & CABLE under REMOVAL & INSTALLATION.

Installation – Install cable, ensuring square-drive cable end seats in recliner drive hinge worm gear. Seat cable housing into transmission housing. Install cable housing-to-transmission clamp. Clamp prongs point toward floor. Install 4 recliner-to-seat frame screws. Install seat outboard side shields. Set system soft limits.

MEMORY CONTROL MODULE

Removal & Installation – Remove seat. See SEAT ASSEMBLY under REMOVAL & INSTALLATION. Place seat upside down on clean surface. Remove memory control module-to-seat track screws. Disconnect control module wiring. Remove memory control module. To install, reverse removal procedure. Set system soft limits. See SYSTEM SOFT LIMITS under OPERATION.

RECLINER SWITCH

Removal & Installation – Remove recliner trim. Disconnect recliner switch wiring. Remove recliner switch screws from side shields. Remove recliner switch. To install, reverse removal procedure.

TESTING

NOTE: Ensure battery is fully charged and all electrical connections are proper before any testing.

MEMORY SEAT SELF-TEST

Press memory switches "1" and "2" and hold 5-10 seconds. Press SET button and hold 5-10 seconds. This will enter self-diagnostic mode.

- Three seconds after releasing switches, control module should move seat to a mid-travel position.
- Within 10 seconds, move seat switch to activate a seat motor. Check for seat movement in all switch positions: seat track forward, rearward, front upward and front downward.
- Within 10 seconds of last seat movement, press memory switches "1" and "2" for at least 5 seconds and release. Seat should move to a full downward and rearward position. Module should move seat until it comes to a stall in 8 positions: forward, rearward, front up, front down, rear up, rear down, recliner forward and recliner downward.
- If a problem exists, control module will not move seat for that function.
- After all motors have run to stall, system will pause for 3 seconds, then return to mid-travel position. Control module will move seat through its positions for a 2-second run.

- Within 10 seconds of last seat movement, press memory switches "1" and "2" for at least 5 seconds and release. This will activate power mirror test. Control module will move right mirror fully horizontally outboard, then fully horizontally inboard. Left mirror will then move inboard, outboard, up and down. Motor will run until each mirror face has been stalled for 1-1/2 seconds at end of travel. If a problem with mirror rheostat is encountered, that particular motor will not be actuated.
- If a problem is found, control module will go into a loop and move only problem part of system.
- To exit loop, repair the fault or press SET or "1" or "2" buttons. When seat and mirror stops, system will return to normal operating mode.
- If a problem is found, see TROUBLE SHOOTING.

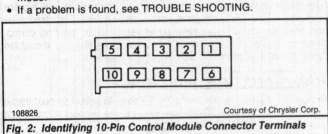

108826   Courtesy of Chrysler Corp.

Fig. 2: Identifying 10-Pin Control Module Connector Terminals

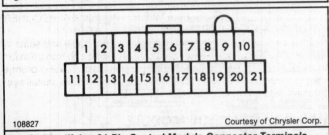

108827   Courtesy of Chrysler Corp.

Fig. 3: Identifying 21-Pin Control Module Connector Terminals

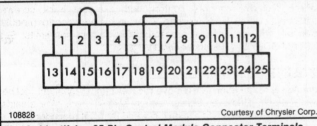

108828   Courtesy of Chrysler Corp.

Fig. 4: Identifying 25-Pin Control Module Connector Terminals

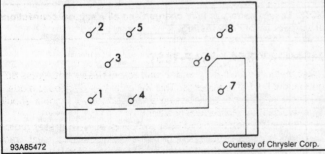

93A85472   Courtesy of Chrysler Corp.

Fig. 5: Identifying Seat Switch Connector Terminals

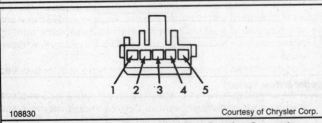

108830   Courtesy of Chrysler Corp.

Fig. 6: Identifying 5-Pin Recliner Position Sensing Connector Terminals

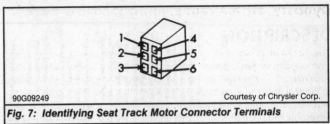

90G09249   Courtesy of Chrysler Corp.

Fig. 7: Identifying Seat Track Motor Connector Terminals

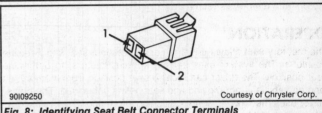

90I09250   Courtesy of Chrysler Corp.

Fig. 8: Identifying Seat Belt Connector Terminals

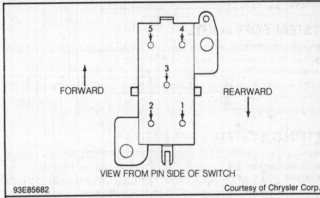

93E85682   Courtesy of Chrysler Corp.

Fig. 9: Identifying Recliner Switch Connector Terminals

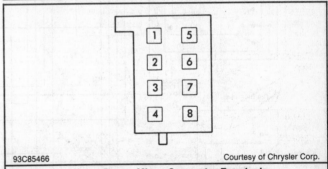

93C85466   Courtesy of Chrysler Corp.

Fig. 10: Identifying Power Mirror Connector Terminals

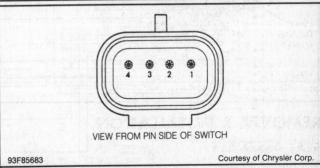

93F85683   Courtesy of Chrysler Corp.

Fig. 11: Identifying Memory Switch Connector Terminals

WIRING DIAGRAMS

NOTE: For terminal identification of power memory seat system connectors, see Figs. 2-11.

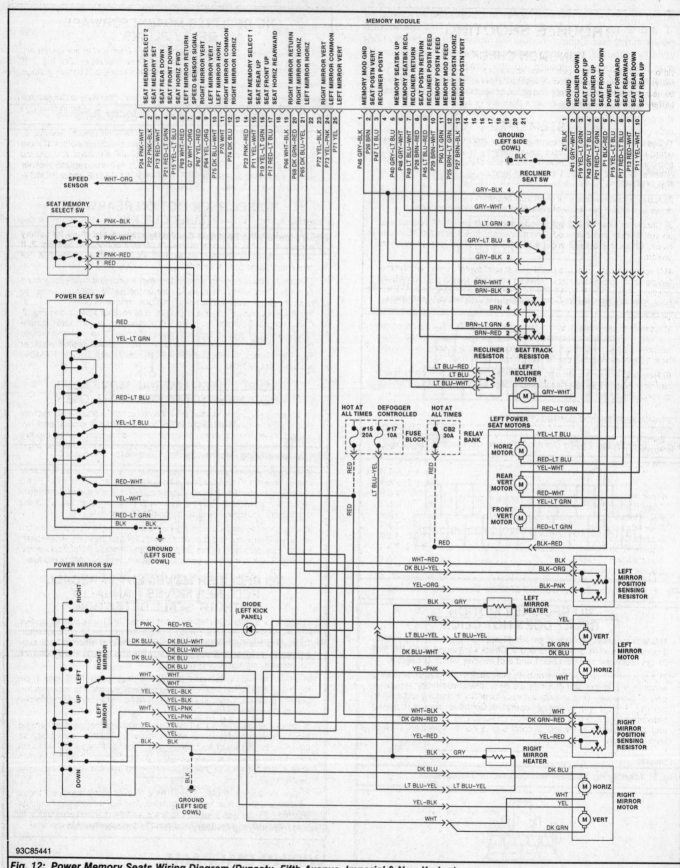

Fig. 12: Power Memory Seats Wiring Diagram (Dynasty, Fifth Avenue, Imperial & New Yorker)

93C85441

TROUBLE SHOOTING

FUNCTION CHECK

Before any diagnosis is performed move seat switches and listen for relays clicking in control module located underneath seat. If relays can be heard clicking, main battery and ground circuits to control module and battery circuit to switches in driver's door are good.

NO SYSTEM OPERATION

1) Check for an open or loose circuit breaker mounted in board on relay board in cavity No. 15. Activate power memory seat and recliner switch and check for continuity between ground side of 2-wire connector under driver's seat and pin No. 1 of control module 10-wire connector. *See Figs. 1 and 2.*

2) Activate switch and check continuity between 2-wire connector under driver's seat and pin No. 6 of control module 10-wire connector.

3) Check for seat movement by operating seat switch. If seat moves, control module circuit is good. If no movement, check fuse No. 15 in fuse block. Check for battery voltage to pin No. 3 of driver's power seat switch.

4) If voltage exists, check driver's power seat switch. Using an ohmmeter, perform continuity check between pins with switch set in specified position. See POWER SEAT SWITCH CONTINUITY SPECIFICATIONS table. *See Fig. 6.* If there is no continuity at any of the switch positions, replace switch.

5) If switch is okay, check all connectors for proper mating. If connectors are okay, replace control module. If replacing control module, open memory module and check printed circuit board. If a burnt area exists near 10-pin connector, recliner switch may be at fault.

6) Remove recliner switch and check movable contacts. If contact arm can be rotated, replace recliner switch. New switch will prevent damage to control module.

POWER SEAT SWITCH CONTINUITY CHECK

Switch Position	Check Continuity Between Pins
Off	6 & 8; 6 & 7
	6 & 5; 6 & 4
	6 & 2; 6 & 1
Front Rocker Up	3 & 5
Front Rocker Down	3 & 2
Rear Rocker Up	3 & 4
Rear Rocker Down	3 & 1
Square Knob Up	3 & 5; 3 & 4
Square Knob Down	3 & 2; 3 & 1
Square Knob Forward	3 & 8
Square Knob Rearward	3 & 7

NO RECLINER MOTION
RELAY DOES NOT CLICK

1) Check for battery voltage at pin No. 11 of 21-pin connector and pin No. 3 of recliner switch. *See Figs. 3 and 9.* Check for ground at pin No. 1 of 21-pin connector and pins No. 1 and 5 of recliner switch connector.

2) If ground in missing at one or both pins, repair or replace seat wiring harness. If voltages and grounds are okay, check continuity of recliner switch. Continuity should exist between pins No. 5 and 2 and between pins No. 1 and 4 with switch not operated. Continuity should also exist between pins No. 3 and 2 with switch forward, and between pins No. 3 and 4 with switch rearward. If continuity is not as specified, replace recliner switch

NO RECLINER MOTION FORWARD
RELAY CLICKS

1) Activate power memory seat and recliner switch and check for battery voltage at pin No. 2 of control module 10-wire connector. *See Fig. 2.* If battery voltage is not present, replace control module. If battery voltage is present, go to next step.

2) Activate power memory seat and recliner switch and check for ground at pin No. 4 of control module 10-wire connector. If ground in okay, go to next step. If ground in not okay, replace control module.

3) Check for battery voltage at pin No. 3 of recliner switch. *See Fig. 9.* Check for ground at pins No. 1 and 5 of recliner switch connector. If there is no voltage or ground, replace control module. If voltage and ground checks are okay and recliner motor will not operate, replace recliner motor and cable. See RECLINER MOTOR AND CABLE under REMOVAL & INSTALLATION.

NO RECLINER MOTION REARWARD
RELAY CLICKS

1) Activate power memory seat and recliner switch and check for battery voltage at pin No. 4 of control module 10-wire connector. *See Fig. 2.* If battery voltage is present, go to next step. If battery voltage is not present, replace control module.

2) Activate power memory seat and recliner switch and check for ground at pin No. 2 of control module 10-wire connector. If ground is okay, go to next step. If ground is not okay, replace control module.

3) Check for battery voltage at pin No. 3 of recliner switch. *See Fig. 9.* Check for ground at pins No. 1 and 5 of recliner switch connector. If there is no voltage or ground, replace control module. If voltage and ground checks are okay and recliner motor will not operate, replace recliner motor and cable. See RECLINER MOTOR AND CABLE under REMOVAL & INSTALLATION.

NO RECLINER MANUAL MOVEMENT
RECLINER MOVES IN RECALL ONLY

1) Check seat wiring harness between control module and recliner switch for shorted wires to ground or crossed wires. If ground pins No. 1 and 5 are in wrong cavities of recliner switch connector, control module may be damaged. Correct wiring and replace control module. If wiring is okay, go to next step.

2) If recliner moves rearward in recall mode only, go to step **3)**. If recliner moves forward in recall mode only, press recliner switch in foreward direction and check for battery voltage at pin No. 2 of recliner switch connector and at pin No. 5 of control module 21 pin connector. *See Fig. 3 and 9.* If battery voltage is present, replace control module.

3) If recliner moves rearward in recall mode only, press recliner switch in rearward direction and check for battery voltage at pin No. 4 of recliner switch connector and at pin No. 6 of control module 21-pin connector. *See Fig. 3 and 9.* If battery voltage is present, replace control module.

NO RECLINER MOVEMENT IN RECALL
RECLINER MOVES MANUALLY
WITHOUT STALL DETECTION

1) Check for 5 volts at pin No. 9 of control module 21-wire connector. *See Fig. 3.* Check for ground at pin No. 7 of control module 21-pin connector. To check ground, one lead of voltmeter must be connected to 5 volt supply (pin No. 9) for control module. If 5 volt sensing voltage and ground are not present, replace control module.

2) If 5 volt sensing voltage and ground are okay, check for 5 volts at pin No. 2 (Light Blue/Red wire) of recliner position sensing Black connector. *See Fig. 6.* Check for ground at pin No. 4 (White wire) of recliner position sensor Black connector.

3) Check voltage at pin No. 3 (Light Blue wire) of recliner position sensing Black connector with recliner switch activated. Voltage should be less than 5 volts with seat fully forward and more than zero volts with seat fully reclined. If voltage is as specified, go to next step. If voltage is zero volts, check for short to ground in seat wiring harness. Repair wiring as necessary.

4) Check voltage at pin No. 3 (Light Blue wire) of control module 21-wire connector with recliner switch activated. *See Fig. 3.* Voltage should be less than 5 volts with seat fully forward and more than zero volts with seat fully reclined. If voltage is as specified, replace control module.

NO SEAT OR RECLINER MOTION
FROM MANUAL SWITCHES
MOVES IN RECALL MODE ONLY

1) Check for stuck switch contact in recliner switch mounted in left side of driver's seat. To do this, check continuity of recliner switch. Continuity should exist between pins No. 5 and 2 and between pins No. 1 and 4 with switch not operated. *See Fig. 9.*

2) Continuity should also exist between pins No. 3 and 2 with switch forward, and between pins No. 3 and 4 with switch rearward. If continuity is as specified, go to next step. If continuity is not as specified, replace recliner switch

3) Check driver's power seat switch. Using an ohmmeter, perform continuity check between pins with switch set in specified position. See POWER SEAT SWITCH CONTINUITY SPECIFICATIONS table under NO SYSTEM OPERATION. If there is no continuity at any of the switch positions, replace switch.

NO MEMORY RECALL OF
SEATS, RECLINER OR MIRRORS
MANUAL ADJUSTMENT ONLY

Check for stuck switch contact in memory switch. See MEMORY SWITCH CONTINUITY table. *See Fig. 11.* Check for battery voltage at pin No. 1 of memory switch.

MEMORY SWITCH CONTINUITY CHECK

Switch Position	Check Continuity Between Pins
No Switch Operated	None
"1" Actuated	1 & 2
"2" Actuated	1 & 3
"S" Actuated	1 & 4

NO MEMORY RECALL OF SEAT,
RECLINER, OR MIRRORS TO POSITION NO. 1
UNABLE TO ENTER DIAGNOSTIC SELF-TEST
MODES, POSITION NO. 2 RECALL OPERATES

1) Using an ohmmeter, check for continuity of actuated memory position No. 1 switch. See MEMORY SWITCH CONTINUITY CHECK table. *See Fig. 11.* If continuity is present, go to next step. If continuity is not present, replace switch.

2) Check for poor terminal contact at memory switch connector terminal No. 2 and repair as necessary. *See Fig. 11.* If terminal contact is okay, go to next step.

3) Activate position No. 1 switch. Using a voltmeter, check for battery voltage between control module 25-pin connector terminal No. 14 and ground. If battery voltage is present, but there is no reaction from control module, manually move seat to a different position than No. 2. If there is still no control module reaction, replace control module.

NO NEW POSITIONS CAN BE SET
UNABLE TO ENTER SELF-TEST MODE
ONLY PREVIOUS MEMORY RECALLED

1) Check for continuity of memory switch circuits. See MEMORY SWITCH CONTINUITY CHECK table. If continuity exists, go to next step. If continuity does not exist, replace memory switch.

2) Check for broken or pushed out pin No. 4 of memory switch. *See Fig. 11.* With SET button actuated, check for battery voltage at pin No. 2 of control module 25-pin connector. If battery voltage exists, no pin is broken or pushed out and connector is properly seated, replace control module

NO MEMORY RECALL OF SEAT RECLINER,
OR MIRRORS TO POSITION 2 ONLY
UNABLE TO ENTER DIAGNOSTIC SELF-TEST
MODES, POSITION 1 RECALL OKAY

1) Check for continuity of actuated memory POSITION 2 button. If continuity is okay, go to next step. If not, replace switch.

2) Check terminal 3 of the memory switch connector for a damaged or pushed out pin. Actuate POSITION 2 button and check for battery voltage at terminal No. 1 of control module 25-pin connector.

3) If battery voltage is present, and terminal pin is not damaged or pushed out, ensure connector is seated correctly. If control module operation is still faulty, manually move seat to a different position to ensure positions are not duplicated. If positions are not duplicated and control module action is still faulty, replace control module.

NO CRUISE CONTROL SPEED SET
NO AUTOMATIC DOOR LOCK AT 15 MPH
SPEEDOMETER REMAINS AT ZERO MPH

Disconnect memory seat control module 25-pin connector. *See Fig. 1.* Road test vehicle. If doors lock, cruise control accepts a set and speedometer registers speed, replace control module.

NO MOVEMENT IN RECALL
SEAT MOVES MANUALLY
WITHOUT STALL DETECTION

1) Check for 5 volts at pin No. 10 of control module 25-pin connector. This is 5-volt feed from control module to seat track sensing position sensing potentiometer.

2) Check for ground at pin No. 8 of control module 25-pin connector while other voltmeter lead is connected to a voltage supply. If voltage and ground do not exist when seat switch is pressed, replace control module. If voltage and ground exist, go to next step.

3) Check for 5 volts at pin No. 5 of seat track 5-pin connector. *See Fig. 6.* Check for ground at pin No. 4 of seat track 5-pin connector. If voltage and ground do not exist, repair harness. If voltage and ground exist but power seat adjuster still has no movement in recall mode, go to next step.

4) Disconnect seat track 5-pin connector. Using an ohmmeter, check for resistance between pins No. 4 and 5 of seat track motor connector. *See Fig. 7.* If resistance is not 2600-4000 ohms, replace seat motor package.

MEMORY RECALLS CAN BE SET
WITH VEHICLE MOVING/BELT UNBUCKLED

1) Check for continuity between pin No. 9 of left side instrument panel Blue 16-pin connector and pin No. 7 of control module 25-pin connector. If continuity does not exist, repair circuit. If continuity exists, go to next step.

2) Check for 5 volts at pin No. 7 of control module 25-pin connector with ignition on and while moving vehicle 3-5 feet. If 5-volt signal does not exist, check for broken or shorted wires and connectors. Repair circuit as necessary.

NO MEMORY POSITIONS RECALLED
SELF-TEST SWITCH CHECK WORKS

1) Unbuckle seat belt. Check for continuity across seat belt switch 2-pin connector. Ensure contact opens when seat belt is buckled. Check continuity between pin No. 2 of seat belt switch 2-pin connector and ground. *See Fig. 8.*

2) Check continuity between pin No. 13 of control module 25-pin connector and pin No. 1 of seat belt switch connector. *See Figs. 4 and 8.* Check for open or shorted wire between control module and seat belt switch.

NO SEAT TRACK FORWARD OR REARWARD
MOVEMENT IN RECALL MODE
SEAT TRACK WILL MOVE FORWARD OR
REARWARD BY MANUAL SWITCH ACTUATION
WITHOUT STALL DETECTION

1) Check for voltage at terminal No. 12 of control module 21-pin connector. *See Fig. 3.* Less than 5 volts should be present for seat track full forward position. Greater than zero volts should be present when in fully rearward position. Voltage should vary with position.

2) Attach ground lead of DVOM to terminal No. 4 of 5-pin connector. Check for voltage at terminal No. 1 of 5-pin (Natural color) connector. Repeat procedure as described in step **1)**. If voltage is zero, disconnect 5-pin (Natural color) connector and check harness for a short to ground. If no short is found, reconnect 5-pin connector and go to next step.

3) Check for voltage as described in step **1)**. If voltage does not vary as seat position is moved forward or rearward, the sensing potentiometer is defective. Replace the seat motor assembly. Reconnect all wiring and reinstall seat in vehicle. Operate switches manually to cause maximum seat movement in all directions. Perform memory seat self-tests to program soft limits to control module. See MEMORY SEAT SELF-TEST under TESTING.

NO SEAT TRACK FRONT UP OR DOWN MOVEMENT IN RECALL MODE
SEAT TRACK FRONT WILL MOVE UP OR DOWN BY MANUAL SWITCH ACTUATION WITHOUT STALL DETECTION

1) Check for voltage at terminal No. 2 of 21-pin connector. *See Fig. 3.* Less than 5 volts should be present for seat track front full up position. Greater than zero volts should be present when in fully down position. Voltage should vary with position.

2) Attach ground lead of DVOM to terminal No. 4 of 5-pin (Natural color) connector. Check for voltage at terminal No. 2 of 5-pin (Natural color) connector. Repeat procedure as described in step **1)**. If voltage is zero, disconnect 5-pin connector and check harness for a short to ground. If no short is found, reconnect 5-pin connector and go to next step.

3) Check for voltage as described in step **1)**. If voltage does not vary as the seat track front is moved up and down, the sensing potentiometer is defective. Replace the seat motor assembly. Reconnect all wiring and reinstall seat in vehicle. Operate switches manually to cause maximum seat movement in all directions. Perform memory seat self-test to program soft limits to control module.

NO SEAT TRACK REAR UP OR DOWN MOVEMENT IN RECALL MODE
SEAT TRACK REAR WILL MOVE UP OR DOWN BY MANUAL SWITCH ACTUATION WITHOUT STALL DETECTION

1) Check for voltage at terminal No. 13 of 21-pin connector. *See Fig. 3.* Less than 5 volts should be present for seat track rear full up position. Greater than zero volts should be present when in fully down position. Voltage should vary with position.

2) Attach ground lead of DVOM to terminal No. 4 of 5-pin connector. Check for voltage at terminal No. 3 of 5-pin (Natural color) connector. Repeat procedure as described in step **1)**. If voltage is zero, disconnect 5-pin connector and check harness for a short to ground. If no short is found, reconnect 5-pin connector and go to next step.

3) Check for voltage as described in step **1)**. If voltage does not vary as the seat track rear is moved up and down, the sensing potentiometer is defective. Replace the seat motor assembly. Reconnect all wiring and reinstall seat in vehicle. Operate switches manually to cause maximum seat movement in all directions. Perform memory seat self-test to program soft limits to control module.

NO MOVEMENT OF SEAT
SEAT WILL MOVE IN RECALL MODE ONLY

1) Check for battery voltage at terminal No. 3 of drivers power seat switch. *See Fig. 5.* Disconnect switch and check continuity of memory switch. See MEMORY SWITCH CONTINUITY table.

MEMORY SWITCH CONTINUITY

Application	Pin Continuity
Memory Portion – Pins 1-5	
Neutral Position	5 & 2, 1 & 4
Recliner Forward	3 & 2
Recliner Rearward	3 & 4

2) If switch tests okay, check continuity between driver's door switch and 25-pin control module connector. Disconnect harness connectors from components. See HARNESS CONTINUITY table.

3) Repair wiring as necessary for open or shorted circuits. Check terminal connections for pushed out pins or faulty crimps. If harness is okay, replace control module.

HARNESS CONTINUITY (SEAT SWITCH-TO-CONTROL MODULE)

Switch Position	Seat Switch	Control Module
Forward	8	5
Rearward	7	17
Front Up	5	16
Front Down	2	4
Rear Up	4	15
Rear Down	1	3

NO SEAT MOVEMENT
RELAYS CLICK WHEN SWITCH ACTIVATED

1) Operate seat and check for battery voltage and grounds at control module 10-pin connector. *See Fig. 2.* See CONTROL MODULE 10-PIN CONNECTOR VOLTAGE & GROUND table. If circuits are okay, go to next step. If circuits are not okay, replace control module.

CONTROL MODULE 10-PIN CONNECTOR VOLTAGE & GROUND

Seat Direction	Terminal No.
Forward	
Battery Voltage	7
Ground	8
Rearward	
Battery Voltage	8
Ground	7
Front Up	
Battery Voltage	3
Ground	5
Front Down	
Battery Voltage	5
Ground	3
Rear Up	
Battery Voltage	10
Ground	9
Rear Down	
Battery Voltage	9
Ground	10

2) Using an ohmmeter, check for continuity between control module 10-pin connector and seat motor 6-pin connector. *See Figs. 2 and 7.* See CONTROL MODULE 10-PIN CONNECTOR & SEAT MOTOR 6-PIN CONNECTOR CONTINUITY table. Repair wiring as necessary. If circuits are okay but seat movement is absent, replace seat motor package assembly. Operate switches manually to obtain maximum seat movement in all directions.

CONTROL MODULE 10-PIN CONNECTOR & SEAT MOTOR 6-PIN CONNECTOR CONTINUITY

Motor Terminal	Control Module Terminal
1	7
2	10
3	3
4	8
5	9
6	5

NO MIRROR MOVEMENT WHEN MIRROR SWITCH ACTIVATED, MIRRORS MOVE DURING RECALL ONLY

1) Remove driver's door panel. Locate mirror switch 8-pin connector in door. *See Fig. 10.* Use a voltmeter and backprobe between 8-pin connector terminal No. 1 and ground. If battery voltage is not present, go to next step. If battery voltage is present, go to step **3)**.

2) If battery voltage was not present in previous step, check diode package located in left cowl side area. Grounded wire on switch side of diode will cause diode package to open. If replacement is necessary, ensure connections are soldered and taped.

3) If battery voltage was present in step **1)**, check for ground at 8-pin connector terminal No. 5. *See Fig. 10.* If ground is okay, check voltage and grounds at mirror switch 8-pin connector. See MIRROR SWITCH 8-PIN CONNECTOR SPECIFICATIONS table. Repair wiring or switch as necessary.

NO MIRROR MOVEMENT WHEN MIRROR SWITCH ACTIVATED, MIRRORS MOVE DURING RECALL ONLY (Cont.)

MIRROR SWITCH 8-PIN CONNECTOR SPECIFICATIONS

Mirror Direction	Terminal No.
Left Mirror	
Up	
Battery Voltage	2
Ground	3
Down	
Battery Voltage	3
Ground	2
Left	
Battery Voltage	1
Ground	3
Right	
Battery Voltage	3
Ground	1
Right Mirror	
Up	
Battery Voltage	6
Ground	7
Down	
Battery Voltage	7
Ground	6
Left	
Battery Voltage	5
Ground	7
Right	
Battery Voltage	7
Ground	5

NO MOVEMENT OF BOTH OR ONE MIRROR DURING RECALL MODE MIRRORS MOVE ONLY WHEN POWER MIRROR SWITCH ACTUATED, MEMORY SEAT & RECLINER MOVE IN RECALL

1) If all memory mirror recall movements are missing, set mirrors to 2 different vertical and horizontal positions for both mirrors. Attempt to recall these set positions. Check for no movement in a specific direction for a specific mirror. If there is no movement of either mirror in any direction, replace control module. Perform memory seat diagnostic self-test so control module will learn soft limits of the assembly. See MEMORY SEAT SELF-TEST under TESTING.

2) If mirror will not move in a specific direction, see MEMORY SEAT SELF-TEST under TESTING to determine if fault is with a motor or position sensing rheostat circuit. If fault is with motor, go to next step. If fault is with rheostat circuit, go to step **4)**.

3) Check continuity of motor drive circuits between control module 25-pin connector and mirror 8-pin connector. *See Figs. 4 and 10.* See CONTROL MODULE 25-PIN CONNECTOR & MIRROR 8-PIN CONNECTOR CONTINUITY table. Repair wiring as necessary. Perform memory seat diagnostic self-test so control module will learn soft limits of the assembly. See MEMORY SEAT SELF-TEST under TESTING.

CONTROL MODULE 25-PIN CONNECTOR & MIRROR 8-PIN CONNECTOR CONTINUITY

25-Pin Connector	8-Pin Connector
Left Mirror	
24	1
10	2
25	3
Right Mirror	
11	1
12	2
23	3

4) Disconnect 25-pin connector under driver's seat. Using an ohmmeter, check resistance between 25-pin connector terminals. See Fig. 4. See LEFT & RIGHT MIRROR RHEOSTAT RESISTANCE specifications table. If resistances are not to specification, go to next step.

5) Check for continuity of position sensing rheostat circuits between control module 25-pin connector and mirror 8-pin connector (for left or right mirror, as necessary). *See Figs. 4 and 10.* See POSITION SENSING RHEOSTAT CIRCUIT RESISTANCE table. If continuity is not present, go to step **7)**. If continuity is present, go to next step.

NO MOVEMENT OF BOTH OR ONE MIRROR DURING RECALL MODE MIRRORS MOVE ONLY WHEN POWER MIRROR SWITCH ACTUATED, MEMORY SEAT & RECLINER MOVE IN RECALL (Cont.)

LEFT & RIGHT MIRROR RHEOSTAT RESISTANCE

Mirror Position/Terminals	Ohms
Left Mirror	
Down (Terminals No. 6 & 9)	Greater Than 100
Left (Terminals No. 6 & 21)	Greater Than 100
Up (Terminals No. 6 & 9)	Less Than 4500
Right (Terminals No. 6 & 21)	Less Than 4500
Right Mirror	
Down (Terminals No. 19 & 8)	Greater Than 100
Left (Terminals No. 19 & 20)	Greater Than 100
Up (Terminals No. 19 & 8)	Less Than 4500
Right (Terminals No. 19 & 20)	Less Than 4500

POSITION SENSING RHEOSTAT CIRCUIT RESISTANCE

25-Pin Connector	8-Pin Connector
Left Mirror	
6	8
21	7
9	6
Right Mirror	
19	8
20	7
8	6

6) Connect an ohmmeter between mirror 8-pin connector terminals. See MEMORY MIRROR RHEOSTAT TEST SPECIFICATIONS table. Move mirror face manually during test. If resistance values do not change between those listed in table, replace mirror assembly.

MEMORY MIRROR RHEOSTAT TEST SPECIFICATIONS

Mirror Position/Terminals	Ohms
Down	
Terminals No. 8 & 6	Greater Than 100
Left	
Terminals No. 8 & 7	Greater Than 100
Up	
Terminals No. 8 & 6	Less Than 4500
Right	
Terminals No. 8 & 7	Less Than 4500

7) Use an ohmmeter and isolate circuits and components at fault. Repair or replace wiring harness as necessary. If fault is in mirror, replace mirror assembly. If all circuits are okay, replace control module.

NO SEAT MOVEMENT RELAYS CLICK WHEN SWITCH ACTIVATED

1) Operate seat and check for battery voltage and grounds at control module 10-pin connector. *See Fig. 2.* See CONTROL MODULE 10-PIN CONNECTOR VOLTAGE & GROUND table. If circuits are okay, go to next step. If circuits are not okay, replace control module.

CONTROL MODULE 10-PIN CONNECTOR VOLTAGE & GROUND

Seat Direction	Terminal No.
Forward	
Battery Voltage	7
Ground	8
Rearward	
Battery Voltage	8
Ground	7
Front Up	
Battery Voltage	3
Ground	5
Front Down	
Battery Voltage	5
Ground	3
Rear Up	
Battery Voltage	10
Ground	9
Rear Down	
Battery Voltage	9
Ground	10

NO SEAT MOVEMENT
RELAYS CLICK WHEN SWITCH ACTIVATED
(Cont.)

2) Using an ohmmeter, check for continuity between control module 10-pin connector and seat motor 6-pin connector. *See Figs. 2 and 7.* See CONTROL MODULE 10-PIN CONNECTOR & SEAT MOTOR 6-PIN CONNECTOR CONTINUITY table. Repair wiring as necessary. If circuits are okay but seat movement is absent, replace seat motor package assembly. Operate switches manually to obtain maximum seat movement in all directions.

CONTROL MODULE 10-PIN CONNECTOR & SEAT MOTOR 6-PIN CONNECTOR CONTINUITY

Motor Terminal	Control Module Terminal
1	7
2	10
3	3
4	8
5	9
6	5

NO MIRROR MOVEMENT WHEN MIRROR SWITCH ACTIVATED, MIRRORS MOVE DURING RECALL ONLY

1) Remove driver's door panel. Locate mirror switch 8-pin connector in door. *See Fig. 10.* Use a voltmeter and backprobe between 8-pin connector terminal No. 1 and ground. If battery voltage is not present, go to next step. If battery voltage is present, go to step 3).

2) If battery voltage was not present in previous step, check diode package located in left cowl side area. Grounded wire on switch side of diode will cause diode package to open. If replacement is necessary, ensure connections are soldered and taped.

3) If battery voltage was present in step 1), check for ground at 8-pin connector terminal No. 5. *See Fig. 10.* If ground is okay, check voltage and grounds at mirror switch 8-pin connector. See MIRROR SWITCH 8-PIN CONNECTOR SPECIFICATIONS table. Repair wiring or switch as necessary.

MIRROR SWITCH 8-PIN CONNECTOR SPECIFICATIONS

Mirror Direction	Terminal No.
Left Mirror	
Up	
Battery Voltage	2
Ground	3
Down	
Battery Voltage	3
Ground	2
Left	
Battery Voltage	1
Ground	3
Right	
Battery Voltage	3
Ground	1
Right Mirror	
Up	
Battery Voltage	6
Ground	7
Down	
Battery Voltage	7
Ground	6
Left	
Battery Voltage	5
Ground	7
Right	
Battery Voltage	7
Ground	5

NO MOVEMENT OF BOTH OR ONE MIRROR DURING RECALL MODE MIRRORS MOVE ONLY WHEN POWER MIRROR SWITCH ACTUATED, MEMORY SEAT & RECLINER MOVE IN RECALL

1) If all memory mirror recall movements are missing, set mirrors to 2 different vertical and horizontal positions for both mirrors. Attempt to recall these set positions. Check for no movement in a specific direction for a specific mirror. If there is no movement of either mirror in any direction, replace control module. Perform memory seat diagnostic self-test so control module will learn soft limits of the assembly. See MEMORY SEAT SELF-TEST under TESTING.

2) If mirror will not move in a specific direction, see MEMORY SEAT SELF-TEST under TESTING to determine if fault is with a motor or position sensing rheostat circuit. If fault is with motor, go to next step. If fault is with rheostat circuit, go to step 4).

3) Check continuity of motor drive circuits between control module 25-pin connector and mirror 8-pin connector. *See Figs. 4 and 10.* See CONTROL MODULE 25-PIN CONNECTOR & MIRROR 8-PIN CONNECTOR CONTINUITY table. Repair wiring as necessary. Perform memory seat diagnostic self-test so control module will learn soft limits of the assembly. See MEMORY SEAT SELF-TEST under TESTING.

CONTROL MODULE 25-PIN CONNECTOR & MIRROR 8-PIN CONNECTOR CONTINUITY

25-Pin Connector	8-Pin Connector
Left Mirror	
24	1
10	2
25	3
Right Mirror	
11	1
12	2
23	3

4) Disconnect 25-pin connector under driver's seat. Using an ohmmeter, check resistance between 25-pin connector terminals. See Fig. 4. See LEFT & RIGHT MIRROR RHEOSTAT RESISTANCE specifications table. If resistances are not to specification, go to next step.

LEFT & RIGHT MIRROR RHEOSTAT RESISTANCE

Mirror Position/Terminals	Ohms
Left Mirror	
Down (Terminals No. 6 & 9)	Greater Than 100
Left (Terminals No. 6 & 21)	Greater Than 100
Up (Terminals No. 6 & 9)	Less Than 4500
Right (Terminals No. 6 & 21)	Less Than 4500
Right Mirror	
Down (Terminals No. 19 & 8)	Greater Than 100
Left (Terminals No. 19 & 20)	Greater Than 100
Up (Terminals No. 19 & 8)	Less Than 4500
Right (Terminals No. 19 & 20)	Less Than 4500

5) Check for continuity of position sensing rheostat circuits between control module 25-pin connector and mirror 8-pin connector (for left or right mirror, as necessary). *See Figs. 4 and 10.* See POSITION SENSING RHEOSTAT CIRCUIT RESISTANCE table. If continuity is not present, go to step 7). If continuity is present, go to next step.

POSITION SENSING RHEOSTAT CIRCUIT RESISTANCE

25-Pin Connector	8-Pin Connector
Left Mirror	
6	8
21	7
9	6
Right Mirror	
19	8
20	7
8	6

6) Connect an ohmmeter between mirror 8-pin connector terminals. See MEMORY MIRROR RHEOSTAT TEST SPECIFICATIONS table. Move mirror face manually during test. If resistance values do not change between those listed in table, replace mirror assembly.

NO MOVEMENT OF BOTH OR ONE MIRROR DURING RECALL MODE MIRRORS MOVE ONLY WHEN POWER MIRROR SWITCH ACTUATED, MEMORY SEAT & RECLINER MOVE IN RECALL (Cont.)

MEMORY MIRROR RHEOSTAT TEST SPECIFICATIONS

Mirror Position/Terminals	Ohms
Down	
Terminals No. 8 & 6	Greater Than 100
Left	
Terminals No. 8 & 7	Greater Than 100
Up	
Terminals No. 8 & 6	Less Than 4500
Right	
Terminals No. 8 & 7	Less Than 4500

7) Use an ohmmeter and isolate circuits and components at fault. Repair or replace wiring harness as necessary. If fault is in mirror, replace mirror assembly. If all circuits are okay, replace control module.

Concorde, Dynasty, Fifth Avenue, Imperial, Intrepid, New Yorker, Vision

DESCRIPTION & OPERATION

All models use a power trunk release system that uses an electric switch located inside the glove box to release the trunk lid. The trunk lid contains a latch and solenoid to release the lid.

Dynasty, Fifth Avenue, Imperial and New Yorker models use a power trunk pull-down system that pulls down and latches the trunk lid during the last 1" (25 mm) of travel. A combination latch/release mechanism is located in the trunk lid. A pull-down motor is located in the trunk lid opening lower panel.

When the trunk lid is closed, very light pressure is required to cause the latch to grab the pull-down bar. The bar will then automatically take the lid to its completely closed position.

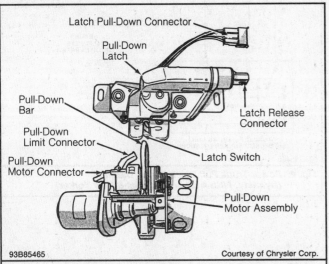

Latch Pull-Down Connector

Pull-Down Latch

Pull-Down Bar

Pull-Down Limit Connector

Pull-Down Motor Connector

Latch Release Connector

Latch Switch

Pull-Down Motor Assembly

93B85465

Courtesy of Chrysler Corp.

Fig. 1: Identifying Power Trunk Release Latch & Pull-Down Motor

TROUBLE SHOOTING

Check the following items for possible causes of system malfunctions before performing individual tests.
- Faulty Fuses Or Circuit Breaker
- Loose Or Corroded Connectors
- Low Battery Charge
- Poor Ground Connections
- Linkage Disconnected, Binding Or Bent
- Inoperative Lock Or Latch Mechanism

TESTING

TRUNK LID RELEASE TEST

Check that solenoid wire is connected. Using voltmeter, check that 10 volts or more are present at solenoid. Check that proper ground is available at latch mounting screws. Remove latch and examine plunger. Plunger should spring back when pressed. Plunger travel should be at least 5/8" (16 mm).

POWER PULL-DOWN LATCH TEST

1) Open trunk lid and ensure latch switch is released. Check for continuity between Black/Red and Black wires.
2) Depress latch switch and check for continuity between Black/White and Black wire terminals. If either test does not show continuity, replace pull-down latch

POWER TRUNK PULL-DOWN MOTOR TEST

1) Disconnect motor connector wiring. Connect battery voltage to Red wire of motor and ground Tan wire. This will cause pull-down bar to retract.
2) With 12 volts still connected to Red wire, ground Gray wire. This will cause pull-down bar to raise to open position. If pull-down limit switch is depressed at this time, motor should stop. If motor fails any of these tests, replace motor.

REMOVAL & INSTALLATION

CAUTION: When battery is disconnected, vehicle computer and memory systems may lose memory data. Driveability problems may exist until computer systems have completed a relearn cycle. See COMPUTER RELEARN PROCEDURES article in GENERAL INFORMATION before disconnecting battery.

TRUNK LID RELEASE SWITCH

Removal & Installation – Using small screwdriver, pry switch from glove box housing. Disconnect harness connector and remove switch. To install, reverse removal procedure.

TRUNK LID SOLENOID

Removal & Installation – Raise trunk lid to full open position. Remove latch cover attaching screws and cover. Remove solenoid mounting screws and remote key cable retainers. Remove solenoid. To install, reverse removal procedure.

TRUNK LID PULL-DOWN MOTOR

Removal & Installation – Raise trunk lid to full open position. Disconnect wiring harness connector. Remove motor-to-mounting bracket attaching screws and remove motor. To install, reverse removal procedure.

WIRING DIAGRAMS

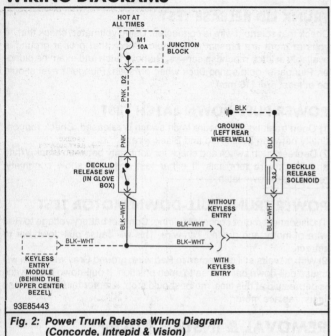

Fig. 2: Power Trunk Release Wiring Diagram (Concorde, Intrepid & Vision)

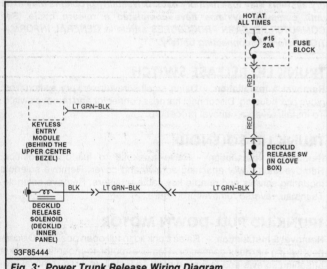

Fig. 3: Power Trunk Release Wiring Diagram (Dynasty, Fifth Avenue, Imperial & New Yorker)

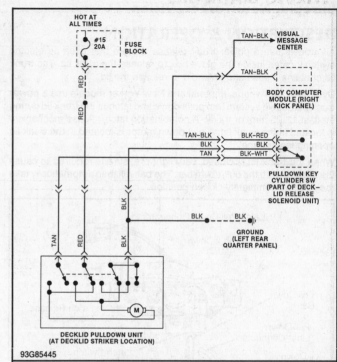

Fig. 4: Power Trunk Pull-Down Wiring Diagram (Dynasty, Fifth Avenue, Imperial & New Yorker)

WIRING DIAGRAMS

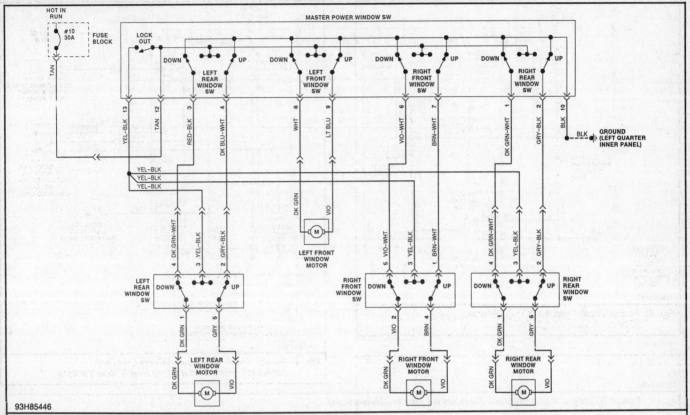

93H85446

Fig. 9: Power Windows Wiring Diagram (Acclaim, LeBaron Sedan & Spirit)

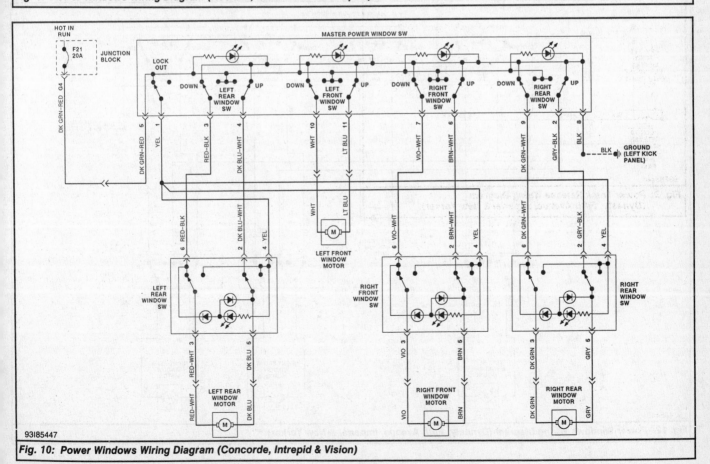

93I85447

Fig. 10: Power Windows Wiring Diagram (Concorde, Intrepid & Vision)

1993 ACCESSORIES & EQUIPMENT
Power Windows – Except Laser & Talon (Cont.)

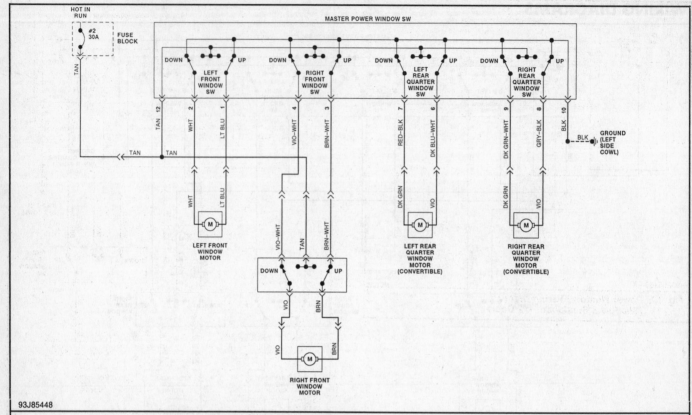

93J85448

Fig. 11: Power Windows Wiring Diagram (Daytona & LeBaron Convertible)

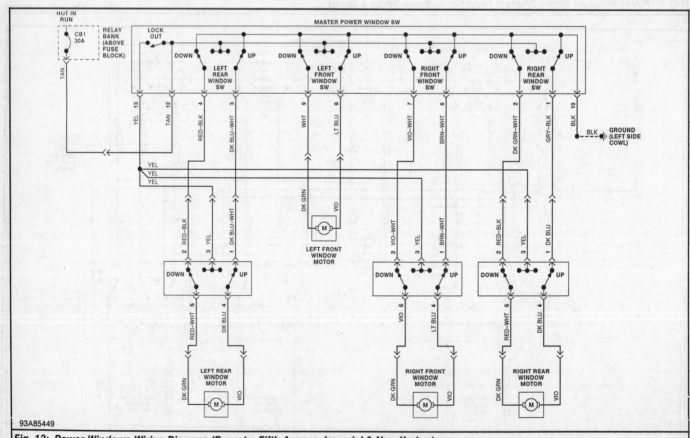

93A85449

Fig. 12: Power Windows Wiring Diagram (Dynasty, Fifth Avenue, Imperial & New Yorker)

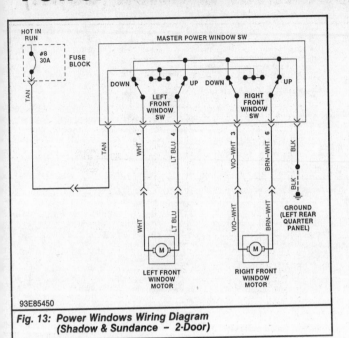

Fig. 13: Power Windows Wiring Diagram (Shadow & Sundance – 2-Door)

Fig. 15: Power Windows Wiring Diagram (LeBaron Coupe)

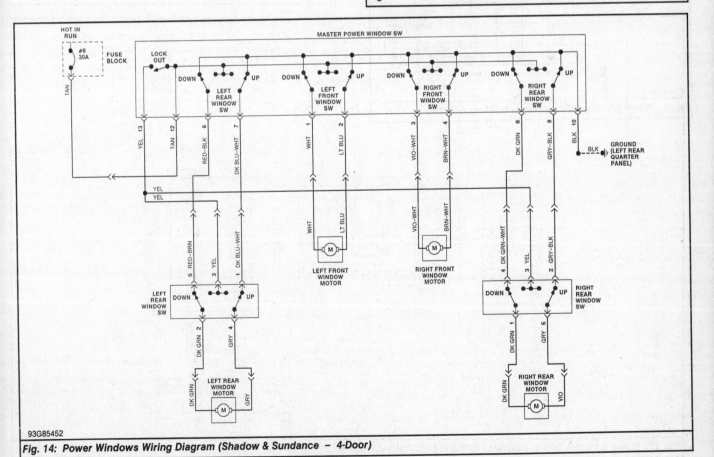

Fig. 14: Power Windows Wiring Diagram (Shadow & Sundance – 4-Door)

1993 ACCESSORIES & EQUIPMENT
Power Windows – Laser & Talon (Cont.)

WIRING DIAGRAMS

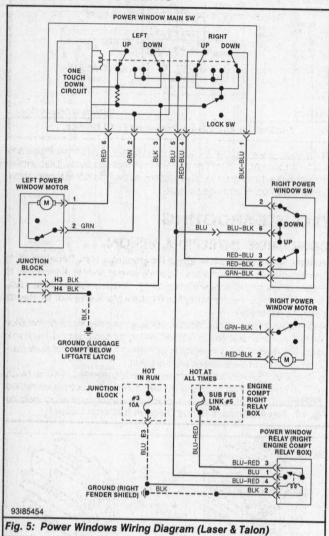

Fig. 5: Power Windows Wiring Diagram (Laser & Talon)

93I85454

AC & AY Bodies: Dynasty, Fifth Avenue, Imperial, New Yorker
LH Body: Concorde, Intrepid, Vision

DESCRIPTION

The remote keyless entry system allows for locking and unlocking of the vehicle doors and trunk by remote control, using a hand-held radio transmitter. The ignition switch must be off before the trunk lid can be unlocked with the transmitter. The receiver may receive signals from 2 transmitters. Each transmitter has its own code which is stored in memory. If the transmitter is replaced, or a second one added, the code on both units have to be placed in memory. The transmitter will operate within 23-30 feet of the vehicle. No more than 2 transmitters can be used. The receiver is capable of retaining memory even when power is removed. The transmitter has two 3-volt batteries which can be replaced. Battery life is about 2 years.

OPERATION

The transmitter has 3 buttons for operation; LOCK, UNLOCK and TRUNK release. The UNLOCK button will unlock the driver's door and light the illuminated entry system. On models with theft alarm system it will also activate theft security system. Pushing and releasing the button once will unlock the driver door. Pushing the button twice within 5 seconds will unlock all doors.

The LOCK button will lock all doors and activate theft security system (if equipped). When pressed, horn will sound a short chirp to signify that the signal was received and doors are locked. The TRUNK button will slightly open the trunk lid when pressed.

TRANSMITTER PROGRAMMING

Concorde, Intrepid & Vision – 1) Remove upper center bezel from instrument panel and locate traction control Black connector. *See Fig. 1.* Disconnect connector. Turn ignition switch to ON position.
2) Ground connector pin No. 4. Door locks will lock and unlock to indicate that system is ready to receive codes. Trunk solenoid will not cycle at this time. Press any button on transmitter to set code. Locks will cycle to confirm programming.
3) If a second transmitter is used, it must be set at this time. Press any button on transmitter and wait for locks to cycle. Disconnect program line from ground. This returns system to normal operation. Replace upper center bezel to instrument panel.

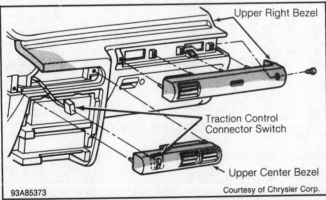

93A85373   Courtesy of Chrysler Corp.

Fig. 1: Keyless Entry Traction Control Switch Location (Concorde, Intrepid & Vision)

Dynasty, Fifth Avenue, Imperial & New Yorker – 1) Remove trim cover or floor console that covers Air Bag Diagnostic Module (ASDM). Pull back carpeting between accelerator pedal and ASDM. Locate programming wire between pedal and ASDM (Dark Green wire with an insulator on the end). Turn ignition switch to ON position.
2) Ground program wire. Door locks will lock and unlock to indicate that system is ready to receive codes. Trunk solenoid will not cycle at this time. Press any button on transmitter to set code. Locks will cycle to confirm programming.

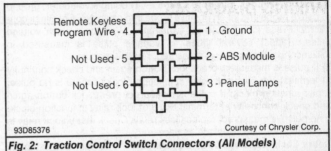

93D85376   Courtesy of Chrysler Corp.

Fig. 2: Traction Control Switch Connectors (All Models)

3) If a second transmitter is used, it must be set at this time. Press any button on second transmitter and wait for locks to cycle. Disconnect program wire from ground. This returns system to normal operation. Replace trim cover or floor console.

TROUBLE SHOOTING

CONCORDE, INTREPID & VISION

No Response From Module When Programming New Receiver – 1) Check batteries in transmitters. Operate power door lock switches to ensure relays and motors are functioning. Check that module has battery voltage at connector cavity No. 8 to fuse block fuse No. 13. Repair wiring as necessary.
2) Check that module has ignition voltage at cavity No. 2 of the Blue connector from fuse No. 14. Repair wiring as necessary. Check that cavity No. 4 on Black connector is grounded to front center floor panel, driver side, of passive restraint bracket.
3) Check that programming wire is properly grounded. This is cavity No. 5 of Black connector and cavity No. 4 of the Black traction control connector. If circuits are okay, replace remote keyless entry module.

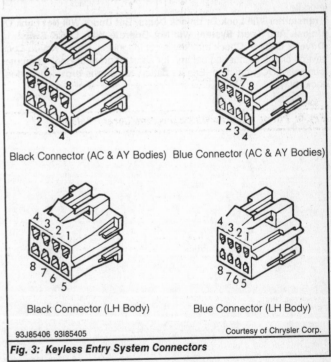

Black Connector (AC & AY Bodies)   Blue Connector (AC & AY Bodies)

Black Connector (LH Body)   Blue Connector (LH Body)

93J85406 93I85405   Courtesy of Chrysler Corp.

Fig. 3: Keyless Entry System Connectors

All Doors Lock Except Driver's – Check cavity No. 3 of Black connector for proper ground. If there is no ground at pin, replace module. If ground is okay, replace door lock motor.
Only Driver's Door Locks – Check for proper ground circuit to the door unlock relay. If ground is okay, replace door unlock relay.

Doors Do Not Lock, But Horn Chirps – **1)** Using a voltmeter, ground negative probe and insert positive probe into cavity No. 6 of Black connector. Press lock button on transmitter. Wait for a quick voltage pulse. Repeat several times as voltage pulse is measured in milliseconds. If no pulse is measured, replace module.

2) If pulse is measured, press lock button again and check continuity at terminal No. 6 of lock relay in junction block. If there is no pulse, repair junction block. If pulse is measured, press lock button again and check continuity at terminal No. 8 of lock relay in junction block. If no pulse is measured, replace lock relay. Check that unlock relay is grounded. Repair or replace as necessary.

Doors Lock, But Horn Does Not Chirp – Press horn and listen for chirp. If there is no chirp, check horn relay and horns. Repair circuit or components as necessary. If horn chirps, check for continuity between cavity No. 7 of Black connector and terminal No. 12 of horn relay. Repair circuit as necessary. If there is still no chirp, replace module.

Transmitter Will Not Lock Or Unlock Remove batteries from transmitter. Check voltage across both batteries. If there is not 6 volts, replace batteries.

DYNASTY, FIFTH AVENUE, IMPERIAL & NEW YORKER

No Response From Module When Programming New Receiver – **1)** Check batteries in transmitters. Operate power door lock switches to ensure relays and motors are functioning. Check that module has battery voltage at Black connector cavity No. 1 to fuse block. Repair as necessary.

2) Check that module has ignition feed at cavity No. 8 of the Black connector to 5-amp fuse in fuse block. Repair circuit as necessary. Check that cavity No. 5 in Black connector is grounded to right side cowl behind body computer. Check that programming wire is properly grounded. If all circuits are okay, replace the remote keyless entry module.

Transmitter Will Lock Or Unlock Doors, But Doors Will Not Lock Or Unlock And Theft System Will Not Operate With LOCK Switch in Driver's Door – Check that key is not in ignition. Check Key-In-Lock switch circuit in steering column for short to ground. Body computer controls LOCK function. Ensure battery voltage is provided to door lock relay.

Transmitter Will Lock Doors, But Not Arm Theft System – Check for battery voltage at cavity No. 10 of theft alarm module to receiver module. If voltage is okay, replace receiver module.

All Doors Lock Except Driver's – Check cavity No. 6 of Black connector for proper ground. If there is no ground at pin, replace module. If ground is okay, replace door lock motor.

Only Driver's Door Locks – Check for proper ground circuit to door unlock relay. If ground is okay, replace door unlock relay.

Doors Lock, But Horn Does Not Chirp – Press horn and listen for chirp. If no chirp, check horn relay and horns. Repair as necessary. If horn chirps, check for continuity between cavity No. 7 of Black connector and terminal No. 12 of horn relay. Repair circuit as necessary. If there is still no chirp, replace module.

REMOVAL & INSTALLATION

CAUTION: When battery is disconnected, vehicle computer and memory systems may lose memory data. Driveability problems may exist until computer systems have completed a relearn cycle. See COMPUTER RELEARN PROCEDURES article in GENERAL INFORMATION before disconnecting battery.

KEYLESS ENTRY MODULE

Removal & Installation (Concorde, Intrepid & Spirit) – Remove instrument panel top cover. Module is mounted to structural duct on passenger side. Remove 2 screws attaching receiver to structural duct. Disconnect wiring connectors. Remove module. To install, reverse removal procedure.

Removal & Installation (Dynasty, Fifth Avenue, Imperial & New Yorker) – Remove lower right instrument panel silencer. Remove glove box assembly. Remove 3 screws attaching mounting bracket to instrument panel. Lower bracket and module and disconnect wiring connectors. Remove module attaching screws and remove module. To install, reverse removal procedure.

WIRING DIAGRAMS

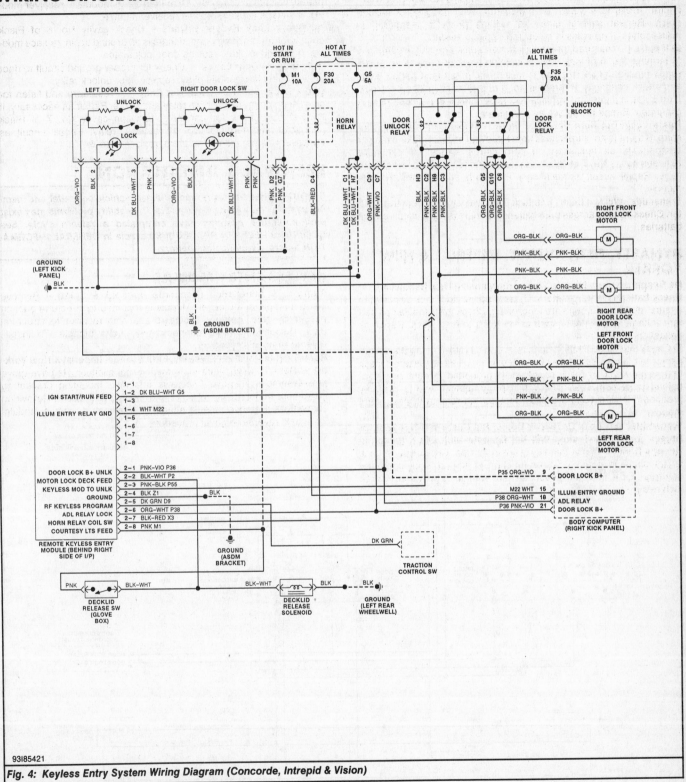

Fig. 4: Keyless Entry System Wiring Diagram (Concorde, Intrepid & Vision)

93I85421

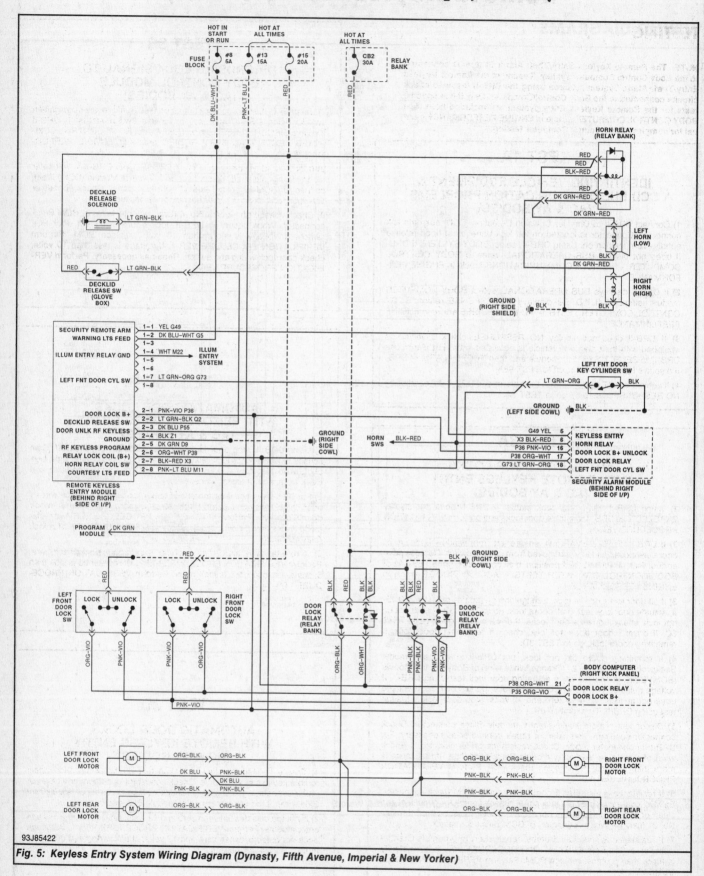

93J85422

Fig. 5: Keyless Entry System Wiring Diagram (Dynasty, Fifth Avenue, Imperial & New Yorker)

TESTING

NOTE: The Remote Keyless Entry/Theft Alarm System is connected to the Body Control Computer system. Testing of the Remote Keyless Entry/Theft Alarm System requires using the DRB-II tester to check circuits connected to the Body Control Computer. Only those specific tests for the Remote Keyless Entry system are included here. See BODY CONTROL COMPUTER article in ENGINE PERFORMANCE manual for complete Body Control Computer testing.

TEST 1A

IDENTIFYING VEHICLE EQUIPMENT & CCD BUS COMMUNICATION PROBLEMS (AC & AY BODIES)

1) Connect DRB-II to Chrysler Collision Detection (CCD) bus data link connector. Connector is located on left kick panel, near hood release handle. Turn ignition on. Using DRB-II, select BODY SYSTEM. If DRB-II does not display BUS OPERATIONAL, refer to BODY CONTROL COMPUTER – VEHICLE COMMUNICATIONS article in ENGINE PERFORMANCE.

2) If DRB-II displays BUS OPERATIONAL, select BODY COMPUTER module using DRB-II. If DRB-II displays NO RESPONSE, refer to BODY CONTROL COMPUTER TESTS – AC & AY BODIES article in ENGINE PERFORMANCE.

3) If DRB-II does not display NO RESPONSE, check if vehicle is equipped with theft alarm. If vehicle is equipped with theft alarm, use DRB-II to SELECT SYSTEM module and then THEFT ALARM. If DRB-II displays NO RESPONSE, go to TEST 98A.

4) If vehicle is NOT equipped with theft alarm or if DRB-II did not display NO RESPONSE in step 5), go to TEST 3A.

TEST 3A

AUTOMATIC DOOR LOCKS WITH REMOTE KEYLESS ENTRY (AC & AY BODIES)

1) Using DRB-II, read door lock status. If DRB-II does not display ENABLED, use DRB-II to enable door locks and perform VERIFICATION PROCEDURE VER-1.

2) If DRB-II displays ENABLED, ensure left front window is down, all doors are closed and key is removed from ignition switch. Depress power door lock switch to LOCK position. If all doors lock, go to TEST 4A of BODY CONTROL COMPUTER TESTS – AC & AY BODIES article in ENGINE PERFORMANCE.

3) If all door locks do not lock, turn ignition on (engine off). Using DRB-II, actuate door lock test. If all doors lock, go to TEST 3B. If all doors do not lock, check if driver's door locks. If driver's door locks, go to TEST 3C. If driver's door does not lock, check if remaining doors lock. If remaining doors lock, go to TEST 3D.

4) If remaining doors did not lock, put DRB-II in voltmeter mode. Backprobe terminal No. 21 (Orange/White wire) of Body Control Module (BCM) Black connector while actuating door lock test using DRB-II. If voltage pulsates between zero and 12 volts, go to TEST 3E. If voltage does not pulsate between zero and 12 volts, stop door lock actuation test using DRB-II. Turn ignition off.

5) Disconnect remote keyless entry module Black connector. Check connector condition, and clean or repair connector as necessary. Put DRB-II in ohmmeter mode. Check resistance on terminal No. 4 (Black wire) of remote keyless entry module Black connector. If resistance is more than 5 ohms, repair open Black wire. Perform VERIFICATION PROCEDURE VER-1.

6) If resistance is less than 5 ohms, disconnect BCM Black connector. BCM is located behind right kick panel. Check connector condition, and clean or repair connector as necessary. Check resistance on terminal No. 21 (Orange/White connector) of BCM Black connector.

7) If resistance is less than 5 ohms, repair short to ground in Orange/White wire. Perform VERIFICATION PROCEDURE VER-1. If resistance is more than 5 ohms, replace BCM. Perform VERIFICATION PROCEDURE VER-1.

TEST 3B

DIAGNOSING LOCK SIGNAL TO BODY CONTROL MODULE (AC & AY BODIES)

1) Using DRB-II, stop door lock actuation test. Remove key from ignition switch. Using DRB-II, read key in ignition switch status. If DRB-II displays CIRCUIT CLOSED, go to TEST 47A of BODY CONTROL COMPUTER TESTS – AC & AY BODIES article in ENGINE PERFORMANCE.

2) If DRB-II did not display CIRCUIT CLOSED, put DRB-II in voltmeter mode. Turn ignition off. Disconnect Body Control Module (BCM) Black connector. BCM is located behind right kick panel. Check connector condition, and clean or repair connector as necessary.

3) Check voltage on terminal No. 4 (Orange/Violet wire) of BCM Black connector. While observing DRB-II, lock doors using left door lock switch. If voltage is more than 10 volts, replace BCM. Perform VERIFICATION PROCEDURE VER-1. If voltage is less than 10 volts, check door lock wiring and switch. Repair as necessary. Perform VERIFICATION PROCEDURE VER-1.

TEST 3C

AUTOMATIC DOOR LOCKS WITH REMOTE KEYLESS ENTRY (AC & AY BODIES)

1) Using DRB-II, stop door lock actuation test. Turn ignition off. Gain access to power door lock relays. Relays are located behind right side of glove box. Remove door unlock relay. Check connector condition, and clean or repair connector as necessary.

2) Put DRB-II in ohmmeter mode and check resistance of Black wire of door unlock relay connector. If resistance is more than 5 ohms, repair open Black wire. Perform VERIFICATION PROCEDURE VER-1. If resistance is less than 5 ohms, check resistance of Pink/Black wire of unlock relay connector.

3) If resistance is more than 5 ohms, repair open Pink/Black wire. Perform VERIFICATION PROCEDURE VER-1. If resistance is less than 5 ohms, replace door unlock relay. Perform VERIFICATION PROCEDURE VER-1.

TEST 3D

AUTOMATIC DOOR LOCKS WITH REMOTE KEYLESS ENTRY (AC & AY BODIES)

1) Ensure DRB-II door lock actuation test is still active. Disconnect remote keyless entry module. Check connector condition, and clean or repair connector as necessary. Check voltage on terminal No. 3 (Dark Blue wire) of remote keyless entry module Black connector.

2) If voltage pulsates between zero and 12 volts, replace remote keyless entry module. Perform VERIFICATION PROCEDURE VER-1. If voltage does not pulse between zero and 12 volts, check wiring and door lock motor. Repair as necessary. Perform VERIFICATION PROCEDURE VER-1.

TEST 3E

AUTOMATIC DOOR LOCKS
WITH REMOTE KEYLESS ENTRY
(AC & AY BODIES)

NOTE: Door lock/door unlock relay must remain in place when back-probing door lock/door unlock relay connector.

1) Ensure DRB-II door lock actuation test is still active. Gain access to power door lock relays. Relays are located behind right side of glove box. Backprobe Orange/White wire of door lock relay connector. If voltage does not pulsate between zero and 12 volts, repair open in Orange/White wire between Body Control Module (BCM) and door lock relay. Perform VERIFICATION PROCEDURE VER-1.

2) If voltage pulsates between zero and 12 volts, backprobe Black wire of door lock relay. If voltage pulsates between zero and 12 volts, repair open Black wire. Perform VERIFICATION PROCEDURE VER-1. If voltage does not pulsate between zero and 12 volts, backprobe Red wire of door lock relay connector. If voltage is less than 10 volts, repair Red wire as necessary. Perform VERIFICATION PROCEDURE VER-1.

3) If voltage is more than 10 volts, backprobe Orange/Black wire at door lock relay. Ensure DRB-II door lock actuation test is still active. If voltage does not pulsate between zero and 12 volts, go to TEST 3F. If voltage pulsates between zero and 12 volts, remove door unlock relay. Check connector condition, and clean or repair connector as necessary.

4) Check voltage of Pink/Black wire at door unlock relay connector. If voltage does not pulsate between zero and 12 volts, repair open Orange/Black or Pink/Black wire. Perform VERIFICATION PROCEDURE VER-1. If voltage pulsates between zero and 12 volts, use DRB-II to stop door lock actuation test. Turn ignition off.

5) Put DRB-II in ohmmeter mode. Check resistance of Black wire of door unlock relay connector. If resistance is less than 5 ohms, replace door unlock relay. Perform VERIFICATION PROCEDURE VER-1. If resistance is more than 5 ohms, repair open Black wire. Perform VERIFICATION PROCEDURE VER-1.

TEST 3F

AUTOMATIC DOOR LOCKS
WITH REMOTE KEYLESS ENTRY
(AC & AY BODIES)

1) Using DRB-II, stop door lock actuation test. Turn ignition off. Disconnect remote keyless entry module connector. Check connector condition, and clean or repair connector as necessary. Remove door lock and unlock relays. Relays are located behind right side of glove box. Check condition of connectors, and clean or repair connectors as necessary.

2) With DRB-II in ohmmeter mode, check resistance of Orange/Black wire at door lock relay connector. If resistance is less than 5 ohms, repair short to ground in Orange/Black wire. Perform VERIFICATION PROCEDURE VER-1. If resistance is more than 5 ohms, replace door lock relay. Perform VERIFICATION PROCEDURE VER-1.

TEST 36A

IDENTIFYING REMOTE KEYLESS
ENTRY (RKE) PROBLEM (LH BODY)

1) If problem is with Remote Keyless Entry (RKE), go to TEST 36D. If problem is not with RKE, close and unlock all doors. Open driver's window and remove ignition key.

2) Using DRB-II, actuate door LOCK test and then actuate door UNLOCK test. If any door locks, repair inoperative door lock motor(s) or wiring. If doors do not lock, check if a door unlock problem exists. If an unlock problem exists, go to TEST 36B.

NOTE: The BCM must be connected while performing step 3). Failure to do so may lead to incorrect circuit/system diagnosis.

3) If an unlock problem does not exist, manually lock all doors. Press door lock switch to unlock position. If doors unlock only, go to TEST 39A of BODY CONTROL COMPUTER TESTS – LH BODY article in ENGINE PERFORMANCE. If doors lock and unlock, use DRB-II in voltmeter mode to backprobe Body Controller Module (BCM) terminal No. 18, door lock relay circuit (Orange/White wire). Module is located behind right kick panel. If voltage is more than 10 volts, replace BCM. Perform VERIFICATION PROCEDURE VER-1.

4) If voltage is less than 10 volts, use DRB-II to stop door lock test. Press driver's power door lock switch to lock and then unlock position. If any doors lock and unlock, repair inoperative door lock motor(s) or wiring.

5) If none of the doors lock or unlock, turn ignition off and disconnect BCM Bone connector. Check voltage on BCM Bone connector terminal No. 9, power door lock switch circuit (Orange/Violet wire). Depress door lock switch. If voltage is less than 10 volts, go to TEST 36C.

6) If voltage is more than 10 volts, reconnect BCM Bone connector and remove door lock relay from fuse/junction block. Fuse/junction block is located behind end cover, on left side of instrument panel. With DRB-II in voltmeter mode, check voltage on door lock relay control circuit (Orange/White wire) on door lock relay connector. Press door lock switch to lock position. If voltage is less than 10 volts, repair open circuit in Orange/White wire between door lock relay and BCM. Perform VERIFICATION PROCEDURE VER-1.

7) If voltage is more than 10 volts, use DRB-II in voltmeter mode to check voltage on door lock circuit (Orange/Black wire) on door lock relay connector. Press door lock switch to unlock position. If voltage is less than 10 volts, repair open circuit in Orange/Black wire. Perform VERIFICATION PROCEDURE VER-1.

8) If voltage is more than 10 volts, use DRB-II to stop door unlock test. Check voltage on door lock relay connector fused battery feed circuit (Red wire). If voltage is less than 10 volts, repair open circuit on Red wire. Perform VERIFICATION PROCEDURE VER-1.

9) If voltage is more than 10 volts, use DRB-II in ohmmeter mode to check resistance on door lock relay connector ground circuit (Black wire). If resistance is more than 5 ohms, repair open circuit on Black wire. Perform VERIFICATION PROCEDURE VER-1. If resistance is less than 5 ohms, replace door lock relay. Perform VERIFICATION PROCEDURE VER-1.

93C40602

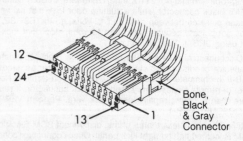

Fig. 5: Identifying Body Controller Connector Terminals (Concorde, Intrepid & Vision)

TEST 36B

REMOTE KEYLESS ENTRY (RKE)
DOOR LOCK SWITCH SENSE (LH BODY)

1) Using DRB-II, stop door lock test. Remove door unlock relay from fuse/junction block. Fuse/junction block is located behind end cover, on left side of instrument panel. Using DRB-II, actuate door unlock test. With DRB-II in voltmeter mode, check voltage on door unlock relay control circuit (Pink/Violet wire) on door unlock relay connector. If voltage is less than 10 volts, repair open circuit in Pink/Violet wire between door unlock relay and Body Controller Module (BCM). Perform VERIFICATION PROCEDURE VER-1.

2) If voltage is more than 10 volts, use DRB-II in voltmeter mode to check voltage on door unlock circuit (Pink/Black wire) on door unlock relay connector. Using DRB-II, actuate door lock test. If voltage is less than 10 volts, repair open circuit in Pink/Black wire. Perform VERIFICATION PROCEDURE VER-1.

3) If voltage is more than 10 volts, use DRB-II to stop door lock test. With DRB-II in voltmeter mode, check voltage on unlock relay connector fused battery feed circuit (Red wire). If voltage is less than 10 volts, repair open circuit in Red wire. Perform VERIFICATION PROCEDURE VER-1.

4) If voltage is more than 10 volts, use DRB-II in ohmmeter mode to check resistance on unlock relay connector ground circuit (Black wire). If resistance is more than 5 ohms, repair open circuit in Black wire. Perform VERIFICATION PROCEDURE VER-1. If resistance is less than 5 ohms, replace door unlock relay. Perform VERIFICATION PROCEDURE VER-1.

TEST 36C

REMOTE KEYLESS ENTRY (RKE)
DOOR LOCK RELAY PROBLEM (LH BODY)

1) Turn ignition off and disconnect Body Controller Module (BCM) Bone connector. Module is located behind right kick panel. Check voltage on BCM Bone connector terminal No. 9, power door lock switch circuit (Orange/Violet wire). Depress opposite (passenger's) door switch to lock position. If voltage is less than 10 volts, repair open circuit in Orange/Violet wire. Perform VERIFICATION PROCEDURE VER-1.

2) If voltage is more than 10 volts, turn ignition off and reconnect BCM Bone connector. Turn ignition on and press door lock switch to lock position. If doors do not lock, replace BCM. Perform VERIFICATION PROCEDURE VER-1. If doors lock, problem is in driver's door. Repair wiring.

TEST 36D

REMOTE KEYLESS ENTRY (RKE)
MODULE PROBLEM (LH BODY)

1) If problem is with trunk release or warning light, go to TEST 36E of BODY CONTROL COMPUTER TESTS – LH BODY article in ENGINE PERFORMANCE. If problem is not with trunk release or warning light, ensure DRB-II door lock test is still active. Disconnect Remote Keyless Entry (RKE) module Black connector. Module is located on top, right side of dashboard.

NOTE: RKE module may be accessed by carefully prying each end of dashboard top cover, then lifting rear edge of top cover and sliding cover forward to disengage front clips.

2) With DRB-II in voltmeter mode, check voltage on RKE Black connector door unlock relay feed circuit (Pink/Violet wire). If voltage fluctuates from zero volts to less than 10 volts, repair open circuit in Pink/Violet wire. Perform VERIFICATION PROCEDURE VER-1.

3) If voltage fluctuates from zero volts to more than 10 volts, use DRB-II to stop door lock test. With DRB-II in ohmmeter mode, check resistance on RKE Black connector ground circuit (Black wire). If resistance is less than 5 ohms, replace RKE module. Perform VERIFICATION PROCEDURE VER-1. If resistance is more than 5 ohms, repair open circuit in Black wire. Perform VERIFICATION PROCEDURE VER-1.

VERIFICATION PROCEDURE VER-1

VERIFICATION OF REPAIRS

Reconnect all previously disconnected components and connections. Ensure all repairs have been made. Actuate system that was not operational. If system operates properly, repair is complete. If system does not operate properly, go to TEST 1A

1993 FORD MOTOR CO. CONTENTS

Continental, Cougar, Mark VIII, Probe, Thunderbird, Town Car

DESCRIPTION

The anti-theft system is designed to prevent unauthorized entry into vehicle passenger and luggage compartments (and engine compartment on Mark VIII, Probe and Town Car). When activated, system provides both audible and visual warning alarms. The horn will sound and the low beam headlights, taillights, parking lights or hazard warning lights, and alarm indicator will flash off and on. In addition, the vehicle starter is disabled, preventing the vehicle from being started until alarm system has been deactivated.

The system is controlled by an Anti-Theft Control module (or Central Processing Unit on Probe). When armed, unauthorized entry is detected by the door ajar switches located in each door, a lock tamper detection switch in the trunk lid or liftgate lock cylinder, a hood switch on right fender panel or the ignition key lock cylinder sensor. An alarm indicator is located on the instrument panel.

The following existing vehicle components are also used in the anti-theft system: power door lock switches, door ajar switches and lights, ignition switch, horns and horn relay, low beam headlights, autolight system (some models), tail and parking lights, starter relay and remote keyless entry system (if equipped). Some models also have an ignition switch monitoring function which detects switch tampering. System does not have to be armed for ignition switch monitoring.

OPERATION

Arming System – Use the following input sequence to arm system. Turn off ignition switch. Open a door. Anti-theft indicator will flash. Lock doors using power door locks or keyless entry code. Close all doors. Wait about 30 seconds for anti-theft indicator to go out. System is now activated.

Disarming System – Unlock driver or passenger door using vehicle key, keyless entry code or remote transmitter. Turn ignition switch to ON or ACC position. Unlock driver's door using power UNLOCK switch if not previously done.

Triggering System – Alarm will be activated when any of the following actions occur with alarm armed:

- Any door is opened without first using key, keyless entry code or remote transmitter.
- Trunk/liftgate lid lock cylinder is removed.
- Hood is opened (Mark VIII, Probe and Town Car).
- Ignition switch is tampered with.

Within 2-4 minutes, horns and lights will shut off automatically. System will then reset to an armed state and will trigger again if another intrusion occurs. Vehicle starting system will remain disabled until system is disarmed.

Disarming A Triggered System – Unlock driver or passenger door with key, or unlock driver's door using keyless entry code or remote transmitter.

TESTING

Use the following diagnosis chart to determine individual pinpoint tests for anti-theft system.

ANTI-THEFT DIAGNOSIS CHART (CONTINENTAL, COUGAR & THUNDERBIRD)

Symptom	Pinpoint Test
Verify Alarm Arming	Test A
Verify Untriggered Alarm Disarming	Test B
Verify Alarm Activation	Test C
Verify Triggered Alarm Disarming	Test D
Vehicle Will Not Crank	Test E
Alarm Light Is Always On	Test F
Alarm Light Does Not Work	Test G
Horn, Headlights & Parking Lights Always On	Test H
System Activates Falsely	Test I
Door & Trunk Switch Diagnostics	Test J

ANTI-THEFT DIAGNOSIS CHART (MARK VII & TOWN CAR)

Symptom	Pinpoint Test
Verify Alarm Arming	Test A
Verify Untriggered Alarm Disarming	Test B
Verify Alarm Activation	Test C
Verify Triggered Alarm Disarming	Test D
Vehicle Will Not Crank	Test E
Alarm Light Is Always On	Test F
Alarm Light Does Not Work	Test G
Horn, Headlights & Parking Lights Always On	Test H
System Activates Falsely	Test I
Verify Ignition Lock Cylinder Sensor	Test J
Door/Trunk/Hood Switch & Ignition Sensor Diagnostics	Test K

ANTI-THEFT DIAGNOSIS CHART (PROBE)

Symptom	See Pinpoint Test K
System Does Not Operate	Step 1
Alarm Light Does Not Light	Step 6
Alarm Light Is Always On	Step 9
System Disarms But Vehicle Will Not Start	Step 11
Vehicle Starts With System Armed	Step 11
Hazard Lights Do Not Flash	Step 12
Horn Does Not Sound Alarm	Step 13
Headlights Do Not Light	Step 14
Alarm Does Not Work When Manual Or Power Door Locks Are Used	Step 15
Alarm Does Not Arm With Power Door Locks	Step 15
Alarm Goes Off When Alarm Is Armed	Step 15
Alarm Does Not Work When Interior Liftgate Switch Is Operated	Step 18
Alarm Does Not Work When Hood Is Opened	Step 19
Alarm Does Not Deactivate When Door Key Is Used	Step 22
Alarm Does Not Deactivate When Liftgate Key Is Used	Step 25

DOOR DISARM SWITCH

Using a digital volt-ohmmeter, measure resistance of door disarm switch with key removed from door lock. Resistance should be more than 25,000 ohms. Measure resistance with key in lock and fully rotated to unlock position. Resistance should be less than 200 ohms. If either specification is not met, replace door disarm switch.

TRUNK/LIFTGATE LID TAMPER SWITCH

Using a digital volt-ohmmeter, measure resistance of trunk/liftgate lid tamper switch. Resistance should be more than 25,000 ohms. If resistance is less than 25,000 ohms, replace tamper switch.

IGNITION KEY LOCK CYLINDER SENSOR

Disconnect anti-theft control module. Using a digital volt-ohmmeter, measure resistance between pins No. 10 and 26 at wiring harness connector. Resistance should be 145-175 ohms. If resistance is not 145-175 ohms, repair circuit No. 936 (Dark Green/White wire), or replace lock cylinder sensor.

REMOVAL & INSTALLATION

CAUTION: When battery is disconnected, vehicle computer and memory systems may lose memory data. Driveability problems may exist until computer systems have completed a relearn cycle. See COMPUTER RELEARN PROCEDURES article in GENERAL INFORMATION before disconnecting battery.

THEFT CONTROL MODULE

Removal & Installation – Disconnect negative battery cable. On Continental, Cougar and Thunderbird, open trunk lid and remove 2 retaining screws attaching module to package tray or relay panel of left side of compartment. On Mark-VIII, open hood and remove trim panel covering evaporator assembly. On Town Car, remove right side trim panel in passenger compartment. On Probe remove left hand trim panel in passenger compartment. On all models, disconnect electrical connectors and remove module. To install, reverse removal procedure.

HOOD TAMPER SWITCH

Removal & Installation – Open hood. On Probe, remove hood latch assembly. Remove wire attaching strap. Remove tamper switch attaching nut and bolt. On all other models, locate hood switch on left hand fender apron. Remove switch attaching screws. Disconnect electrical connector and remove switch. To install, reverse removal procedure.

LIFTGATE TAMPER SWITCH

Removal & Installation – Open liftgate. Remove liftgate latch. Remove arming switch ground wire. Remove switch attaching bolt. Disconnect electrical connector and remove switch from latch. To install, reverse removal procedure.

STARTER & HORN RELAYS

Removal & Installation – Disconnect negative battery cable. Remove main fuse block cover. Open tabs and remove horn and/or starter relay from fuse block.

IGNITION KEY LOCK CYLINDER SENSOR

Removal & Installation – Disconnect negative battery cable. Remove ignition key lock cylinder from steering column housing. Slide ignition key lock cylinder sensor off steering column casting. Sensor is located next to key warning buzzer switch. Remove clock spring assembly to access sensor ground. Disconnect sensor ground terminal. Disconnect electrical connector and remove sensor. To install, reverse removal procedure.

PINPOINT TESTING

NOTE: See appropriate ANTI-THEFT DIAGNOSIS CHART under TESTING to determine testing according to vehicle system problem.

Before performing any tests on anti-theft system, check the following items to eliminate common problems:
- Hood/trunk/liftgate properly aligned.
- Door locks not binding.
- Fuses not blown.
- Loose or corroded connections.
- Damaged wiring harness.
- Damaged Central Processing Unit (CPU).
- Horn, headlights, hazard flashers, interior lights, trunk lights, power door locks and remote entry systems operational.

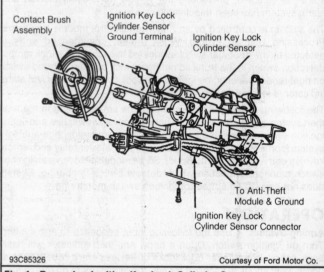

Contact Brush Assembly

Ignition Key Lock Cylinder Sensor Ground Terminal

Ignition Key Lock Cylinder Sensor

To Anti-Theft Module & Ground

Ignition Key Lock Cylinder Sensor Connector

93C85326   Courtesy of Ford Motor Co.

Fig. 1: Removing Ignition Key Lock Cylinder Sensor

WIRING DIAGRAMS

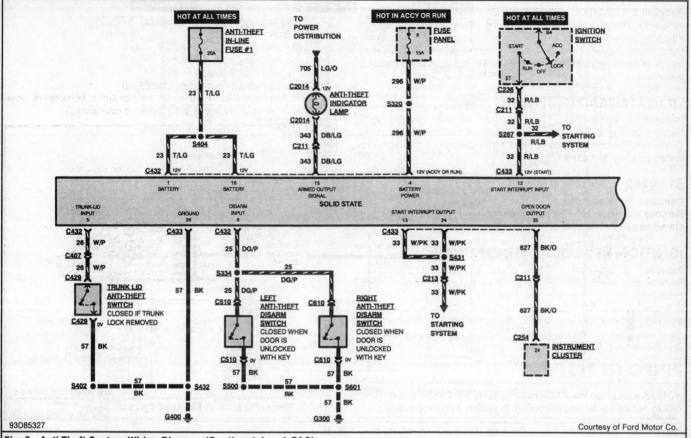

Fig. 2: Anti-Theft System Wiring Diagram (Continental – 1 Of 2)

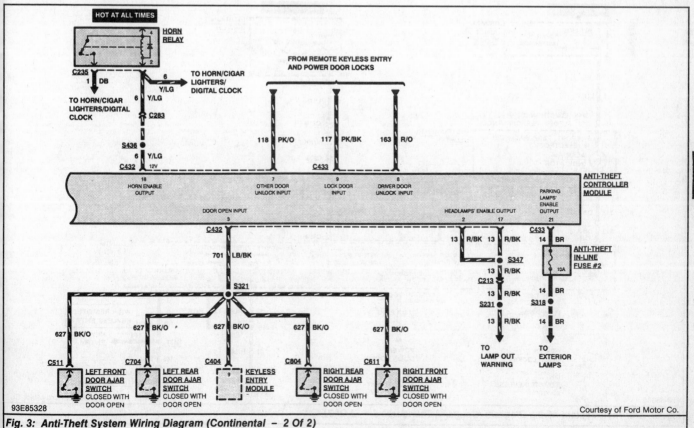

Fig. 3: Anti-Theft System Wiring Diagram (Continental – 2 Of 2)

1993 ACCESSORIES & EQUIPMENT
Anti-Theft System (Cont.)

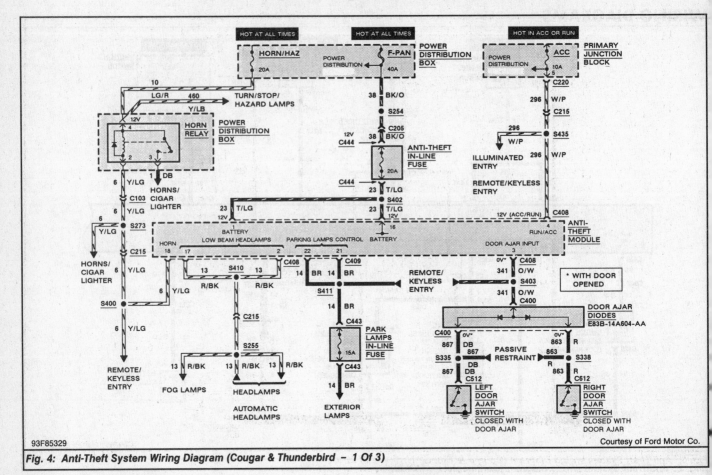

Fig. 4: *Anti-Theft System Wiring Diagram (Cougar & Thunderbird – 1 Of 3)*

93F85329

Courtesy of Ford Motor Co.

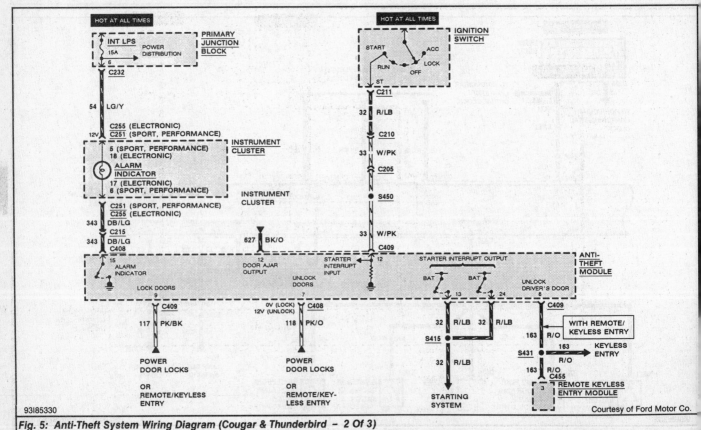

Fig. 5: *Anti-Theft System Wiring Diagram (Cougar & Thunderbird – 2 Of 3)*

93I85330

Courtesy of Ford Motor Co.

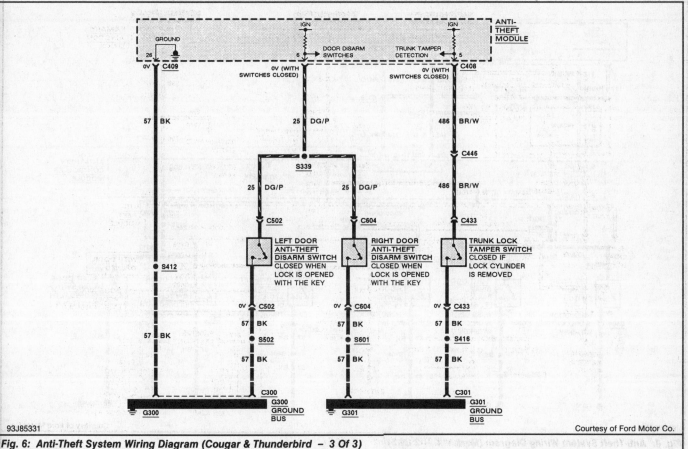

Fig. 6: Anti-Theft System Wiring Diagram (Cougar & Thunderbird – 3 Of 3)

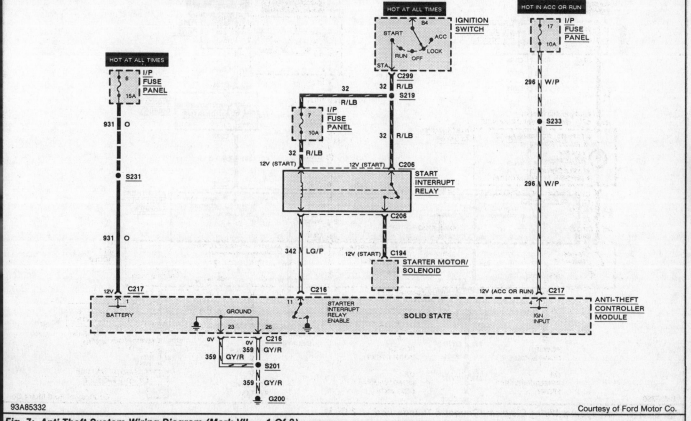

Fig. 7: Anti-Theft System Wiring Diagram (Mark VII – 1 Of 3)

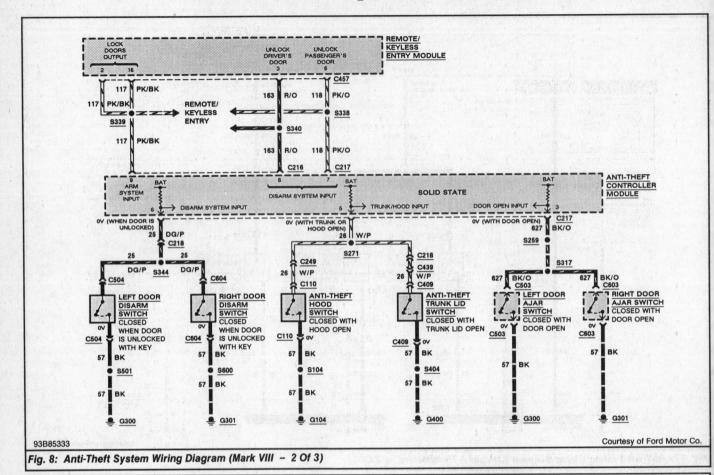

93B85333

Courtesy of Ford Motor Co.

Fig. 8: Anti-Theft System Wiring Diagram (Mark VIII – 2 Of 3)

93C85334

Courtesy of Ford Motor Co.

Fig. 9: Anti-Theft System Wiring Diagram (Mark VII – 3 Of 3)

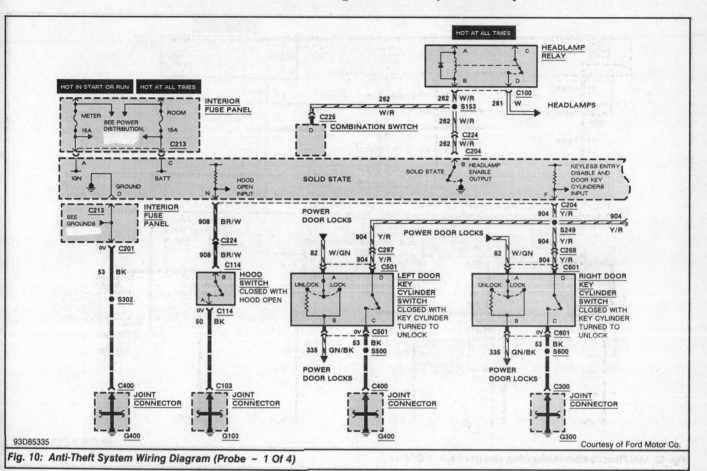

93D85335

Fig. 10: Anti-Theft System Wiring Diagram (Probe – 1 Of 4)

Courtesy of Ford Motor Co.

93E85336

Fig. 11: Anti-Theft System Wiring Diagram (Probe – 2 Of 4)

Courtesy of Ford Motor Co.

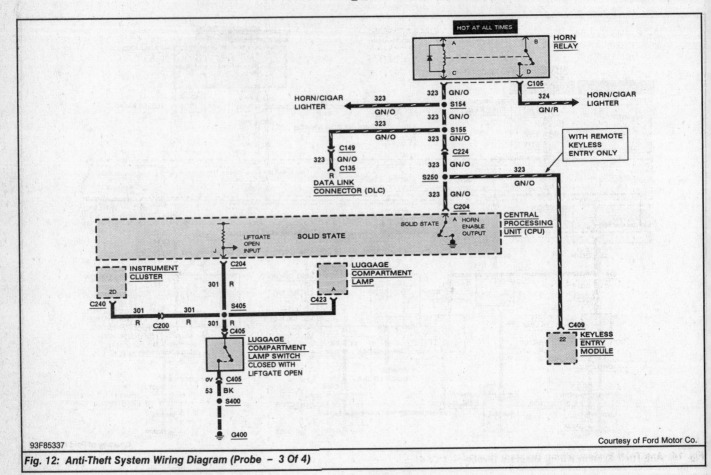

Fig. 12: *Anti-Theft System Wiring Diagram (Probe – 3 Of 4)*

93F85337

Courtesy of Ford Motor Co.

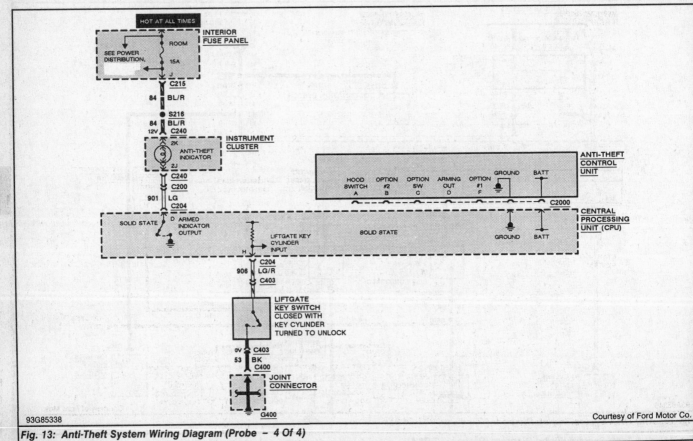

Fig. 13: *Anti-Theft System Wiring Diagram (Probe – 4 Of 4)*

93G85338

Courtesy of Ford Motor Co.

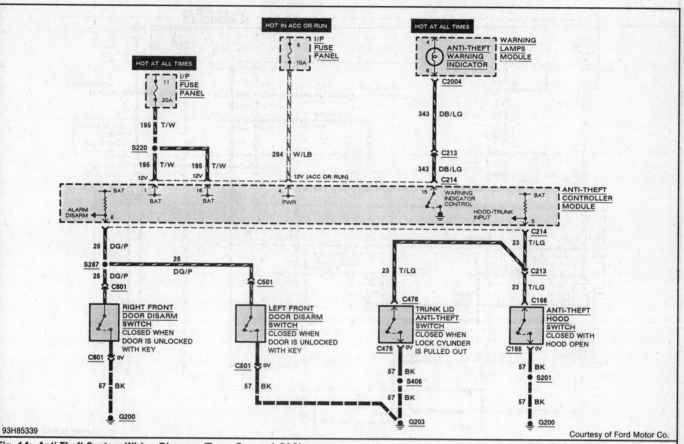

Fig. 14: Anti-Theft System Wiring Diagram (Town Car – 1 Of 3)

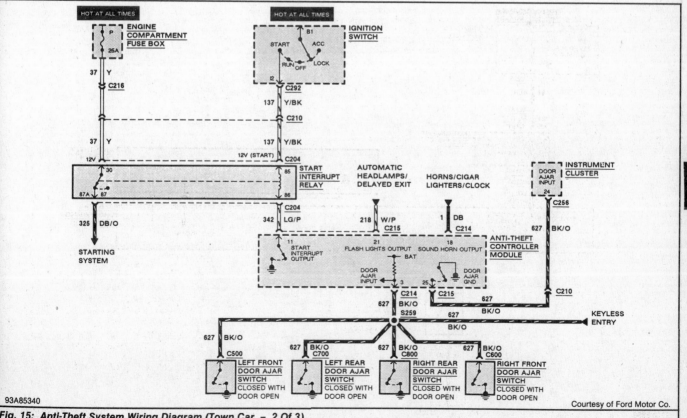

Fig. 15: Anti-Theft System Wiring Diagram (Town Car – 2 Of 3)

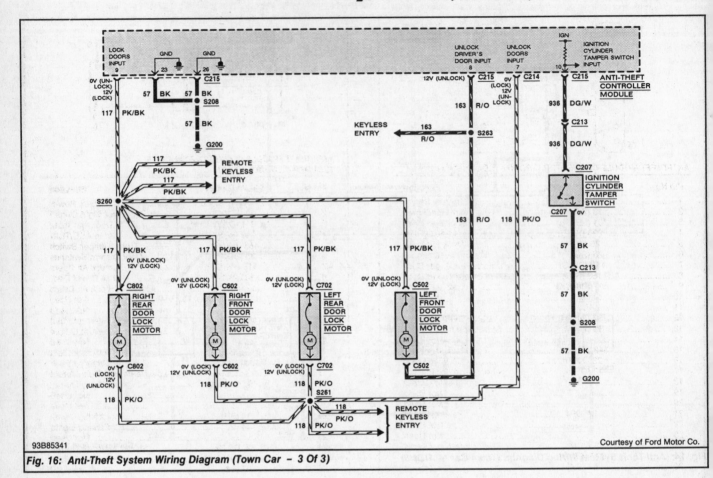

Fig. 16: Anti-Theft System Wiring Diagram (Town Car – 3 Of 3)

93B85341

Courtesy of Ford Motor Co.

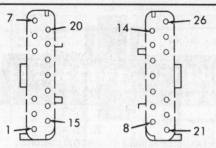

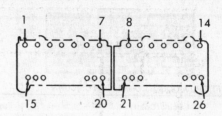

ANTI-THEFT MODULE CONNECTOR CIRCUITS (CONTINENTAL)

Pin No.	Circuit (Color)	Function
1	23 (T/LG)	Battery Power
2	13 (R/BK)	Low Beam Headlights
3	701 (LB/BK)	Door Ajar Input
4	296 (W/P)	Hot In ACC/RUN
5	26 (W/P)	Deck Lid Input
6	25 (DG/P)	Disarm Switch Input
7	118 (PK/O)	Unlock Passenger Door
8	163 (R/O)	Unlock Driver Door
9	117 (PK/BK)	Lock All Doors
10		Not Used
11		Not Used
12	32 (R/LB)	Starter Interrupt Input
13	33 (W/PK)	Starter Interrupt Output
14		Not Used
15	343 (DB/LG)	Alarm Indicator Light
16	23 (T/LG)	Battery Power
17	13 (R/BK)	Low Beam Headlights
18	6 (Y/LG)	Horn Enable Output
19		Not Used
20		Not Used
21	14 (BR)	Parking Lights
22		Not Used
23		Not Used
24	33 (W/PK)	Starter Interrupt Output
25	627 (BK/O)	Door Ajar Output
26	57 (BK)	Ground

ANTI-THEFT MODULE CONNECTOR CIRCUITS (COUGAR & THUNDERBIRD)

Pin No.	Circuit (Color)	Function
1	23 (T/LG)	Battery Power
2	13 (R/BK)	Low Beam Headlight Output
3	341 (O/W)	Door Ajar Input
4	296 (W/P)	Hot In ACC/RUN
5	486 (BR/W)	Trunk Tamper Switch
6	25 (DG/P)	Door Disarm Switches
7	118 (PK/O)	Unlock All Doors
8	163 (R/O)	Unlock Driver Door
9	117 (PK/BK)	Lock All Doors
10		Not Used
11		Not Used
12	33 (W/PK)	Starter Interrupt Input
13	32 (R/LB)	Starter Interrupt Output
14		Not Used
15	343 (DB/LG)	Alarm Indicator Light
16	23 (T/LG)	Battery Power
17	13 (R/BK)	Low Beam Headlight Output
18	6 (Y/LG)	Horn Relay Output
19		Not Used
20		Not Used
21	14 (BR)	Parking Lights
22	14 (BR)	Parking Lights
23		Not Used
24	32 (R/LB)	Starter Interrupt Output
25	267 (BK/O)	Door Ajar Output
26	57 (BK)	Ground

ANTI-THEFT MODULE CONNECTOR CIRCUITS (TOWN CAR)

Pin No.	Circuit (Color)	Function
1	195 (T/W)	Battery Power
2		Not Used
3	627 (BK/O)	Door Ajar Input
4	640 (R/Y)	Hot In ACC/RUN
5	23 (T/LG)	Trunk/Hood Tamper Switch
6	25 (T/LG)	Door Disarm Switches
7	118 (PK/O)	Unlock Passenger Door
8	163 (R/O)	Unlock Driver Door
9	117 (PK/BK)	Lock All Doors
10	936 (DG/W)	Ignition Tamper Input
11	342 (LG/P)	Starter Interrupt Output
12		Not Used
13		Not Used
14		Not Used
15	343 (DB/LG)	Alarm Indicator Light
16	195 (T/W)	Battery Power
17		Not Used
18	1 (DB)	Horn Relay
19		Not Used
20		Not Used
21	218 (W/P)	Flash Lights Output
22		Not Used
23	57 (BK)	Ground
24		Not Used
25	267 (BK/O)	Door Ajar Output
26	57 (BK)	Module Ground

ANTI-THEFT MODULE CONNECTOR CIRCUITS (MARK VIII)

Pin No.	Circuit (Color)	Function
1	931 (T/LG)	Battery Power
2		Not Used
3	627 (BK/O)	Door Ajar Switches
4	294 (W/LB)	Ignition Switch Input
5	26 (W/P)	Trunk/Hood Tamper Switches
6	25 (DG/P)	Door Disarm Switches
7	118 (PK/O)	Unlock All Doors
8	163 (R/O)	Unlock Driver Door
9	117 (PK/BK)	Lock All Doors
10	936 (DG/W)	Ignition Key Sensor
11	342 (LG/P)	Starter Interrupt
12		Not Used
13		Not Used
14		Not Used
15	343 (DB/LG)	Alarm Indicator Light
16		Not Used
17		Not Used
18	1 (DB)	Horn Relay Output
19		Not Used
20		Not Used
21	218 (W/P)	Exterior Lights Output
22		Not Used
23	57 (BK)	Ground
24		Not Used
25		Not Used
26	57 (BK)	Ground

93C85342
Courtesy of Ford Motor Co.

Fig. 17: Identifying Anti-Theft Control Module Connector Terminals (Continental & Town Car)

93G85346
Courtesy of Ford Motor Co.

Fig. 18: Identifying Anti-Theft Control Module Connector Terminals (Cougar, Mark VIII & Thunderbird)

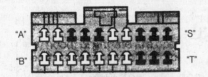

ANTI-THEFT/CPU MODULE CONNECTOR CIRCUITS

Pin No.	Circuit (Color)	Function
A	323 (GN/O)	Horn Relay
B	262A (W/R)	Headlight Relay
C	909 (LG/Y)	Starter Interrupt Relay
D	901 (LG)	Instrument Cluster
E		Not Used
F	904 (Y/R)	Power Door Lock Switches
G		Not Used
H	906 (LG/R)	Liftgate Switch
I		Not Used
J	301A (R)	Liftgate Lamp Switch
K	905 (BR/Y)	LH Pwr. Door Motor Switch
L	910 (Y)	RH Pwr. Door Motor Switch
M	115 (GN/R)	Flasher Module
N	908 (BR/W)	Hood Switch
O-T		Not Used

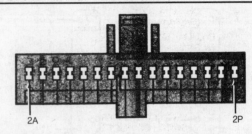

2A ← → 2P

INSTRUMENT CLUSTER MODULE CONNECTOR CIRCUITS

Pin No.	Circuit (Color)	Function
2A	52F (BK)	Ground
2B	305C (GN/Y)	Inst. Panel Dimmer Switch
2C	80H (O)	Parking Light Relay
2D	301B (R)	Trunk Compart. Light Sw.
2E	731 (GN)	Tach Signal From Ignition
2F	110 (P/Y)	Oil Pressure Sender
2G	746 (BL)	Malfunction Light Signal
2H	307 (BR/BK)	Seat Belt Light Sig. From CPU
2I	824 (BR/Y)	O/D Off Light Signal
2J	901A (LG)	Theft Warning Light Signal
2K	84R (BL/R)	Power
2L	952A (R/GN)	Air Bag Diag. Module
2M	244 (W/R)	Inertia Fuel Cutoff Switch
2N	117C (GN/W)	RH Signal From Flasher
2O	300A (R/W)	Door Switches & CPU
2P	20 (W/BK)	Generator/Voltage Reg. Signal

"A" ← → "P"

WARNING CHIME/CPU MODULE CONNECTOR CIRCUITS

Pin No.	Circuit (Color)	Function
A		Power
B	300 (R/W)	Seat Belt Indicator
C	84G (BL/R)	Pwr. & Key Reminder Switch
D	53F (BK)	Ground
E	300 (R/W)	Door Jamb Switches & Ajar Light
F	333D (GN)	Dome, Map & Foot Lights
G	304 (PK)	Illuminated Entry Lights
H		Not Used
I	303 (BL/Y)	Key Reminder Switch
J	302 (R/Y)	Door Handle Switches
K	308 (BR/W)	Seat Belt Buckle Switch
L		Not Used
M		Not Used
N		Not Used
O	108 (R/Y)	Backup Lights & Switch
P	80 (O)	Rear & Dimmer Lights & Parking Light Relay

93H85347 93I85348 93J85349

Fig. 19: Identifying Anti-Theft Control Module, Instrument Cluster Module & Warning Chime/CPU Module Connector Terminals (Probe)

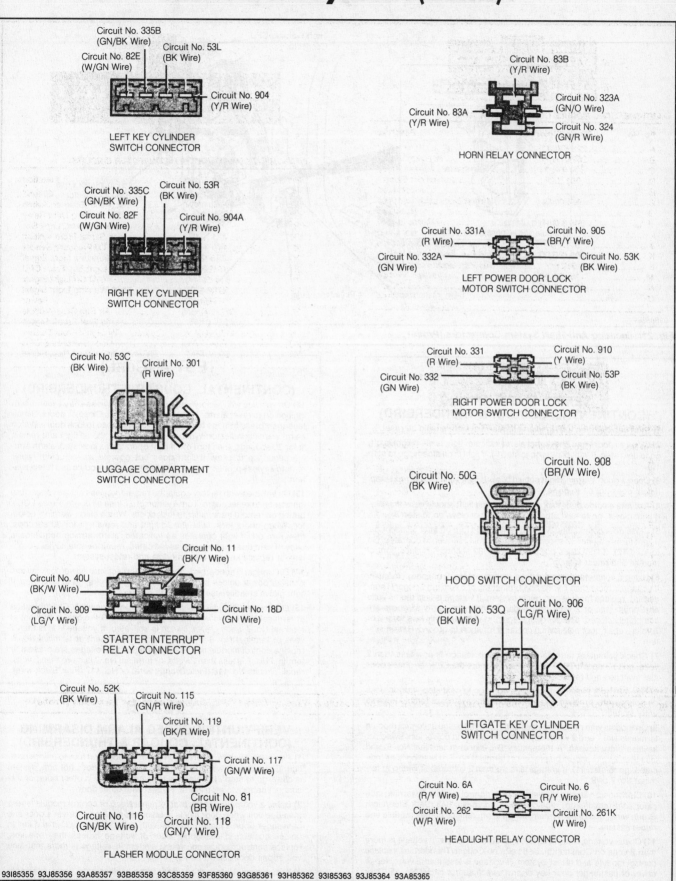

Circuit No. 335B
(GN/BK Wire)

Circuit No. 82E
(W/GN Wire)

Circuit No. 53L
(BK Wire)

Circuit No. 904
(Y/R Wire)

**LEFT KEY CYLINDER
SWITCH CONNECTOR**

Circuit No. 83B
(Y/R Wire)

Circuit No. 83A
(Y/R Wire)

Circuit No. 323A
(GN/O Wire)

Circuit No. 324
(GN/R Wire)

HORN RELAY CONNECTOR

Circuit No. 335C
(GN/BK Wire)

Circuit No. 53R
(BK Wire)

Circuit No. 82F
(W/GN Wire)

Circuit No. 904A
(Y/R Wire)

**RIGHT KEY CYLINDER
SWITCH CONNECTOR**

Circuit No. 331A
(R Wire)

Circuit No. 905
(BR/Y Wire)

Circuit No. 332A
(GN Wire)

Circuit No. 53K
(BK Wire)

**LEFT POWER DOOR LOCK
MOTOR SWITCH CONNECTOR**

Circuit No. 53C
(BK Wire)

Circuit No. 301
(R Wire)

**LUGGAGE COMPARTMENT
SWITCH CONNECTOR**

Circuit No. 331
(R Wire)

Circuit No. 910
(Y Wire)

Circuit No. 332
(GN Wire)

Circuit No. 53P
(BK Wire)

**RIGHT POWER DOOR LOCK
MOTOR SWITCH CONNECTOR**

Circuit No. 11
(BK/Y Wire)

Circuit No. 40U
(BK/W Wire)

Circuit No. 909
(LG/Y Wire)

Circuit No. 18D
(GN Wire)

**STARTER INTERRUPT
RELAY CONNECTOR**

Circuit No. 50G
(BK Wire)

Circuit No. 908
(BR/W Wire)

HOOD SWITCH CONNECTOR

Circuit No. 52K
(BK Wire)

Circuit No. 115
(GN/R Wire)

Circuit No. 119
(BK/R Wire)

Circuit No. 117
(GN/W Wire)

Circuit No. 81
(BR Wire)

Circuit No. 116
(GN/BK Wire)

Circuit No. 118
(GN/Y Wire)

FLASHER MODULE CONNECTOR

Circuit No. 53Q
(BK Wire)

Circuit No. 906
(LG/R Wire)

**LIFTGATE KEY CYLINDER
SWITCH CONNECTOR**

Circuit No. 6A
(R/Y Wire)

Circuit No. 6
(R/Y Wire)

Circuit No. 262
(W/R Wire)

Circuit No. 261K
(W Wire)

HEADLIGHT RELAY CONNECTOR

93I85355 93J85356 93A85357 93B85358 93C85359 93F85360 93G85361 93H85362 93I85363 93J85364 93A85365

Fig. 20: Identifying Related Anti-Theft System Connector Terminals (Probe)

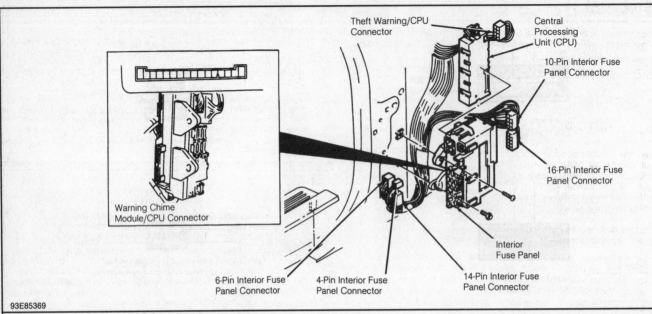

Theft Warning/CPU Connector

Central Processing Unit (CPU)

10-Pin Interior Fuse Panel Connector

16-Pin Interior Fuse Panel Connector

Warning Chime Module/CPU Connector

Interior Fuse Panel

6-Pin Interior Fuse Panel Connector

4-Pin Interior Fuse Panel Connector

14-Pin Interior Fuse Panel Connector

93E85369

Fig. 21: Locating Anti-Theft System Connectors (Probe)

TEST A

VERIFY ALARM ARMING
(CONTINENTAL, COUGAR & THUNDERBIRD)

1) Start vehicle, then turn ignition off. Alarm system should be reset.

2) Close all doors and check that alarm indicator light is off. If light is off, go to next step. If light blinks, go to step **6)**. If light is on steady, go to step **10)**.

3) Open a door. Warning light should blink. If light blinks, go to next step. If light does not blink, go to step **7)**.

4) Activate electric door lock switch. Warning light should glow steadily. If light glows, go to next step. If light does not glow, go to step **8)**.

5) Close door completely. Warning light should turn off after 32 seconds. If light turns off after 32 seconds, manual arming sequence operates. Go to step **12)**. If light does not turn off after 32 seconds, replace control module and retest system.

6) Using a voltmeter, check voltage at terminal No. 3 of control module. If voltage is more than 7 volts on Continental, or 5 volts on Cougar/Thunderbird, replace module and retest system. If voltage is less than 7 volts on Continental, or 2 volts on Cougar/Thunderbird, verify all doors are completely closed. Check voltage again. If voltage is still less than 2 or 7 volts, repair door ajar switch contacts for short to ground. Retest system.

7) Check voltage at terminal No. 3 again. If voltage is now less than 2 volts, go to Pinpoint TEST G. If voltage is more than 2 volts, check door ajar switches and retest.

8) Operate door locks. If door locks work, go to next step. If door locks do not operate, problem is in power door lock system or remote keyless entry system.

9) On models with remote keyless entry, check voltage at control module terminals No. 7 and 9 when doors are locked using power lock switch or keyless entry keypad. A momentary B+ signal at terminal No. 9, and less than 2 volts should be present at terminal No. 7. If reading is as indicated, go to step **11)**. If voltage is more than 2 volts repair wiring at terminal No. 7 or 9.

10) Disconnect harness connectors from control module. If warning indicator light remains on, repair short in circuit No. 343 (Dark Blue/Light Green wire), and retest system. If light is off, replace control module and retest system.

11) Check voltage at terminal No. 6 on control module. If voltage is more than 2 volts on Continental, or 5 volts on Cougar/Thunderbird, replace control module and retest system. If voltage is less than 2 volts, repair driver or passenger door key disarm switch and/or circuit No. 25 (Dark Green/Purple wire).

TEST A (Cont.)
(CONTINENTAL, COUGAR & THUNDERBIRD)

12) On vehicles with factory equipped remote/keyless entry system, turn ignition on to reset alarm. Turn ignition switch off. Close all doors. Simultaneously press buttons No. 7/8 and 9/0 on keypad to lock doors. Watch alarm warning indicator. When doors lock, light should light and remain lit for 30 seconds, then turn off. If light operates as indicated, alarm arming sequence is okay. If light does not operate as indicated, repair remote keyless problem, or replace keyless entry module and retest system.

13) On vehicles with factory equipped remote/keyless entry system, turn ignition on to reset alarm. Turn ignition off. Close all doors. Press LOCK button on remote transmitter to lock doors. Watch alarm warning indicator. When doors lock, light should light and remain lit for 30 seconds, then turn off. If light operates as indicated, alarm arming sequence is okay. If light does not operate as indicated, repair remote keyless problem, or replace keyless entry module and retest system.

14) On Cougar/Thunderbird, open door and activate power lock switch. Activate power unlock switch. If warning light blinks, go to next step. If light glows steadily, use door key to disarm system.

15) On Cougar/Thunderbird, press power unlock switch. Check voltage at terminal No. 9, and verify that a momentary B+ signal is present at terminal No. 7 when unlock switch is activated. If voltage is less than 2 volts at terminal No. 9 and a B+ signal is present at terminal No. 7, replace control module and retest system. If no voltages are present or terminal No. 7 is less than 2 volts, or terminal No. 9 is more than 2 volts, repair circuits No. 118 (Pink/Orange wire) or No. 117 (Pink/Black wire).

TEST B
VERIFY UNTRIGGERED ALARM DISARMING
(CONTINENTAL, COUGAR & THUNDERBIRD)

1) Arm alarm system. Insert key in driver's doors and turn to unlock position. Open door. If warning light blinks and alarm does not arm, system is okay, go to step **3)**. If alarm is triggered, try key in other door, or disconnect battery to stop alarm. Repeat with other door.

2) Using a voltmeter, check that terminal No. 6 of control module is less than one volt when door key is in unlocked position in driver's door and passenger door is locked. Repeat with driver's door locked and key in unlock position in passenger door. If voltage is less than one volt, replace control module and retest system. If voltage is more than one volt, repair door disarm switch.

3) Arm system. Unlock driver door using keyless entry code, or remote transmitter UNLOCK button. Open a door. If warning light blinks and alarm remains off, system is okay, go to next step. If alarm is triggered, use key to stop alarm and go to step **6)**.

TEST B (Cont.)
(CONTINENTAL, COUGAR & THUNDERBIRD)

4) Arm system and sit in driver's seat. Open any door. Watch alarm indicator. Insert ignition key and turn to RUN or ACC. If warning light turns off, ignition input is okay, and test is ended. If warning light blinks or alarm is triggered, go to next step.

5) Using a voltmeter, check voltage of terminal No. 9 (Continental) or terminal No. 4 (Cougar/Thunderbird) of control module with ignition key in RUN or ACC position. If voltage is more than 9 volts, replace control module and retest. If voltage is less than 9 volts, service ignition switch or check circuit No. 296 (White/Pink wire) for an open circuit. Retest system.

6) On models with remote/keyless entry, check voltage at control module terminals No. 7 and 8 when doors are unlocked using keyless entry code. A momentary B+ signal should be present at terminal No. 8, and less than 2 volts should be present at terminal No. 7. Repeat on passenger door using UNLOCK button of remote transmitter. If voltage is less than 2 volts and B+ is present, replace control module and retest system. If no voltage is present, service keyless entry system and retest system.

TEST C
VERIFY ALARM ACTIVATION
(CONTINENTAL)

1) Arm system with a front window down. Reach through window and open door using inside handle. If alarm triggers, go to next step. If alarm does not trigger, go to step 7). If alarm goes off continuously, replace control module and retest system.

2) With alarm triggered, check that horn sounds. If horn sounds, go to next step. If horn does not sound, go to step 9).

3) With alarm triggered, check that tail, parking and alarm indicator lights flash. If all lights flash, go to next step. If all lights do not flash, check in-line fuse leading from alarm relay (located in luggage compartment), circuit No. 14 (Brown wire) or circuit No. 343 (Dark Blue/Light Green wire) and retest system.

4) With alarm triggered, check that low beam headlights flash. If headlights flash, go to next step. If headlights do not flash, repair circuit No. 13 (Red/Black wire) and retest system.

5) With alarm triggered, check that vehicle does not start. If vehicle does not start, system is okay. Stop test and disarm system by unlocking door with key. If vehicle starts, go to next step.

6) Disconnect anti-theft module from wiring harness. Measure resistance between pins No. 12 and 24 of wiring connector. If resistance is less than 100 ohms, repair shorts in circuits No. 32 and 33. If resistance is more than 100 ohms, replace control module and retest.

7) Arm system. Open trunk lid. Short contacts of lock switch and check that system triggers. If system triggers, system is okay. Stop test and disarm system by unlocking door with key. If system did not trigger, go to next step.

8) Using a voltmeter, measure voltage at terminal No. 5 of control module. If voltage is less than 2 volts, replace control module and retest system. If voltage is more than 2 volts, repair circuit No. 26 (White/Pink wire) and/or replace trunk lid lock cylinder and retest system.

9) Activate horn from steering wheel. If horn sounds, go to next step. If horn does not sound, repair horn circuit, horn or horn relay.

10) Using voltmeter, check voltage at terminal No. 18 of control module. If voltage is less than 2 volts, repair open in circuit No. 6 (Yellow/Light Green wire) and retest system. If voltage is more than 2 volts, replace control module and retest system.

TEST C
VERIFY ALARM ACTIVATION
(COUGAR & THUNDERBIRD)

1) Arm system with a front window down. Reach through window and open door using inside handle. If alarm triggers, go to next step. If alarm does not trigger, replace control module and retest system. If alarm goes off continuously, replace control module and retest system.

TEST C (Cont.)
(CONTINENTAL)

2) With alarm triggered, check that horn sounds. If horn sounds, go to next step. If horn does not sound, go to step 8).

3) With alarm triggered, check that tail, parking and alarm indicator lights flash. If all lights flash, go to next step. If all lights do not flash, check in-line fuse (located in luggage compartment leading from alarm relay), circuit No. 14 (Brown wire) or circuit No. 343 (Dark Blue/Light Green wire) and retest system.

4) With alarm triggered, check that low beam headlights flash. If headlights flash, go to next step. If headlights do not flash, repair circuit No. 13 (Red/Black wire) and retest system.

5) With alarm triggered, check that vehicle does not start. If vehicle does not start, system is okay. Stop test and disarm system by unlocking door with key. If vehicle starts, replace control module and retest system.

6) Arm system. Open trunk lid. Short contacts of lock switch and check that system is triggered. If system triggers, system is okay. Stop test and disarm system by unlocking door with key. If system did not trigger, go to next step.

7) Using a voltmeter, measure voltage at terminal No. 5 of control module. If voltage is less than 2 volts, replace control module and retest system. If voltage is more than 2 volts, repair circuit No. 486 (Black/White wire) and/or replace trunk lid lock cylinder and retest system.

8) Activate horn from steering wheel. If horn sounds, go to next step. If horn does not sound repair horn circuit, horn or horn relay.

9) Using voltmeter, check voltage at terminal No. 18 of control module. If voltage is less than 2 volts, repair open in circuit No. 6 (Yellow/Light Green wire) and retest system. If voltage is more than 2 volts, replace control module and retest system.

TEST D
VERIFY TRIGGERED ALARM DISARMING
(CONTINENTAL, COUGAR & THUNDERBIRD)

1) Arm system with a front window down. Reach through window and open door using inside handle. Insert key and turn to unlock position. If alarm triggers, then turns off and warning light blinks, system is okay. Go to step 3). If alarm does not turn off, go to next step.

2) Using voltmeter, check voltage at control module terminal No. 6 with door key in unlock position. If voltage is more than one volt, repair door disarm switch or check for open in circuits No. 25 (Dark Green/Pink wire) or No. 57 (Black wire) and retest system. If voltage is less than one volt, replace control module and retest system.

3) Arm system with a front window down. Reach through window and open door using inside handle. Activate keyless entry door unlock code. If alarm triggers, then turns off and warning light blinks, system is okay. Go to step 5). If alarm does not turn off, go to next step. Repeat test using UNLOCK button of remote transmitter.

4) Using a voltmeter, check that a momentary B+ signal is present at terminal No. 8, when keyless entry unlock code, or remote transmitter UNLOCK button is activated. If B+ is present, replace control module and retest system. If less than one volt is present, repair circuit No. 163 (Red/Orange wire) and retest system.

5) Arm system with front window down. Open door using inside door handle. Wait 4 minutes. If alarm triggers, then shuts off after 3-4 minutes and vehicle will not start, system is okay. Test is complete, disarm system and retest system. If alarm does not shut off, or vehicle starts, replace control module and retest system.

TEST E
VEHICLE WILL NOT CRANK
(CONTINENTAL, COUGAR & THUNDERBIRD)

1) Insert door key and turn to unlock position. Open a door. Alarm system should trigger. If alarm triggers, go to TEST D, step 1). If alarm does not trigger, go to next step.

2) Measure battery voltage. If voltage is more than 9 volts, go to next step. If voltage is less than 9 volts, service battery as needed and retest.

TEST E (Cont.)
(CONTINENTAL, COUGAR & THUNDERBIRD)

3) Measure resistance between terminals No. 12 and 24 of control module. If resistance is more than 100 ohms, replace control module and retest system. If resistance is less than 100 ohms, anti-theft system is okay, problem is in vehicle starting system.

TEST F
ALARM LIGHT IS ALWAYS ON
(CONTINENTAL, COUGAR & THUNDERBIRD)

1) Arm alarm system. Within 30 seconds, insert door key and turn to unlock position. Warning light should turn off. If warning light turns off, system is okay. If warning light does not turn off, go to next step.

2) Disconnect control module connectors. If warning light turns off, replace control module and retest system. If warning light does not turn off, check for short in circuit No. 343 (Dark. Blue/Light Green wire). Repair circuit and retest system.

TEST G
ALARM LIGHT DOES NOT WORK
(CONTINENTAL, COUGAR & THUNDERBIRD)

1) Connect a jumper wire between ground and terminal No. 15 of control module. If light turns on, go to next step. If light does not turn on, check circuits No. 343 (Dark Blue/Light Green wire) or No. 705 (Light Green/Orange wire) for opens and repair. Retest system.

2) Using a voltmeter, check voltage at control module terminal No. 1. If voltage is more than 9 volts, go to next step. If voltage is less than 9 volts, check fuse and/or circuits No. 23 (Tan/Light Green wire) and 38 (Black/Yellow wire) and retest system.

3) Check voltage at control module terminal No. 4. If voltage is less than 9 volts, go to next step. If voltage is more than 9 volts, check for short in circuit No. 296 (White/Pink wire) and retest system.

4) Open any door. Activate electric door lock switch. If warning light blinks then glows steadily, system is okay. If light does not blink or glow steadily, replace control module and retest system.

TEST H
HORN, HEADLIGHTS & PARKING LIGHTS ALWAYS ON
(CONTINENTAL, COUGAR & THUNDERBIRD)

1) Disconnect control module. If horn turns off, replace control module and retest system. If horn remains on, service horn system and retest system.

2) Disconnect control module. If low beam headlights turn off, replace control module and retest system. If low beams remain on, check circuit No. 13 (Red/Black wire) and retest system.

3) Disconnect control module. If parking light turn off, replace control module and retest system. If parking lights remain on, check circuit No. 14 (Brown wire) and retest system.

TEST I
SYSTEM ACTIVATES FALSELY
(CONTINENTAL, COUGAR & THUNDERBIRD)

1) Arm alarm system. Verify system does not trigger immediately after arming. If system arms and does not trigger, go to next step. If system triggers, disarm system by unlocking door with key. Go to step **3)**.

TEST I (Cont.)
(CONTINENTAL, COUGAR & THUNDERBIRD)

2) While system remains armed, open trunk lid and apply movement to trunk lid lock switch connector and cable. If system does not trigger, go to next step. If system triggers, disarm system. Replace trunk lid lock cylinder and glove box cylinder. Retest system.

3) Using a voltmeter, check voltage at control module terminal No. 3 with all doors closed. If voltage is more than 7 volts, go to next step. If voltage is less than 7 volts, service circuits No. 627 (Black/Orange wire – Continental), No. 701 (Light Blue/Black wire – Continental), No. 567 (Dark Green wire – Cougar/Thunderbird), No. 563 (Red wire – Cougar/Thunderbird), No. 341 (Orange/White wire – Cougar/Thunderbird), or door ajar switches.

4) Using a voltmeter, measure voltage at control module terminal No. 5. If voltage is more than 2 volts on Continental, go to step **6)**. If voltage is more than 7 volts on Cougar/Thunderbird, replace control module and retest system. If voltage is less than 2 volts on all models, go to next step.

5) Disconnect anti-theft trunk lid lock cylinder switch from wiring harness. Arm system. If system arms and does not trigger, replace trunk lid and glove box lock cylinders and retest system. If system is triggered on Continental, go to next step. If system is triggered on Cougar/Thunderbird, replace control module and retest system.

6) On Continental, disconnect control module connectors. Disconnect trunk lid lock cylinder connector. Check continuity of circuit No. 26 (White/Pink wire) to known good ground. If continuity exists, locate and service short-to-ground. Reconnect connectors and retest system. If continuity does not exist, replace control module and retest system.

7) On models with remote/keyless entry system, when alarm activates falsely, turn ignition key to RUN/ACC position. If alarm continues to sound, replace control module and retest system. If alarm shuts off, see PINPOINT TEST J in KEYLESS ENTRY SYSTEM – EXCEPT PROBE article.

TEST J
DOOR & TRUNK SWITCH DIAGNOSTICS
(CONTINENTAL, COUGAR & THUNDERBIRD)

Diagnostic test provides capability to identify a short to ground condition for door disarm and/or trunk lid tamper circuits. Turn ignition switch to RUN position. Activate power door locks 5 times in 10 seconds. Watch alarm indicator light and count flashes. Warning light will repeat every 10 seconds. If light flashes one time, all inputs are normal. If light flashes 2 times, door disarm switch(es) input is shorted. If light flashes 3 times, trunk lid switch input is shorted. If light flashes 4 times, both door disarm and trunk lid inputs are shorted. Repair inputs as necessary.

Diagnostic mode will automatically cancel after 2 minutes or when key is turned from RUN to OFF position. If door disarm circuit is shorted to ground, alarm system will not arm because control module is receiving a disarm input. Refer to TEST A, step **11)**. If trunk lid circuit is shorted to ground, alarm system will trigger immediately after it is armed. Refer to TEST I, steps **1)**, **2)**, **4)** and **5)**.

TEST A
VERIFY ALARM ARMING
(MARK VIII & TOWN CAR)

1) Start vehicle, then turn ignition off. Alarm system should be reset.

2) Close all doors and check that alarm indicator light is off. If light is off, go to next step. If light blinks, go to step **6)**. If light is on steady, go to step **10)**.

3) Open a door. Warning light should blink. If light blinks, go to next step. If light does not blink, go to step **7)**.

4) Activate electric door lock switch. Warning light should glow steadily. If light glows, go to next step. If light does not glow, go to step **8)**.

5) Close door completely. Warning light should turn off after 32 seconds. If light turns off, manual arming sequence operates, go to step **12)**. If light does not turn off, replace control module and retest system.

TEST A (Cont.)
(MARK VIII & TOWN CAR)

6) Using a voltmeter, check voltage between terminals No. 3 and 26 of control module. If voltage is more than 7 volts on Town Car, or 5 volts on Mark VIII, replace module and retest system. If voltage is less than 7 volts on Town Car, or 5 volts on Mark VII, verify that all doors are completely closed. Check voltage again. If voltage is still less than 5 or 7 volts, repair door ajar switch contacts for short to ground and/or check for open is circuit No. 627 (Black/Orange wire). Retest system.

7) Check voltage at terminal No. 3 again. If voltage is now less than 2 volts, go to Pinpoint TEST G. If voltage is more than 2 volts, check door ajar switches and retest.

8) Operate door locks. If door locks work, go to step **9)**. If door locks do not operate, problem is in power door lock system or remote keyless entry system.

9) On models with remote keyless entry, check voltage at control module terminal No. 7 and 9 when doors are locked using power lock switch or keyless entry keypad. A momentary B+ signal at terminal No. 9, and less than 2 volts should be present at terminal No. 7. If voltage is less than 2 volts, go to step **11)**. If voltage is more than 2 volts, repair circuits No. 117 (Pink/Black wire) and/or No. 118 (Pink/Orange wire).

10) Disconnect harness connectors from control module. Check warning indicator. If light is on, repair short in circuit No. 343 (Dark Blue/Light Green wire), and retest system. If light is off, replace control module and retest system.

11) Check voltage at terminal No. 6 on control module. If voltage is more than 2 volts, replace control module and retest system. If voltage is less than 2 volts, repair driver or passenger door key disarm switch and/or circuit No. 25 (Dark Green/Purple wire).

12) On vehicles with factory equipped remote/keyless entry system, turn ignition on to reset alarm. Turn ignition switch off. Close all doors. Simultaneously press buttons No. 7/8 and 9/0 on keypad to lock doors. Watch alarm warning indicator. When doors lock, light should glow and remain lit for 30 seconds, then turn off. If light operates as indicated, alarm arming sequence is okay. If light does not operate as indicated, repair remote keyless problem, or replace keyless entry module and retest system.

13) On vehicles with factory equipped remote/keyless entry system, turn ignition on to reset alarm. Turn ignition off. Close all doors. Press LOCK button on remote transmitter to lock doors. Watch alarm warning indicator. When doors lock, light should glow and remain lit for 30 seconds, then turn off. If light operates as indicated, alarm arming sequence is okay. If light does not operate as indicated, repair remote keyless problem, or replace keyless entry module and retest system.

TEST B
VERIFY UNTRIGGERED ALARM DISARMING
(TOWN CAR)

1) Arm alarm system. Insert key in driver's door and turn to unlock position. Open door. If warning light blinks and alarm does not arm, system is okay, go to step **3)**. If alarm is triggered, try key in other door, or disconnect battery to stop alarm. Repeat with other door.

2) Using a voltmeter, check that terminal No. 6 of control module is less than one volt when door key is in unlocked position in driver's door and passenger door is locked. Repeat with driver's door locked and key in unlock position in passenger door. If voltage is less than one volt, replace control module and retest system. If voltage is more than one volt, repair door disarm switch.

3) Arm system. Unlock driver door using keyless entry code, or remote transmitter UNLOCK button. Open a door. If warning light blinks and alarm remains off, system is okay, go to next step. If alarm is triggered, use key to stop alarm and go to step **6)**.

4) Arm system and sit in driver's seat. Open any door. Watch alarm indicator light. Insert ignition key and turn to RUN or ACC position. If light glows steadily and then turns off, ignition input is okay, and test is ended. If light does not turn off, go to next step.

5) Using a voltmeter, check voltage of terminal No. 4 of control module with ignition key in RUN or ACC. If voltage is more than 2 volts, replace control module and retest. If less than 2 volts, service ignition switch or check circuit No. 294 (White/Light Blue wire) for an open circuit. Retest system.

TEST B (Cont.)
(TOWN CAR)

6) On models with remote/keyless entry, check voltage at control module terminals No. 7 and 8 when doors are unlocked using keyless entry code. A momentary B+ signal should be present at terminal No. 8, and less than 2 volts should be present at terminal No. 7. Repeat on passenger door using UNLOCK button of remote transmitter. If voltage is less than 2 volts and B+ is present, replace control module and retest system. If no voltage is present, service keyless entry system and retest system.

TEST B
VERIFY UNTRIGGERED ALARM DISARMING
(MARK VIII)

1) Arm alarm system. Insert key in driver's doors and turn to unlock position. Open door. If warning light blinks and alarm does not arm, system is okay, go to step **3)**. If alarm is triggered, try key in other door, or disconnect battery to stop alarm. Repeat with other door.

2) Using a voltmeter, check that terminal No. 6 of control module is less than one volt when door key is in unlocked position in driver's door and passenger door is locked. Repeat with driver's door locked and key in unlock position in passenger door. If voltage is less than one volt, replace control module and retest system. If voltage is more than one volt, repair door disarm switch.

3) Arm system. Unlock driver door using keyless entry code, or remote transmitter UNLOCK button. Open a door. If warning light blinks and alarm remains off, system is okay, go to next step. If alarm is triggered, use key to stop alarm and go to step **8)**.

4) Open a front door and activate power door lock switch. Activate power door unlock switch. If warning light blinks, go to step **6)**. If warning light glows steadily, use door key to disarm system and go to next step.

5) Using a voltmeter, check voltage at terminals No. 9 and 7 of control module. B+ signal should be present at terminal No. 7 of control module when unlock switch is activated. If B+ is present, but voltage at terminal No. 9 is less than 2 volts, replace control module and retest system. If no voltage is present, or voltage at terminal No. 9 is more than 2 volts, repair circuits No. 117 (Pink/Black wire) and No. 118 (Pink/Orange wire) and retest system.

6) Disarm system. Open any door. Watch alarm indicator. Insert ignition key and turn to RUN or ACC position. If light blinks and then turns off, ignition input is okay, and test is ended. If light does not turn off, go to next step.

7) Using a voltmeter, check voltage of terminal No. 4 of control module with ignition switch in RUN or ACC position. If voltage is more than 9 volts, replace control module and retest. If less than 9 volts, service ignition switch or check circuit No. 294 (White/Light Blue wire) for an open circuit. Retest system.

8) On models with remote/keyless entry, check voltage at control module terminals No. 7 and 8 when doors are unlocked using keyless entry code. A momentary B+ signal should be present at terminal No. 8, and less than 2 volts should be present at terminal No. 7. If voltage is less than 2 volts and B+ is present, replace control module and retest system. If no voltage is present, service keyless entry system and retest system.

TEST C
VERIFY ALARM ACTIVATION
(MARK VIII & TOWN CAR)

1) Arm system with a front window down. Reach through window and open door using inside handle. If alarm triggers, system is okay. Unlock door with key. Test complete. If alarm does not trigger, go to step **7)**. If alarm goes off continuously, replace control module and retest system.

2) With alarm triggered, check that horn sounds. If horn sounds, go to next step. If horn does not sound, go to step **9)**.

3) With alarm triggered, check that tail, parking, low beam headlights (Town Car) and alarm indicator lights flash. If all lights flash, go to next step. If all lights do not flash, go to step **11)**.

4) On Mark VIII, with alarm triggered, check that low beam headlights flash. If lights flash, go to next step. If lights do not flash, repair circuit No. 218 (White/Pink wire) and retest system.

TEST C (Cont.)
(MARK VIII & TOWN CAR)

5) On all models, with alarm triggered, check that vehicle does not start. If vehicle does not start, system is okay. Stop test and disarm system by unlocking door with key. If vehicle starts, go to next step.

6) Disconnect anti-theft module from wiring harness. On Mark VIII, measure voltage at terminal No. 11 of control module. If voltage is less than one volt, service starter interrupt relay and/or repair circuit No. 342 (Light Green/Pink wire). If voltage is more than one volt, replace control module and retest. On Town Car, measure resistance between pins No. 12 and 24 of wiring harness connector. If resistance is less than 100 ohms, repair circuits No. 342 (Light Green/Pink wire) and No. 137 (Yellow/Black wire) and/or service starter interrupt relay. If resistance is more than 100 ohms, replace control module and retest.

7) Arm system. Open trunk lid. Short contacts of lock switch and check that system is triggered. If system triggers, system is okay. Stop test and disarm system by unlocking door with key. If system did not trigger, go to next step.

8) If equipped with hood tamper switch, open hood and arm system. If alarm triggers, system is okay. Stop test and disarm system. If system does not trigger, go to next step.

9) Using a voltmeter, measure voltage at terminal No. 5 of control module. If voltage is less than 2 volts, replace control module and retest system. If voltage is more than 2 volts, repair circuit No. 26 (White/Pink wire – Mark VIII) or circuit No. 23 (Tan/Light Green wire – Town Car) and/or replace trunk lid lock cylinder and retest system.

10) Activate horn from steering wheel. If horn sounds, go to next step. If horn does not sound repair horn circuit, horn or horn relay.

11) Using voltmeter, check voltage at terminal No. 18 of control module. If voltage is less than 2 volts, repair open in circuit No. 6 (Yellow/Light Green wire – Mark VIII) or circuit No. 1 (Dark Blue wire – Town Car) and retest system. If voltage is more than 2 volts, replace control module and retest system.

12) Using a voltmeter, backprobe terminal No. 21 of control module and measure voltage. If voltage is more than one volt on Mark VIII or less than 9 volts on Town Car, replace control module and retest system. If voltage is less than one volt on Mark VIII or more than 9 volts on Town Car, repair circuit No. 218 (White/Pink wire – All models) or circuit No. 221 (Orange/White wire – Town Car), or autolight system circuit No. 502 (Gray wire – Mark VIII) or autolight relay.

TEST D
VERIFY TRIGGERED ALARM DISARMING
(MARK VIII & TOWN CAR)

1) Arm system with a front window down. Reach through window and open door using inside handle. Insert key and turn to unlock position. If alarm triggers, then turns off and warning light blinks, system is okay. Go to step **3)**. If alarm does not turn off, go to next step.

2) Using voltmeter, check voltage at control module terminal No. 6 with door key in unlock position. If voltage is more than one volt, repair door disarm switch or check for open in circuits No. 25 (Dark Green/Pink wire) or No. 57 (Black wire) and retest system. If voltage is less than one volt, replace control module and retest system.

3) Arm system with a front window down. Reach through window and open door using inside handle. Activate keyless entry door unlock code. If alarm triggers, then turns off and warning light blinks, system is okay. Go to step **5)**. If alarm does not turn off, go to next step. Repeat test using UNLOCK button of remote transmitter.

4) Using a voltmeter, check that a momentary B+ signal is present at terminal No. 8, when keyless entry unlock code, or remote transmitter UNLOCK button is activated. If B+ is present, replace control module and retest system. If voltage is less than one, repair circuit No. 163 (Red/Orange wire) and retest system.

5) Arm system with front window down. Open door using inside door handle. Wait 4 minutes. If alarm triggers, then shuts off after 3-4 minutes and vehicle will not start, system is okay. Test is complete, disarm system. If alarm does not shut off, or vehicle starts, replace control module and retest system.

TEST E
VEHICLE WILL NOT CRANK
(MARK VIII & TOWN CAR)

1) Insert door key and turn to unlock position. Open a door. Alarm system should be disarmed. If system is disarmed, go to next step. If system is not disarmed, go to TEST B, step **1)**.

2) Measure battery voltage. If voltage is more than 9 volts, go to next step. If voltage is less than 9 volts, service battery as needed and retest.

3) On Mark VIII, measure resistance between terminals No. 11 and 13 of control module. If resistance is more than 1000 ohms, replace control module and retest system. If resistance is less than 1000 ohms, anti-theft system is okay, problem is in vehicle starting system.

4) On Town Car, use a voltmeter to measure voltage at terminal No. 11 of control module. If voltage is less than 2 volts, replace control module and retest system. If voltage is more than 2 volts, problem is in starter interrupt relay or starting system.

TEST F
ALARM LIGHT IS ALWAYS ON
(MARK VIII & TOWN CAR)

1) Arm alarm system. Within 30 seconds, insert door key and turn to unlock position. Warning light should turn off. If light is off, system is okay. If light is on, go to next step.

2) Disconnect control module connectors. If light turns off, replace control module and retest system. If light is on, check for short in circuit No. 343 (Dark Blue/Light Green wire). Repair circuit and retest system.

TEST G
ALARM LIGHT DOES NOT WORK
(MARK VIII & TOWN CAR)

1) Connect a jumper wire between ground and terminal No. 15 of control module. If light turns on, go to next step. If light is off, check circuits No. 343 (Dark Blue/Light Green wire) or No. 54 (Light Green/Yellow wire) for an open and repair as necessary. Retest system.

2) Using a voltmeter, check voltage at control module terminal No. 1. If voltage is more than 9 volts, go to next step. If voltage is less than 9 volts, check fuse and/or circuits No. 23 (Tan/Light Green wire – Mark VIII), No. 37 (Yellow wire – Mark VIII) or No. 195 (Tan/White wire – Town Car) and retest system.

3) Check voltage at control module terminal No. 4. If voltage is less than 9 volts, go to next step. If voltage is more than 9 volts, check for short in circuit No. 294 (White/Light Blue wire – Town Car) or No. 296 (White/Pink wire – Mark VIII) and retest system.

4) Open any door. Activate electric door lock switch. If warning light blinks then glows steadily, system is okay. If warning light does not blink or glow steadily, replace control module and retest system.

TEST H
HORN, HEADLIGHTS & PARKING LIGHTS
ALWAYS ON
(MARK VIII & TOWN CAR)

1) Disconnect control module. If horn turns off, replace control module and retest system. If horn remains on, service horn system and retest system.

2) Disconnect control module. If low beam headlights turn off, replace control module and retest system. If low beam headlights remain on, check circuit No. 218 (White/Pink wire) and retest system.

3) Disconnect control module. If parking lights turn off, replace control module and retest system. If parking lights remain on, check circuit No. 218 (White/Pink wire) and retest system.

TEST I

SYSTEM ACTIVATES FALSELY
(MARK VIII & TOWN CAR)

1) With hood closed, arm alarm system. Verify that system does not trigger immediately after arming. If system arms and does not trigger, go to next step. If system triggers, disarm system by unlocking door with key. Go to step **3)**.

2) While system remains armed, open trunk lid and apply movement to trunk lid lock switch connector and cable. If system does not trigger, go to next step. If system triggers, disarm system. Replace trunk lid lock cylinder and glove box cylinder. Retest system.

3) Using a voltmeter, check voltage at control module terminal No. 3 with all doors closed. If voltage is more than 2 volts, go to next step. If voltage is less than 2 volts, service circuit No. 627 (Black/Orange wire – Town Car) or No. 341 (Orange/White wire – Mark VII) or door ajar switches.

4) Using a voltmeter, measure voltage at control module terminal No. 5. If voltage is more than 2 volts, go to step **7)**. If voltage is less than 2 volts, go to next step.

5) Disconnect anti-theft trunk lid lock cylinder switch from wiring harness. Measure voltage at terminal No. 5 of harness connector. If voltage is less than 2 volts, go to next step. If voltage is more than 2 volts, replace trunk lid and glove box lock cylinders and retest system.

6) Disconnect hood switch from wiring harness. Backprobe terminal No. 5 and measure voltage. If voltage is more than 2 volts, check hood for flush fit and/or replace hood switch. If voltage is less than 2 volts, service circuit No. 26 (White/Pink wire – Mark VII) or No. 23 (Tan/Light Green wire – Town Car) for short-to-ground and retest system.

7) Disconnect control module from wiring harness. Measure resistance between terminals No. 10 and 26 through harness. If resistance measures 145-175 ohms, circuit is okay, go to next step. If resistance is less than 145 or more than 175 ohms, replace ignition lock cylinder sensor and/or service circuit No. 936 (Dark Green/White wire).

8) On models with remote/keyless entry system, when alarm activates falsely, turn ignition key to RUN/ACC position. If alarm continues to sound, replace control module and retest system. If alarm shuts off, see PINPOINT TEST J in KEYLESS ENTRY SYSTEM – EXCEPT PROBE article

TEST J

VERIFY IGNITION LOCK CYLINDER SENSOR
(MARK VIII & TOWN CAR)

1) Disarm alarm system by unlocking door with key. Disconnect battery ground cable. Wait 40 seconds. Reconnect battery ground cable. If alarm triggers 8 seconds after reconnecting battery cable, go to step **4)**. If alarm remains silent, go to next step.

2) With ignition off, disconnect ignition key lock cylinder sensor from wiring harness. If alarm triggers, system is okay, reconnect sensor. End of test. If system does not trigger, go to next step.

3) Check that continuity exists between terminals No. 23 and 26 at control module. If continuity exists, go to next step. If continuity does not exist, repair circuit No. 57 (Black wire) and retest system.

4) Disconnect control module and measure resistance between terminals No. 10 and 26. If resistance is 145-175 ohms, replace control module and retest. If resistance is less than 145 or more than 175 ohms, service ignition key lock cylinder sensor and/or circuit No. 936 (Dark Green/White wire) and retest system.

TEST K

DOOR/TRUNK/HOOD SWITCH
& IGNITION SENSOR DIAGNOSTICS
(MARK VIII & TOWN CAR)

Diagnostic test provides capability to identify a short to ground condition for door disarm and/or trunk lid tamper circuits. Turn ignition to RUN position. Watch alarm indicator light. If light remains off, ignition key lock cylinder sensor is okay. If light comes on, ignition key lock cylinder is shorted and needs repair. Activate power door locks 5 times in 10 seconds. Watch alarm indicator light and count flashes. Warning light will

TEST K (Cont.)

(MARK VIII & TOWN CAR)

repeat every 10 seconds. If light flashes one time, all inputs are normal. If light flashes 2 times, door disarm switch(es) input is shorted. If light flashes 3 times, hood or trunk lid switch input is shorted. If light flashes 4 times, both door disarm and hood/trunk lid inputs are shorted. Repair inputs as necessary.

Diagnostic mode will automatically cancel after 2 minutes or when ignition is turned from RUN to OFF position. If door disarm circuit is shorted to ground, alarm system will not arm because control module is receiving a disarm input. Refer to TEST A, step **11)**. If hood or trunk lid circuit is shorted to ground, alarm system will trigger immediately after it is armed. Refer to TEST I, steps **4), 5) and 6)**.

TEST K

THEFT WARNING SYSTEM TESTS (PROBE)

NOTE: In all of the following tests, ignition key should always be in OFF position unless otherwise specified in a specific test.

1) With ignition key off, check 15-amp fuse in passenger compartment fuse panel. If fuse is blown, go to next step. If fuse is okay, go to step **3)**.

2) Replace fuse. If fuse blows again, repair short to ground in anti-theft fuse circuit. If fuse does not fail, go to next step.

3) Disconnect CPU from top of interior fuse panel located at left side kick panel. Using a voltmeter, measure voltage at pin "C" of 16-pin CPU connector. If voltage is more than 10 volts, go to next step. If voltage is less than 10 volts, replace interior fuse panel.

4) Disconnect CPU from fuse panel. Measure resistance between pin "D" of 16-pin fuse panel connector and ground. If resistance is less than 5 ohms, replace CPU. If resistance is more than 5 ohms, go to next step.

5) Disconnect 16-pin fuse panel connector. Measure resistance of Black wire between connector and ground. If resistance is less than 5 ohms, replace fuse panel. If resistance is more than 5 ohms, repair Black wire.

6) Disconnect 20-pin connector from CPU. Apply ground to Light Green wire at CPU connector. If Anti-Theft indicator lights, replace CPU. If light does not light go to next step.

7) Disconnect 16-pin instrument panel cluster connector. Using a voltmeter, measure voltage of Black/Red wire at connector. If voltage is more than 10 volts, go to next step. If voltage is less than 10 volts, repair Black/Red wire.

8) Reconnect 16-pin instrument panel cluster connector. Remove anti-theft indicator bulb from cluster. Measure voltage at bulb terminal on instrument panel printed circuit board. If voltage is more than 10 volts, go to next step. If voltage is less than 10 volts, replace printed circuit board.

9) Disconnect 16-pin instrument panel cluster connector and 20-pin CPU connector. Measure resistance of Light Green wire between 20-pin connector and ground. Resistance should be less than 5 ohms between 20-pin CPU connector and 16-pin cluster connector, and more than 10,000 ohms between 20-pin CPU connector and ground. If resistance readings are correct and warning indicator light is off, go to next step. If resistance readings are correct but warning indicator is on, replace CPU. If resistance readings are incorrect, repair Light Green wire.

10) Reconnect 16-pin instrument panel cluster connector and disconnect 20-pin CPU connector. Remove anti-theft indicator bulb. Measure resistance between bulb terminal on printed cluster and Light Green wire at 20-pin CPU connector. Measure resistance of Light Green wire between 20-pin connector and ground. Resistance should be less than 5 ohms between 20-pin CPU connector and printed circuit bulb terminal, and more than 10,000 ohms between 20-pin CPU connector and ground. If resistance readings are correct, replace anti-theft indicator bulb. If resistance readings are incorrect, repair printed circuit board.

11) Disconnect starter interrupt relay from main fuse panel and 20-pin connector from CPU. Measure resistance of Light Green/Yellow wire between relay connector and CPU connector. Measure resistance of Light Green/Yellow wire between CPU connector and ground. If resistance is less than 5 ohms between starter relay connector and CPU connector and more than 10,000 ohms between CPU connector and ground, replace CPU. If resistance is not as indicated, repair Light Green/Yellow wire.

12) Disconnect 20-pin connector from CPU and flasher module connector. Measure resistance of Green/Red wire between CPU connector and flasher connector. If resistance is less than 5 ohms, replace CPU. If resistance is more than 5 ohms, repair Green/Red wire.

TEST K (Cont.)
(PROBE)

13) Disconnect 20-pin connector from CPU and horn relay from main fuse panel. Measure resistance of Green/Orange wire between CPU connector and horn relay connector. If resistance is less than 5 ohms, replace CPU. If resistance is more than 5 ohms, repair Green/Orange wire.

14) Disconnect 20-pin connector from CPU and headlight relay from main fuse panel. Measure resistance of White/Red wire between CPU connector and headlight relay connector. If resistance is less than 5 ohms, replace CPU. If resistance is more than 5 ohms, repair White/Red wire.

15) Disconnect 20-pin connector from CPU and both door power door lock motor switch connectors. Measure resistance of Brown/Yellow wire between CPU connector and left door switch connector, and Yellow wire between CPU connector and right door switch connector. Measure resistance of Brown/Yellow wire and Yellow wire between CPU connector and ground. Resistance should be less than 5 ohms between CPU connector and door lock motor switch connectors, and more than 10,000 ohms between CPU connector and ground. If resistance is correct but system cannot be armed, go to step **17)**. If resistance is correct but alarm does not activate, go to step **16)**. If resistance is correct but alarm is always on, go to step **19)**. If resistances are incorrect, repair wire(s) in question.

16) Disconnect both power door lock motor switch connectors. Measure resistance of Black wires between each motor switch connector and ground. Resistance should be less than 5 ohms. If resistance is less than 5 ohms, go to next step. If resistance is more than 5 ohms, repair Black wire(s) in question.

17) Reconnect both power door lock motor switch connectors. Disconnect 20-pin CPU connector. Unlock doors manually. Measure resistance of Brown/Yellow wire between CPU connector and ground. Measure resistance of Yellow wire between CPU connector and ground. Lock doors manually. Measure resistance of Brown/Yellow wire between CPU connector and ground. Measure resistance of Yellow wire between CPU connector and ground. If there is continuity with doors unlocked, and more than 10,000 ohms resistance with doors locked, replace CPU. If there is no continuity with doors unlocked, or less than 10,000 ohms resistance with doors locked, replace power door lock motor(s).

18) Disconnect 20-pin connector from CPU and trunk light switch connector. Measure resistance of Red wire between CPU connector and light switch connector. If resistance is less than 5 ohms, replace CPU. If resistance is more than 5 ohms, repair Red wire.

19) Disconnect 20-pin connector from CPU. Open hood. Measure resistance of Brown/White wire between CPU connector and ground. Close hood. Measure resistance again. Resistance should be less than 5 ohms with hood opened and more than 10,000 ohms with hood closed. If resistance is correct, but alarm does not trigger, replace CPU. If resistance is correct, but alarm is always on, go to step **25)**. If resistance is incorrect, repair Brown/White wire.

TEST K (Cont.)
(PROBE)

20) Disconnect 20-pin CPU connector and hood switch connector. Measure resistance of Brown/White wire between CPU connector and hood switch connector. Measure resistance of Brown/White wire between CPU connector and ground. Resistance should be less than 5 ohms between CPU connector and hood switch and more than 10,000 ohms between CPU connector and ground. If resistance is correct, go to step **21)**. If resistance is not correct, repair Brown/White wire.

21) Disconnect hood switch connector. Measure resistance of Black wire between hood switch connector and ground. If resistance is less than 5 ohms, replace hood switch. If resistance is more than 5 ohms, repair Black wire.

22) Disconnect 20-pin connector from CPU. Place key in driver's door lock in unlock position. Measure resistance of Yellow/Red wire between CPU connector and ground. Remove key from lock. Measure resistance of Yellow/Red wire between CPU connector and ground. Repeat procedure for passenger door lock. If resistance is less than 5 ohms with key in unlock position and more than 10,000 ohms with key removed, replace CPU. If resistance is not as indicated, go to next step.

23) Disconnect 20-pin connector from CPU, both door key cylinder switch connectors and remote entry module connector No. 2 (if equipped). Measure resistance of Yellow/Red wires between CPU connector and key cylinder switch connectors. Measure resistance of Yellow/Red wire between CPU connector and ground. If resistance is less than 5 ohms between CPU connector and key cylinder switch connectors, and more than 10,000 ohms between CPU connector and ground, go to next step. If resistance is not as indicated, repair Yellow/Red wire(s).

24) Disconnect both door key cylinder connectors. Measure resistance of Black wire between connectors and ground. If resistance readings are less than 5 ohms, replace key cylinder switch(es). If resistance readings are more than 5 ohms, repair Black wire(s).

25) Disconnect 20-pin CPU connector. Place key in liftgate lock cylinder in unlock position. Measure resistance of Light Green/Red wire between CPU connector and ground. Remove key. Measure resistance again. If resistance is less than 5 ohms with key in unlock position and more than 10,000 ohms with key removed, replace CPU. If resistances are not as indicated go to next step.

26) Disconnect 20-pin CPU connector and liftgate key cylinder switch connector. Measure resistance of Light Green/Red wire between CPU connector and switch connector. Measure resistance of Light Green/Red wire between CPU connector and ground. If resistance is less than 5 ohms between CPU and switch connector and more than 10,000 ohms between CPU and ground, go to next step. If resistance is not as specified, repair Light Green/Red wire.

27) Disconnect liftgate key cylinder switch connector. Measure resistance of Black wire between key switch and ground. If resistance is less than 5 ohms, replace key cylinder switch. If resistance is more than 5 ohms, repair Black wire.

WIRING DIAGRAMS

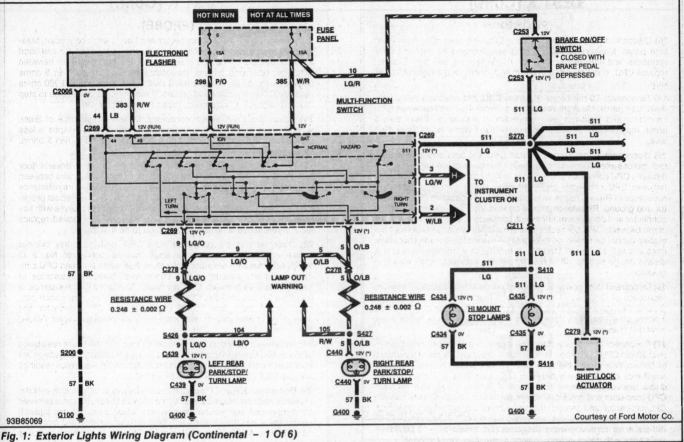

Fig. 1: Exterior Lights Wiring Diagram (Continental – 1 Of 6)

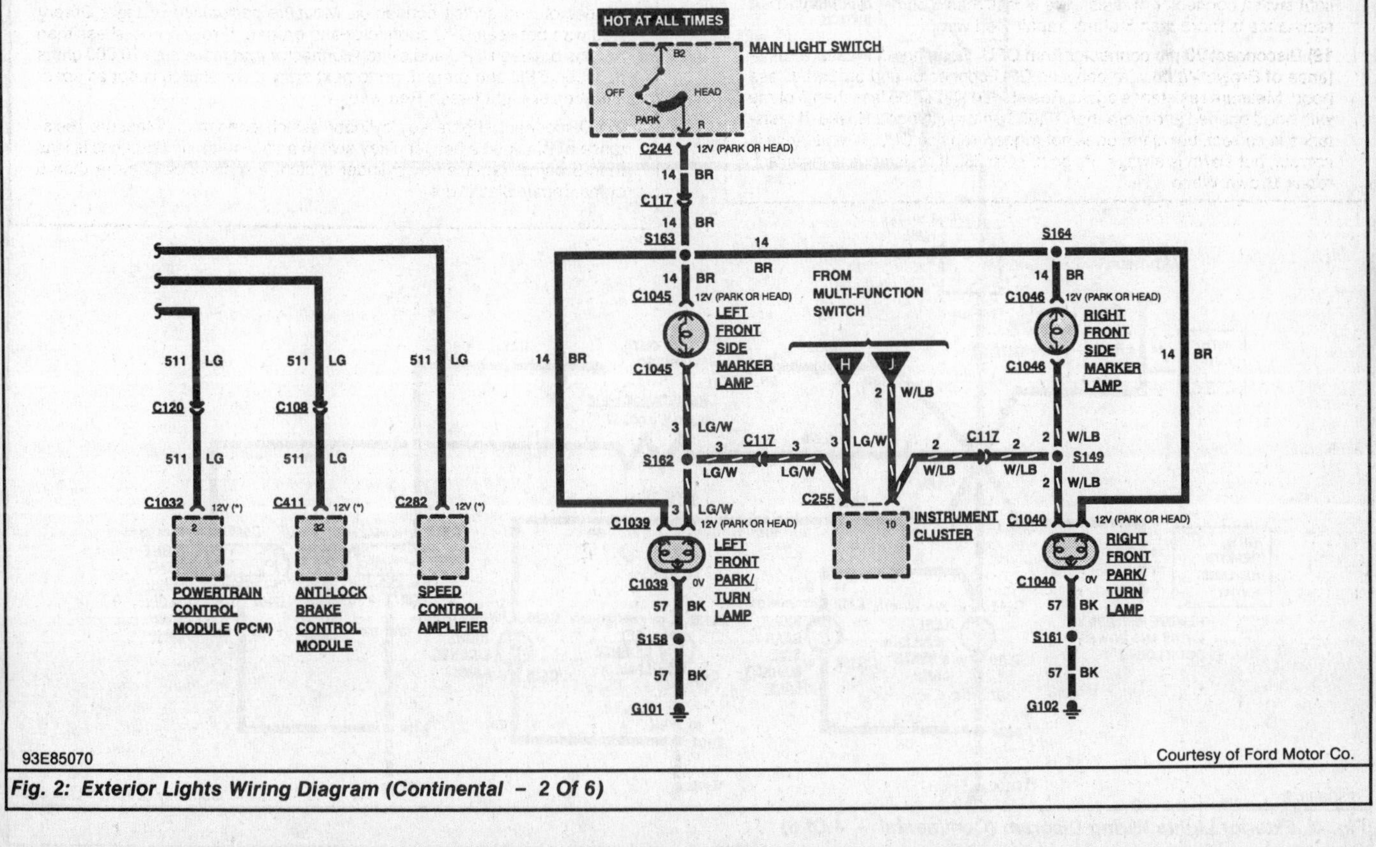

Courtesy of Ford Motor Co.

Fig. 2: Exterior Lights Wiring Diagram (Continental – 2 Of 6)

Courtesy of Ford Motor Co.

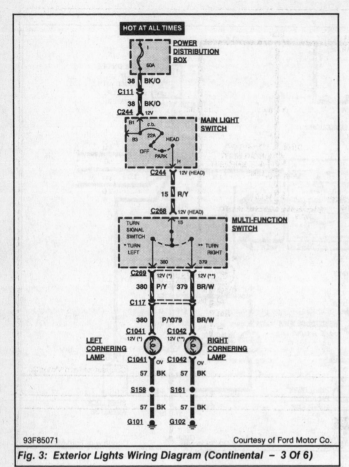

93F85071   Courtesy of Ford Motor Co.

Fig. 3: Exterior Lights Wiring Diagram (Continental – 3 Of 6)

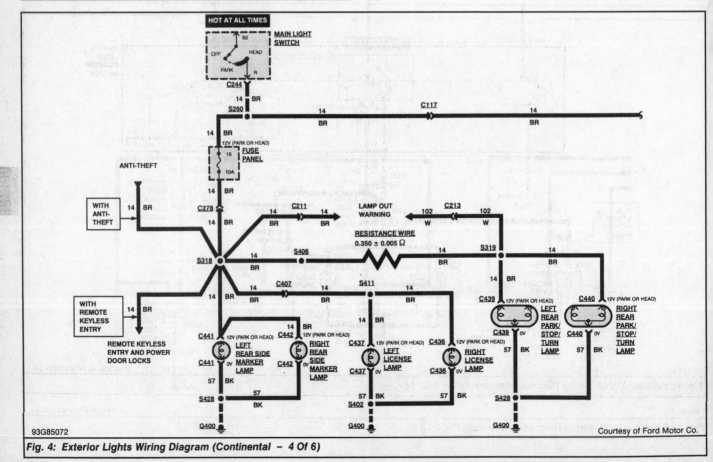

93G85072   Courtesy of Ford Motor Co.

Fig. 4: Exterior Lights Wiring Diagram (Continental – 4 Of 6)

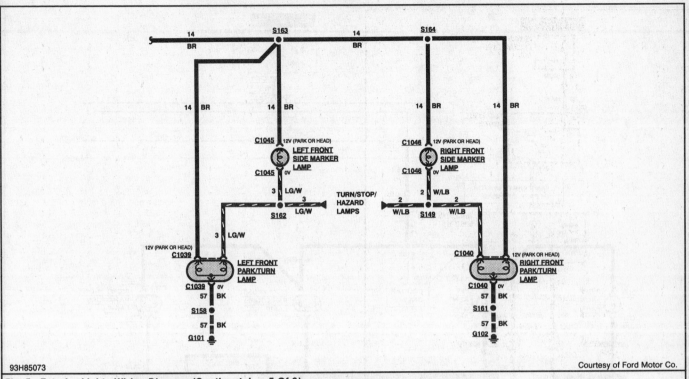

93H85073   Courtesy of Ford Motor Co.

Fig. 5: Exterior Lights Wiring Diagram (Continental – 5 Of 6)

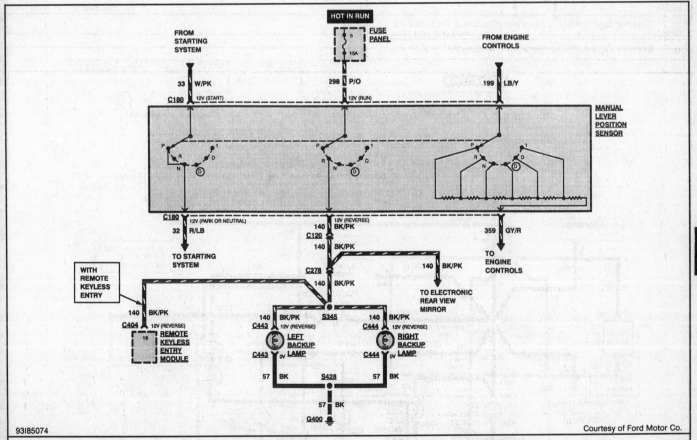

93I85074   Courtesy of Ford Motor Co.

Fig. 6: Exterior Lights Wiring Diagram (Continental – 6 Of 6)

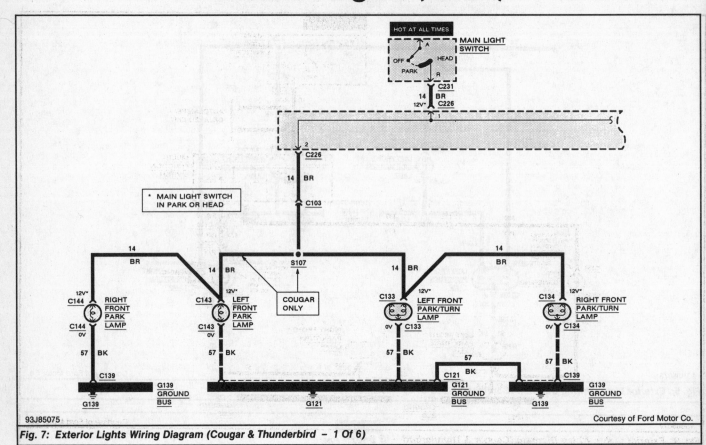

93J85075   Courtesy of Ford Motor Co.

Fig. 7: Exterior Lights Wiring Diagram (Cougar & Thunderbird – 1 Of 6)

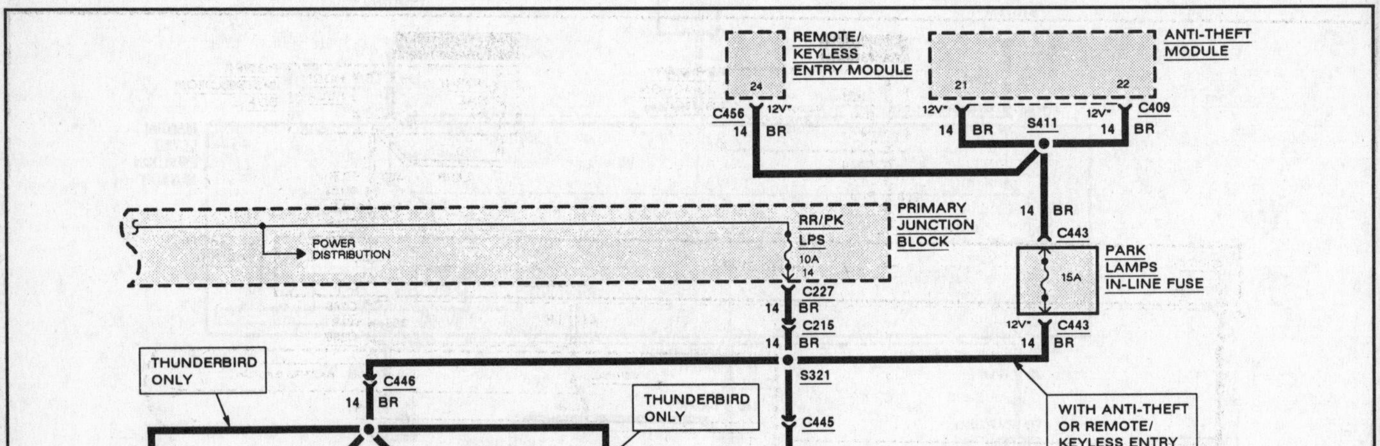

93A85076   Courtesy of Ford Motor Co.

Fig. 8: Exterior Lights Wiring Diagram (Cougar & Thunderbird – 2 Of 6)

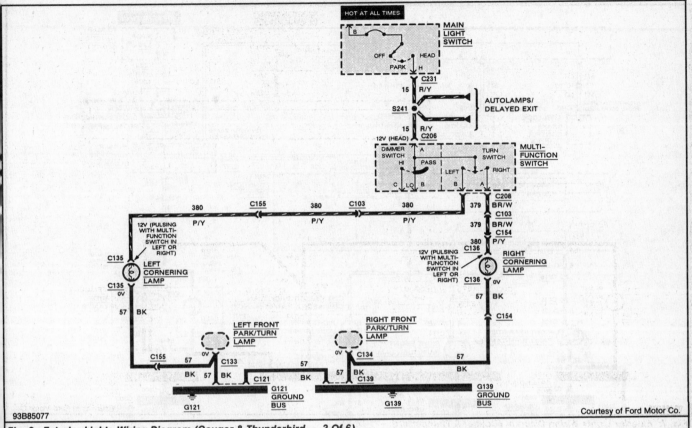

Fig. 9: Exterior Lights Wiring Diagram (Cougar & Thunderbird – 3 Of 6)

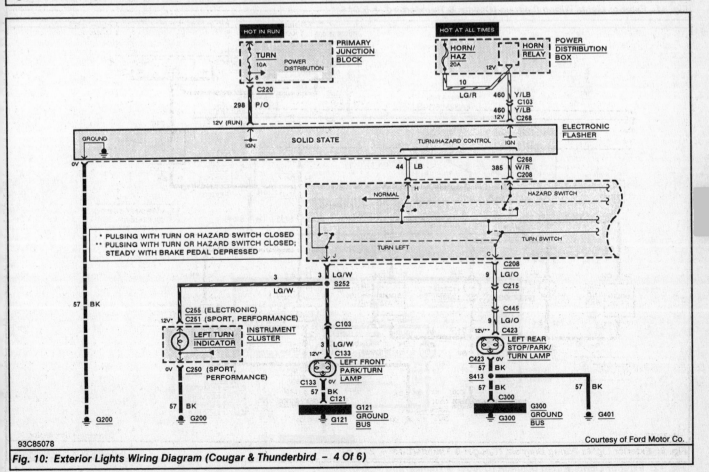

Fig. 10: Exterior Lights Wiring Diagram (Cougar & Thunderbird – 4 Of 6)

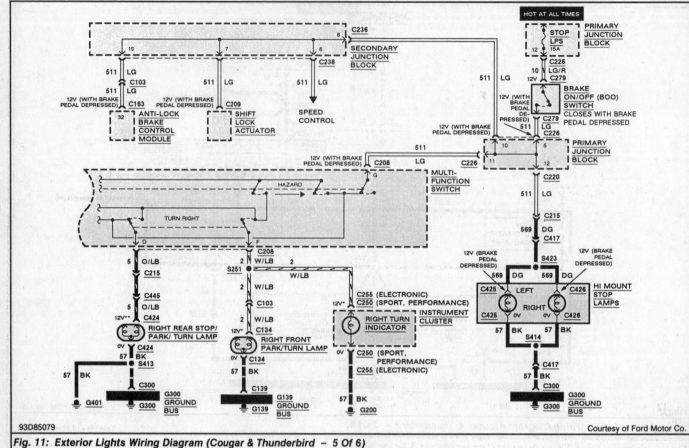

93D85079 — Courtesy of Ford Motor Co.

Fig. 11: Exterior Lights Wiring Diagram (Cougar & Thunderbird – 5 Of 6)

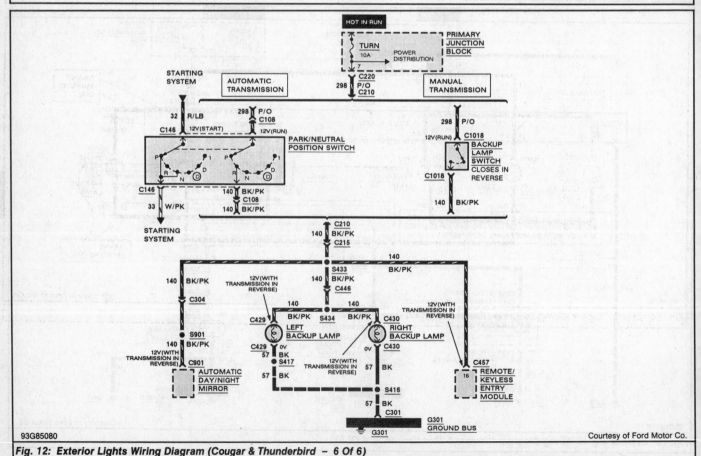

93G85080 — Courtesy of Ford Motor Co.

Fig. 12: Exterior Lights Wiring Diagram (Cougar & Thunderbird – 6 Of 6)

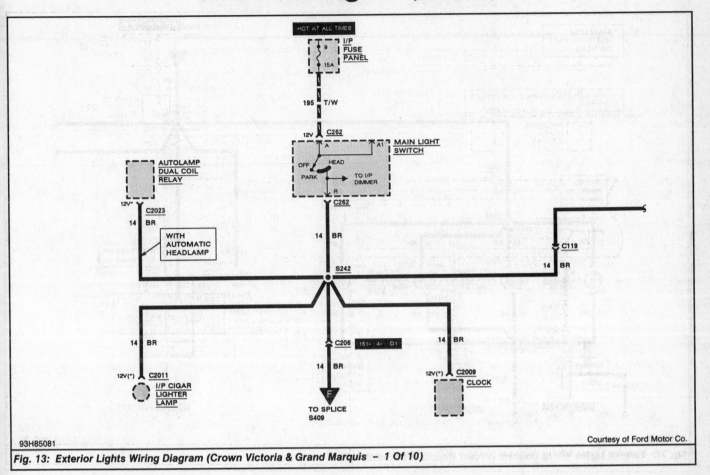

93H85081

Fig. 13: Exterior Lights Wiring Diagram (Crown Victoria & Grand Marquis – 1 Of 10)

93I85082

Fig. 14: Exterior Lights Wiring Diagram (Crown Victoria & Grand Marquis – 2 Of 10)

Courtesy of Ford Motor Co.

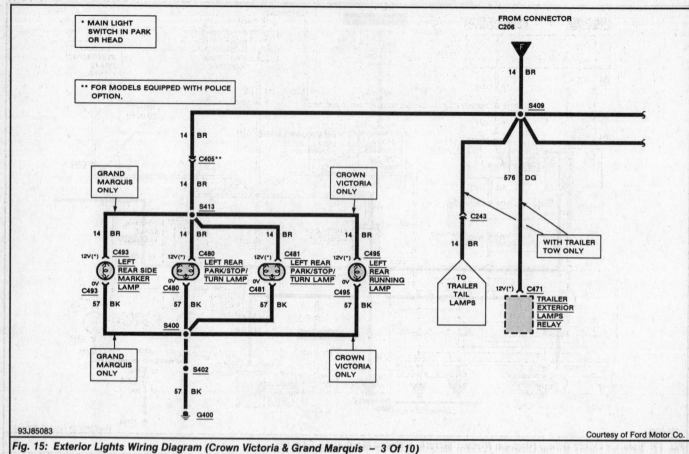

93J85083
Courtesy of Ford Motor Co.

Fig. 15: Exterior Lights Wiring Diagram (Crown Victoria & Grand Marquis – 3 Of 10)

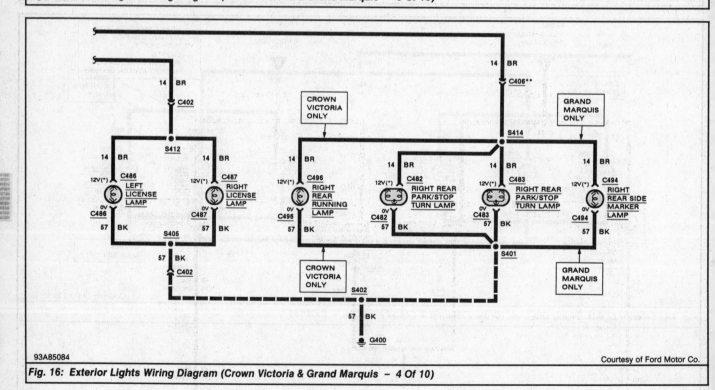

93A85084
Courtesy of Ford Motor Co.

Fig. 16: Exterior Lights Wiring Diagram (Crown Victoria & Grand Marquis – 4 Of 10)

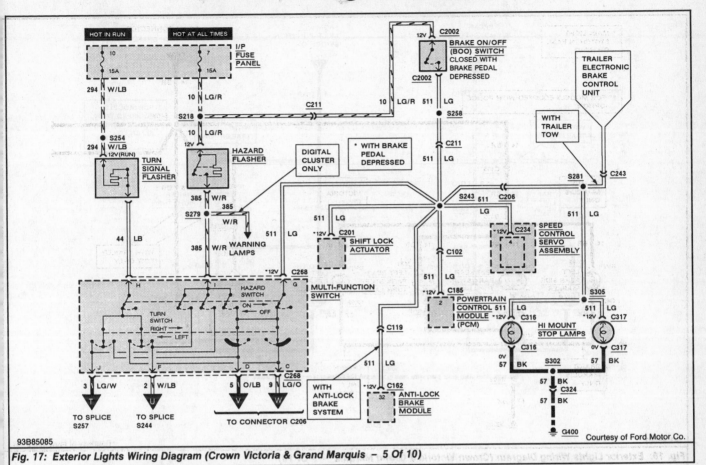

Fig. 17: Exterior Lights Wiring Diagram (Crown Victoria & Grand Marquis – 5 Of 10)

Fig. 18: Exterior Lights Wiring Diagram (Crown Victoria & Grand Marquis – 6 Of 10)

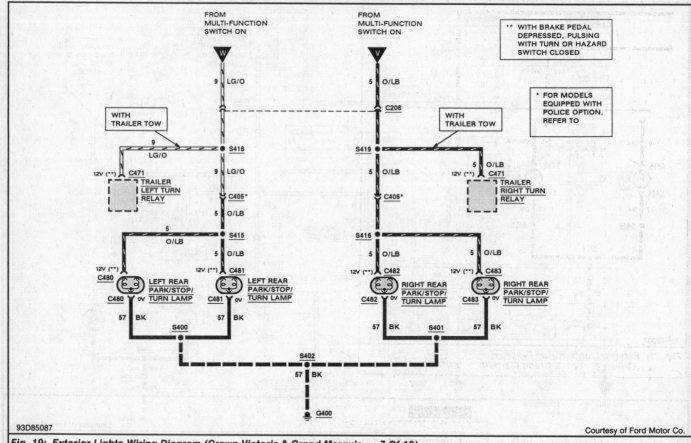

93D85087   Courtesy of Ford Motor Co.

Fig. 19: Exterior Lights Wiring Diagram (Crown Victoria & Grand Marquis – 7 Of 10)

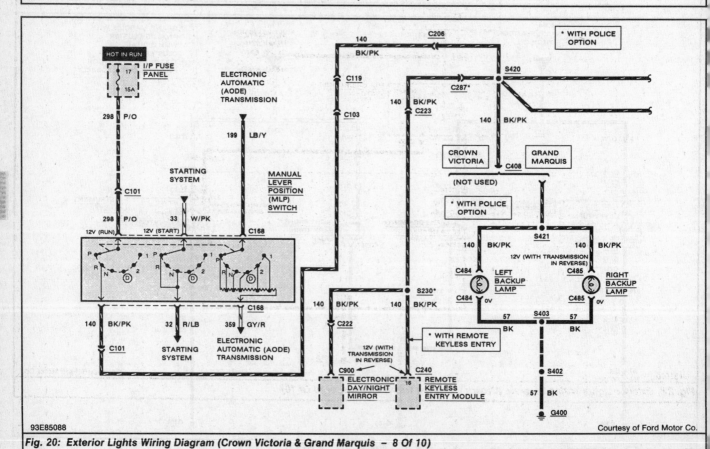

93E85088   Courtesy of Ford Motor Co.

Fig. 20: Exterior Lights Wiring Diagram (Crown Victoria & Grand Marquis – 8 Of 10)

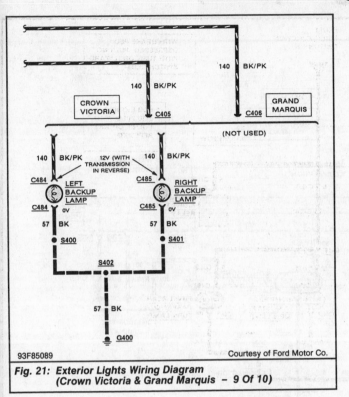

Fig. 21: *Exterior Lights Wiring Diagram (Crown Victoria & Grand Marquis – 9 Of 10)*

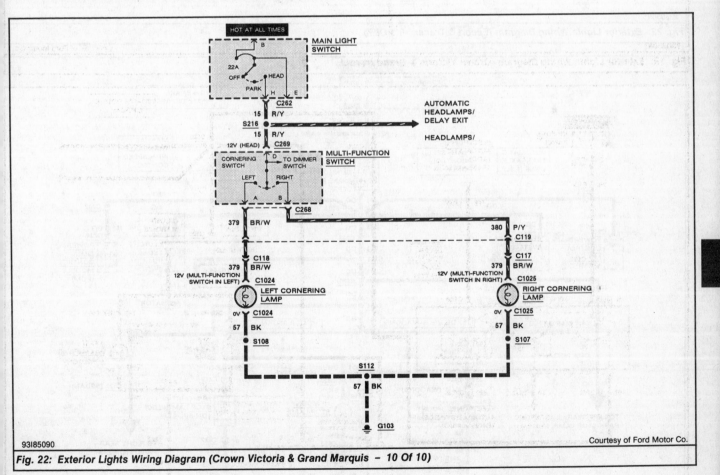

Fig. 22: *Exterior Lights Wiring Diagram (Crown Victoria & Grand Marquis – 10 Of 10)*

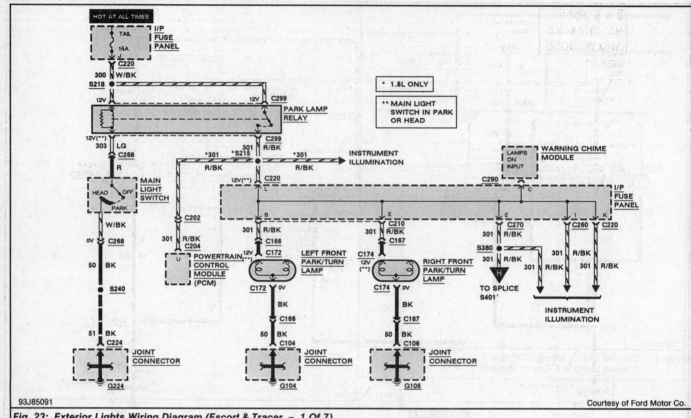

Fig. 23: Exterior Lights Wiring Diagram (Escort & Tracer – 1 Of 7)

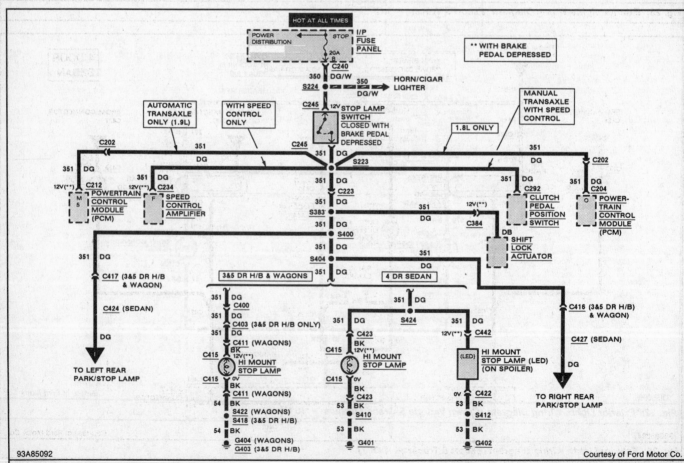

Fig. 24: Exterior Lights Wiring Diagram (Escort & Tracer – 2 Of 7)

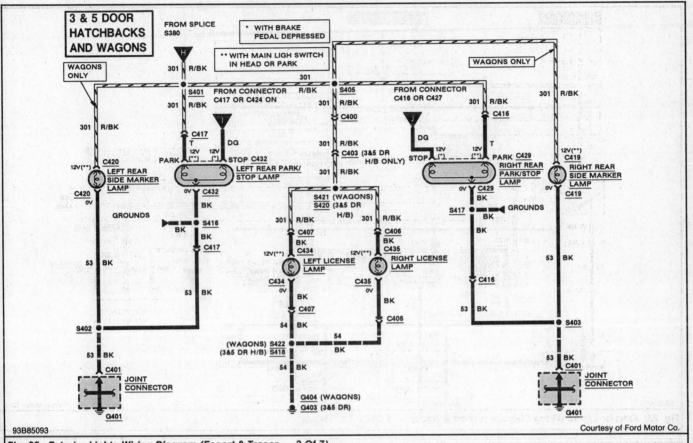

Fig. 25: Exterior Lights Wiring Diagram (Escort & Tracer – 3 Of 7)

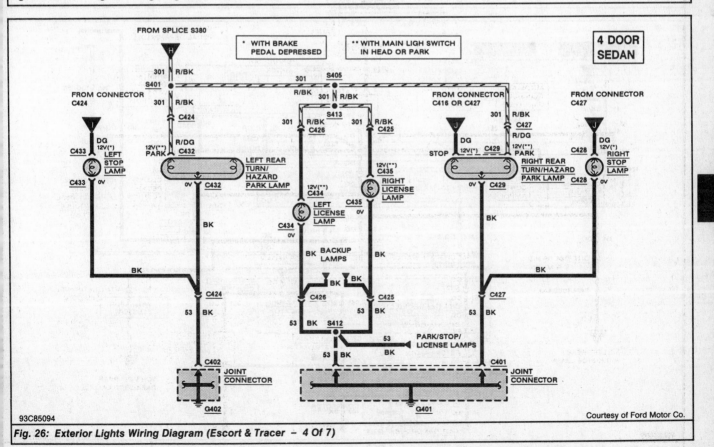

Fig. 26: Exterior Lights Wiring Diagram (Escort & Tracer – 4 Of 7)

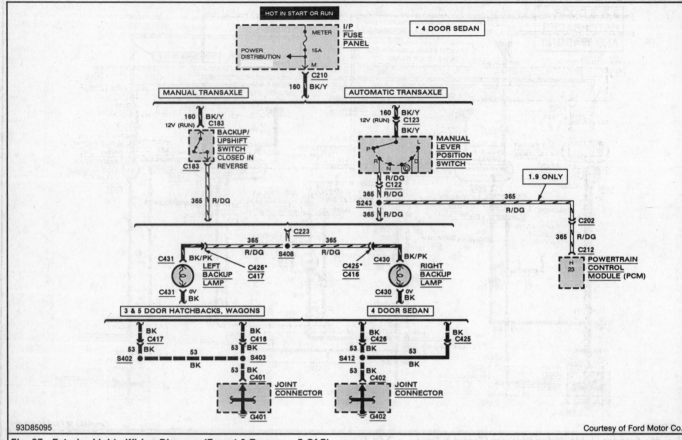

Fig. 27: Exterior Lights Wiring Diagram (Escort & Tracer – 5 Of 7)

93D85095

Courtesy of Ford Motor Co.

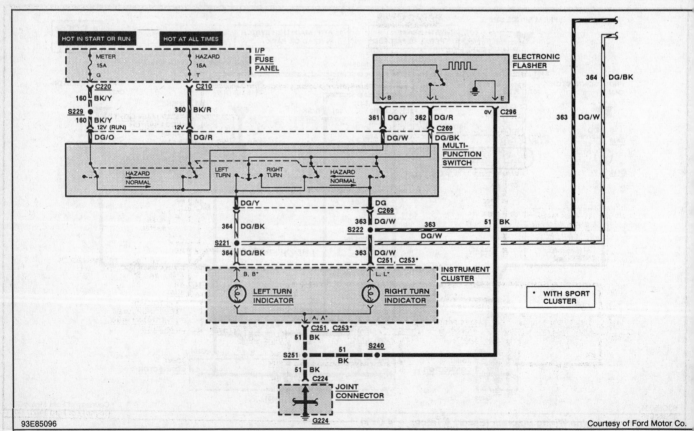

Fig. 28: Exterior Lights Wiring Diagram (Escort & Tracer – 6 Of 7)

93E85096

Courtesy of Ford Motor Co.

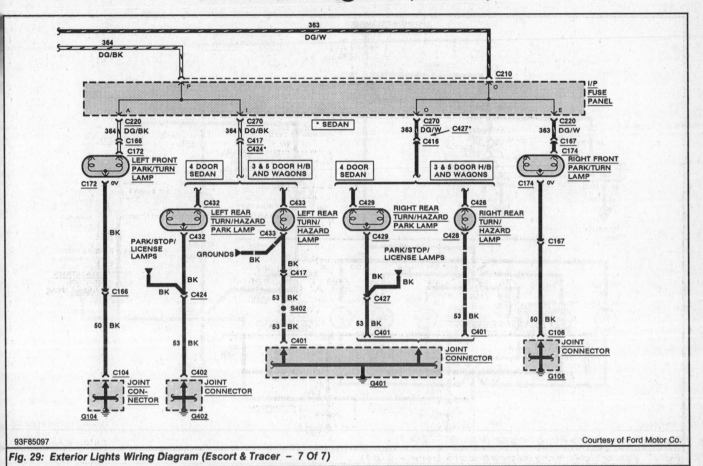

93F85097

Courtesy of Ford Motor Co.

Fig. 29: Exterior Lights Wiring Diagram (Escort & Tracer – 7 Of 7)

93G85098

Courtesy of Ford Motor Co.

Fig. 30: Exterior Lights Wiring Diagram (Mark VIII – 1 Of 7)

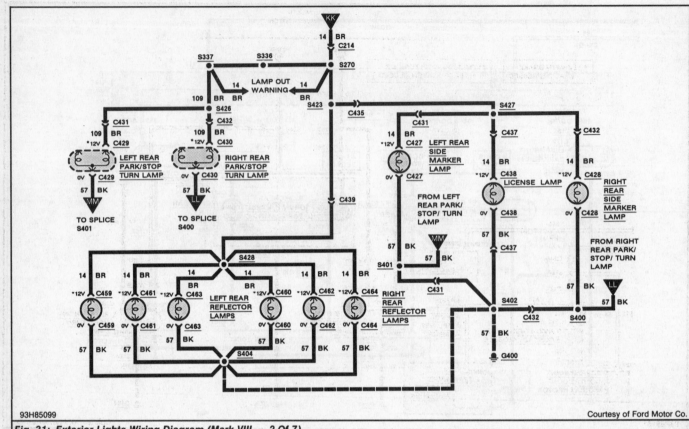

93H85099   Courtesy of Ford Motor Co.

Fig. 31: Exterior Lights Wiring Diagram (Mark VIII – 2 Of 7)

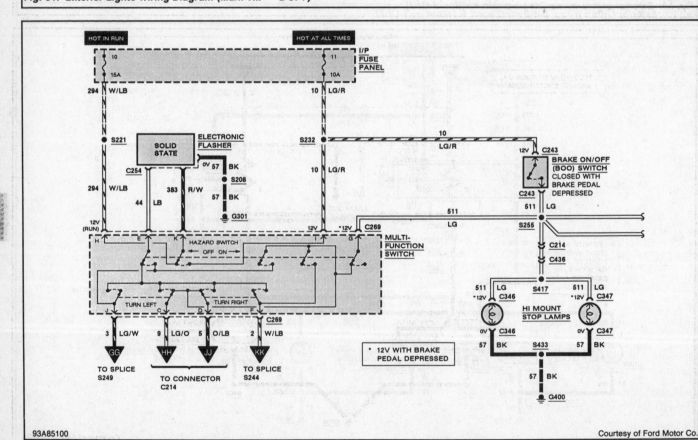

93A85100   Courtesy of Ford Motor Co.

Fig. 32: Exterior Lights Wiring Diagram (Mark VIII – 3 Of 7)

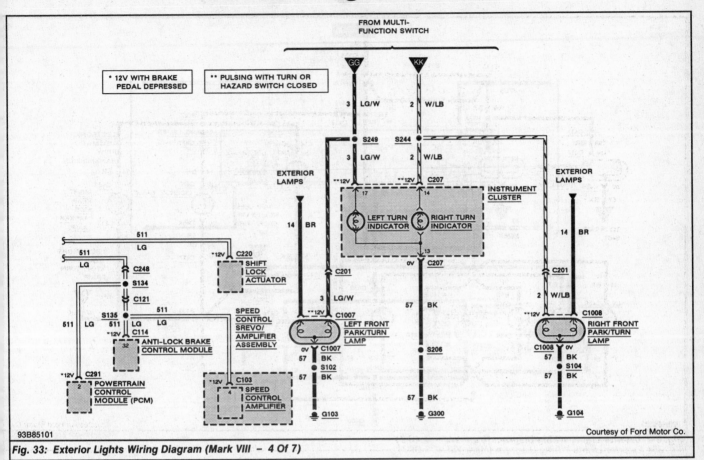

Fig. 33: *Exterior Lights Wiring Diagram (Mark VIII – 4 Of 7)*

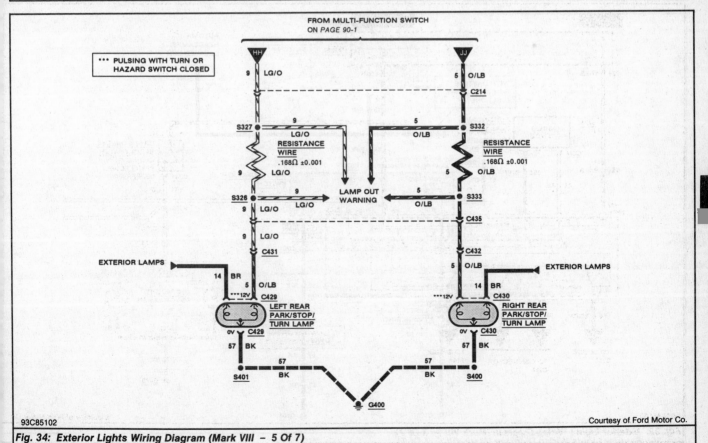

Fig. 34: *Exterior Lights Wiring Diagram (Mark VIII – 5 Of 7)*

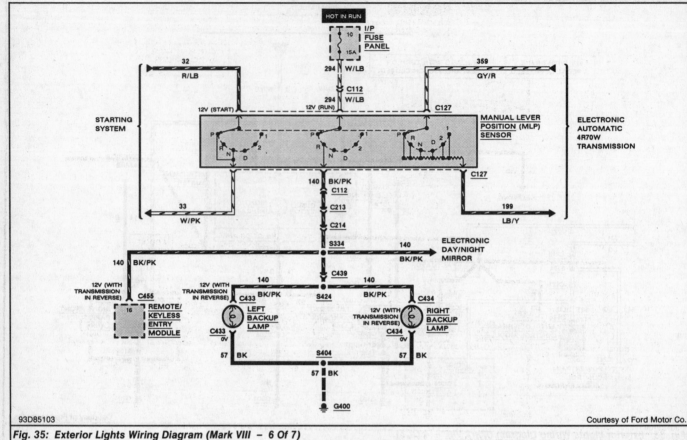

93D85103

Courtesy of Ford Motor Co.

Fig. 35: Exterior Lights Wiring Diagram (Mark VIII – 6 Of 7)

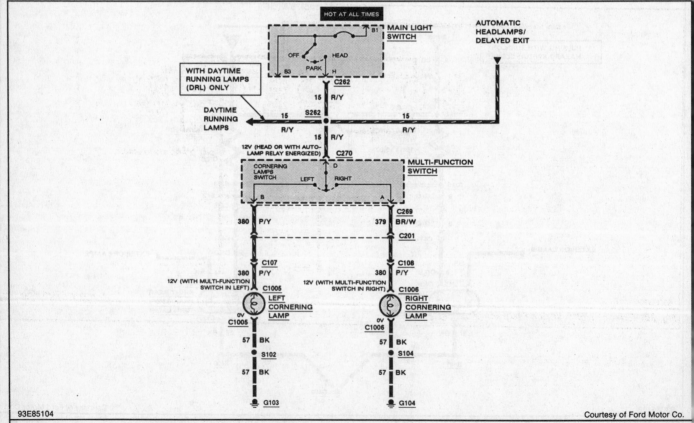

93E85104

Courtesy of Ford Motor Co.

Fig. 36: Exterior Lights Wiring Diagram (Mark VIII – 7 Of 7)

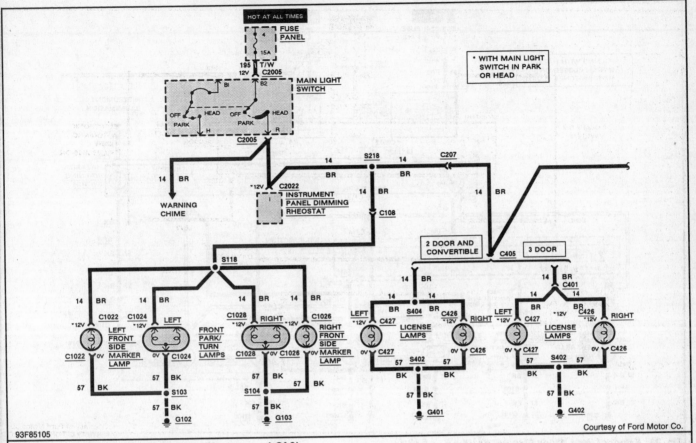

Fig. 37: Exterior Lights Wiring Diagram (Mustang – 1 Of 6)

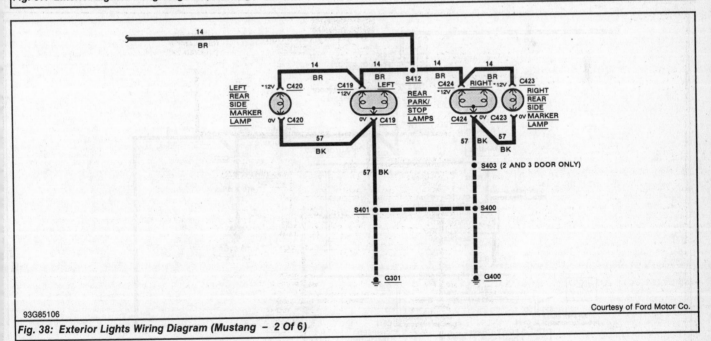

Fig. 38: Exterior Lights Wiring Diagram (Mustang – 2 Of 6)

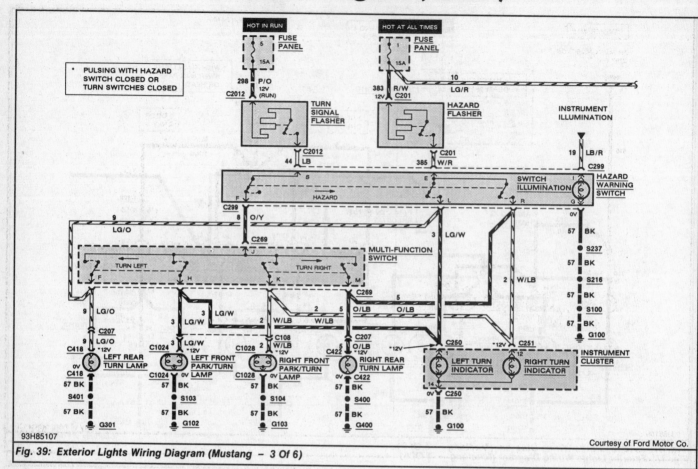

Fig. 39: Exterior Lights Wiring Diagram (Mustang – 3 Of 6)

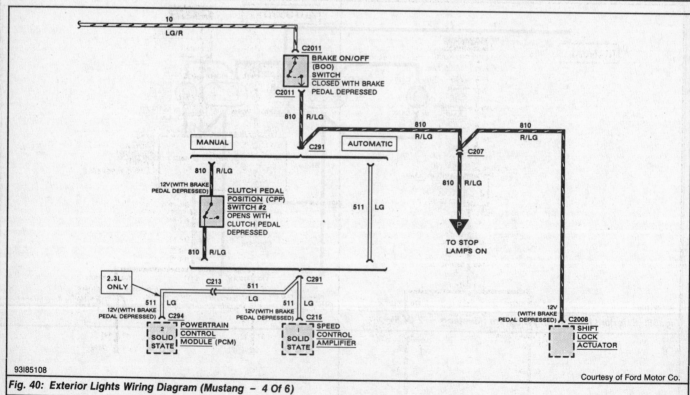

Fig. 40: Exterior Lights Wiring Diagram (Mustang – 4 Of 6)

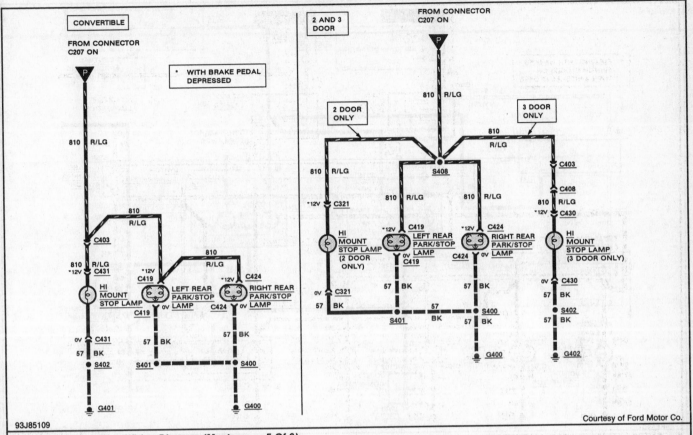

Fig. 41: Exterior Lights Wiring Diagram (Mustang – 5 Of 6)

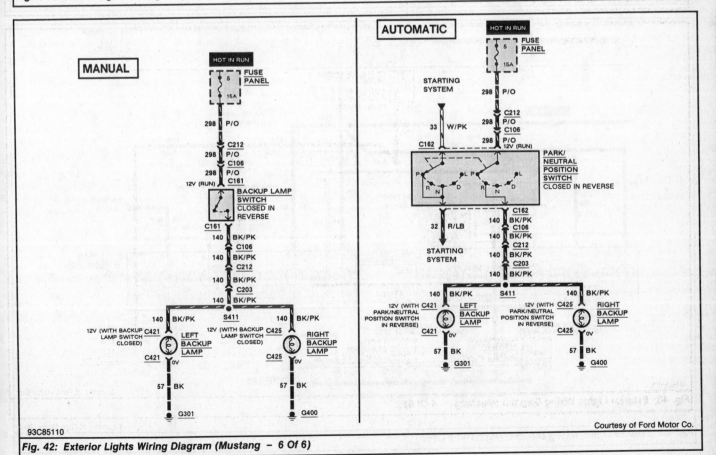

Fig. 42: Exterior Lights Wiring Diagram (Mustang – 6 Of 6)

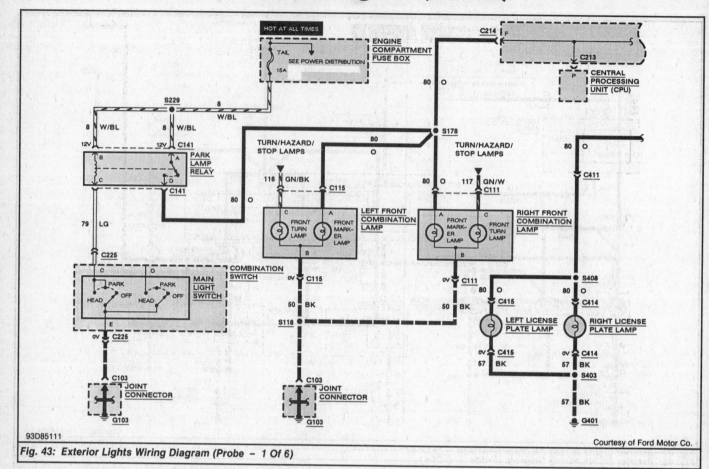

93D85111

Courtesy of Ford Motor Co.

Fig. 43: Exterior Lights Wiring Diagram (Probe – 1 Of 6)

93E85112

Courtesy of Ford Motor Co.

Fig. 44: Exterior Lights Wiring Diagram (Probe – 2 Of 6)

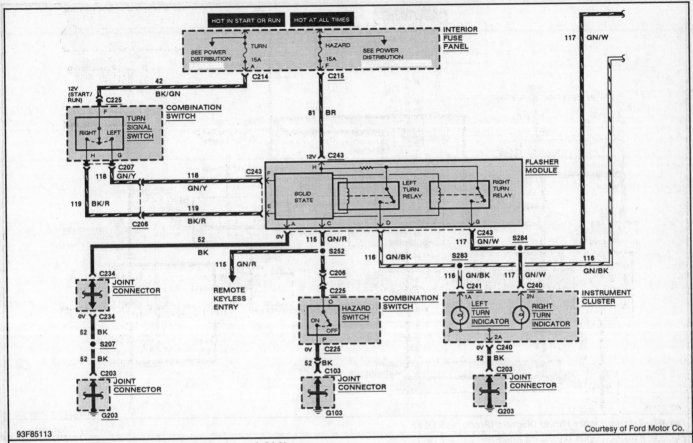

Fig. 45: Exterior Lights Wiring Diagram (Probe - 3 Of 6)

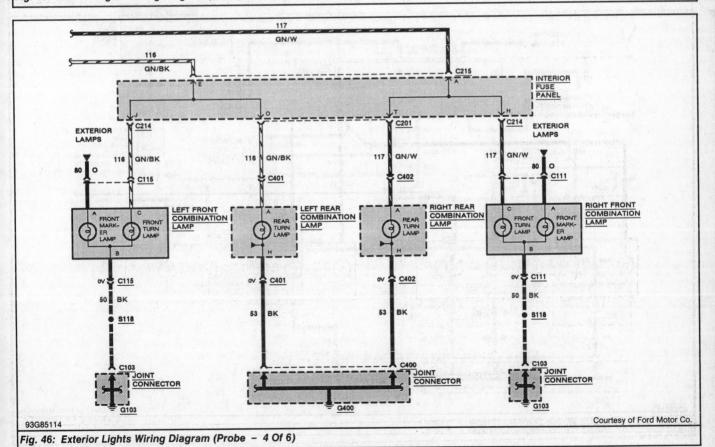

Fig. 46: Exterior Lights Wiring Diagram (Probe - 4 Of 6)

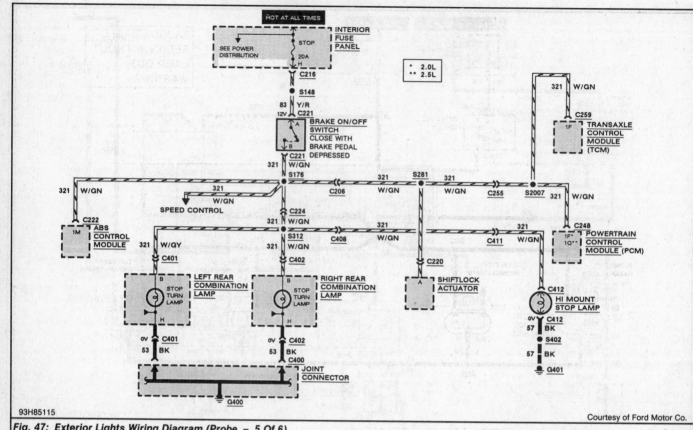

93H85115

Courtesy of Ford Motor Co.

Fig. 47: Exterior Lights Wiring Diagram (Probe – 5 Of 6)

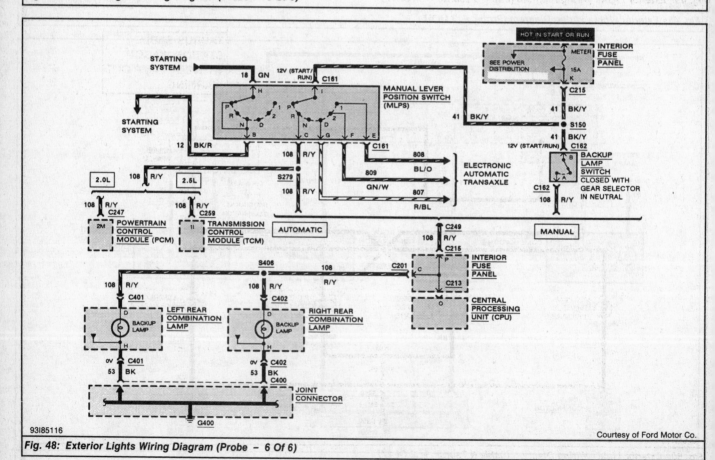

93I85116

Courtesy of Ford Motor Co.

Fig. 48: Exterior Lights Wiring Diagram (Probe – 6 Of 6)

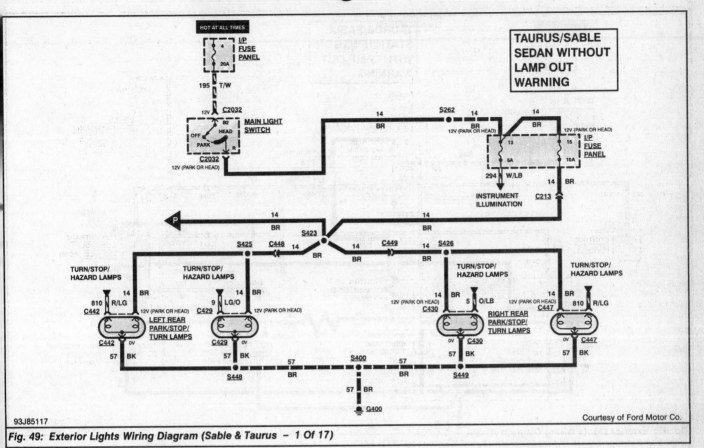

Fig. 49: Exterior Lights Wiring Diagram (Sable & Taurus – 1 Of 17)

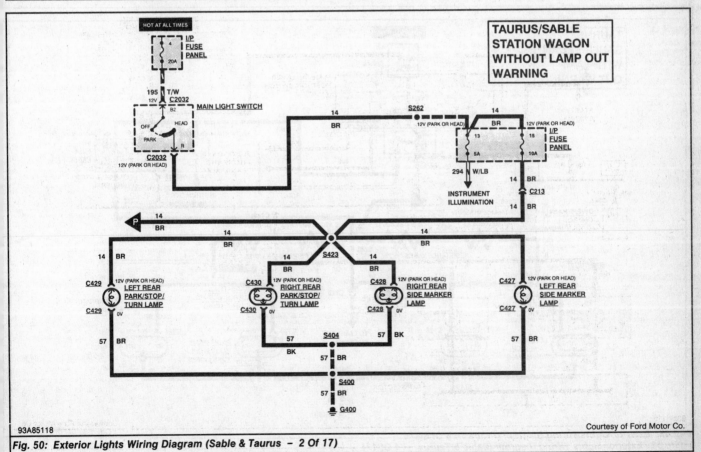

Fig. 50: Exterior Lights Wiring Diagram (Sable & Taurus – 2 Of 17)

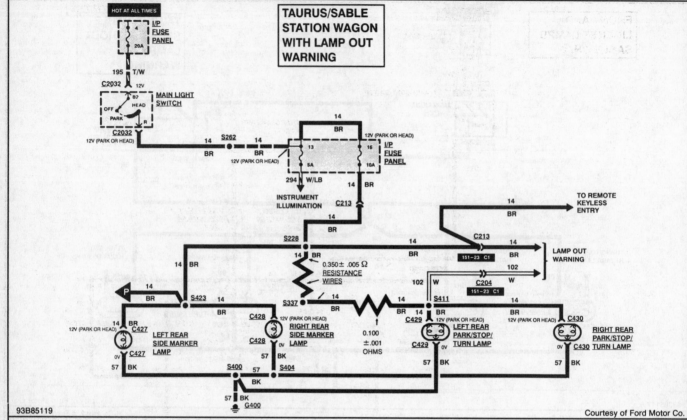

Fig. 51: Exterior Lights Wiring Diagram (Sable & Taurus – 3 Of 17)

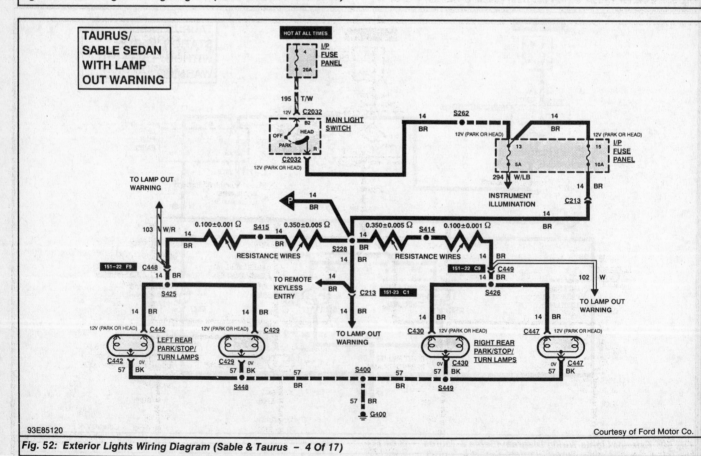

Fig. 52: Exterior Lights Wiring Diagram (Sable & Taurus – 4 Of 17)

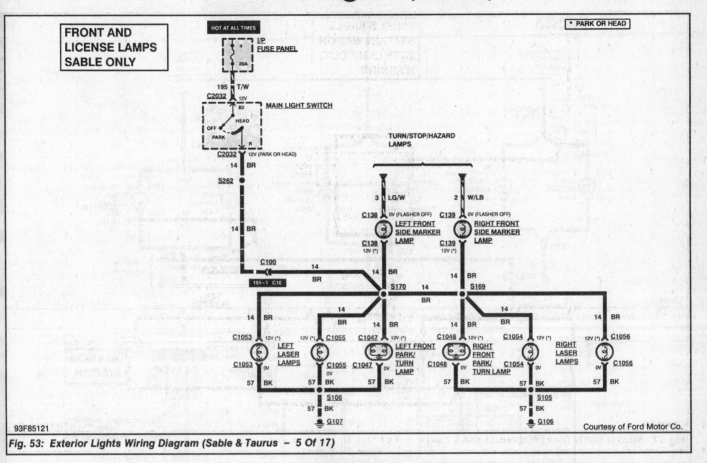

Fig. 53: Exterior Lights Wiring Diagram (Sable & Taurus – 5 Of 17)

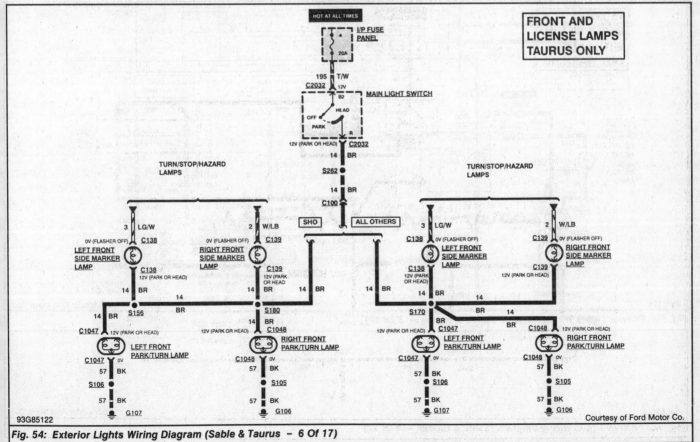

Fig. 54: Exterior Lights Wiring Diagram (Sable & Taurus – 6 Of 17)

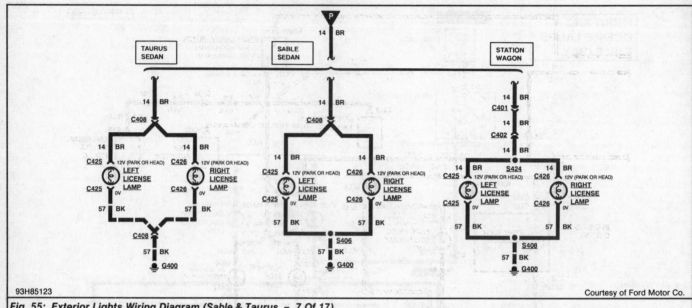

93H85123   Courtesy of Ford Motor Co.

Fig. 55: Exterior Lights Wiring Diagram (Sable & Taurus – 7 Of 17)

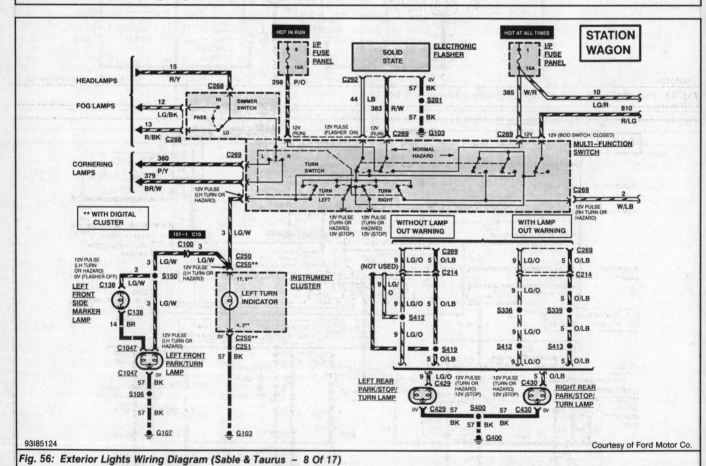

93I85124   Courtesy of Ford Motor Co.

Fig. 56: Exterior Lights Wiring Diagram (Sable & Taurus – 8 Of 17)

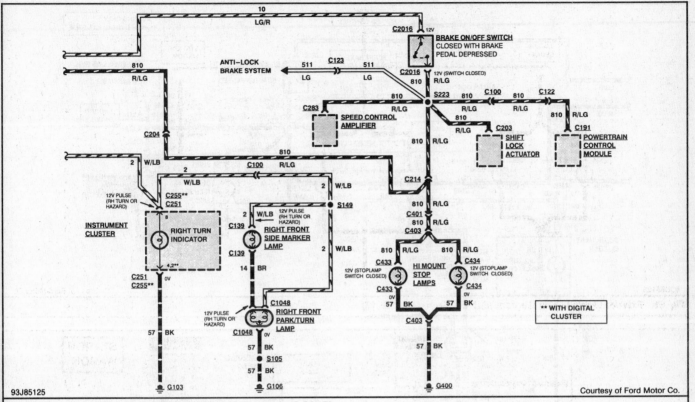

Fig. 57: Exterior Lights Wiring Diagram (Sable & Taurus – 9 Of 17)

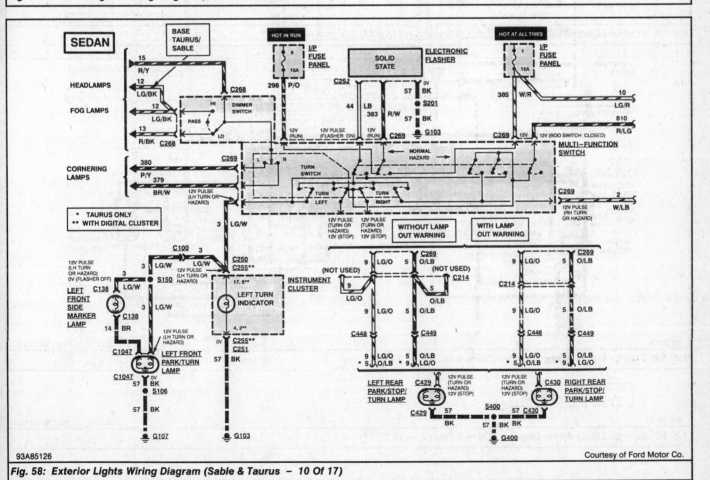

Fig. 58: Exterior Lights Wiring Diagram (Sable & Taurus – 10 Of 17)

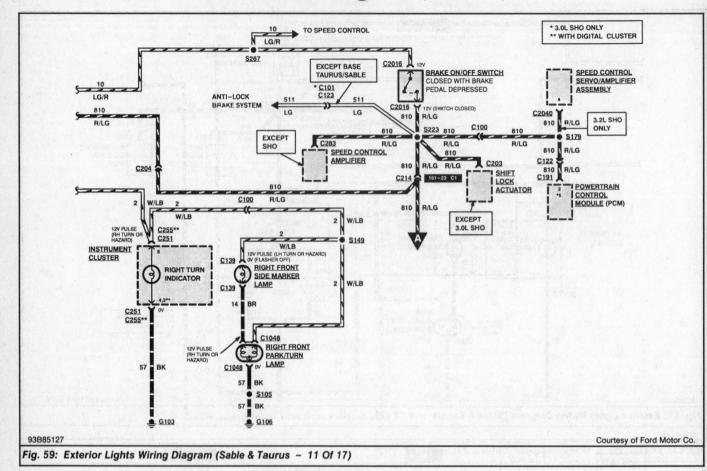

93B85127   Courtesy of Ford Motor Co.

Fig. 59: Exterior Lights Wiring Diagram (Sable & Taurus – 11 Of 17)

93C85128   Courtesy of Ford Motor Co.

Fig. 60: Exterior Lights Wiring Diagram (Sable & Taurus – 12 Of 17)

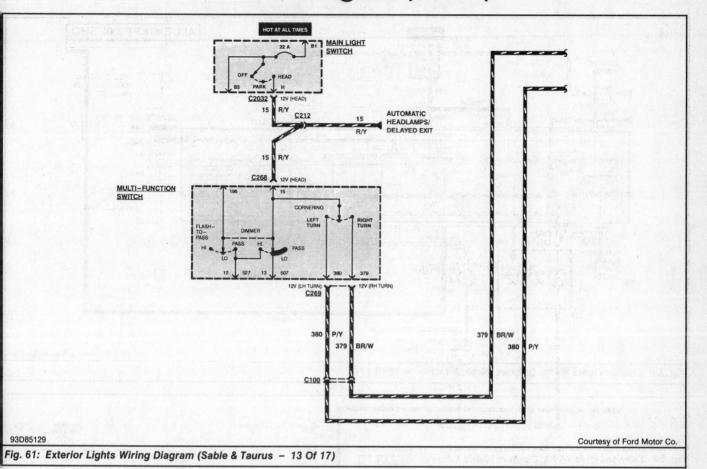

93D85129

Courtesy of Ford Motor Co.

Fig. 61: Exterior Lights Wiring Diagram (Sable & Taurus – 13 Of 17)

93G85130

Courtesy of Ford Motor Co.

Fig. 62: Exterior Lights Wiring Diagram (Sable & Taurus – 14 Of 17)

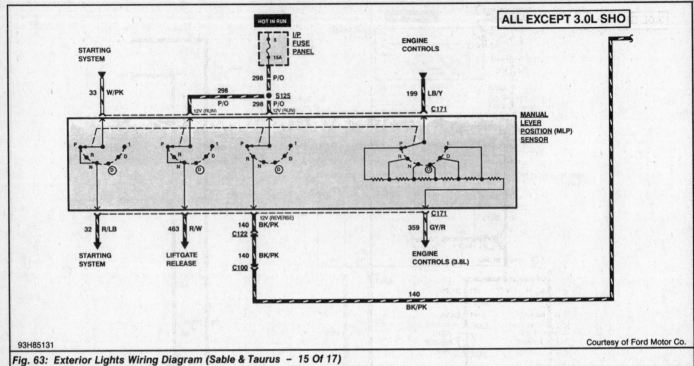

93H85131

Courtesy of Ford Motor Co.

Fig. 63: Exterior Lights Wiring Diagram (Sable & Taurus – 15 Of 17)

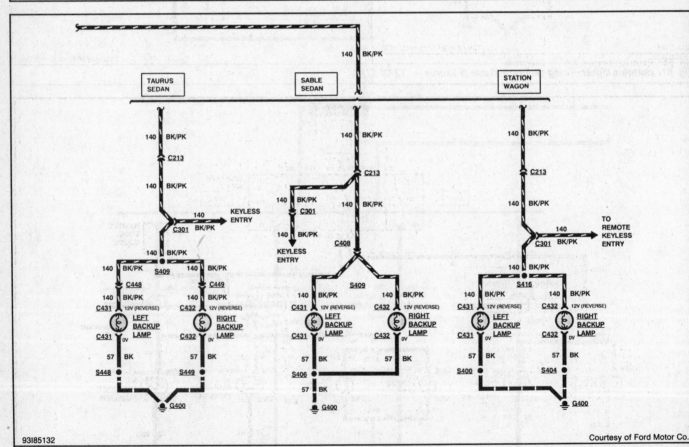

93I85132

Courtesy of Ford Motor Co.

Fig. 64: Exterior Lights Wiring Diagram (Sable & Taurus – 16 Of 17)

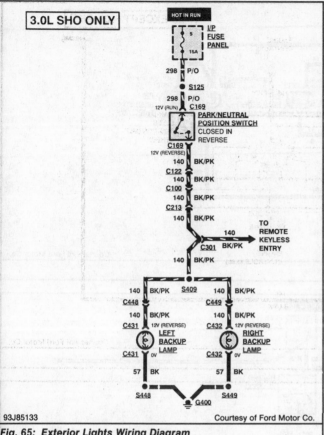

Fig. 65: Exterior Lights Wiring Diagram (Sable & Taurus – 17 Of 17)

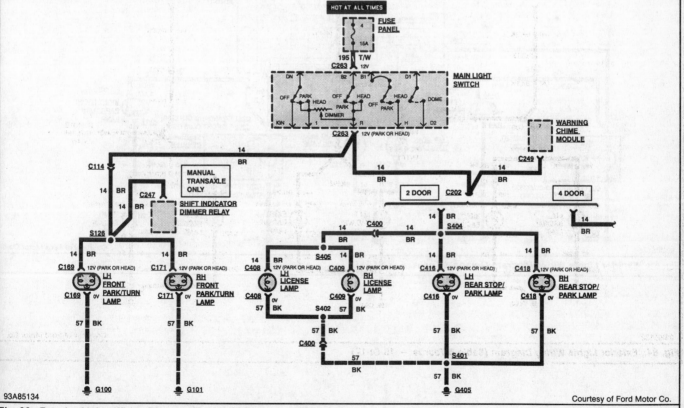

Fig. 66: Exterior Lights Wiring Diagram (Tempo & Topaz – 1 Of 6)

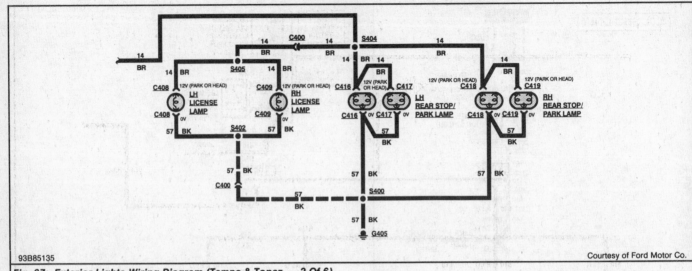

93B85135

Courtesy of Ford Motor Co.

Fig. 67: Exterior Lights Wiring Diagram (Tempo & Topaz − 2 Of 6)

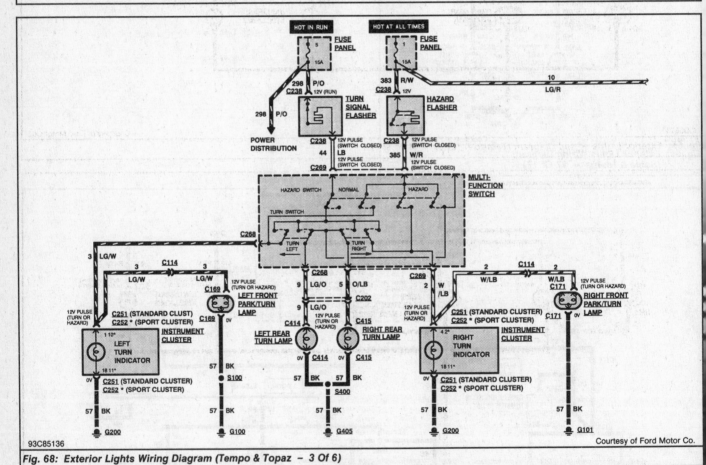

93C85136

Courtesy of Ford Motor Co.

Fig. 68: Exterior Lights Wiring Diagram (Tempo & Topaz − 3 Of 6)

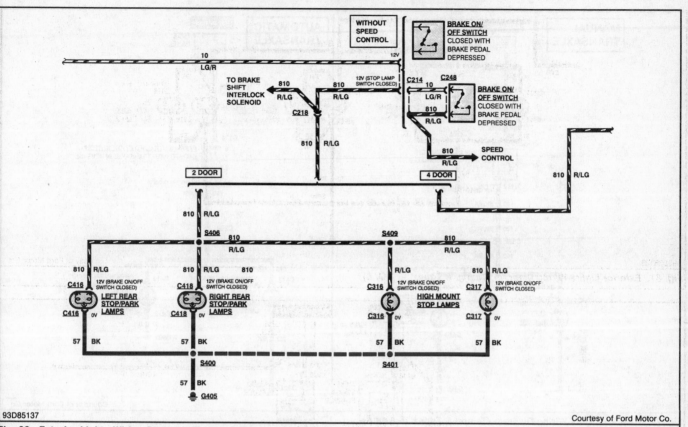

93D85137

Courtesy of Ford Motor Co.

Fig. 69: Exterior Lights Wiring Diagram (Tempo & Topaz – 4 Of 6)

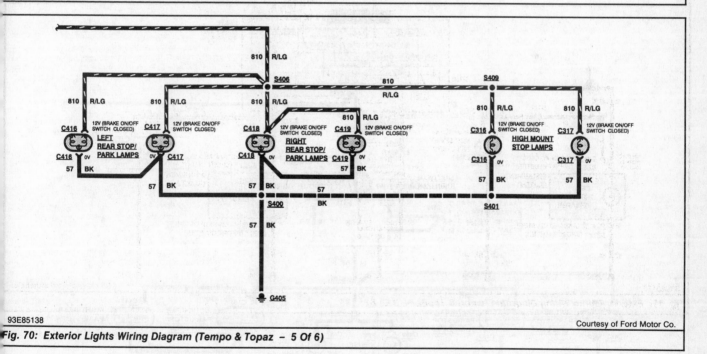

93E85138

Courtesy of Ford Motor Co.

Fig. 70: Exterior Lights Wiring Diagram (Tempo & Topaz – 5 Of 6)

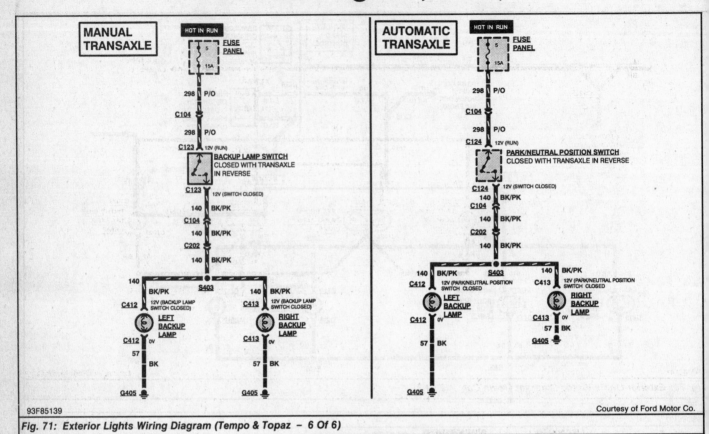

93F85139

Courtesy of Ford Motor Co.

Fig. 71: Exterior Lights Wiring Diagram (Tempo & Topaz – 6 Of 6)

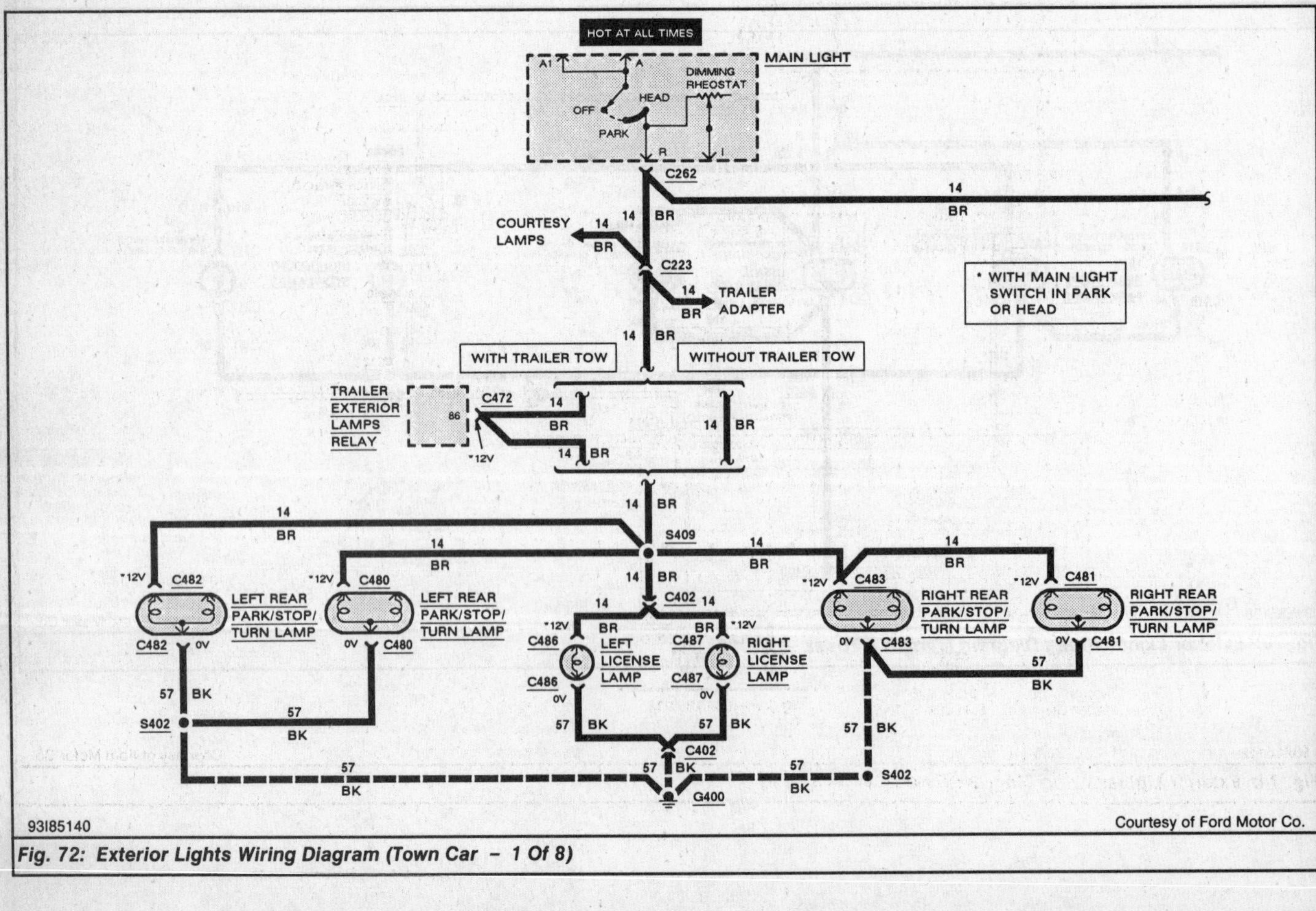

93I85140

Courtesy of Ford Motor Co.

Fig. 72: Exterior Lights Wiring Diagram (Town Car – 1 Of 8)

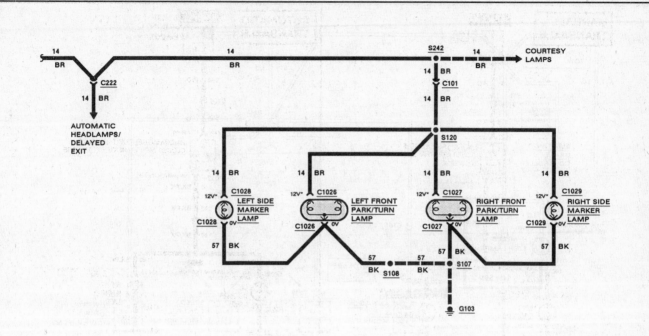

93J85141   Courtesy of Ford Motor Co.

Fig. 73: Exterior Lights Wiring Diagram (Town Car – 2 Of 8)

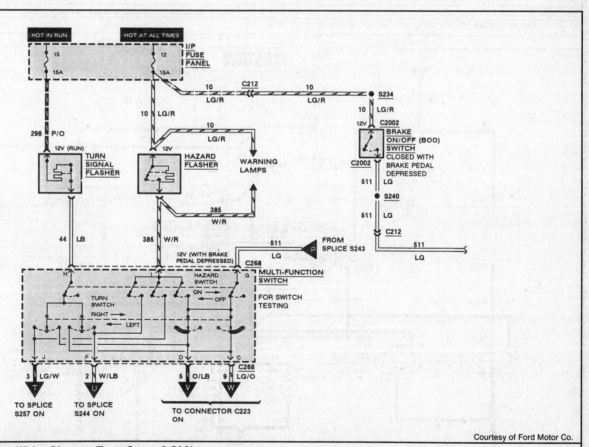

93A85142   Courtesy of Ford Motor Co.

Fig. 74: Exterior Lights Wiring Diagram (Town Car – 3 Of 8)

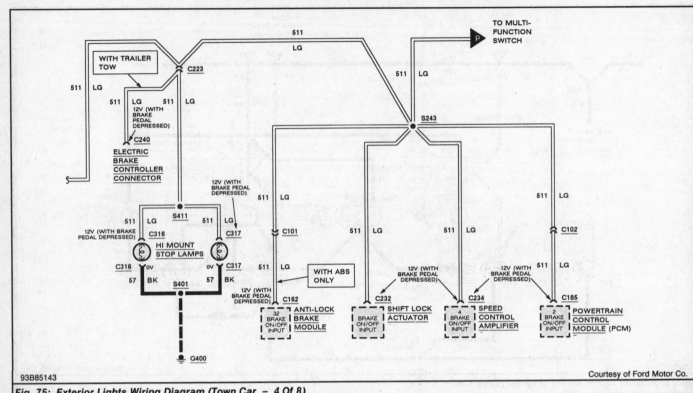

93B85143

Courtesy of Ford Motor Co.

Fig. 75: Exterior Lights Wiring Diagram (Town Car – 4 Of 8)

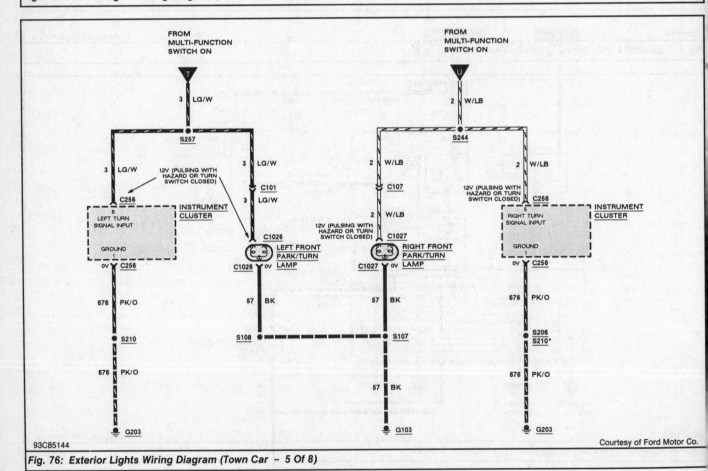

93C85144

Courtesy of Ford Motor Co.

Fig. 76: Exterior Lights Wiring Diagram (Town Car – 5 Of 8)

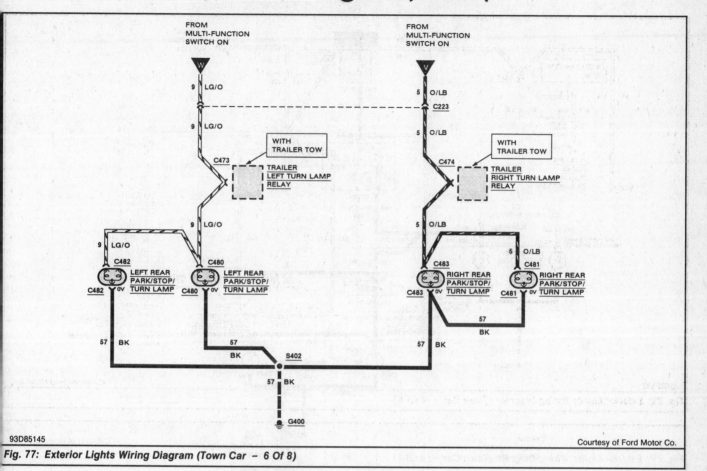

93D85145

Courtesy of Ford Motor Co.

Fig. 77: Exterior Lights Wiring Diagram (Town Car – 6 Of 8)

93E85146

Courtesy of Ford Motor Co.

Fig. 78: Exterior Lights Wiring Diagram (Town Car – 7 Of 8)

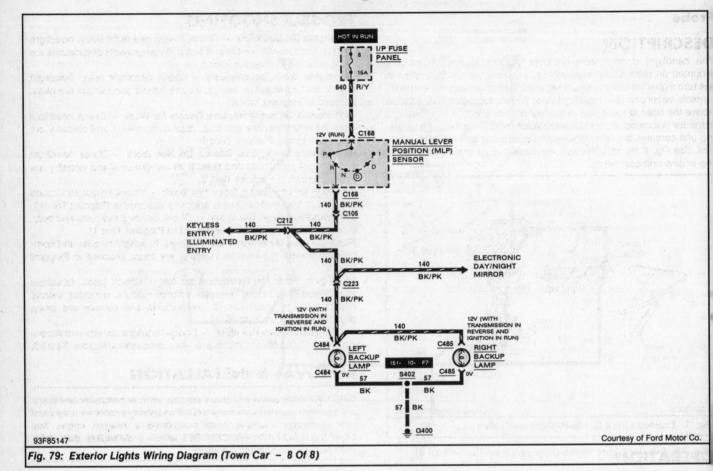

Fig. 79: Exterior Lights Wiring Diagram (Town Car – 8 Of 8)

93F85147

Courtesy of Ford Motor Co.

Probe

DESCRIPTION

The headlight door system consists of dual halogen headlights mounted on retractable mechanisms, a 3-position switch located in the turn signal lever, a headlight retractor switch located in the control console bezel and dual headlight door and motor assemblies located above the front fascia panel. A manual control knob for the headlight retractor is located on top of the retractor motor. The headlight housing unit contains the headlight, mounting bracket and retractor hinge unit. See Fig. 1. Headlight relays are located in the main fuse block in the engine compartment.

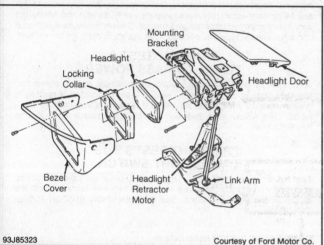

93J85323   Courtesy of Ford Motor Co.

Fig. 1: Exploded View Of Headlight Door System

OPERATION

The 3-position switch, located on the turn signal stalk, controls all exterior lighting operation. In the first position, all exterior lights are lit, except the headlights. When the switch is moved to the second position, the headlights are activated and the retractors lift the door and headlights up to the ON position. The headlight retractor switch on the instrument panel is used to raise the headlights up without the lights being lit. This allows for cleaning and replacement.

The headlight retractor motor is located under the retractor hinge unit. The motor pushes up and pulls down the motor link arm attaching the housing to the motor. Headlight aiming is not affected. The manual control knob is used to open the headlights in case of a system failure. See Fig. 2. The manual control knob should only be used when the negative battery cable is disconnected, or the retractor motor fuse is removed from the fuse block.

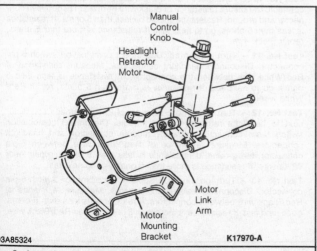

93A85324   K17970-A

Fig. 2: Locating Headlight Door Manual Control

TROUBLE SHOOTING

Headlights Do Not Work – Check fuses, headlight relay, headlight circuits, combination switch and bulbs. If components and circuits are okay, proceed to Pinpoint Test 1.

Headlights Work Continuously – Check headlight relay, headlight circuits and combination switch. If components and circuits are okay, proceed to Pinpoint Test 5.

High Beams Do Not Work, Low Beams Do Work – Check headlight relay, headlight circuits and bulb. If all components and circuitry are okay, proceed to Pinpoint Test 9.

High Beams Work, Low Beams Do Not Work – Check headlight relay, headlight circuits and bulb. If all components and circuitry are okay, proceed to Pinpoint Test 9.

One High Or Low Beam Does Not Work – Check headlight circuits and bulb. If bulb and all circuits are okay, proceed to Pinpoint Test 11.

One Headlight Does Not Work – Check headlight circuits and bulb. If bulb and circuits are okay, proceed to Pinpoint Test 11.

Flash-To-Pass Does Not Work – Check headlight circuits and combination switch. If switch and circuits are okay, proceed to Pinpoint Test 8.

Headlights Work But Retractors Do Not – Check fuses, headlight relay, headlight circuits, retractor control module, retractor switch, retractor motor and bulbs. If components and circuits are okay, proceed to Pinpoint Test 16.

One Retractor Does Not Work – Check headlight circuits and retractor motor. If circuits and motor are okay, proceed to Pinpoint Test 23.

REMOVAL & INSTALLATION

CAUTION: When battery is disconnected, vehicle computer and memory systems may lose memory data. Driveability problems may exist until computer systems have completed a relearn cycle. See COMPUTER RELEARN PROCEDURES article in GENERAL INFORMATION before disconnecting battery.

CONTROL MODULE

Removal & Installation – Module is located under instrument panel near left hand kick panel, next to turn signal flasher. Disconnect connector. Carefully slide module out of metal bracket in a sideways motion. DO NOT pull module straight down and out of bracket as it may break plastic tabs holding module. To install, reverse removal procedure.

HEADLIGHT DOOR

Removal & Installation – Push retractor switch to extend headlights. Disconnect negative battery cable. If removing left side door, remove battery. Remove 2 bracket mounting screws. Support headlight door and snap link arm from motor arm. If removing link arms, also snap arm from hinge unit. Disconnect electrical connector. Remove headlight door. To install, reverse removal procedure. Check headlight aiming and adjust if necessary.

HEADLIGHT DOOR MOTOR

Removal & Installation – Remove splash shield. Remove coolant reservoir, if necessary. DO NOT remove retractor motor arm from shaft. This will affect automatic stop operation. Snap the link arm from motor arm. See Fig. 2. Remove bracket mounting bolts. Disconnect electrical connector. Remove motor and mounting bracket. To install, reverse removal procedure.

HEADLIGHT DOOR RELAY

Removal & Installation – Relay is located in main fuse block in engine compartment. Lift relay straight out of the fuse block. To install, push new relay straight into plug openings.

HEADLIGHT

Removal & Installation – Push headlight retractor switch to extend headlights. Disconnect negative battery cable. Remove bezel attaching screws and remove bezel. Remove headlight housing attaching screws. Remove locking collar and headlight as an assembly. Disconnect electrical connector. To install, reverse removal procedure. Check headlight aiming and adjust if necessary.

HEADLIGHT RETRACTOR SWITCH

Removal & Installation – Remove floor console. Remove 2 console bezel screws located behind ashtray. Move console forward and disconnect switch electrical connector. Squeeze lock tabs on retractor switch and remove switch from console. To install, reverse removal procedure.

HEADLIGHT SWITCH

Removal & Installation – 1) Headlight switch is part of turn signal combination switch located on steering column. Deactivate air bag system. See AIR BAG RESTRAINT SYSTEM article. Remove air bag module and steering wheel. Remove 4 lower steering column panel attaching screws. Separate upper and lower panels. Remove lock cylinder bulb from lower column panel.

2) Remove upper and lower column panels. Remove clockspring. Remove turn signal canceling cam and spring. Remove 3 screws attaching combination switch. Disconnect electrical connectors. Slide the combination switch off the steering column shaft. To install, reverse removal procedure.

TESTING

Before performing any Pinpoint Tests of the headlight door system, check that all of the following are okay:
- Headlight retractor is properly adjusted.
- Retractor hinge is not damaged.
- Fuses are not blown.
- Fog light bulbs are okay.
- Connections are not loose or corroded.
- Wiring harness does not have obvious signs of shorts, opens, bad connections or damage.

PINPOINT TESTS

PINPOINT TESTS 1-4
HEADLIGHT FUSE & POWER SUPPLY

Test No. 1 – Check 30-amp headlight fuse in main fuse panel. If fuse is okay go to TEST NO. 4. If fuse is not okay, go to next test.

Test No. 2 – Turn ignition off. Replace 30-amp fuse and recheck. If fuse did not fail, go to TEST NO. 4. If fuse did fail, go to next test.

Test No. 3 – Turn ignition off. Remove 30-amp fuse. Disconnect 6-pin combination switch connector. Disconnect headlight relay and retractor control module. Measure resistance of Red/Yellow wire between fuse terminal and ground. If resistance is less than 5 ohms, repair Red/Yellow wire. If resistance is more than 5 ohms, replace 30-amp fuse and go to next test.

Test No. 4 – Turn ignition off. Disconnect headlight relay. Measure voltage of Red/Yellow wires at relay connector. If voltage readings are greater than 10 volts, go to next test. If voltage readings are less than 10 volts, repair Red/Yellow wire between fuse terminal and headlight relay.

PINPOINT TESTS 5-7
HEADLIGHT RELAY

Test No. 5 – Turn ignition off. Remove headlight relay. Apply 12 volts to Red/Yellow wire terminals at relay. Measure voltage at White wire terminal with White/Red wire terminal or relay grounded. Voltage should be greater than 10 volts. Measure voltage at White wire with White/Red wire terminal or relay open. Voltage should be less than one volt. If voltages are okay, go to next test. If voltages are not okay, replace headlight relay.

PINPOINT TESTS 5-7 (Cont.)

Test No. 6 – Turn ignition off. Disconnect headlight relay. Disconnect combination switch 6-pin and 14-pin connectors. Measure resistance of White wire between headlight relay connector and 6-pin combination switch connector. Measure resistance of White/Red wire between headlight relay connector and 14-pin combination switch connector. Both wires should measure less than 5 ohms resistance. If resistance readings are not as specified, repair wires as needed. If resistance readings are okay, go to next test.

Test No. 7 – Turn ignition off. Disconnect retractor control module connector. Disconnect headlight relay. Disconnect combination switch 6-pin and 14-pin connectors. Measure resistance of White wire and White/Red wire between relay connector and ground. If wires measure less than 5 ohms resistance, repair as needed. If resistance is okay, go to next test.

PINPOINT TEST 8
FLASH-TO-PASS POWER

Turn ignition off. Disconnect 6-pin combination switch connector. Measure voltage on Red/Yellow wire at 6-pin connector. If reading is greater than 10 volts, go to next test. If reading is less than 10 volts, repair Red/Yellow wire between combination switch and 30-amp headlight fuse.

PINPOINT TESTS 9-15
HEADLIGHT SWITCH

Test No. 9 – Turn ignition off. Disconnect 6-pin and 14-pin connectors at combination switch. Measure resistance between terminals with the switch in the listed positions. See COMBINATION SWITCH RESISTANCE table.

COMBINATION SWITCH RESISTANCE

Switch Position	Terminals	Ohms
Flash-To-Pass	[1] A-D	Less Than 5
High Beam	[2] A-F	Less Than 5
	[3] B-F	More Than 10,000
Low Beam	[3] B-F	Less Than 5
	[2] A-F	More Than 10,000
All Others	[1] A-D	More Than 10,000

[1] – Check between Red/Yellow wire and Red/Black wire terminals.
[2] – Check between White wire and Red/Black wire terminals.
[3] – Check between White wire and Red/White wire terminals.

Measure resistance between White/Red wire (terminal D) and Black wire (terminal E) on 14-pin combination switch connector with switch in Off, Parking and Headlight positions. Resistance readings should be greater than 10,000 ohms with switch in Off and Parking positions. Resistance reading should be less than 5 ohms with switch in Headlight position. If resistance readings are okay, go to next test. If any resistance reading is not to specification, replace combination switch.

Test No. 10 – Turn ignition off. Disconnect 14-pin combination switch connector. Measure resistance of Black wire (terminal 1E) between connector and ground. Resistance should be less than 5 ohms. If resistance is less than 5 ohms, go to next test. If resistance is more than 5 ohms, repair Black wire.

Test No. 11 – Turn ignition off. Disconnect combination switch 6-pin connector. Disconnect headlight connectors. Measure resistance of Red/White wire between the connectors. If resistance is less than 5 ohms, go to next test. If resistance is more than 5 ohms, repair Red/White wire.

Test No. 12 – Turn ignition off. Disconnect 21-pin harness connector next to headlight retractor control module. Disconnect combination switch 6-pin connector, retractor module connector and headlight connectors. Measure resistance of Red/White wire between 6-pin connector and ground. If resistance is less than 5 ohms, repair Red/White wire. If resistance is more than 5 ohms, go to next test.

Test No. 13 – Turn ignition off. Disconnect combination switch 6-pin connector. Disconnect headlight connectors. Measure resistance of Red/Black wire between connectors. If resistance is less than 5 ohms, go to next test. If resistance is more than 5 ohms, repair Red/Black wire.

PINPOINT TESTS 9-15

Test No. 14 – Turn ignition off. Disconnect combination switch 6-pin connector. Disconnect headlight connectors. Measure resistance of Red/Black wire between 6-pin connector and ground. If resistance is less than 5 ohms, repair Red/Black wire. If resistance is more than 5 ohms, go to next test.

Test No. 15 – Turn ignition off. Disconnect headlight connectors. Measure resistance of Black wires between connectors and ground. If resistance is less than 5 ohms, replace headlight bulb(s). If resistance is more than 5 ohms, repair Black wire(s).

PINPOINT TESTS 16-22
HEADLIGHT RETRACTOR CONTROL MODULE

Test No. 16 – Check 20-amp retractor fuse in main fuse panel. If fuse is okay, go to TEST NO. 19. If fuse is not okay, go to next test.

Test No. 17 – Turn ignition off. Replace 20-amp fuse. If the fuse failed again, go to next test. If fuse is okay, go to TEST NO. 19.

Test No. 18 – Turn ignition off. Disconnect headlight retractor motor connector. Remove 20-amp fuse. Measure resistance of Red/White wire between fuse terminal and ground. If resistance is greater than 10,000 ohms, replace 20-amp fuse and go to next test. If resistance is less than 10,000 ohms, repair Red/White wire.

Test No. 19 – Turn ignition off. Disconnect retractor control module connector. Measure voltage on Red/Yellow wire at connector. If reading is greater than 10 volts, go to next test. If reading is less than 10 volts, repair Red/Yellow wire between control module and 30-amp fuse in main fuse block.

Test No. 20 – Turn ignition off. Disconnect headlight relay and retractor module connector. Measure resistance of White wire between module connector and relay connector. If resistance is less than 5 ohms, go to next test. If resistance is more than 5 ohms, repair White wire.

Test No. 21 – Turn ignition off. Disconnect combination switch 6-pin connector and control module connector. Measure resistance of Red/White wire between the connectors. If resistance is less than 5 ohms, go to next test. If resistance is more than 5 ohms, repair Red/White wire.

Test No. 22 – Turn ignition off. Disconnect control module connector. Measure resistance of Black wire between connector and ground. If resistance is less than 5 ohms, go to next test. If resistance is more than 5 ohms, repair Black wire.

PINPOINT TESTS 23-24
HEADLIGHT RETRACTOR CONTROL MODULE
& HEADLIGHT RETRACTOR MOTORS

Test No. 23 – Turn ignition off. Disconnect retractor control module connector and retractor motor connectors. Measure resistance of Red wire between connectors. If resistance is less than 5 ohms, go to next test. If resistance is more than 5 ohms, repair Red wire.

Test No. 24 – Turn ignition off. Disconnect retractor control module connector and retractor motor connectors. Disconnect retractor switch connector. Measure resistance of Red wire between control module connector and ground. If resistance is greater than 10,000 ohms, go to next test. If resistance is less than 10,000 ohms, repair Red wire between control module connector and retractor motors.

PINPOINT TESTS 25-26
HEADLIGHT RETRACTOR CONTROL MODULE
& HEADLIGHT RETRACTOR SWITCH

Test No. 25 – Turn ignition off. Disconnect retractor switch connector and control module connector. Measure resistance of White/Red wire between connectors. If resistance is less than 5 ohms, go to next test. If resistance is more than 5 ohms, repair White/Red wire.

Test No. 26 – Turn ignition off. Disconnect retractor switch connector and control module connector. Measure resistance of White/Red wire between control module connector and ground. If resistance is greater than 10,000 ohms, go to next test. If less than 10,000 ohms, repair White/Red wire between control module and retractor switch.

PINPOINT TEST 27
HEADLIGHT RETRACTOR CONTROL MODULE

Test No. 27 – Turn ignition off. Reconnect retractor control module connector. Measure voltages of Red and White/Red wires at control module with headlight switch in following positions:
Flash-To-Pass – White/Red = 0 volts. Red = 12 volts
Headlights On – White/Red = 0 volts. Red = 12 volts
Headlights Off – White/Red = 12 volts. Red = 0 volts
If voltages are okay, go to next test. If voltages are incorrect, replace headlight retractor control module.

PINPOINT TESTS 28-30
HEADLIGHT RETRACTOR SWITCH

Test No. 28 – Turn ignition off. Disconnect retractor switch. Measure resistance between headlight retractor switch terminals. See COMBINATION SWITCH RESISTANCE table. If resistance is within specification, go to next test. If resistance is not to specification, replace headlight retractor switch.

HEADLIGHT RETRACTOR SWITCH RESISTANCE

Switch	Terminal Wire Color	Ohms
Pressed In	1	Less Than 5
	2	More Than 10,000
Released	1	More Than 10,000
	2	Less Than 5

1 – Check between White/Red wire and Red wire terminals.
2 – Check between White/Red wire and Red wire terminals.

Test No. 29 – Turn ignition off. Disconnect headlight switch connector and retractor motor connectors. Measure resistance of Red and Orange/Black wires between the connectors. If both reading are less than 5 ohms, go to next test. If any are more than 5 ohms, repair the wire(s) in question.

Test No. 30 – Turn ignition off. Disconnect headlight switch connector and retractor motor connectors. Measure resistance of Orange/Black wire between switch connector and ground. If resistance is greater than 10,000 ohms, go to next test. If less than 10,000 ohms, repair Orange/Black wire.

PINPOINT TEST 31
HEADLIGHT RETRACTOR MOTOR GROUND

Turn ignition off. Disconnect retractor motor connectors. Measure resistance of Black wires between motor connectors and ground. If readings are less than 5 ohms, replace retractor motor in question. If readings are than 5 ohms, repair Black wire(s) in question.

WIRING DIAGRAMS

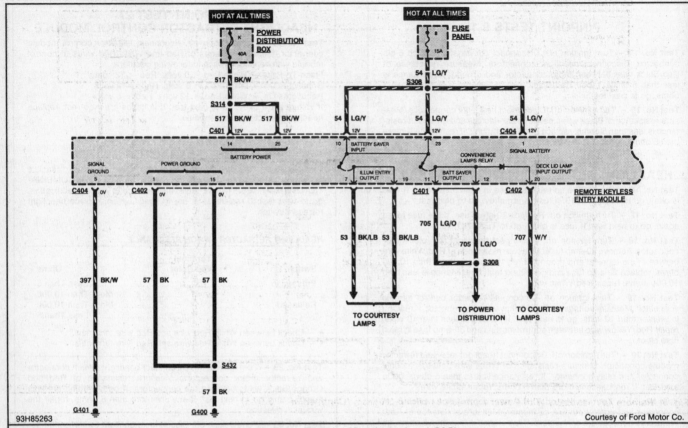

Fig. 1: Remote Keyless Entry With Power Door Locks Wiring Diagram (Continental – 1 Of 5)

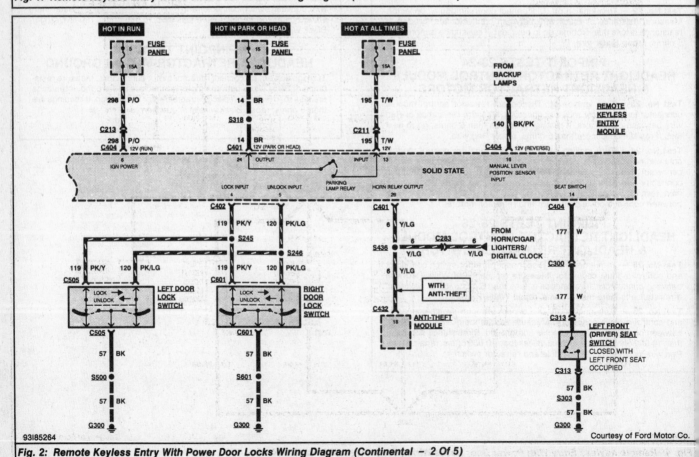

Fig. 2: Remote Keyless Entry With Power Door Locks Wiring Diagram (Continental – 2 Of 5)

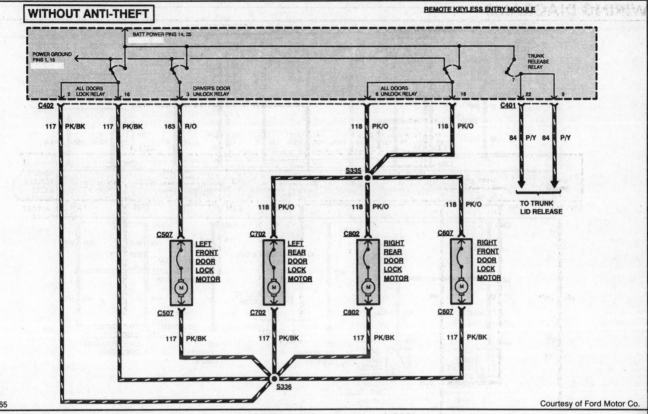

Fig. 3: Remote Keyless Entry With Power Door Locks Wiring Diagram (Continental – 3 Of 5)

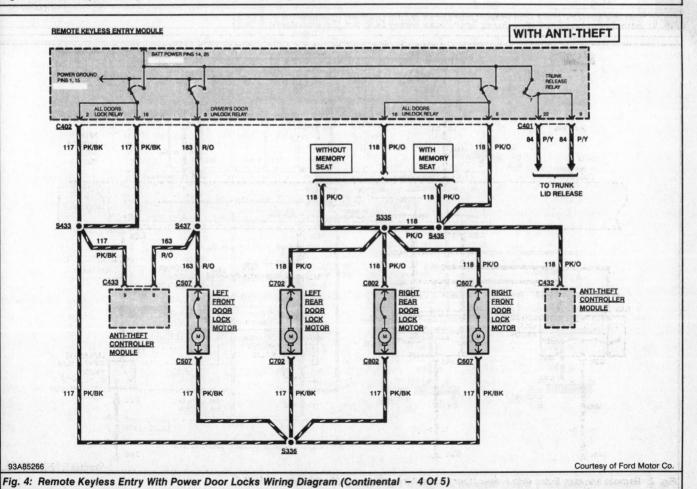

Fig. 4: Remote Keyless Entry With Power Door Locks Wiring Diagram (Continental – 4 Of 5)

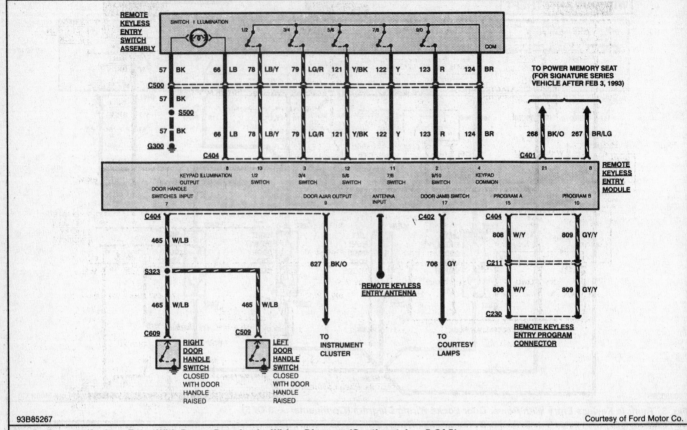

93B85267

Courtesy of Ford Motor Co.

Fig. 5: Remote Keyless Entry With Power Door Locks Wiring Diagram (Continental – 5 Of 5)

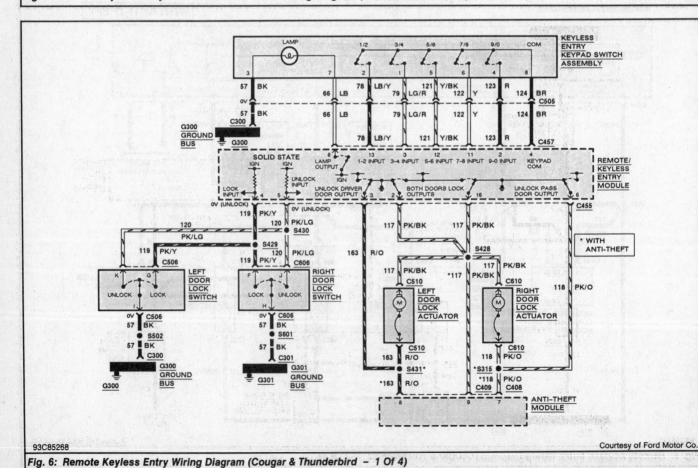

93C85268

Courtesy of Ford Motor Co.

Fig. 6: Remote Keyless Entry Wiring Diagram (Cougar & Thunderbird – 1 Of 4)

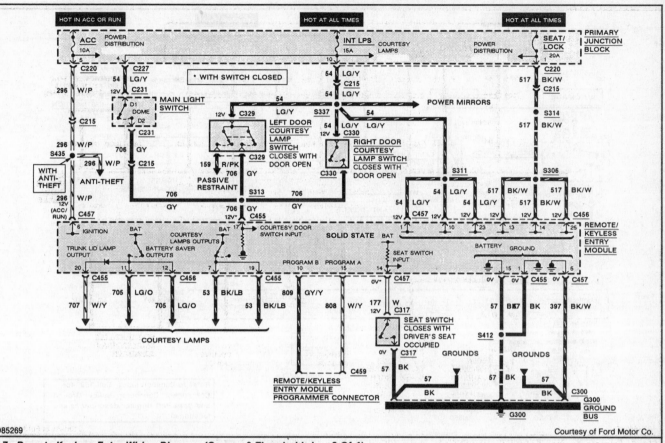

Fig. 7: Remote Keyless Entry Wiring Diagram (Cougar & Thunderbird – 2 Of 4)

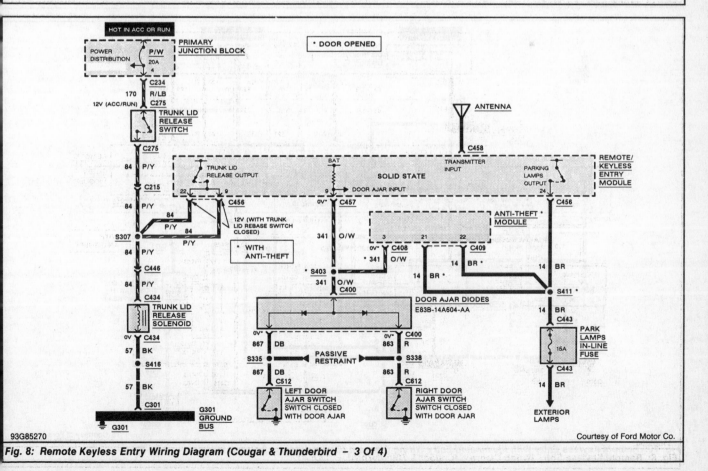

Fig. 8: Remote Keyless Entry Wiring Diagram (Cougar & Thunderbird – 3 Of 4)

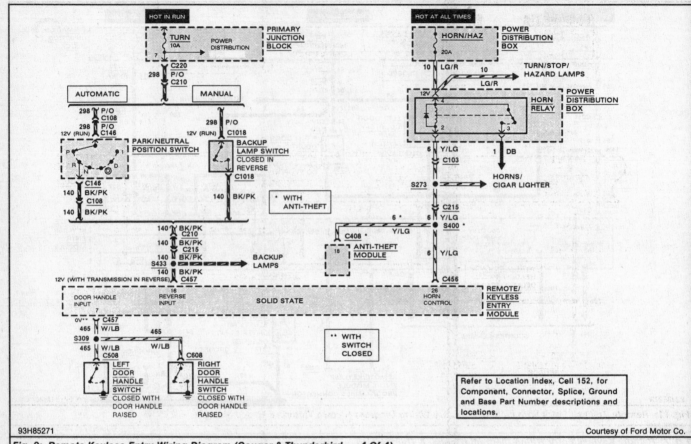

Fig. 9: Remote Keyless Entry Wiring Diagram (Cougar & Thunderbird – 4 Of 4)

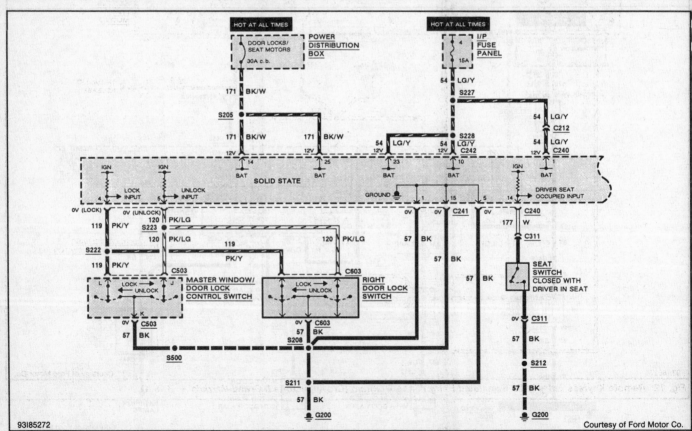

Fig. 10: Remote Keyless Entry With Illuminated Entry Wiring Diagram (Crown Victoria & Grand Marquis – 1 Of 4)

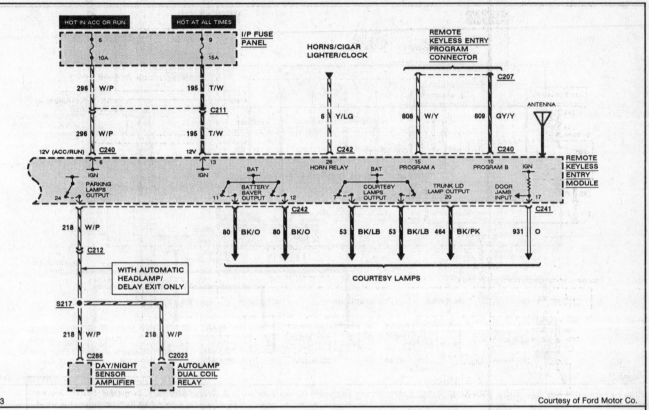

93J85273

Courtesy of Ford Motor Co.

Fig. 11: Remote Keyless Entry With Illuminated Entry Wiring Diagram (Crown Victoria & Grand Marquis – 2 Of 4)

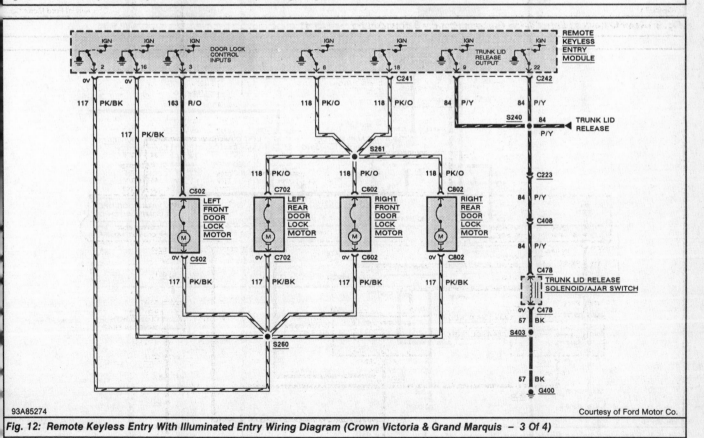

93A85274

Courtesy of Ford Motor Co.

Fig. 12: Remote Keyless Entry With Illuminated Entry Wiring Diagram (Crown Victoria & Grand Marquis – 3 Of 4)

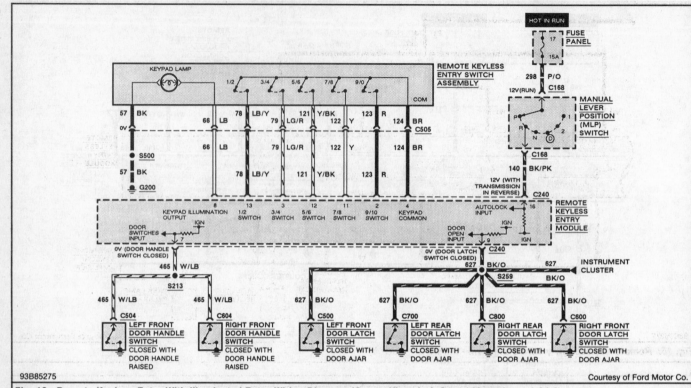

Fig. 13: Remote Keyless Entry With Illuminated Entry Wiring Diagram (Crown Victoria & Grand Marquis – 4 Of 4)

93B85275

Courtesy of Ford Motor Co.

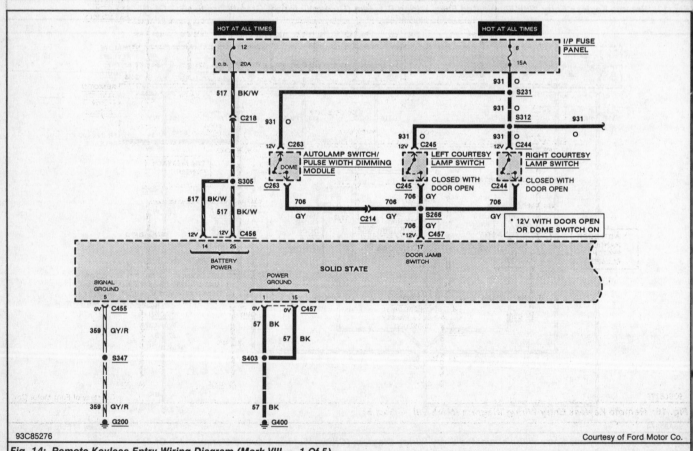

Fig. 14: Remote Keyless Entry Wiring Diagram (Mark VIII – 1 Of 5)

93C85276

Courtesy of Ford Motor Co.

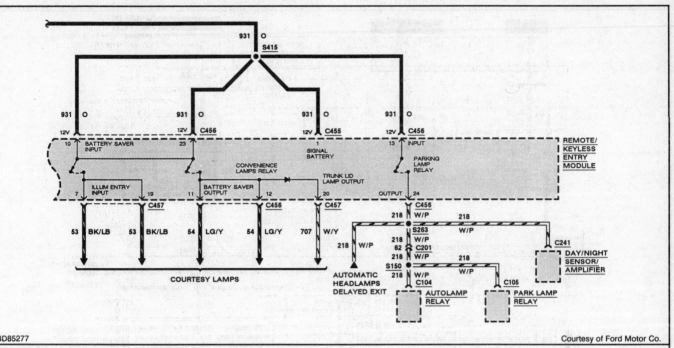

Fig. 15: Remote Keyless Entry Wiring Diagram (Mark VIII – 2 Of 5)

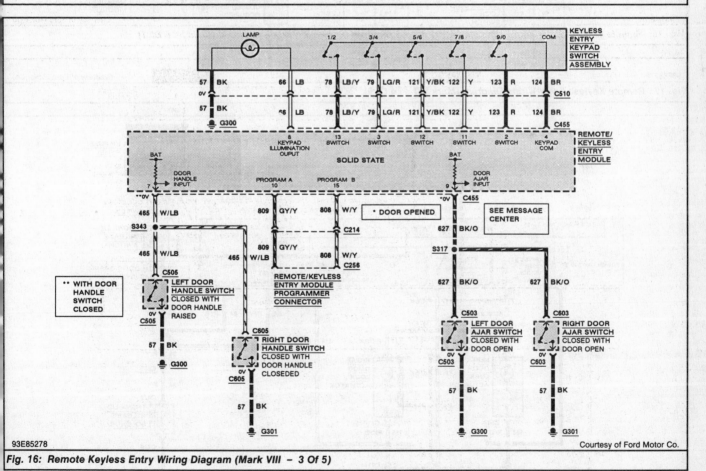

Fig. 16: Remote Keyless Entry Wiring Diagram (Mark VIII – 3 Of 5)

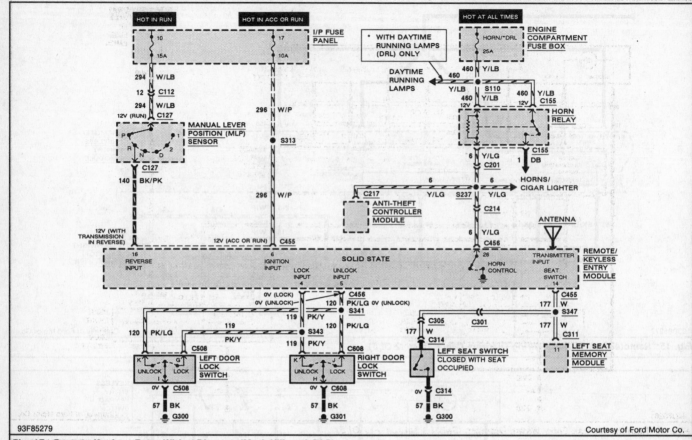

Fig. 17: Remote Keyless Entry Wiring Diagram (Mark VIII – 4 Of 5)

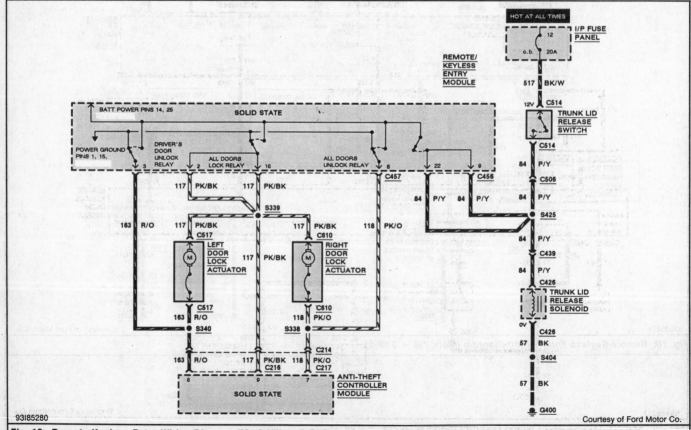

Fig. 18: Remote Keyless Entry Wiring Diagram (Mark VIII – 5 Of 5)

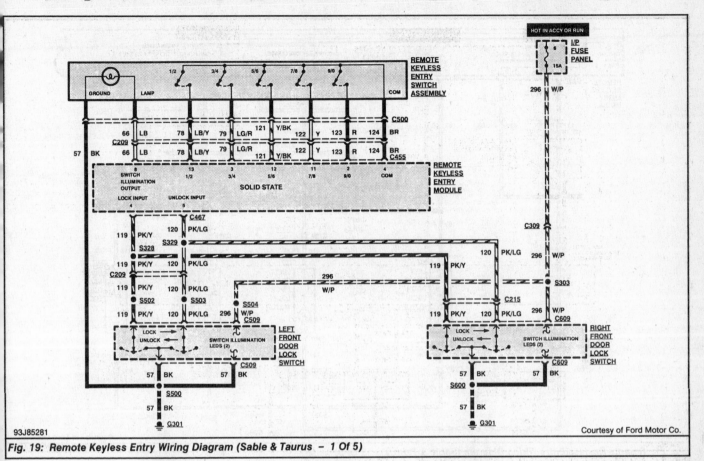

Fig. 19: **Remote Keyless Entry Wiring Diagram (Sable & Taurus – 1 Of 5)**

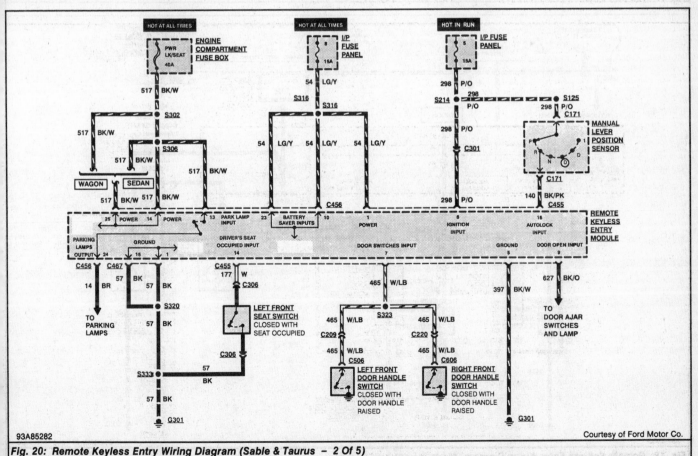

Fig. 20: **Remote Keyless Entry Wiring Diagram (Sable & Taurus – 2 Of 5)**

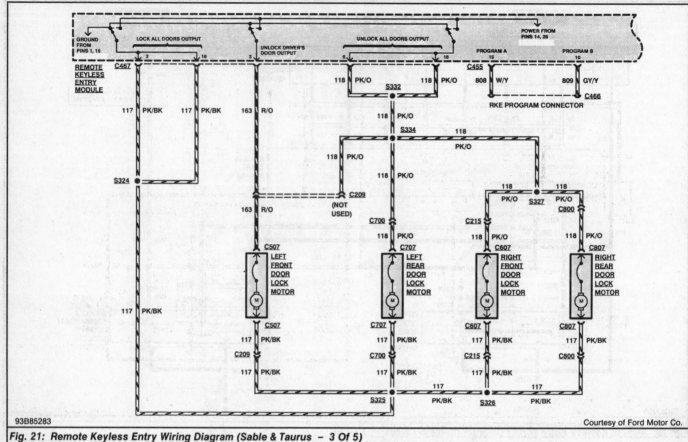

93B85283

Courtesy of Ford Motor Co.

Fig. 21: Remote Keyless Entry Wiring Diagram (Sable & Taurus – 3 Of 5)

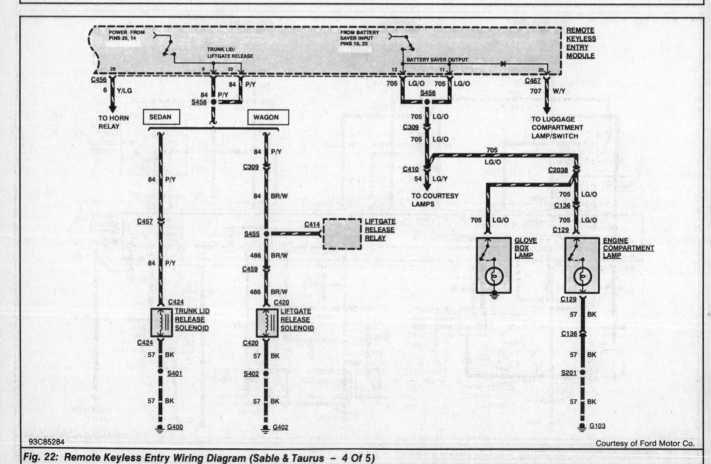

93C85284

Courtesy of Ford Motor Co.

Fig. 22: Remote Keyless Entry Wiring Diagram (Sable & Taurus – 4 Of 5)

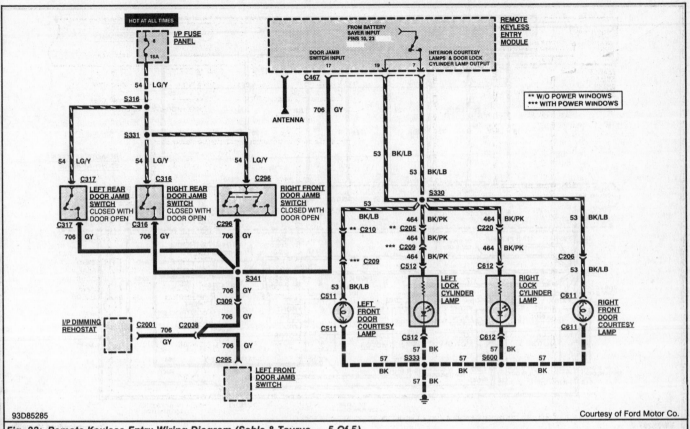

Fig. 23: Remote Keyless Entry Wiring Diagram (Sable & Taurus – 5 Of 5)

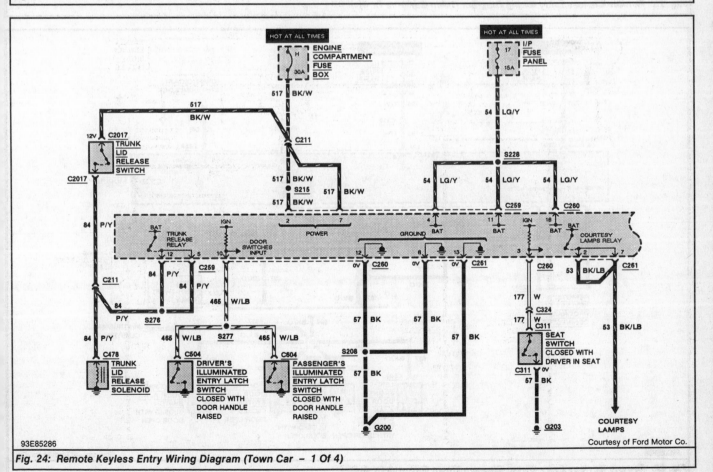

Fig. 24: Remote Keyless Entry Wiring Diagram (Town Car – 1 Of 4)

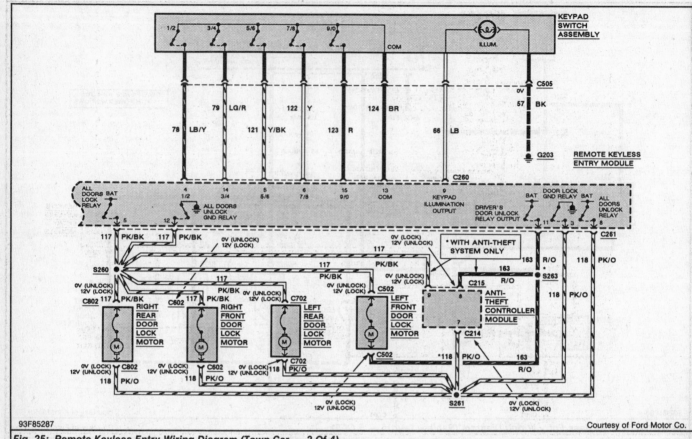

93F85287   Courtesy of Ford Motor Co.

Fig. 25: Remote Keyless Entry Wiring Diagram (Town Car – 2 Of 4)

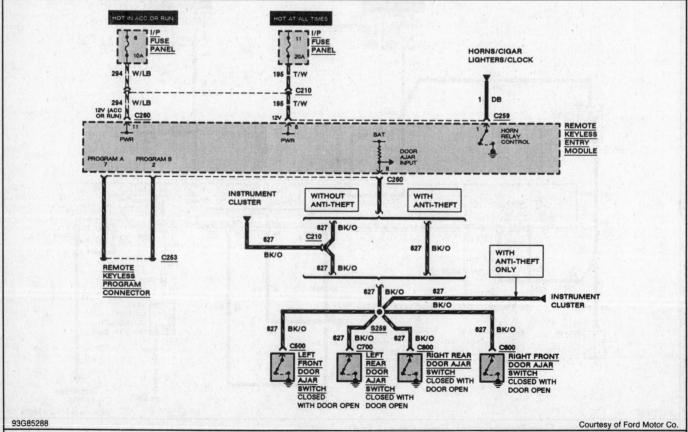

93G85288   Courtesy of Ford Motor Co.

Fig. 26: Remote Keyless Entry Wiring Diagram (Town Car – 3 Of 4)

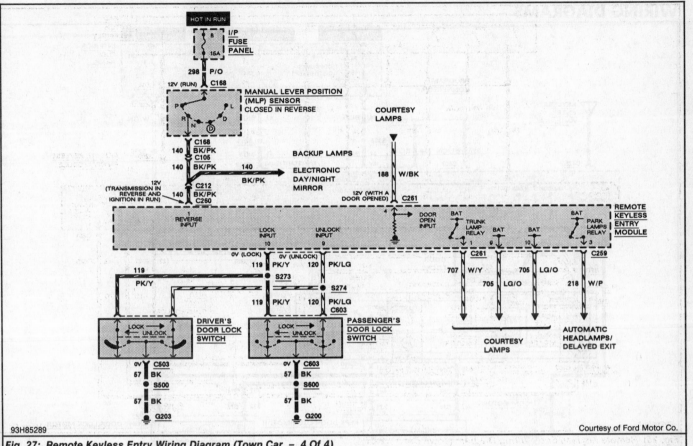

93H85289

Courtesy of Ford Motor Co.

Fig. 27: Remote Keyless Entry Wiring Diagram (Town Car – 4 Of 4)

WIRING DIAGRAMS

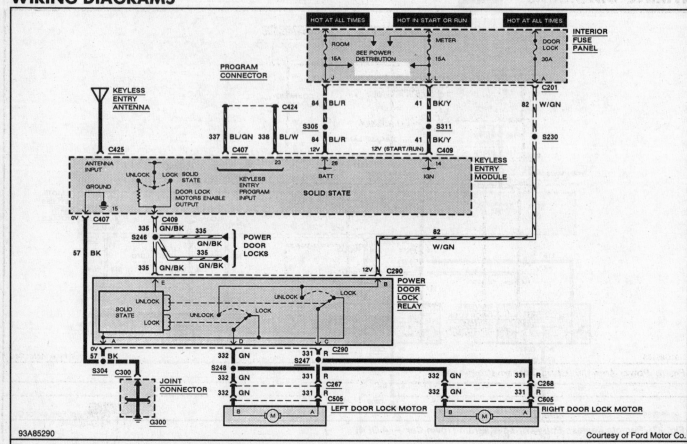

Fig. 3: Remote Keyless Entry Wiring Diagram (Probe – 1 Of 2)

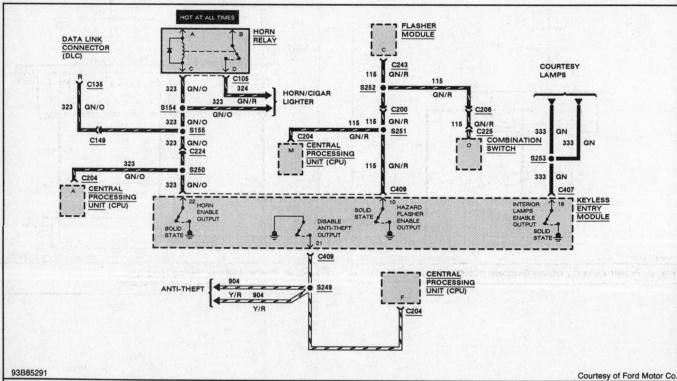

Fig. 4: Remote Keyless Entry Wiring Diagram (Probe – 2 Of 2)

WIRING DIAGRAMS

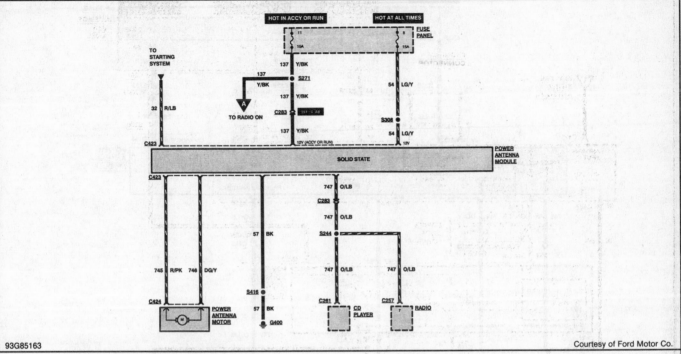

93G85163
Courtesy of Ford Motor Co.

Fig. 1: Power Antenna Wiring Diagram (Continental)

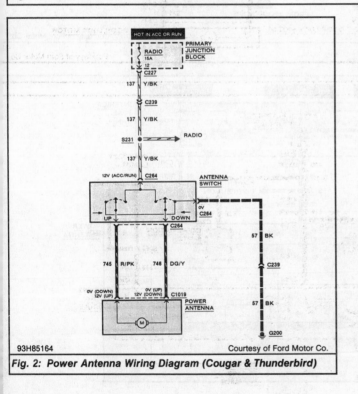

93H85164
Courtesy of Ford Motor Co.

Fig. 2: Power Antenna Wiring Diagram (Cougar & Thunderbird)

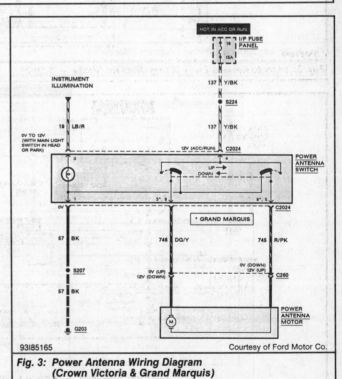

93I85165
Courtesy of Ford Motor Co.

Fig. 3: Power Antenna Wiring Diagram (Crown Victoria & Grand Marquis)

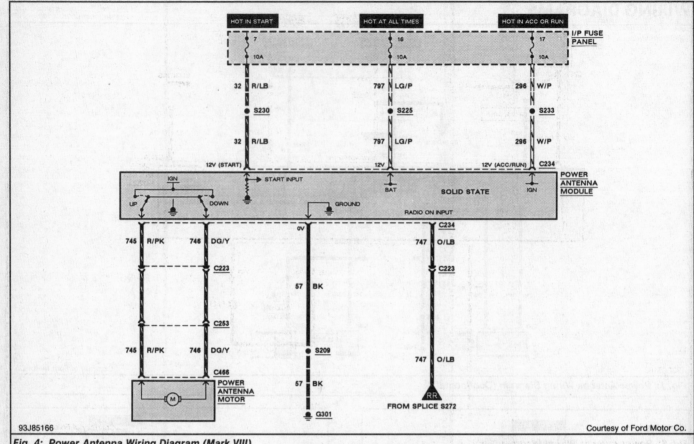

Fig. 4: *Power Antenna Wiring Diagram (Mark VIII)*

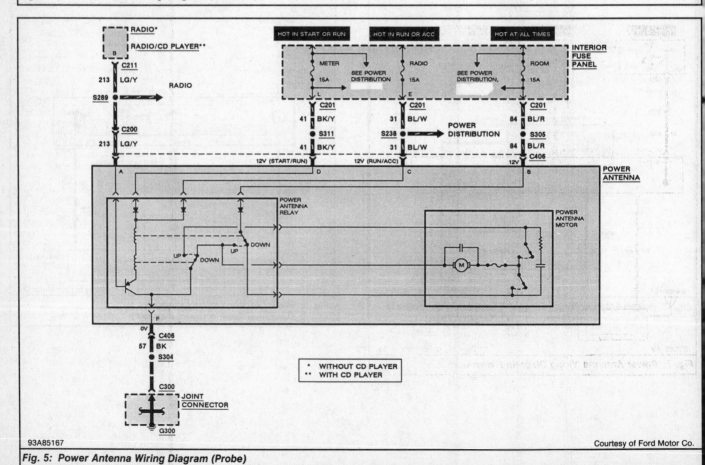

Fig. 5: *Power Antenna Wiring Diagram (Probe)*

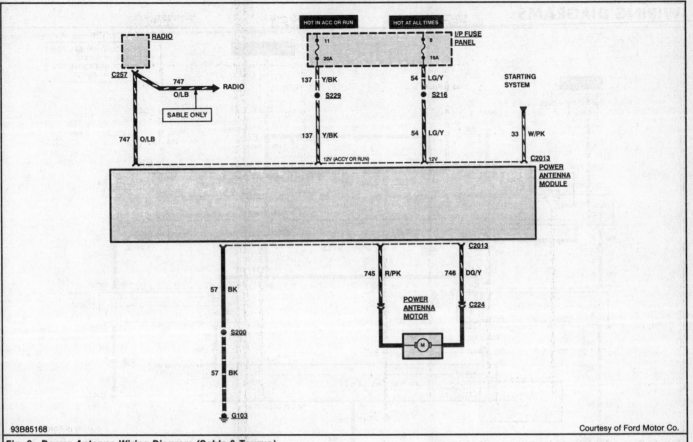

Fig. 6: *Power Antenna Wiring Diagram (Sable & Taurus)*

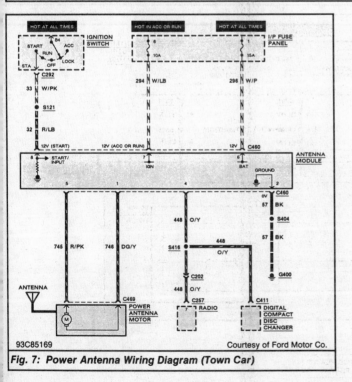

Fig. 7: *Power Antenna Wiring Diagram (Town Car)*

1993 ACCESSORIES & EQUIPMENT
Power Convertible Tops

WIRING DIAGRAMS

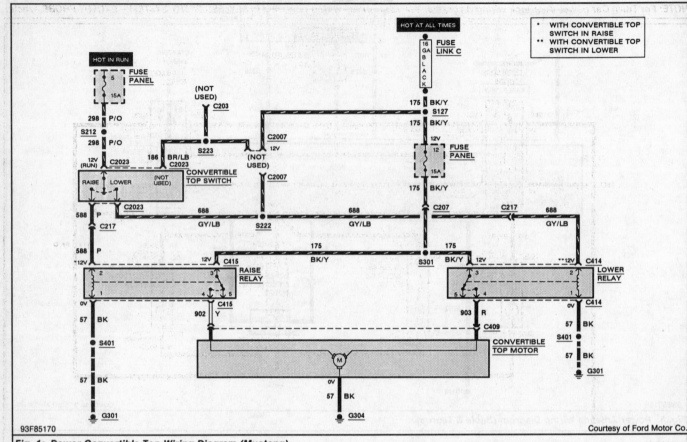

Fig. 1: Power Convertible Top Wiring Diagram (Mustang)

93F85170

Courtesy of Ford Motor Co.

WIRING DIAGRAMS

NOTE: For Town Car power door lock wiring diagrams, see appropriate wiring diagrams in KEYLESS ENTRY SYSTEM – EXCEPT PROBE article.

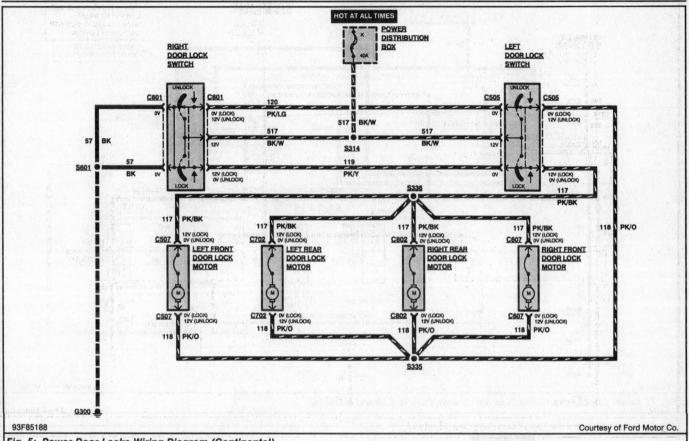

93F85188

Courtesy of Ford Motor Co.

Fig. 5: Power Door Locks Wiring Diagram (Continental)

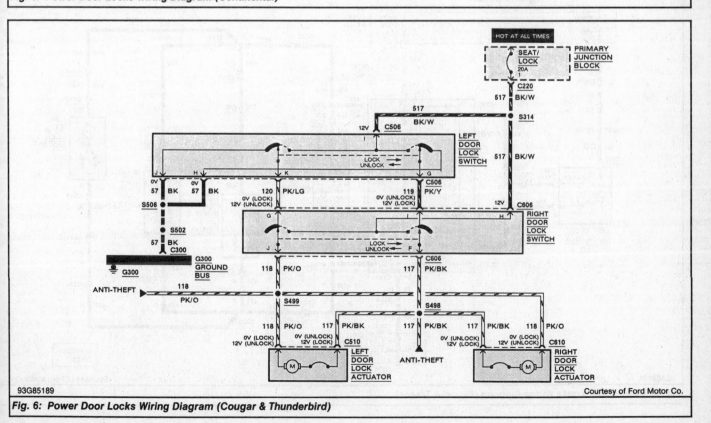

93G85189

Courtesy of Ford Motor Co.

Fig. 6: Power Door Locks Wiring Diagram (Cougar & Thunderbird)

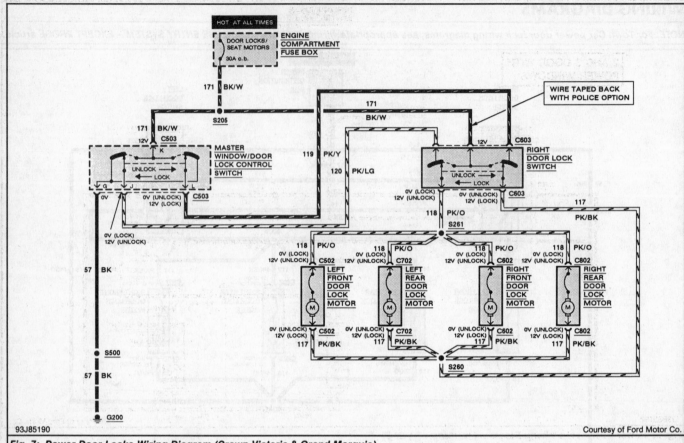

93J85190   Courtesy of Ford Motor Co.

Fig. 7: Power Door Locks Wiring Diagram (Crown Victoria & Grand Marquis)

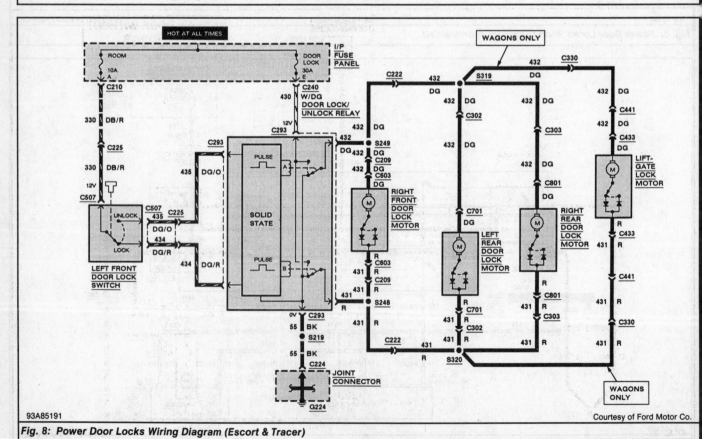

93A85191   Courtesy of Ford Motor Co.

Fig. 8: Power Door Locks Wiring Diagram (Escort & Tracer)

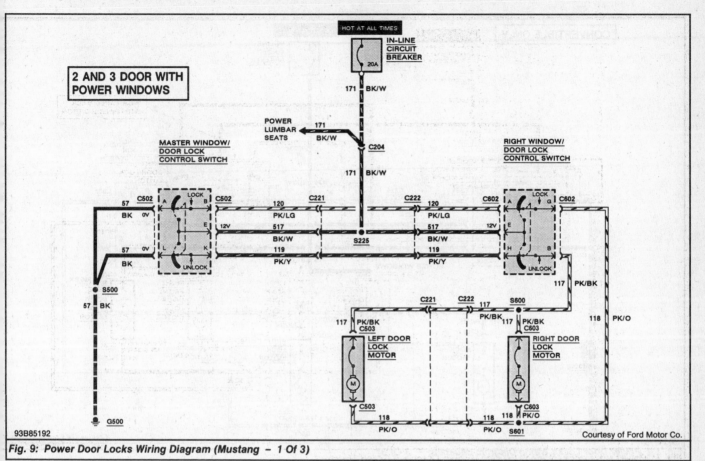

Fig. 9: Power Door Locks Wiring Diagram (Mustang – 1 Of 3)

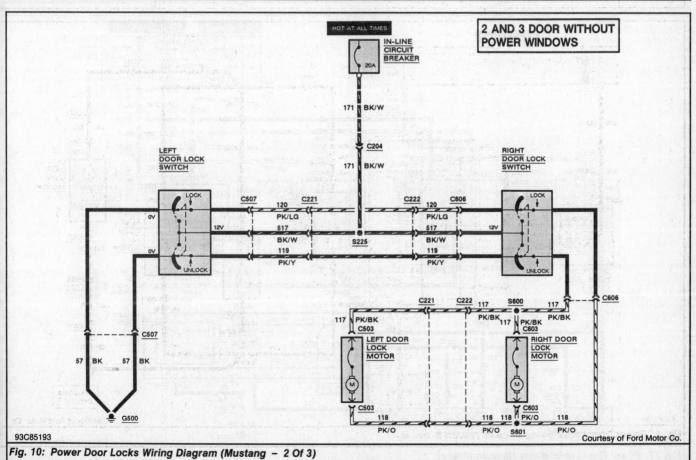

Fig. 10: Power Door Locks Wiring Diagram (Mustang – 2 Of 3)

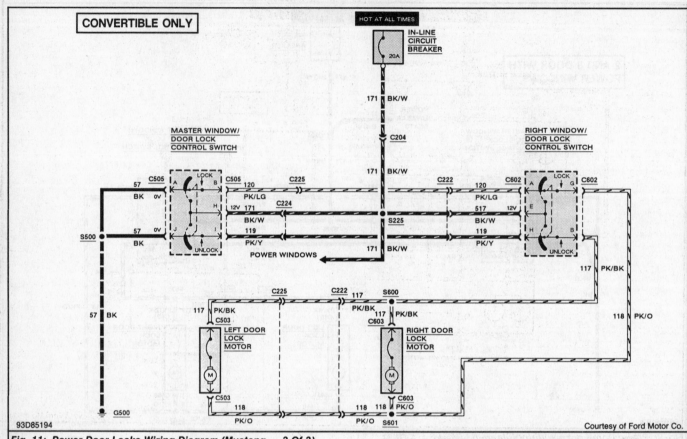

Fig. 11: **Power Door Locks Wiring Diagram (Mustang – 3 Of 3)**

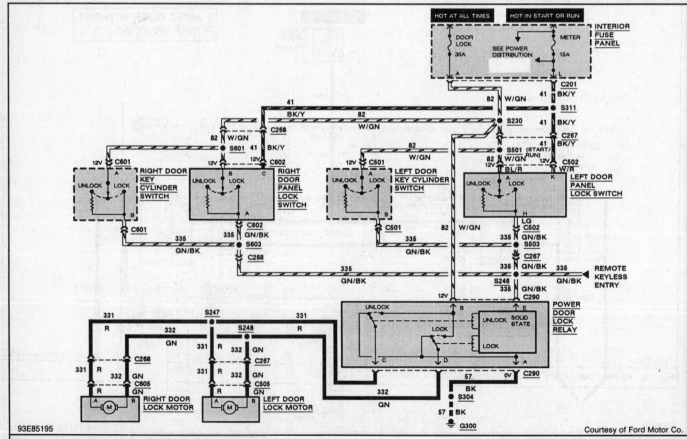

Fig. 12: **Power Door Locks Wiring Diagram (Probe)**

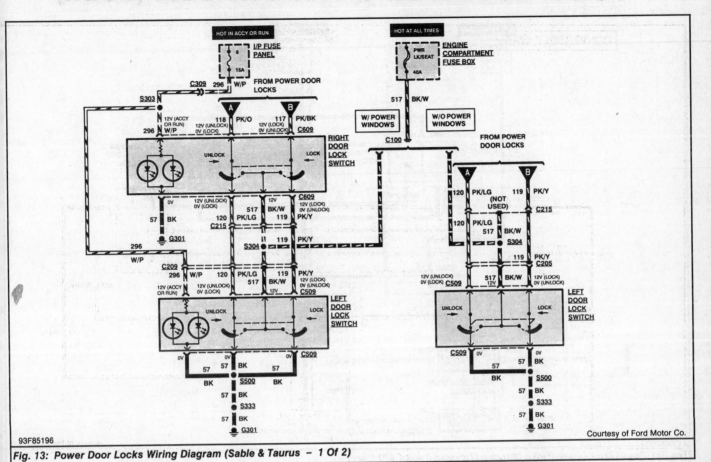

Fig. 13: Power Door Locks Wiring Diagram (Sable & Taurus – 1 Of 2)

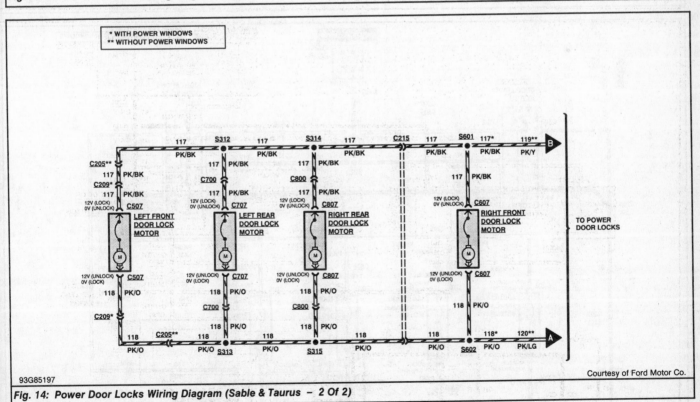

Fig. 14: Power Door Locks Wiring Diagram (Sable & Taurus – 2 Of 2)

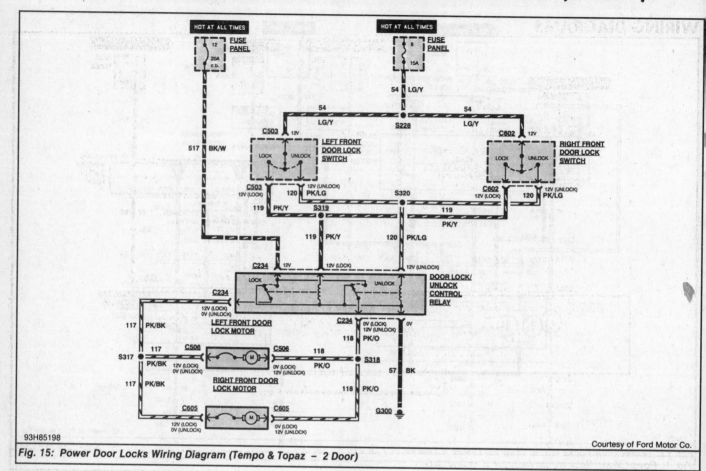

Fig. 15: Power Door Locks Wiring Diagram (Tempo & Topaz – 2 Door)

Courtesy of Ford Motor Co.

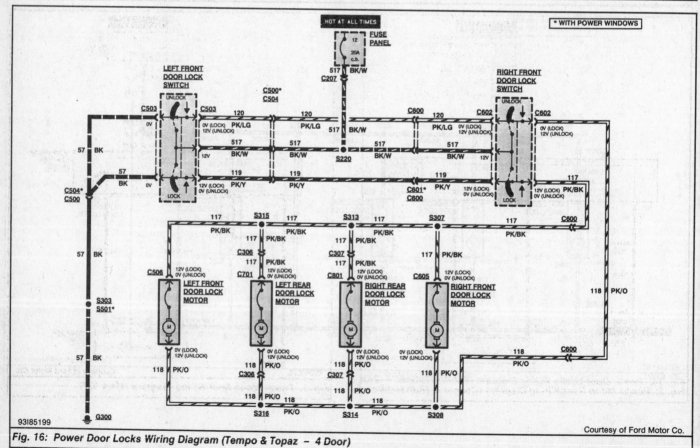

Fig. 16: Power Door Locks Wiring Diagram (Tempo & Topaz – 4 Door)

Courtesy of Ford Motor Co.

WIRING DIAGRAMS

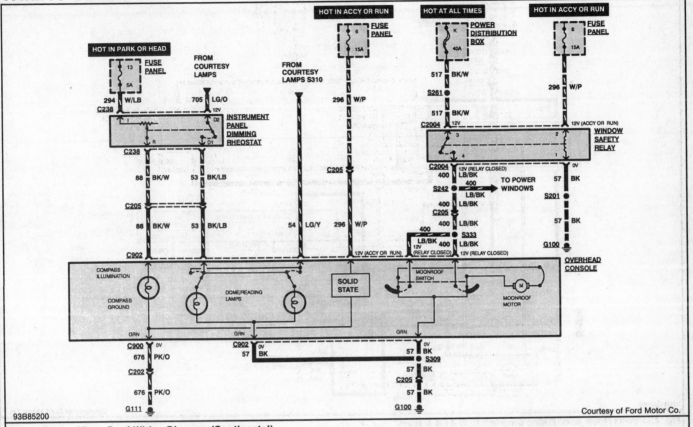

Fig. 1: Power Moon Roof Wiring Diagram (Continental)

93B85200

Courtesy of Ford Motor Co.

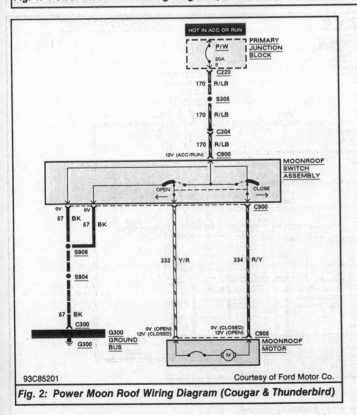

Fig. 2: Power Moon Roof Wiring Diagram (Cougar & Thunderbird)

93C85201

Courtesy of Ford Motor Co.

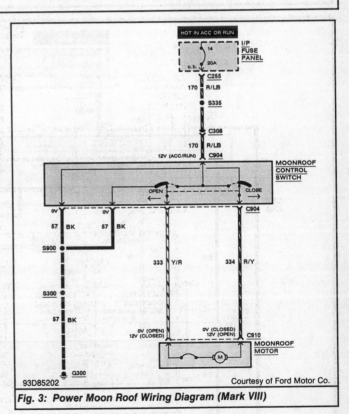

Fig. 3: Power Moon Roof Wiring Diagram (Mark VIII)

93D85202

Courtesy of Ford Motor Co.

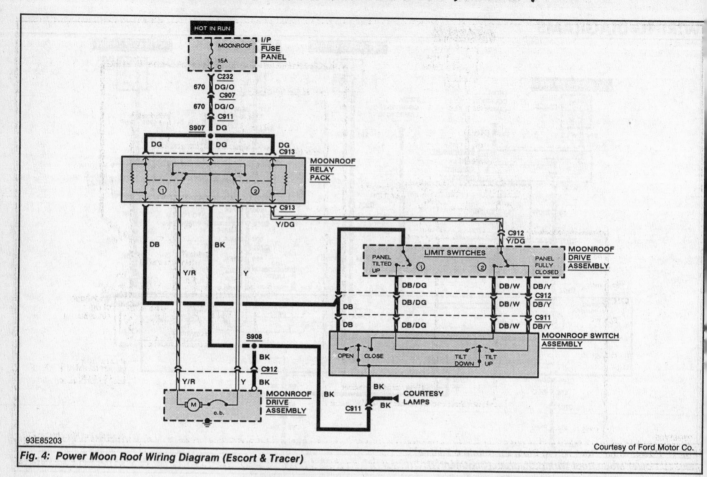

Fig. 4: Power Moon Roof Wiring Diagram (Escort & Tracer)

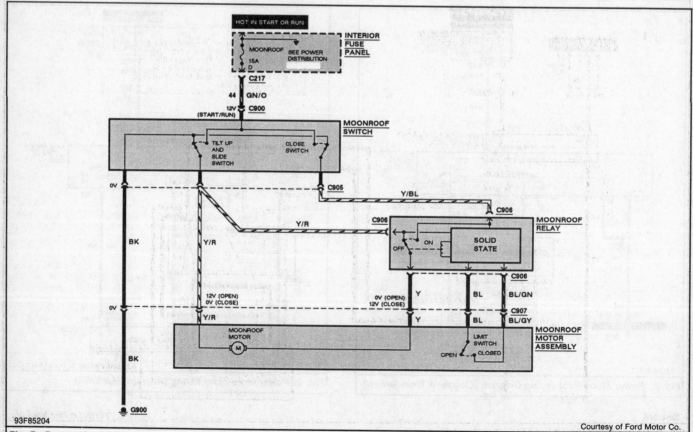

Fig. 5: Power Moon Roof Wiring Diagram (Probe)

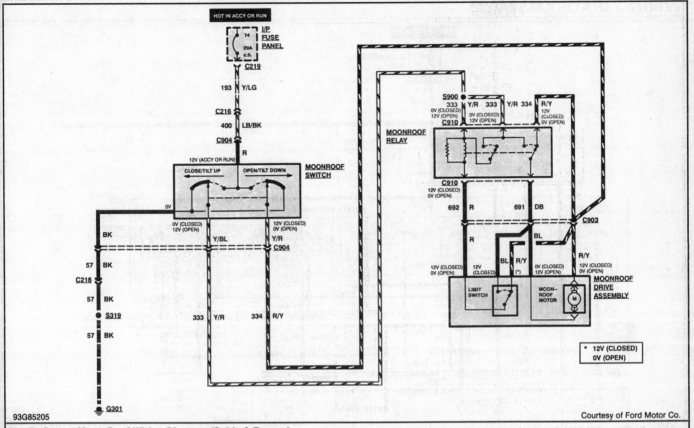

93G85205

Courtesy of Ford Motor Co.

Fig. 6: Power Moon Roof Wiring Diagram (Sable & Taurus)

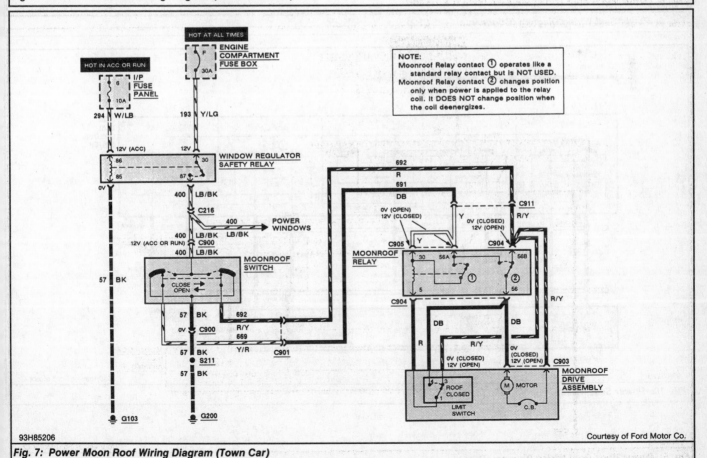

93H85206

Courtesy of Ford Motor Co.

Fig. 7: Power Moon Roof Wiring Diagram (Town Car)

FORD
4-92

1993 ACCESSORIES & EQUIPMENT
Power Seats – Continental, Mark VIII & Town Car (Cont.)

WIRING DIAGRAMS

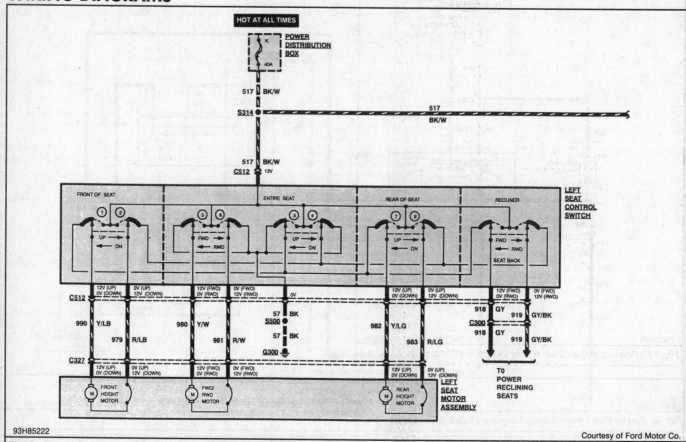

93H85222

Courtesy of Ford Motor Co.

Fig. 9: Power Seat Wiring Diagram (Continental – 1 Of 2)

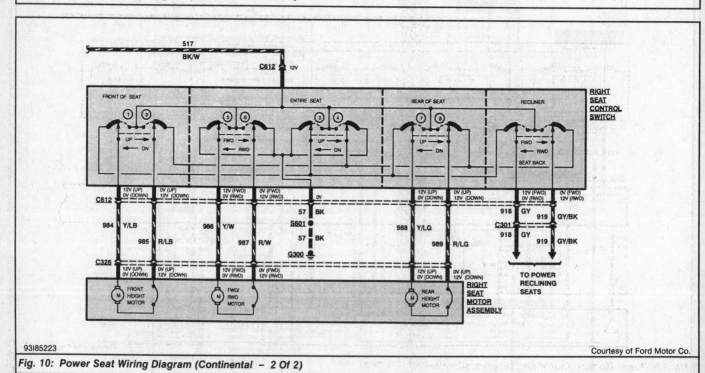

93I85223

Courtesy of Ford Motor Co.

Fig. 10: Power Seat Wiring Diagram (Continental – 2 Of 2)

1993 ACCESSORIES & EQUIPMENT
Power Seats – Continental, Mark VIII & Town Car (Cont.)

FORD
4-93

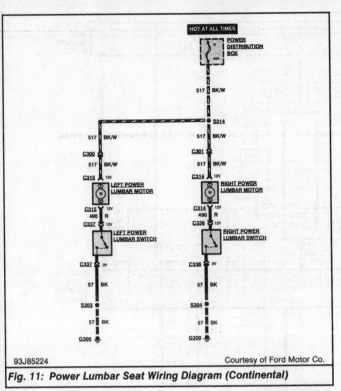

Fig. 11: Power Lumbar Seat Wiring Diagram (Continental)

93J85224

Courtesy of Ford Motor Co.

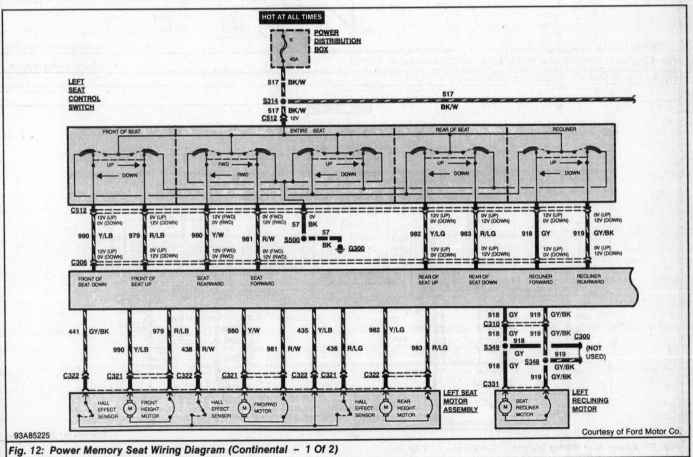

Fig. 12: Power Memory Seat Wiring Diagram (Continental – 1 Of 2)

93A85225

Courtesy of Ford Motor Co.

FORD
4-94

1993 ACCESSORIES & EQUIPMENT
Power Seats – Continental, Mark VIII & Town Car (Cont.)

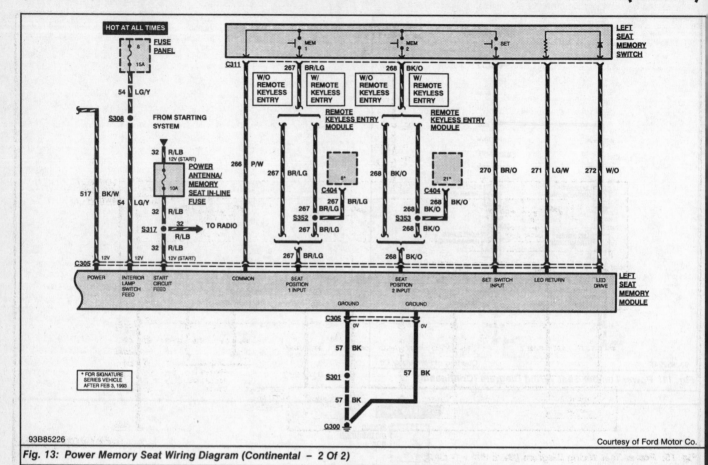

93B85226

Courtesy of Ford Motor Co.

Fig. 13: Power Memory Seat Wiring Diagram (Continental – 2 Of 2)

93C85227

Courtesy of Ford Motor Co.

Fig. 14: Power Reclining Seat Wiring Diagram (Continental)

1993 ACCESSORIES & EQUIPMENT
Power Seats – Continental, Mark VIII & Town Car (Cont.)

FORD
4-95

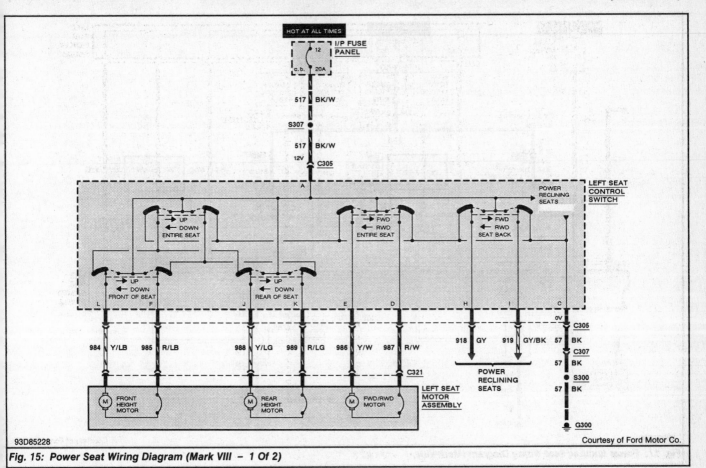

93D85228

Courtesy of Ford Motor Co.

Fig. 15: Power Seat Wiring Diagram (Mark VIII – 1 Of 2)

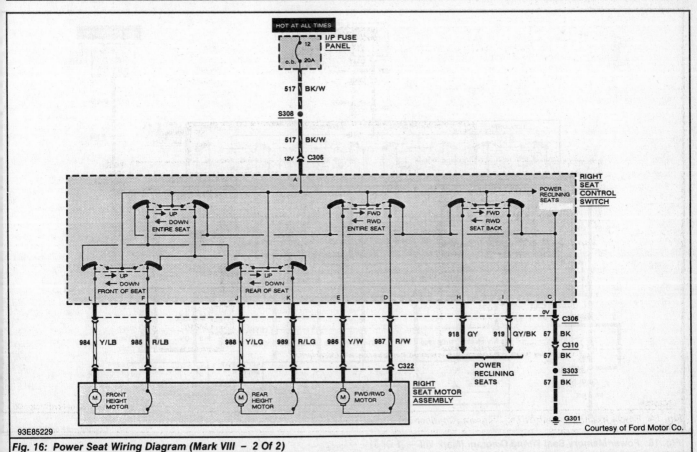

93E85229

Courtesy of Ford Motor Co.

Fig. 16: Power Seat Wiring Diagram (Mark VIII – 2 Of 2)

FORD
4-96

1993 ACCESSORIES & EQUIPMENT
Power Seats – Continental, Mark VIII & Town Car (Cont.)

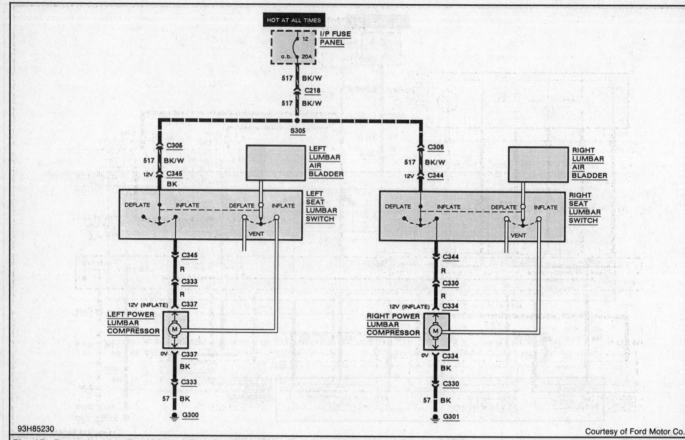

93H85230

Courtesy of Ford Motor Co.

Fig. 17: Power Lumbar Seat Wiring Diagram (Mark VIII)

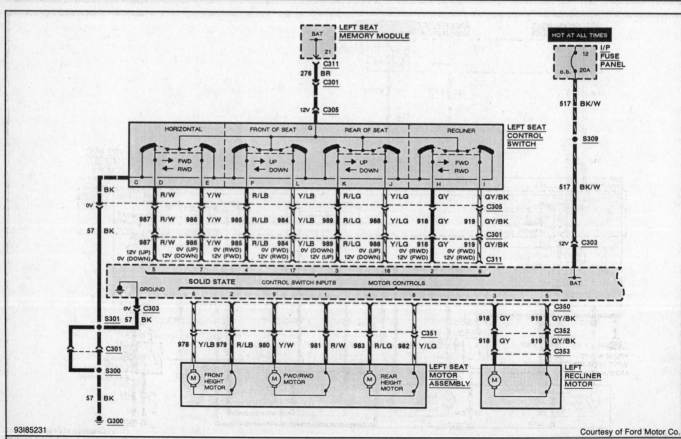

93I85231

Courtesy of Ford Motor Co.

Fig. 18: Power Memory Seat Wiring Diagram (Mark VIII – 1 Of 5)

1993 ACCESSORIES & EQUIPMENT
Power Seats – Continental, Mark VIII & Town Car (Cont.)

FORD
4-97

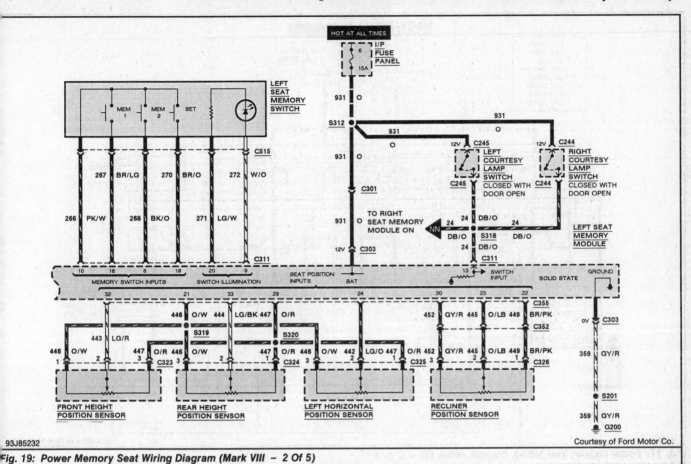

93J85232

Courtesy of Ford Motor Co.

Fig. 19: Power Memory Seat Wiring Diagram (Mark VIII – 2 Of 5)

93A85233

Courtesy of Ford Motor Co.

Fig. 20: Power Memory Seat Wiring Diagram (Mark VIII – 3 Of 5)

FORD
4-98

1993 ACCESSORIES & EQUIPMENT
Power Seats – Continental, Mark VIII & Town Car (Cont.)

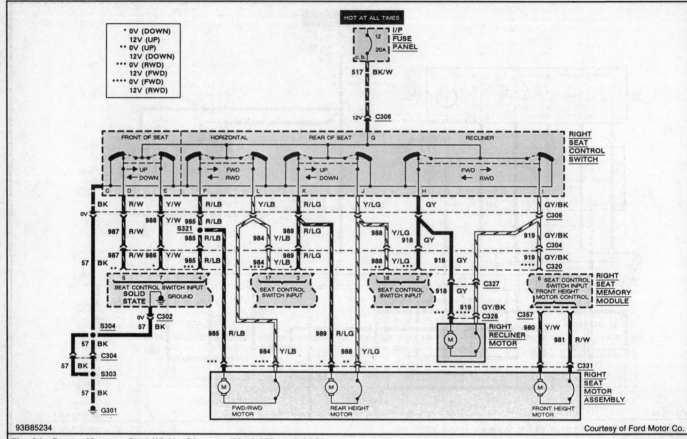

93B85234

Courtesy of Ford Motor Co.

Fig. 21: Power Memory Seat Wiring Diagram (Mark VIII – 4 Of 5)

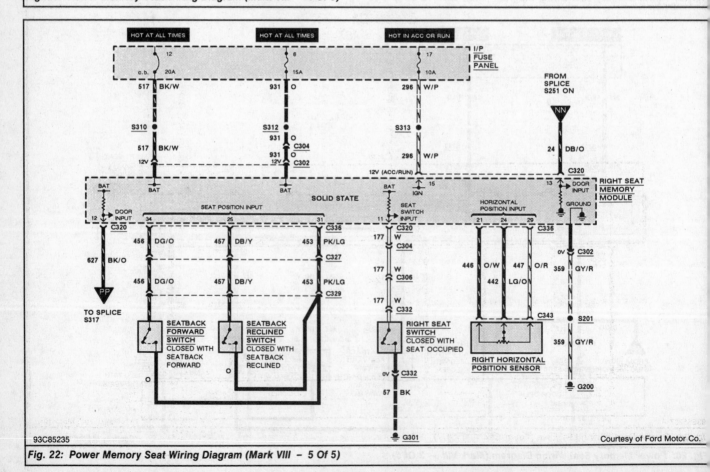

93C85235

Courtesy of Ford Motor Co.

Fig. 22: Power Memory Seat Wiring Diagram (Mark VIII – 5 Of 5)

1993 ACCESSORIES & EQUIPMENT
Power Seats – Continental, Mark VIII & Town Car (Cont.)

FORD
4-99

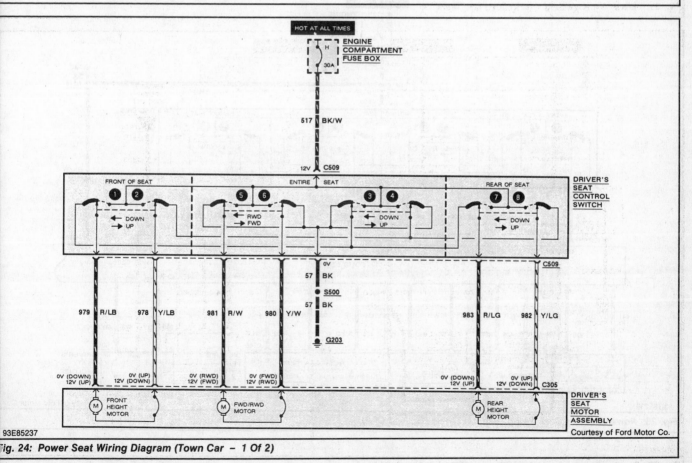

Fig. 23: Power Reclining Seat Wiring Diagram (Mark VIII)

Courtesy of Ford Motor Co.

93D85236

Fig. 24: Power Seat Wiring Diagram (Town Car – 1 Of 2)

Courtesy of Ford Motor Co.

93E85237

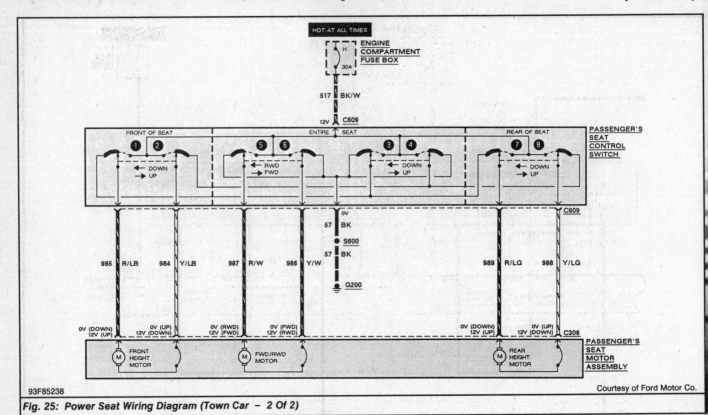

Fig. 25: Power Seat Wiring Diagram (Town Car – 2 Of 2)

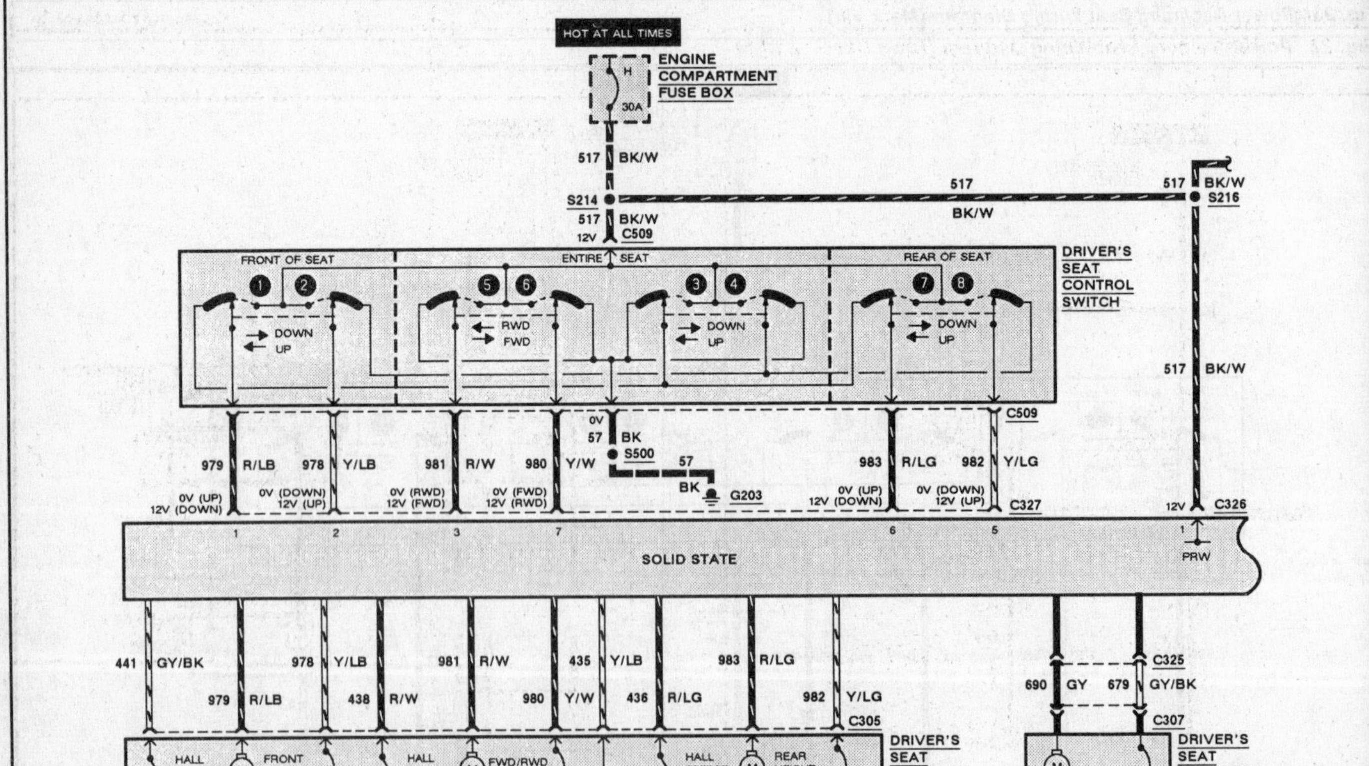

93F85238

Courtesy of Ford Motor Co.

Fig. 26: Power Memory Seat Wiring Diagram (Town Car – 1 Of 2)

93G85239

Courtesy of Ford Motor Co.

1993 ACCESSORIES & EQUIPMENT
Power Seats – Continental, Mark VIII & Town Car (Cont.)

FORD
4-101

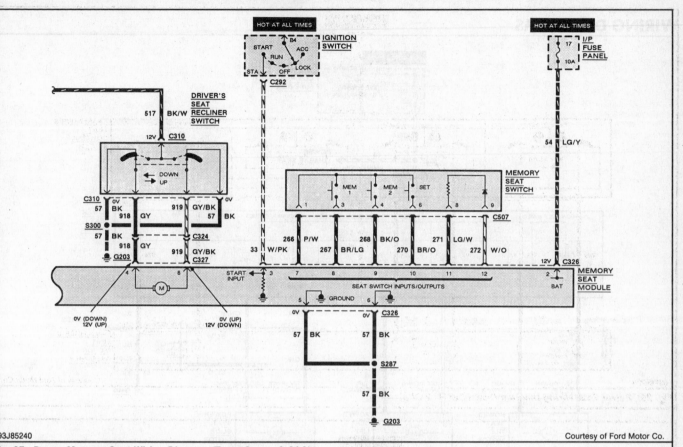

Fig. 27: Power Memory Seat Wiring Diagram (Town Car – 2 Of 2)

93J85240

Courtesy of Ford Motor Co.

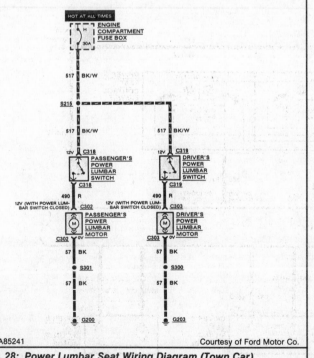

Fig. 28: Power Lumbar Seat Wiring Diagram (Town Car)

93A85241

Courtesy of Ford Motor Co.

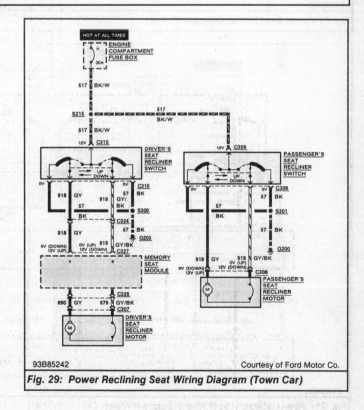

Fig. 29: Power Reclining Seat Wiring Diagram (Town Car)

93B85242

Courtesy of Ford Motor Co.

WIRING DIAGRAMS

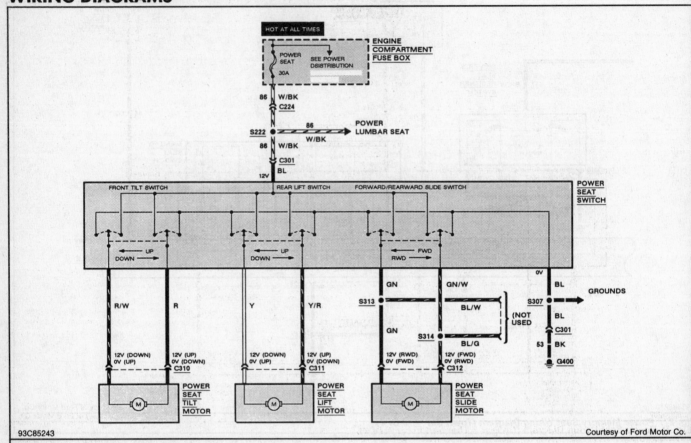

93C85243

Courtesy of Ford Motor Co.

Fig. 7: Power Seat Wiring Diagram (Probe)

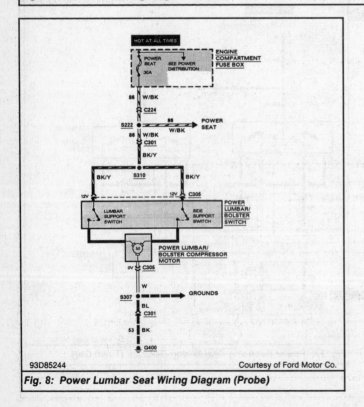

93D85244

Courtesy of Ford Motor Co.

Fig. 8: Power Lumbar Seat Wiring Diagram (Probe)

WIRING DIAGRAMS

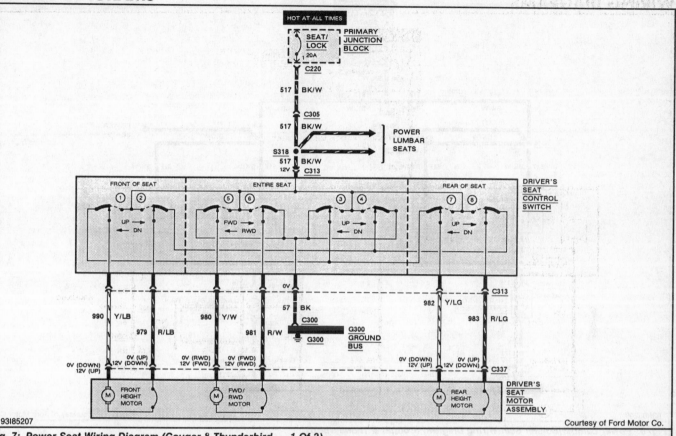

93185207

Courtesy of Ford Motor Co.

Fig. 7: Power Seat Wiring Diagram (Cougar & Thunderbird – 1 Of 2)

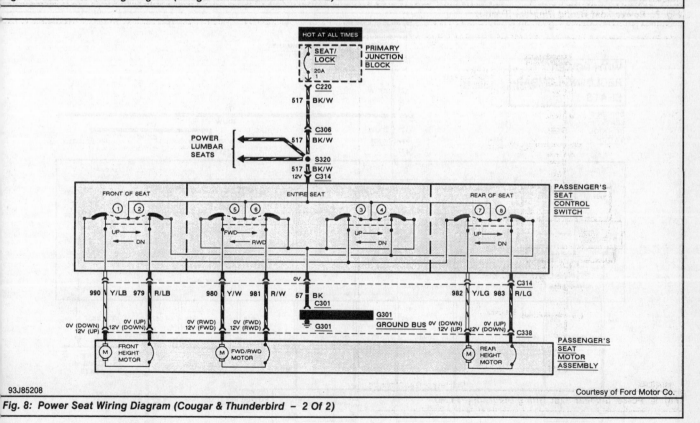

93J85208

Courtesy of Ford Motor Co.

Fig. 8: Power Seat Wiring Diagram (Cougar & Thunderbird – 2 Of 2)

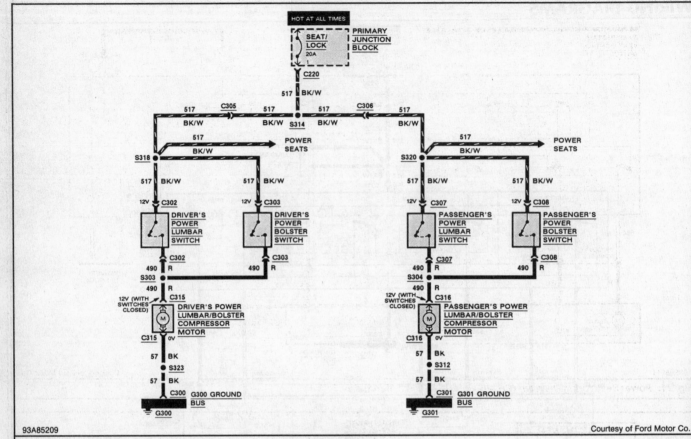

93A85209

Courtesy of Ford Motor Co.

Fig. 9: Power Lumbar/Bolster Seat Wiring Diagram (Cougar & Thunderbird)

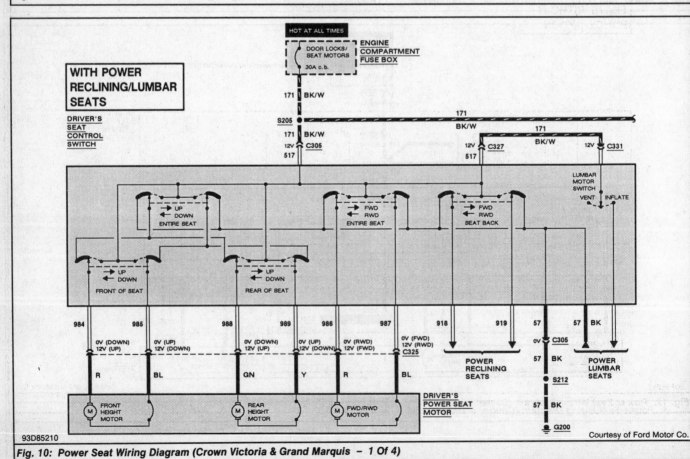

93D85210

Courtesy of Ford Motor Co.

Fig. 10: Power Seat Wiring Diagram (Crown Victoria & Grand Marquis – 1 Of 4)

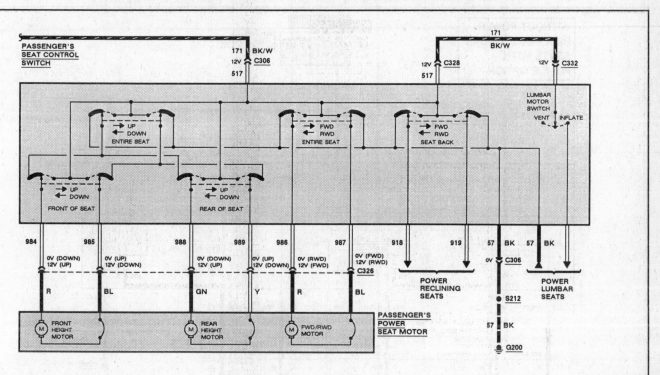

93E85211

Courtesy of Ford Motor Co.

Fig. 11: Power Seat Wiring Diagram (Crown Victoria & Grand Marquis – 2 Of 4)

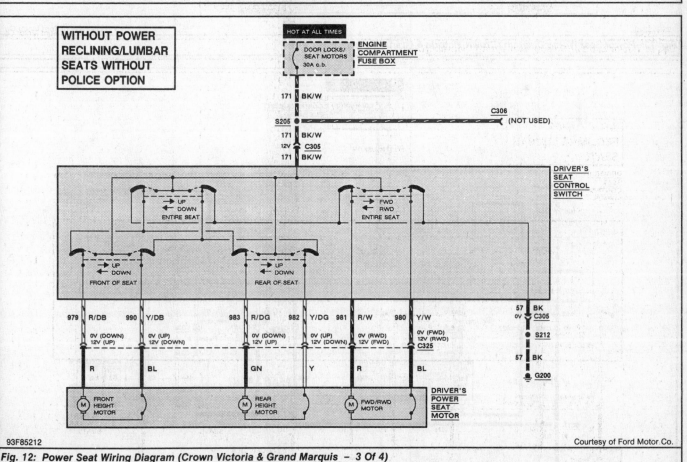

93F85212

Courtesy of Ford Motor Co.

Fig. 12: Power Seat Wiring Diagram (Crown Victoria & Grand Marquis – 3 Of 4)

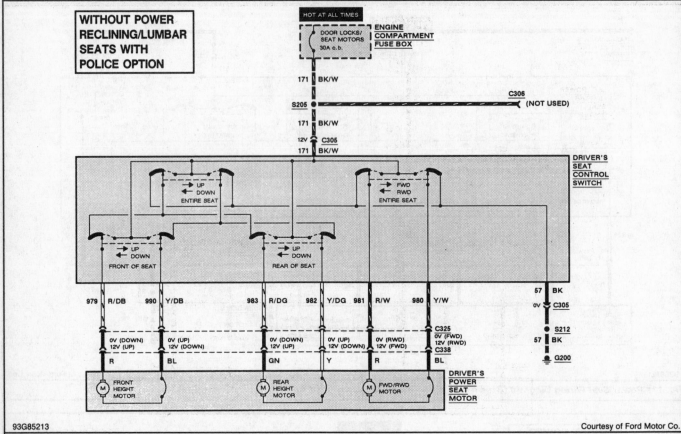

Fig. 13: **Power Seat Wiring Diagram (Crown Victoria & Grand Marquis – 4 Of 4)**

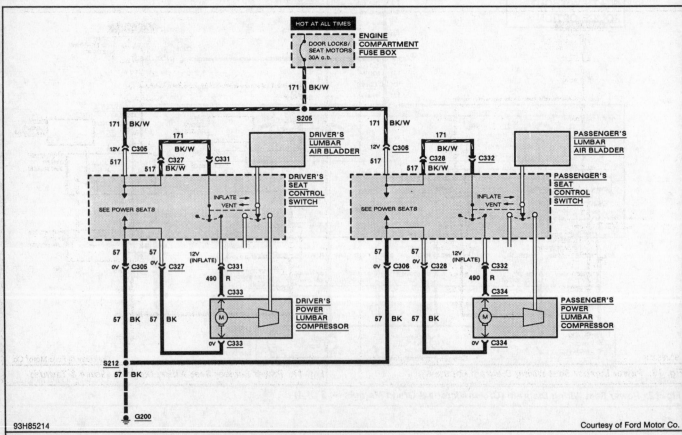

Fig. 14: **Power Lumbar Seat Wiring Diagram (Crown Victoria & Grand Marquis)**

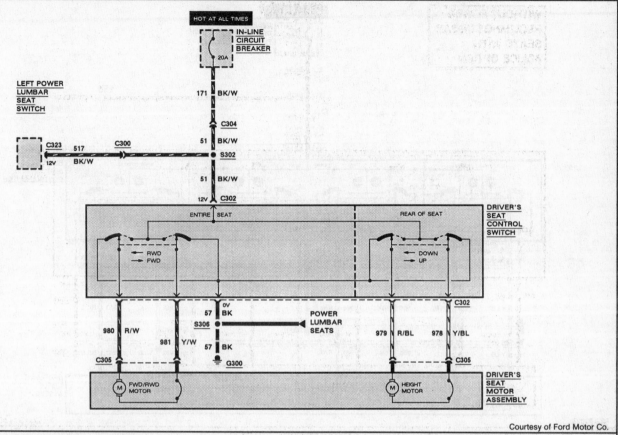

93I85215

Courtesy of Ford Motor Co.

Fig. 15: Power Seat Wiring Diagram (Mustang)

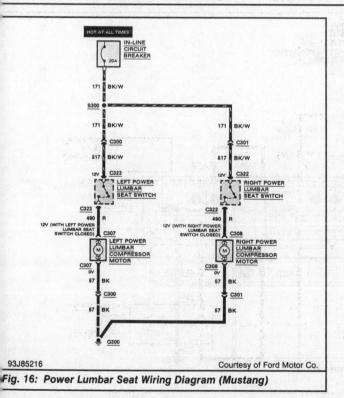

93J85216

Courtesy of Ford Motor Co.

Fig. 16: Power Lumbar Seat Wiring Diagram (Mustang)

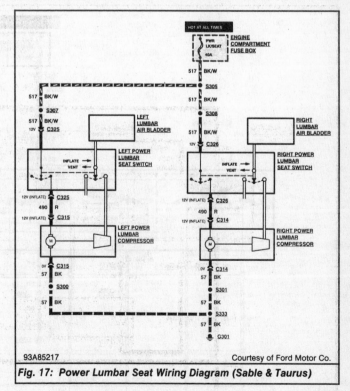

93A85217

Courtesy of Ford Motor Co.

Fig. 17: Power Lumbar Seat Wiring Diagram (Sable & Taurus)

1993 ACCESSORIES & EQUIPMENT
Power Seats – All Others (Cont.)

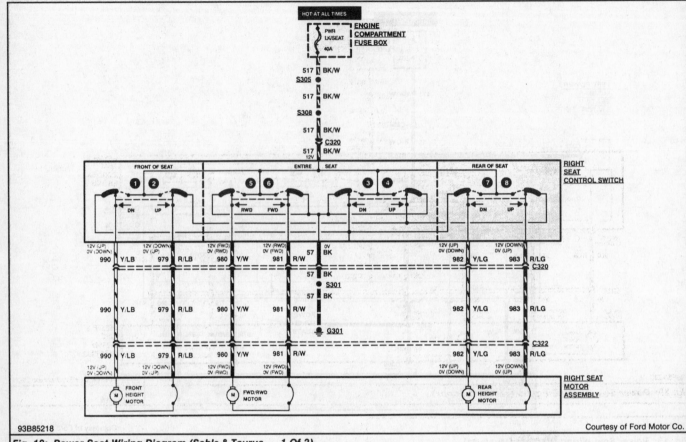

Fig. 18: Power Seat Wiring Diagram (Sable & Taurus – 1 Of 2)

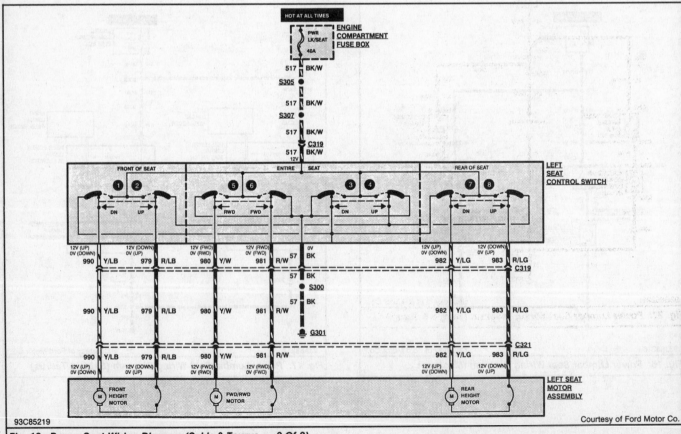

Fig. 19: Power Seat Wiring Diagram (Sable & Taurus – 2 Of 2)

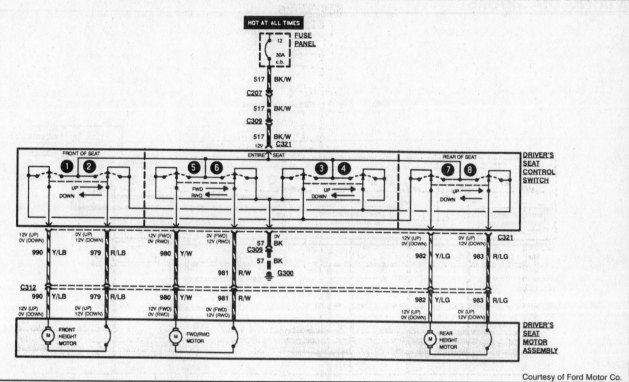

93F85220

Courtesy of Ford Motor Co.

Fig. 20: Power Seat Wiring Diagram (Tempo & Topaz)

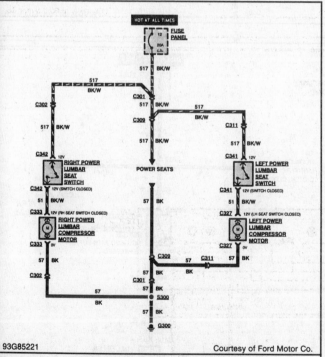

93G85221

Courtesy of Ford Motor Co.

Fig. 21: Power Lumbar Seat Wiring Diagram (Tempo & Topaz)

1993 ACCESSORIES & EQUIPMENT
Power Trunk & Fuel Filler Doors

WIRING DIAGRAMS

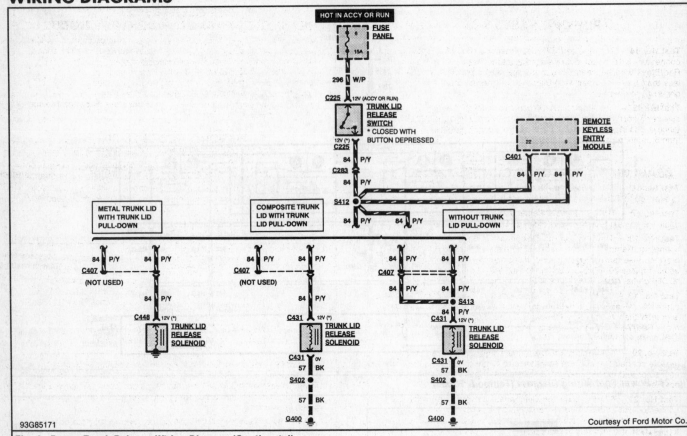

Fig. 1: Power Trunk Release Wiring Diagram (Continental)

93G85171   Courtesy of Ford Motor Co.

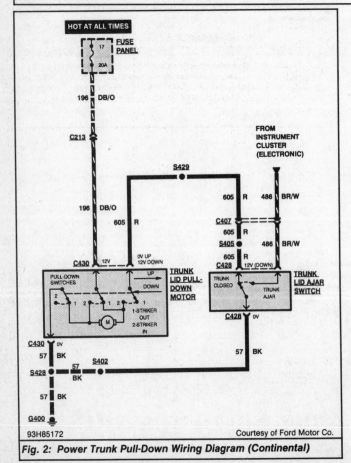

93H85172   Courtesy of Ford Motor Co.

Fig. 2: Power Trunk Pull-Down Wiring Diagram (Continental)

93I85173   Courtesy of Ford Motor Co.

Fig. 3: Power Fuel Filler Door Release Wiring Diagram (Continental)

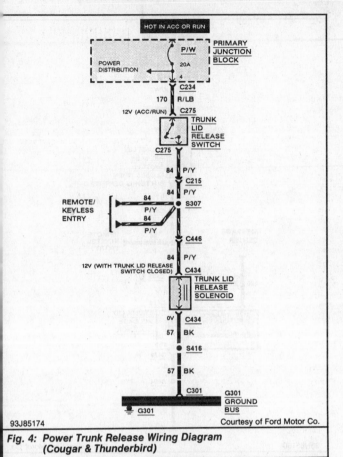

Fig. 4: Power Trunk Release Wiring Diagram (Cougar & Thunderbird)

93J85174

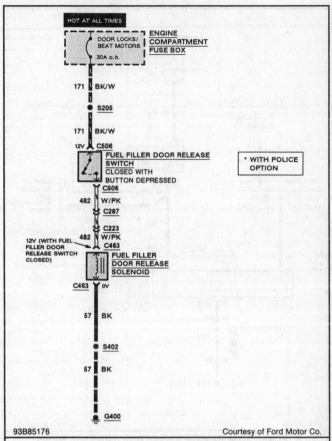

Fig. 6: Power Fuel Filler Door Release Wiring Diagram (Crown Victoria & Grand Marquis)

93B85176

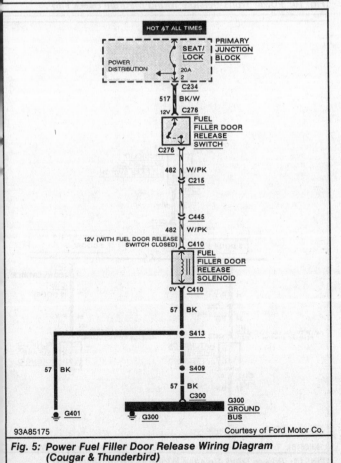

Fig. 5: Power Fuel Filler Door Release Wiring Diagram (Cougar & Thunderbird)

93A85175

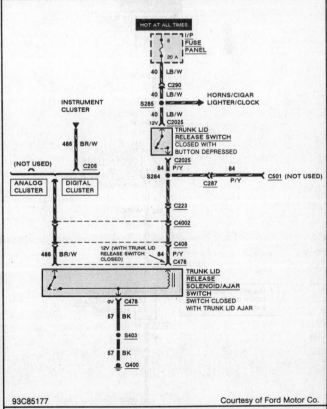

Fig. 7: Power Trunk Release With Police Package Wiring Diagram (Crown Victoria & Grand Marquis)

93C85177

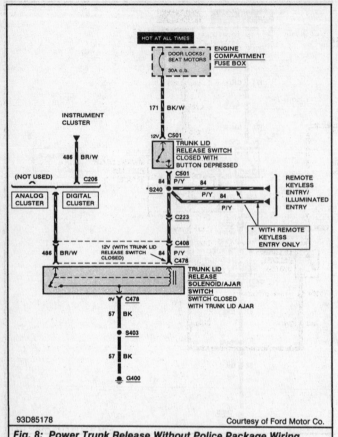

Fig. 8: Power Trunk Release Without Police Package Wiring Diagram (Crown Victoria & Grand Marquis)

93D85178   Courtesy of Ford Motor Co.

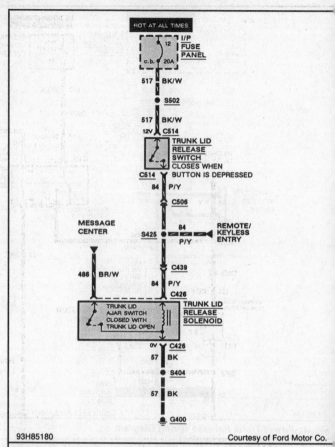

Fig. 10: Power Trunk Release Wiring Diagram (Mark VIII)

93H85180   Courtesy of Ford Motor Co.

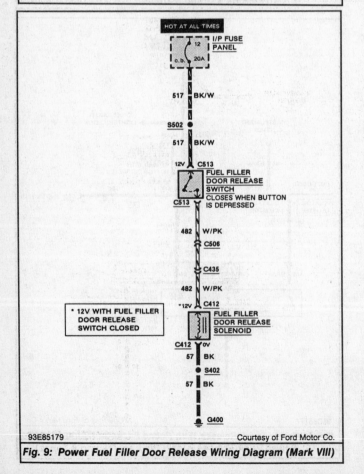

Fig. 9: Power Fuel Filler Door Release Wiring Diagram (Mark VIII)

93E85179   Courtesy of Ford Motor Co.

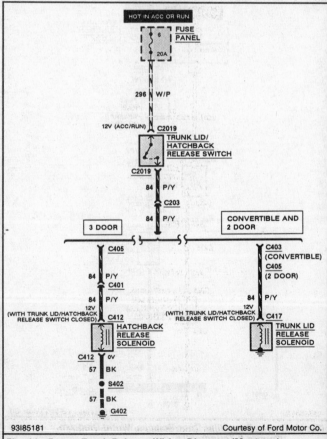

Fig. 11: Power Trunk Release Wiring Diagram (Mustang)

93I85181   Courtesy of Ford Motor Co.

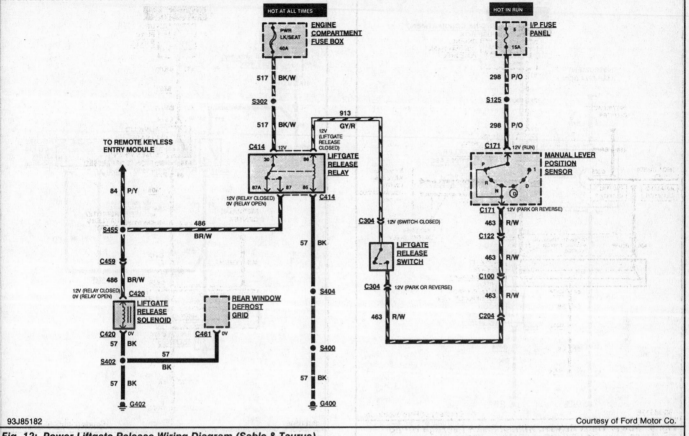

Fig. 12: *Power Liftgate Release Wiring Diagram (Sable & Taurus)*

93J85182

Courtesy of Ford Motor Co.

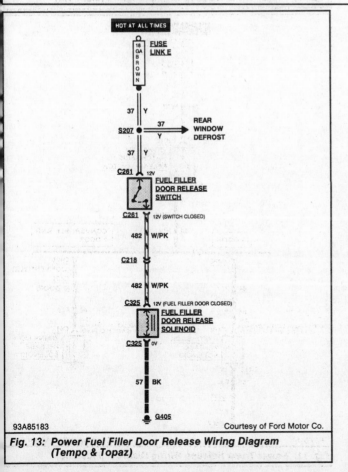

93A85183

Courtesy of Ford Motor Co.

Fig. 13: *Power Fuel Filler Door Release Wiring Diagram (Tempo & Topaz)*

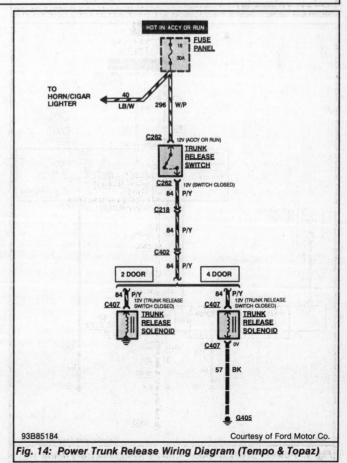

93B85184

Courtesy of Ford Motor Co.

Fig. 14: *Power Trunk Release Wiring Diagram (Tempo & Topaz)*

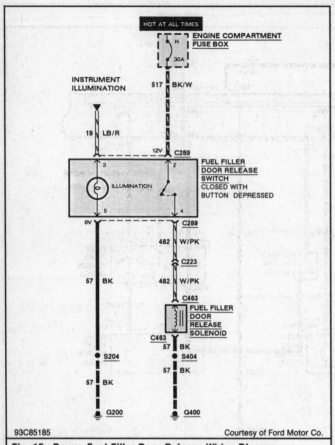

93C85185   Courtesy of Ford Motor Co.

Fig. 15: Power Fuel Filler Door Release Wiring Diagram (Town Car)

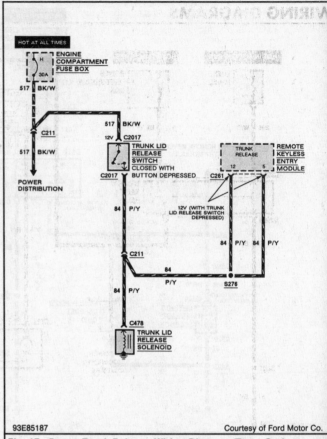

93E85187   Courtesy of Ford Motor Co.

Fig. 17: Power Trunk Release Wiring Diagram (Town Car)

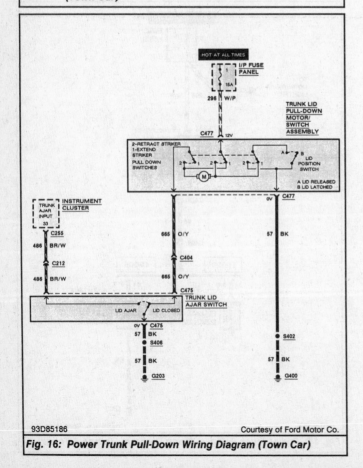

93D85186   Courtesy of Ford Motor Co.

Fig. 16: Power Trunk Pull-Down Wiring Diagram (Town Car)

WIRING DIAGRAMS

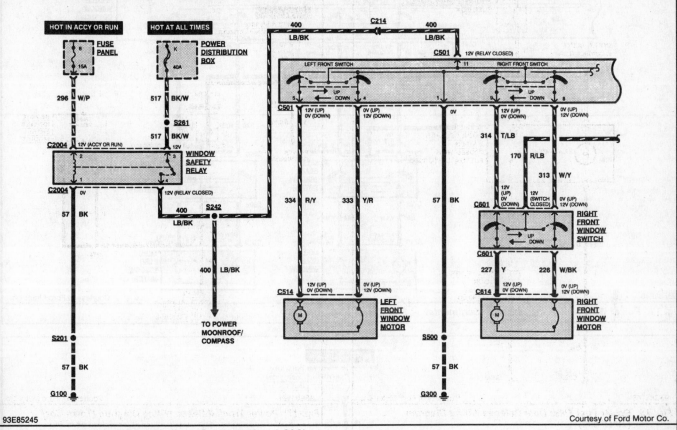

93E85245

Courtesy of Ford Motor Co.

Fig. 10: Power Windows Wiring Diagram (Continental – 1 Of 2)

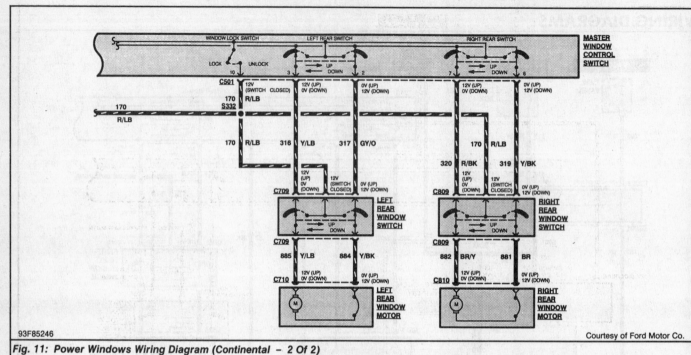

93F85246   Courtesy of Ford Motor Co.

Fig. 11: Power Windows Wiring Diagram (Continental – 2 Of 2)

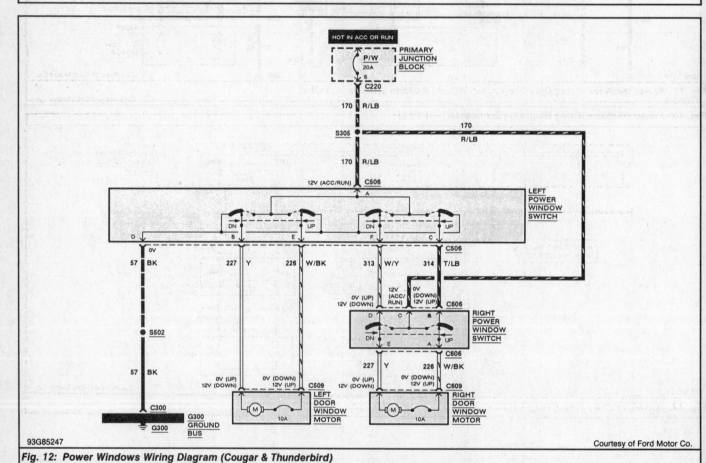

93G85247   Courtesy of Ford Motor Co.

Fig. 12: Power Windows Wiring Diagram (Cougar & Thunderbird)

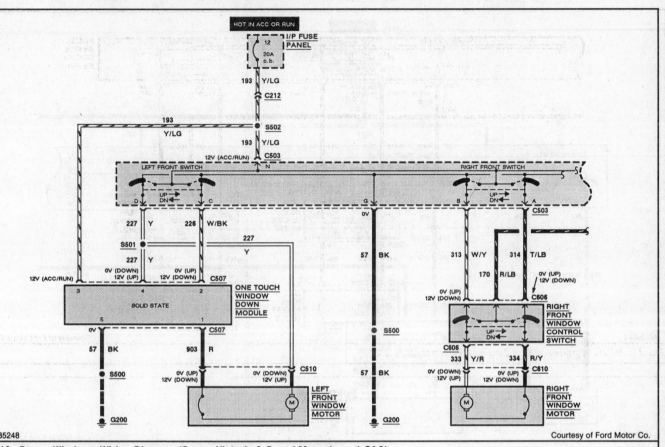

93H85248

Courtesy of Ford Motor Co.

Fig. 13: Power Windows Wiring Diagram (Crown Victoria & Grand Marquis – 1 Of 2)

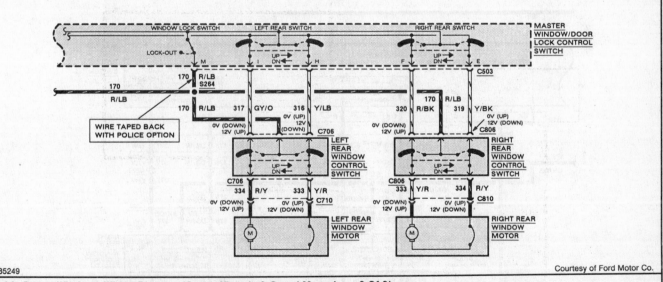

93I85249

Courtesy of Ford Motor Co.

Fig. 14: Power Windows Wiring Diagram (Crown Victoria & Grand Marquis – 2 Of 2)

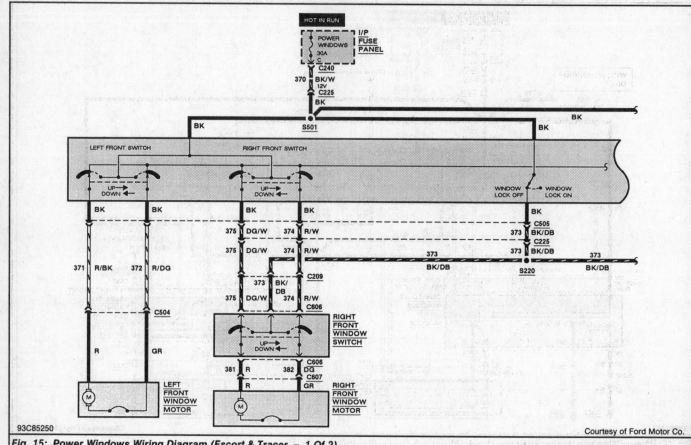

93C85250

Courtesy of Ford Motor Co.

Fig. 15: Power Windows Wiring Diagram (Escort & Tracer – 1 Of 2)

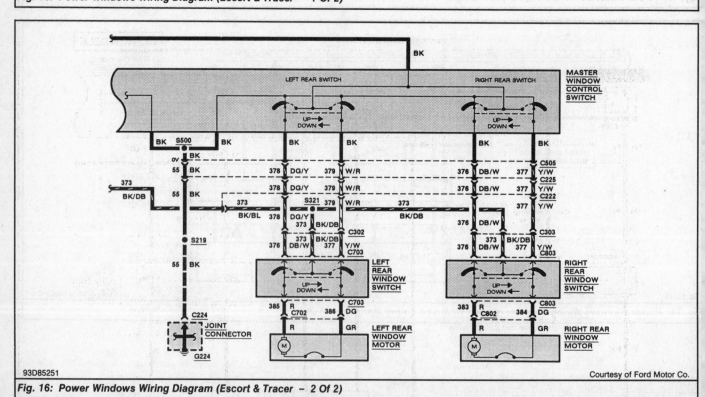

93D85251

Courtesy of Ford Motor Co.

Fig. 16: Power Windows Wiring Diagram (Escort & Tracer – 2 Of 2)

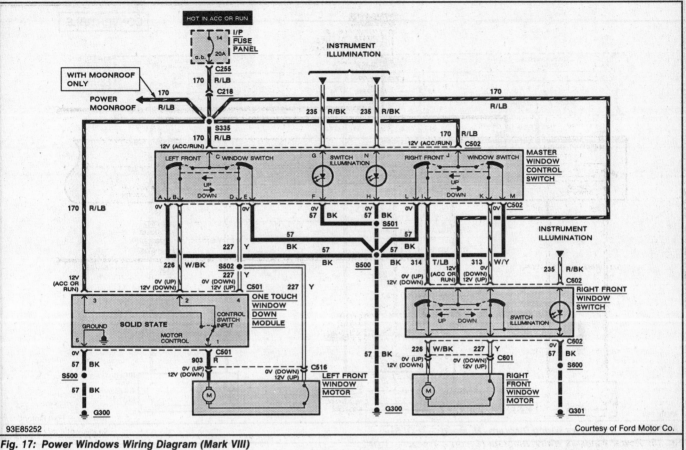

93E85252

Courtesy of Ford Motor Co.

Fig. 17: Power Windows Wiring Diagram (Mark VIII)

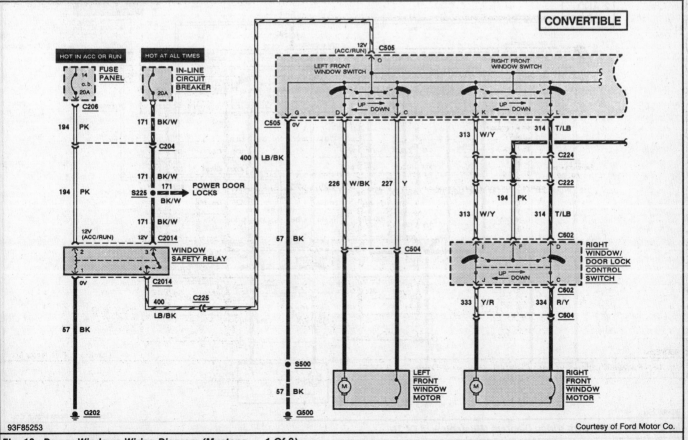

93F85253

Courtesy of Ford Motor Co.

Fig. 18: Power Windows Wiring Diagram (Mustang – 1 Of 3)

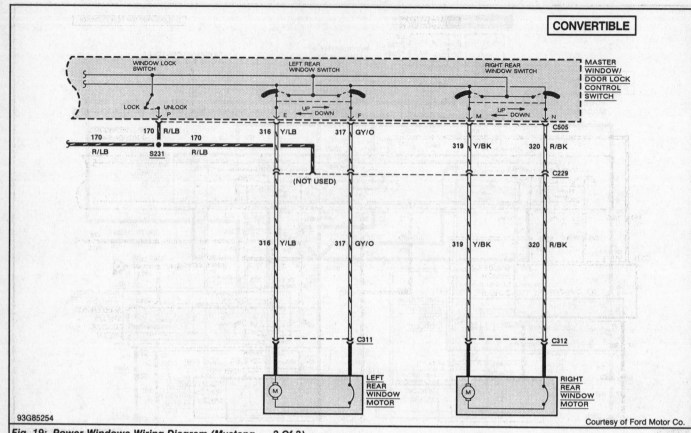

Fig. 19: Power Windows Wiring Diagram (Mustang – 2 Of 3)

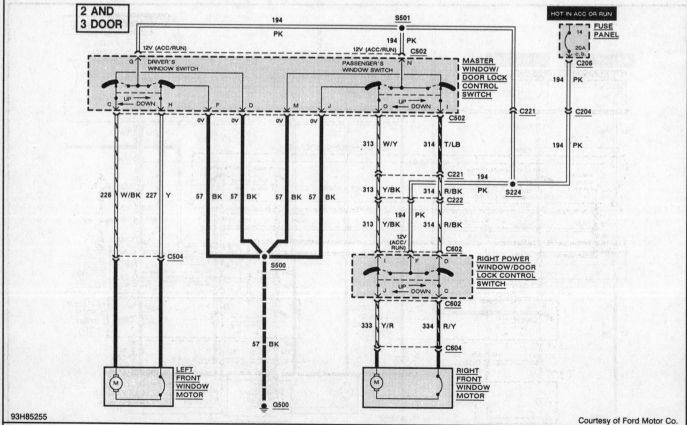

Fig. 20: Power Windows Wiring Diagram (Mustang – 3 Of 3)

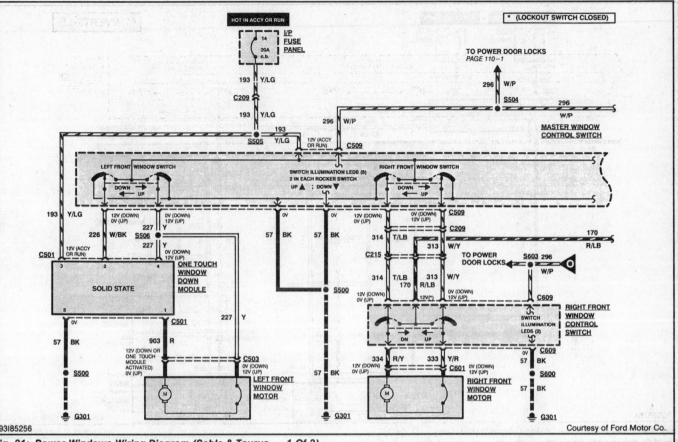

Fig. 21: Power Windows Wiring Diagram (Sable & Taurus – 1 Of 2)

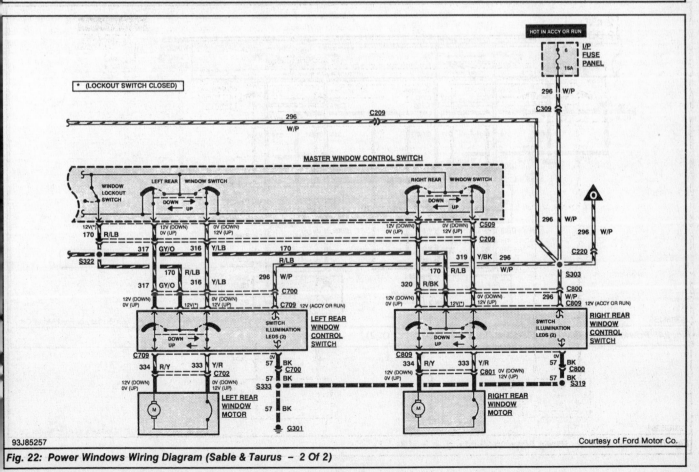

Fig. 22: Power Windows Wiring Diagram (Sable & Taurus – 2 Of 2)

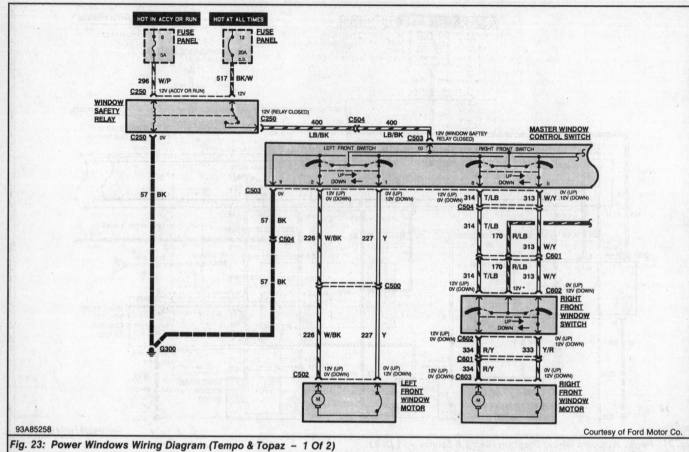

Fig. 23: Power Windows Wiring Diagram (Tempo & Topaz – 1 Of 2)

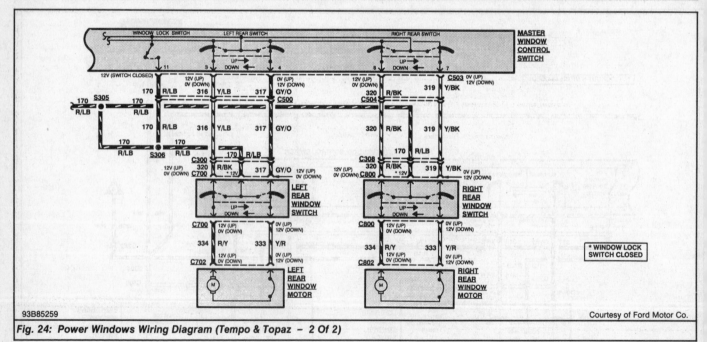

Fig. 24: Power Windows Wiring Diagram (Tempo & Topaz – 2 Of 2)

1993 ACCESSORIES & EQUIPMENT
Power Windows – Except Probe (Cont.)

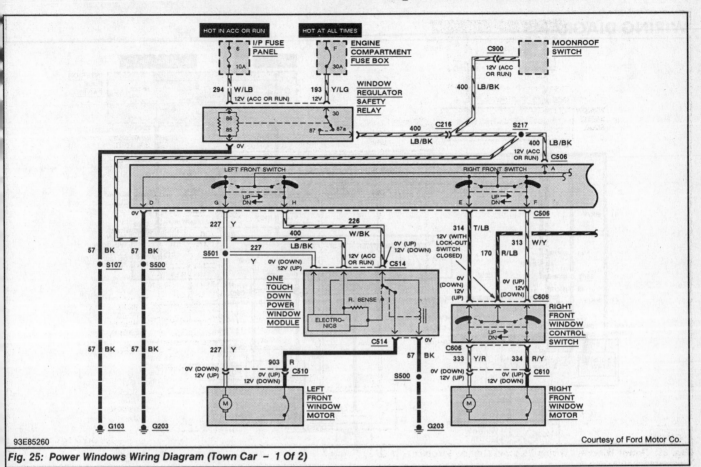

93E85260

Courtesy of Ford Motor Co.

Fig. 25: Power Windows Wiring Diagram (Town Car – 1 Of 2)

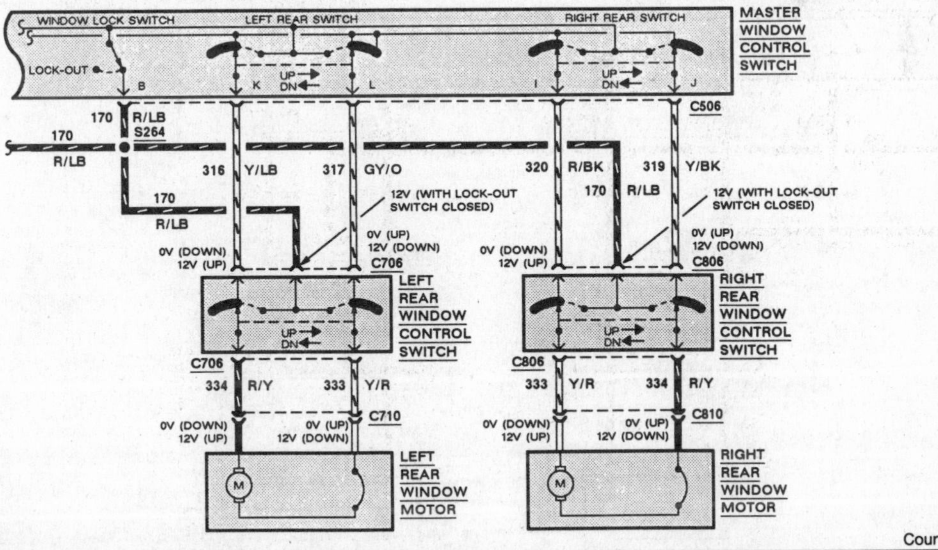

93F85261

Courtesy of Ford Motor Co.

Fig. 26: Power Windows Wiring Diagram (Town Car – 2 Of 2)

WIRING DIAGRAMS

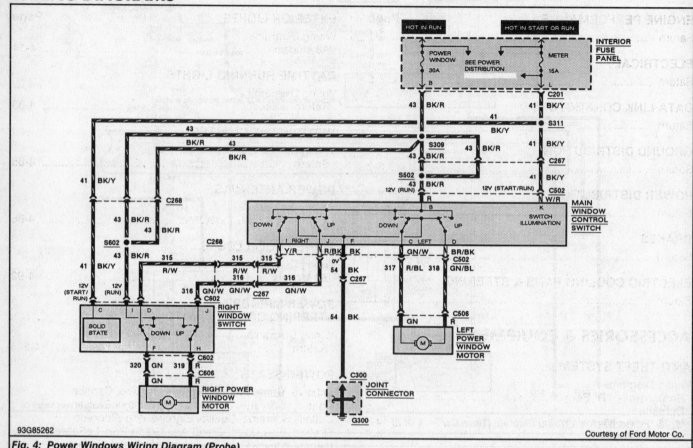

93G85262

Courtesy of Ford Motor Co.

Fig. 4: Power Windows Wiring Diagram (Probe)

ACCESSORIES & EQUIPMENT (Cont.)

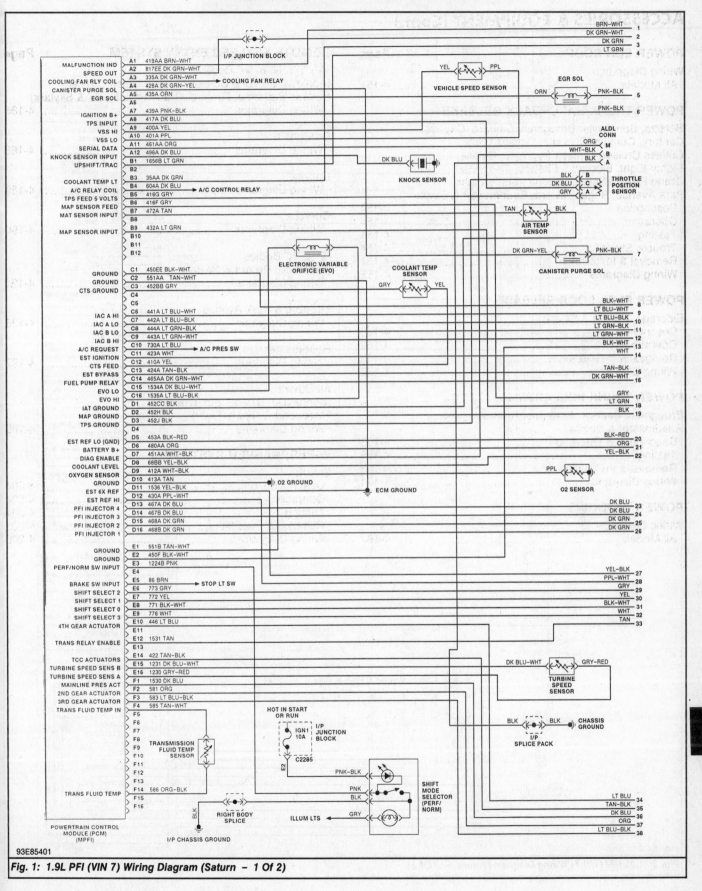

93E85401

Fig. 1: 1.9L PFI (VIN 7) Wiring Diagram (Saturn - 1 Of 2)

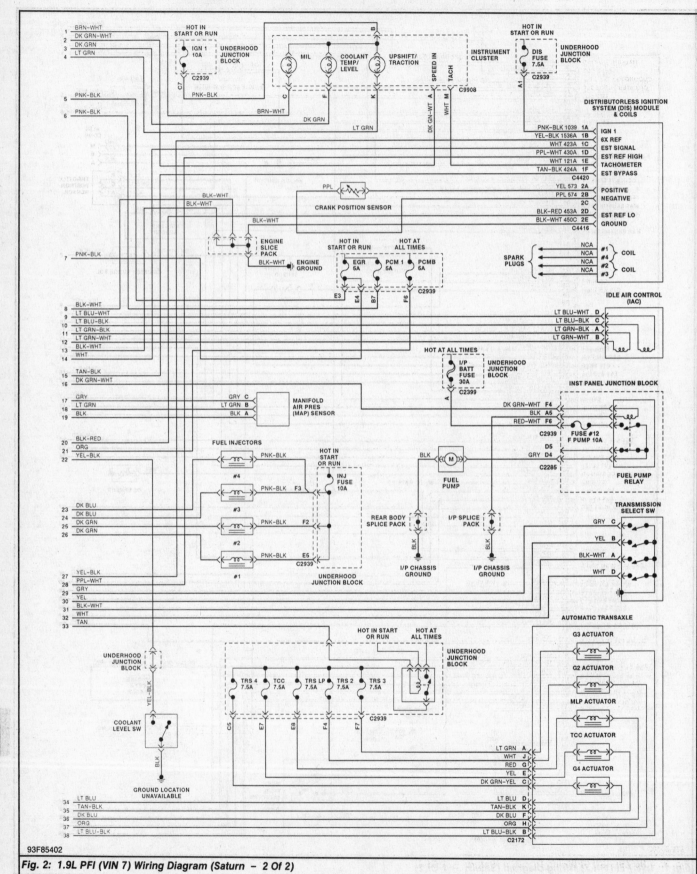

Fig. 2: 1.9L PFI (VIN 7) Wiring Diagram (Saturn - 2 Of 2)

93F85402

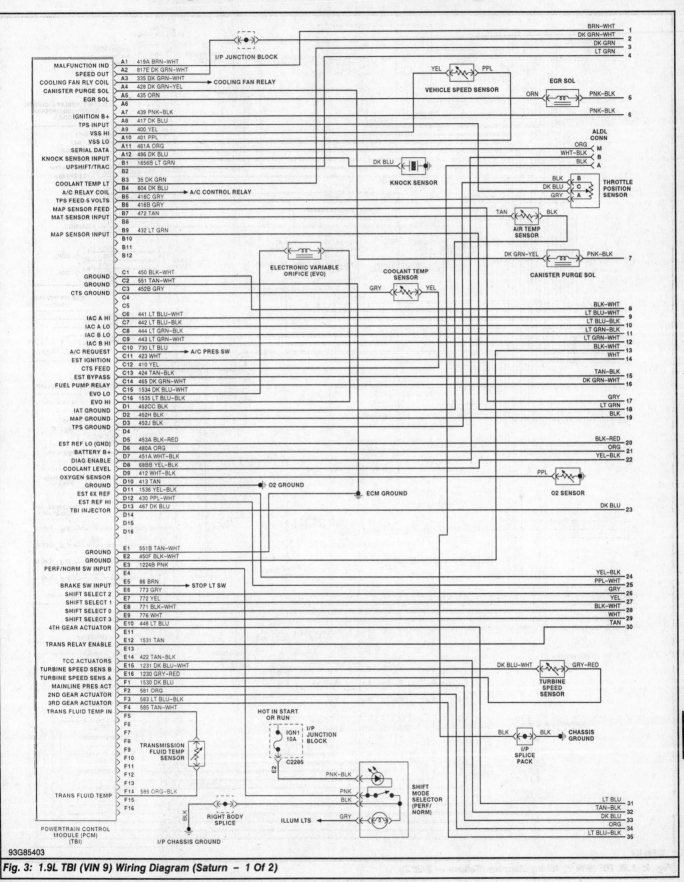

Fig. 3: 1.9L TBI (VIN 9) Wiring Diagram (Saturn - 1 Of 2)

93G85403

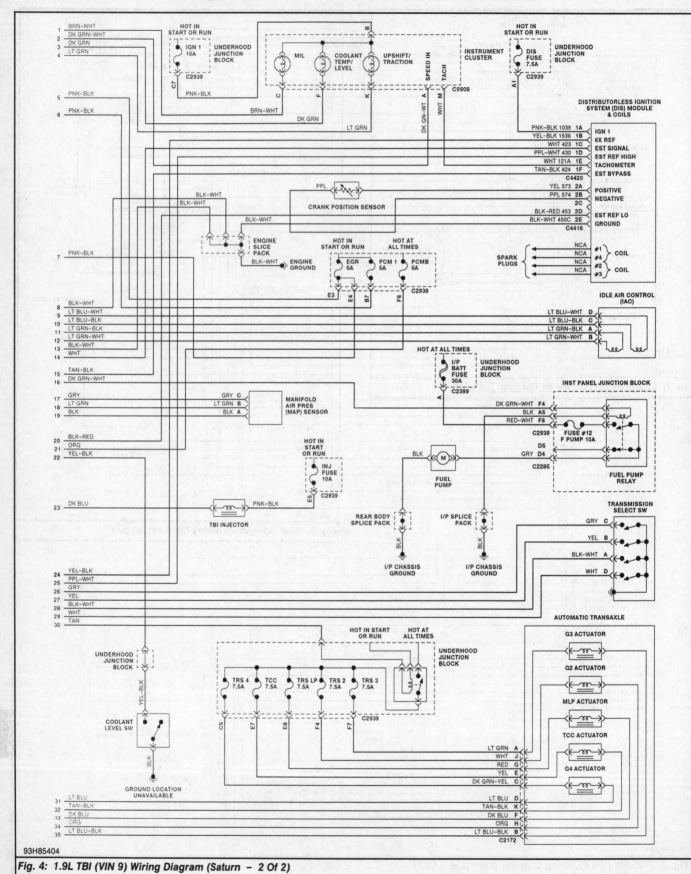

Fig. 4: 1.9L TBI (VIN 9) Wiring Diagram (Saturn - 2 Of 2)

93H85404

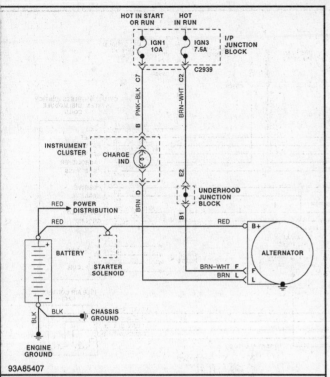

93A85407

Fig. 1: Charging System Wiring Diagram (Saturn)

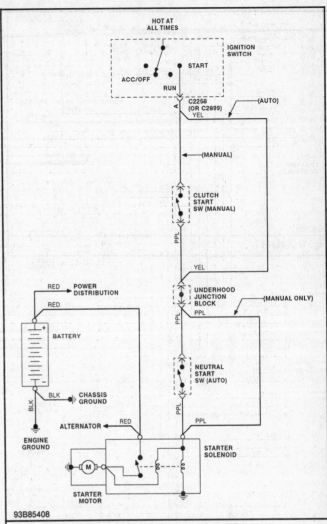

93B85408

Fig. 2: Starting System Wiring Diagram (Saturn)

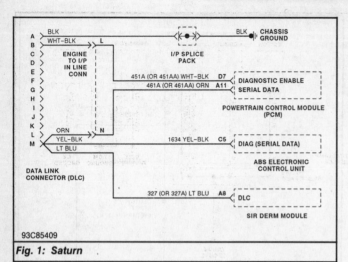

93C85409

Fig. 1: Saturn

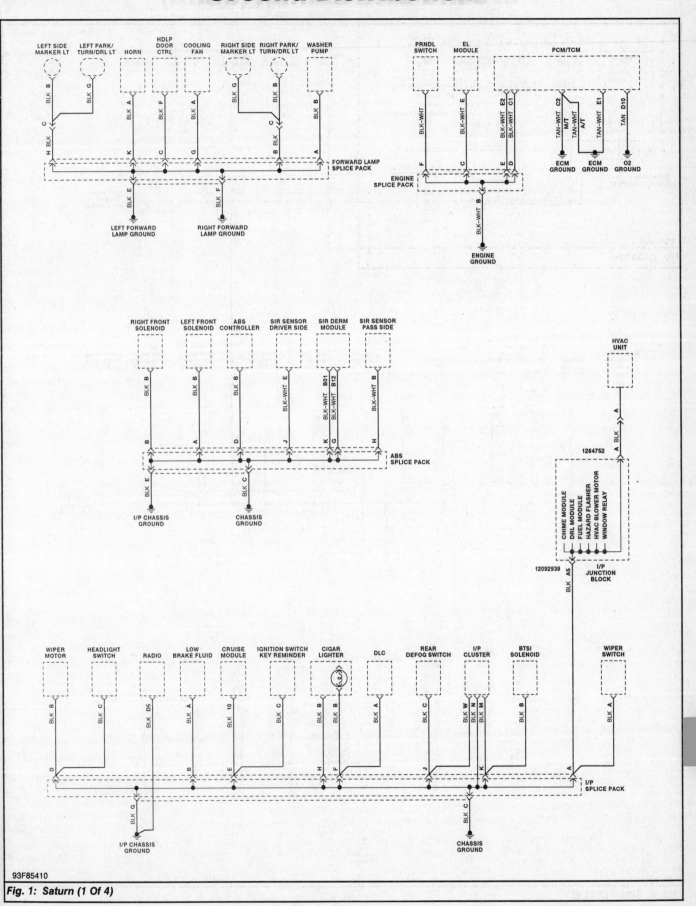

93F85410

Fig. 1: Saturn (1 Of 4)

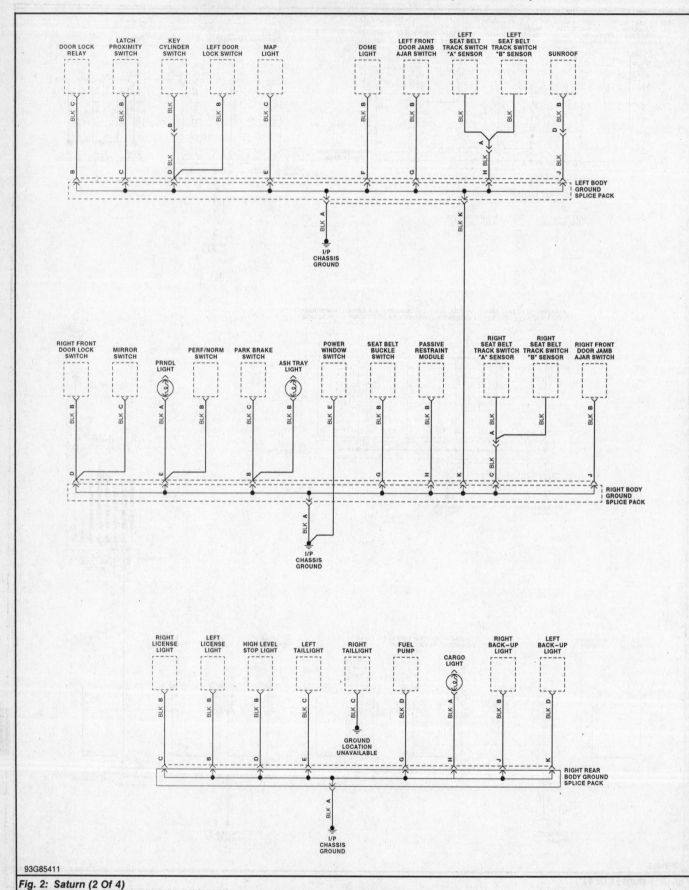

Fig. 2: Saturn (2 Of 4)

93G85411

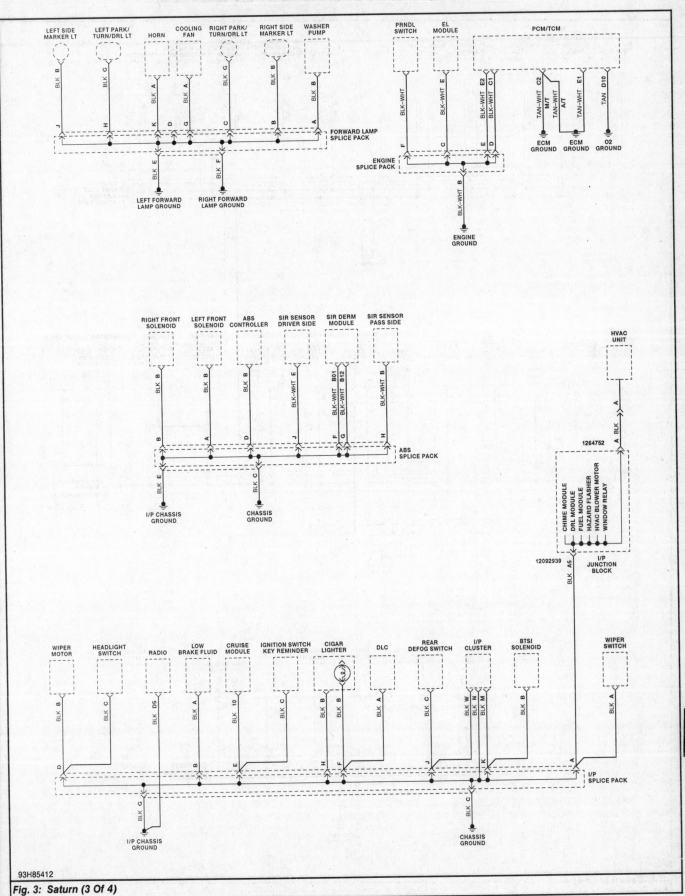

93H85412

Fig. 3: Saturn (3 Of 4)

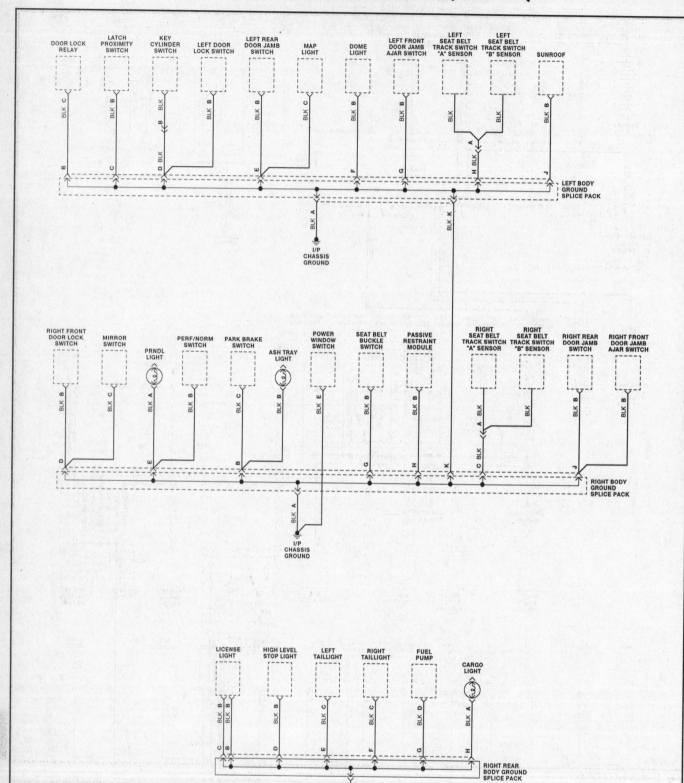

93I85413

Fig. 4: Saturn (4 Of 4)

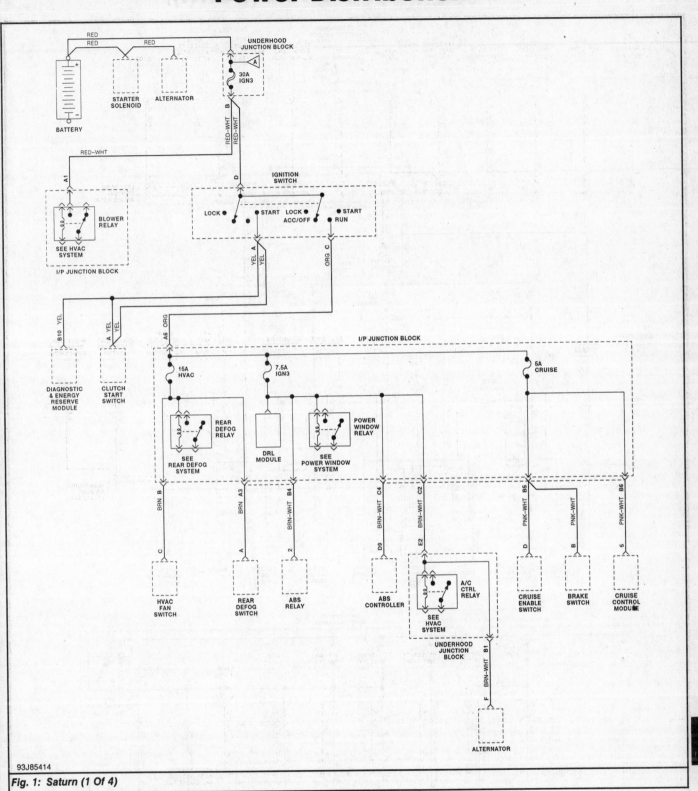

93J85414

Fig. 1: Saturn (1 Of 4)

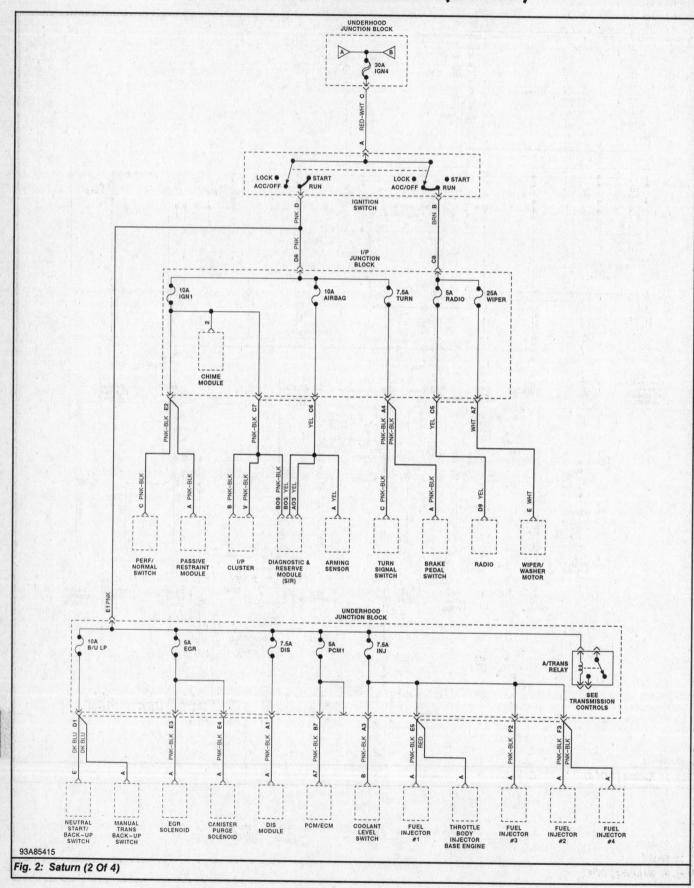

93A85415

Fig. 2: Saturn (2 Of 4)

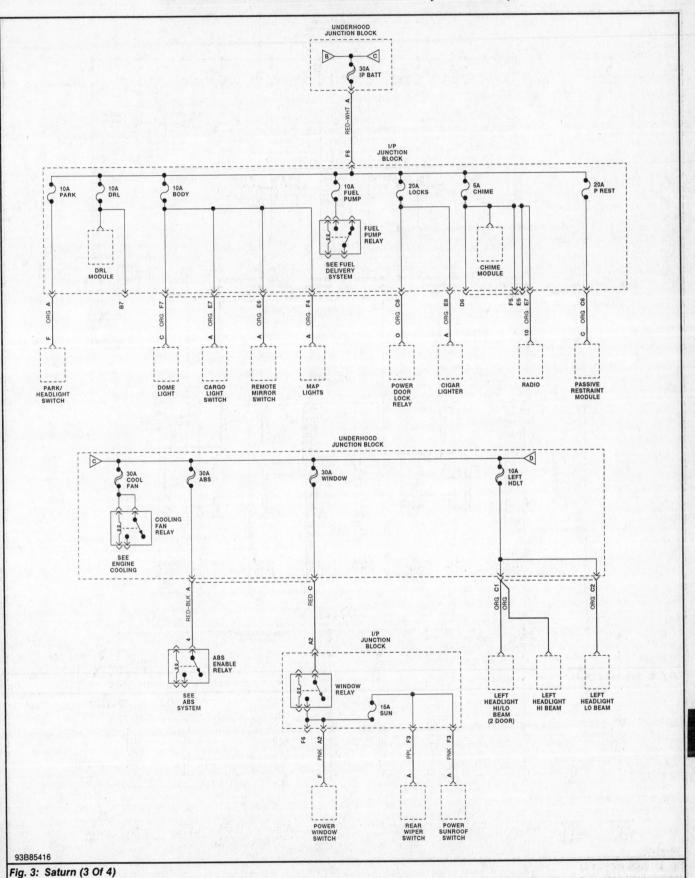

93B85416

Fig. 3: Saturn (3 Of 4)

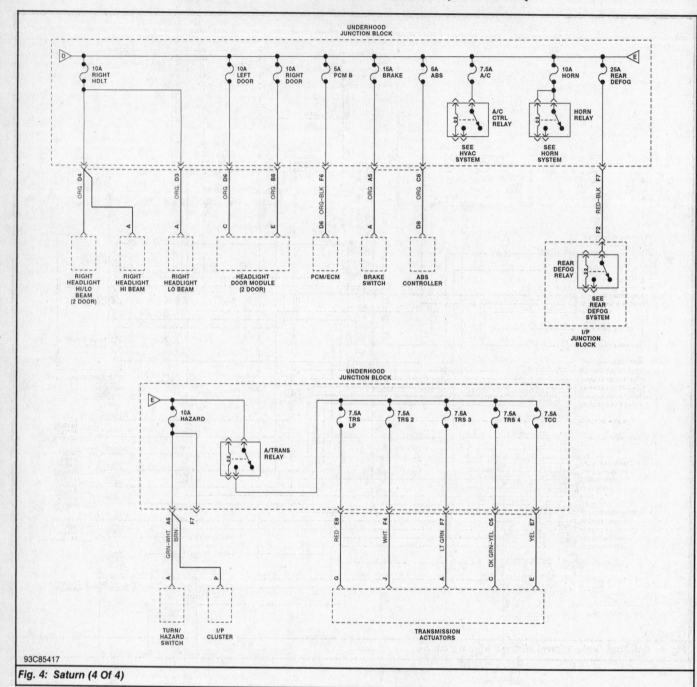

93C85417

Fig. 4: Saturn (4 Of 4)

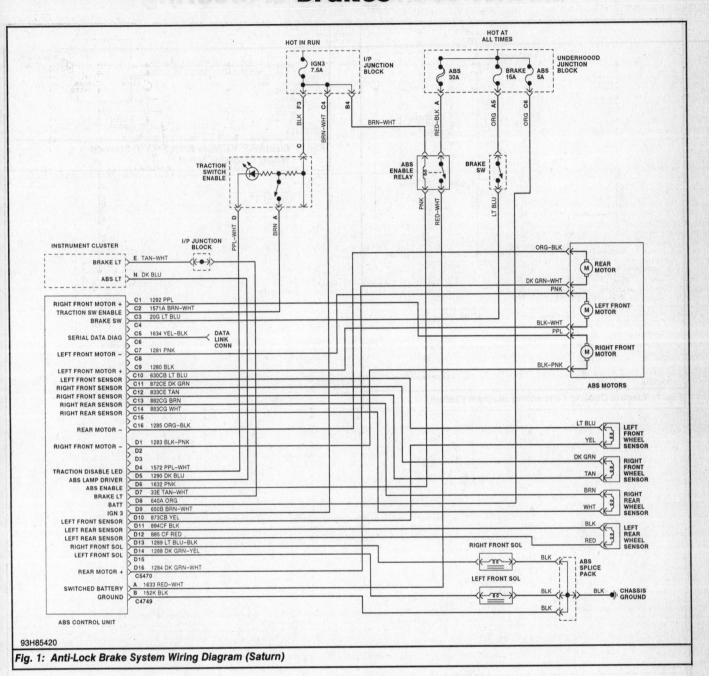

Fig. 1: Anti-Lock Brake System Wiring Diagram (Saturn)

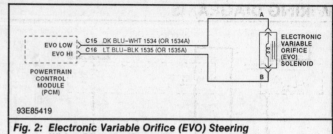

Fig. 2: Electronic Variable Orifice (EVO) Steering Wiring Diagram (Saturn)

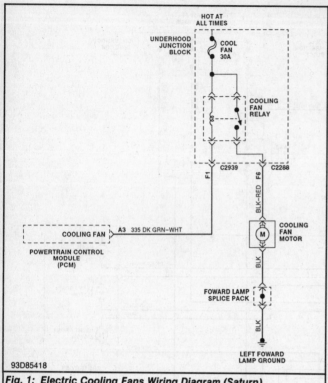

Fig. 1: Electric Cooling Fans Wiring Diagram (Saturn)

WIRING DIAGRAMS

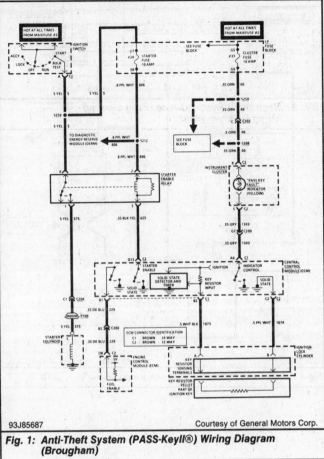

93J85687   Courtesy of General Motors Corp.

Fig. 1: Anti-Theft System (PASS-KeyII®) Wiring Diagram (Brougham)

WIRING DIAGRAMS

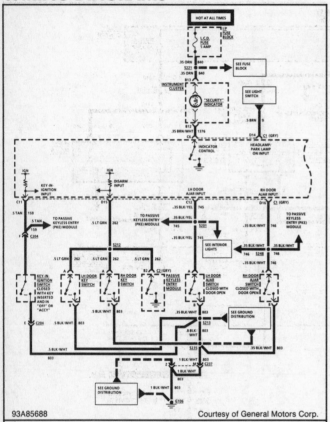

93A85688   Courtesy of General Motors Corp.

Fig.2 : Anti-Theft System Wiring Diagram (Corvette – 1 Of 3)

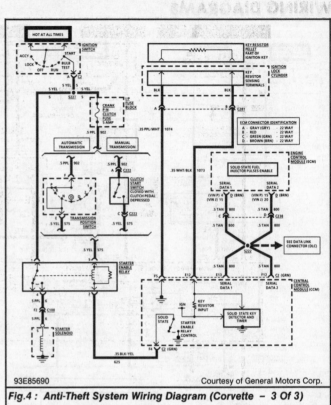

93E85690   Courtesy of General Motors Corp.

Fig.4 : Anti-Theft System Wiring Diagram (Corvette – 3 Of 3)

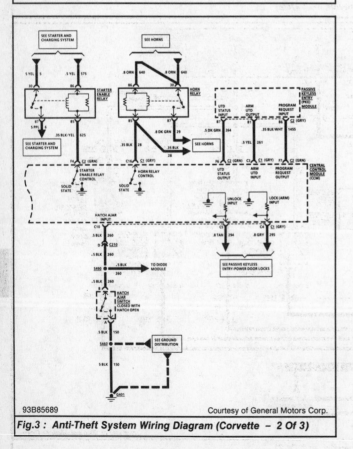

93B85689   Courtesy of General Motors Corp.

Fig.3 : Anti-Theft System Wiring Diagram (Corvette – 2 Of 3)

GM
4-3

1993 ACCESSORIES & EQUIPMENT
Anti-Theft System — "C" & "H" Bodies (Cont.)

WIRING DIAGRAMS

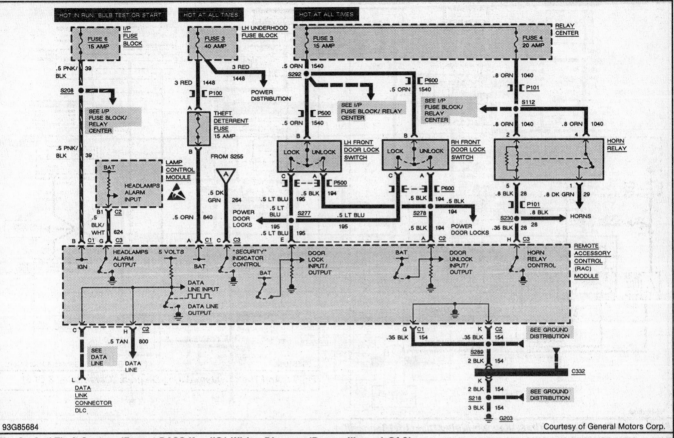

Fig. 3: **Anti-Theft System (Except PASS-Key II®) Wiring Diagram (Bonneville – 1 Of 2)**

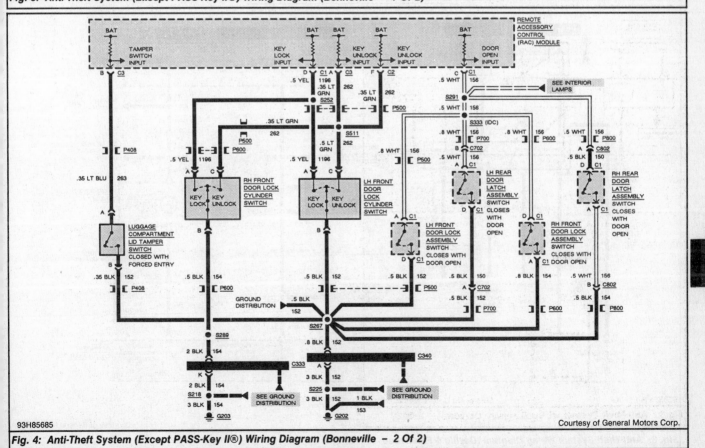

Fig. 4: **Anti-Theft System (Except PASS-Key II®) Wiring Diagram (Bonneville – 2 Of 2)**

Courtesy of General Motors Corp.

93G85684

93H85685

GM
4-4

1993 ACCESSORIES & EQUIPMENT
Anti-Theft System – "C" & "H" Bodies (Cont.)

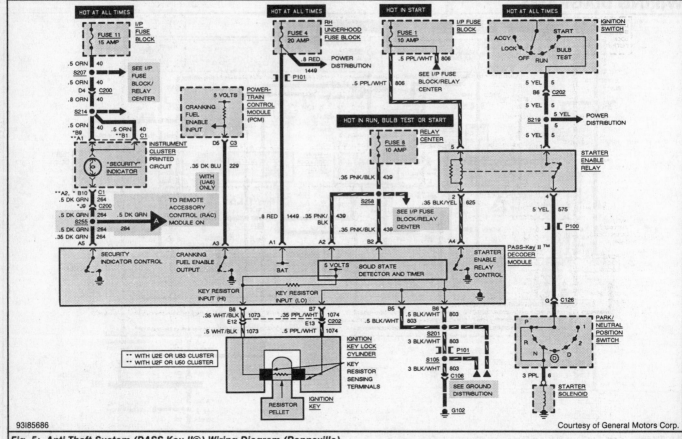

Fig. 5: Anti-Theft System (PASS-Key II®) Wiring Diagram (Bonneville)

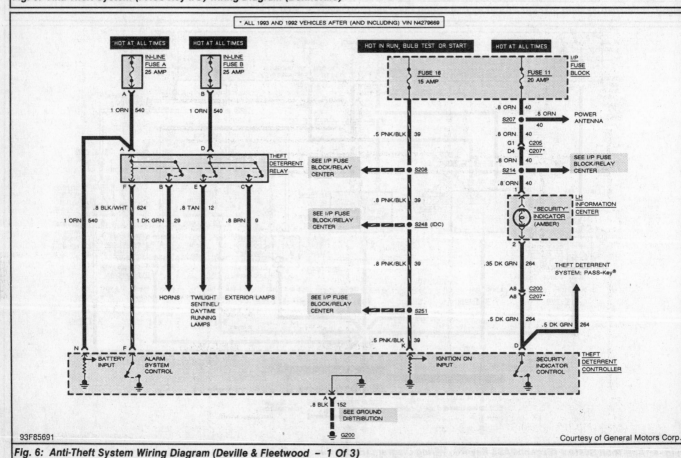

Fig. 6: Anti-Theft System Wiring Diagram (Deville & Fleetwood – 1 Of 3)

1993 ACCESSORIES & EQUIPMENT
Anti-Theft System – "C" & "H" Bodies (Cont.)

GM
4-5

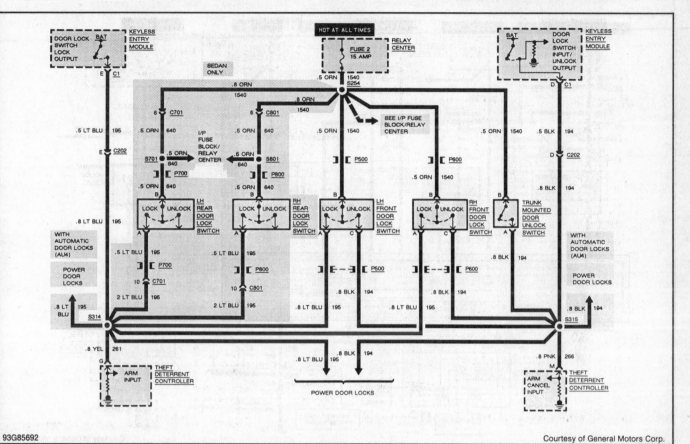

93G85692

Courtesy of General Motors Corp.

Fig. 7: Anti-Theft System Wiring Diagram (Deville & Fleetwood – 2 Of 3)

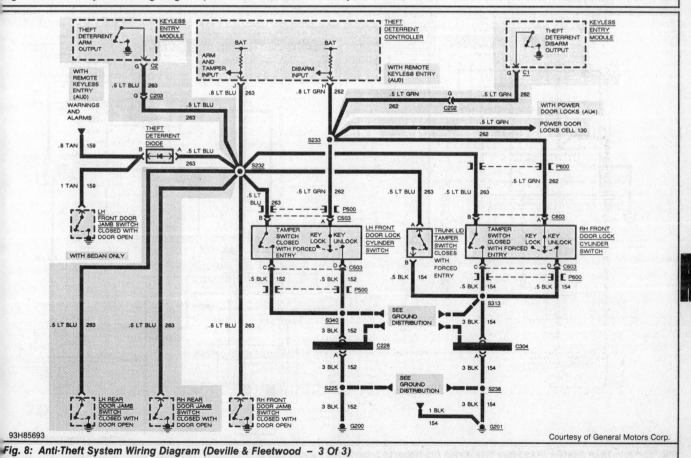

93H85693

Courtesy of General Motors Corp.

Fig. 8: Anti-Theft System Wiring Diagram (Deville & Fleetwood – 3 Of 3)

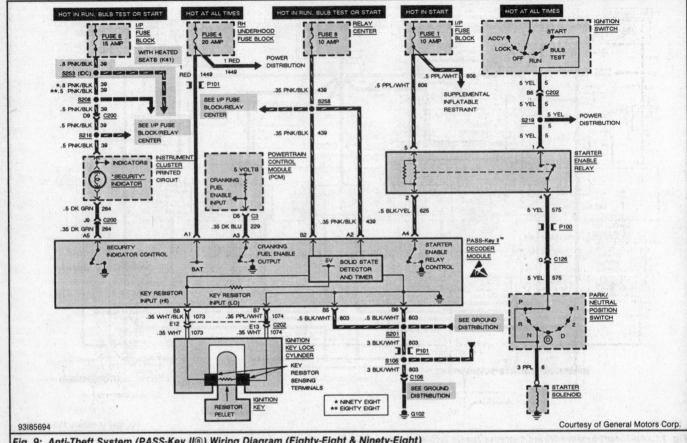

Fig. 9: Anti-Theft System (PASS-Key II®) Wiring Diagram (Eighty-Eight & Ninety-Eight)

93I85694

Courtesy of General Motors Corp.

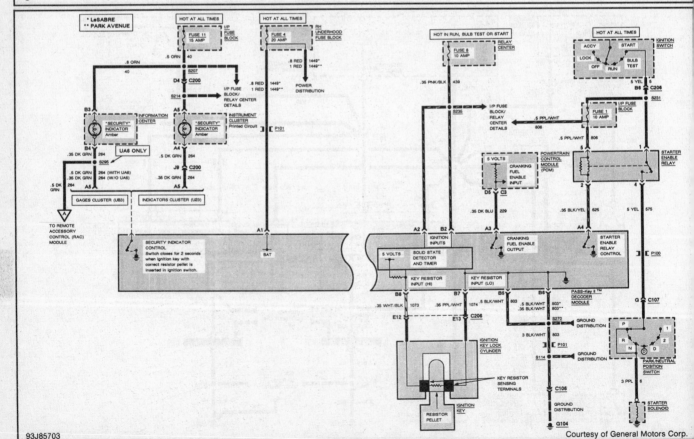

Fig. 10: Anti-Theft System (PASS-Key II®) Wiring Diagram (LeSabre & Park Avenue)

93J85703

Courtesy of General Motors Corp.

1993 ACCESSORIES & EQUIPMENT
Anti-Theft System – "C" & "H" Bodies (Cont.)

GM
4-7

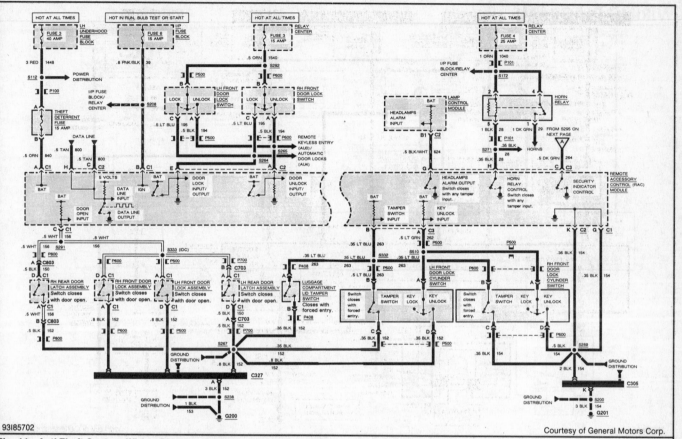

93I85702

Courtesy of General Motors Corp.

Fig. 11: Anti-Theft System Wiring Diagram (LeSabre & Park Avenue)

GM
4-8

1993 ACCESSORIES & EQUIPMENT
Anti-Theft System — "E" & "K" Bodies (Cont.)

WIRING DIAGRAMS

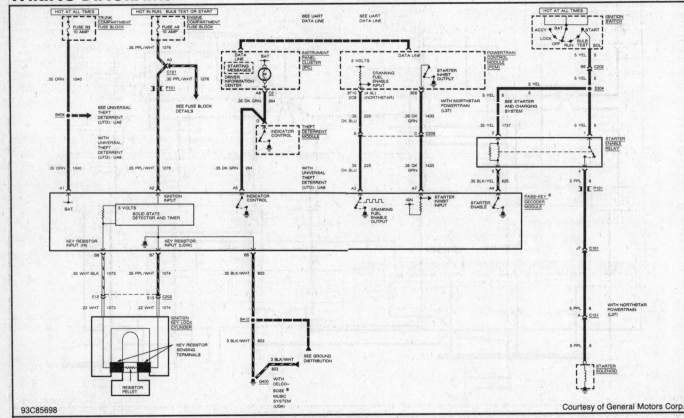

Fig. 3: Anti-Theft System (PASS-Key) Wiring Diagram (Eldorado & Seville)

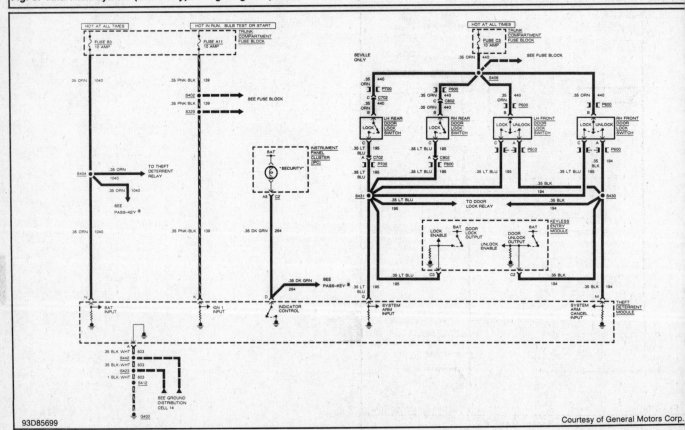

Fig. 4: Anti-Theft System (Except PASS-Key) Wiring Diagram (Eldorado & Seville — 1 Of 3)

1993 ACCESSORIES & EQUIPMENT
Anti-Theft System — "E" & "K" Bodies (Cont.)

GM
4-9

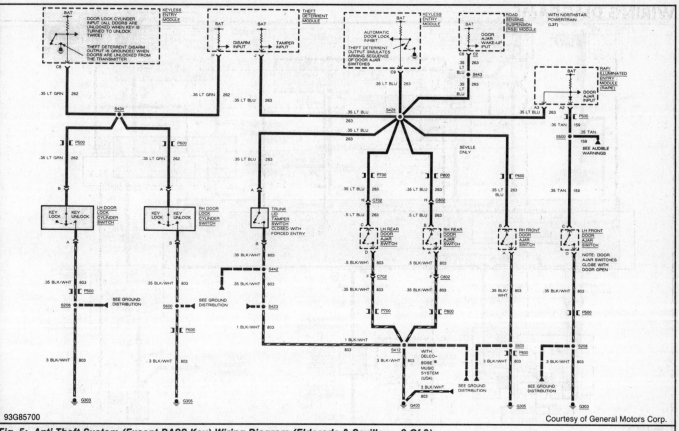

Fig. 5: Anti-Theft System (Except PASS-Key) Wiring Diagram (Eldorado & Seville — 2 Of 3)

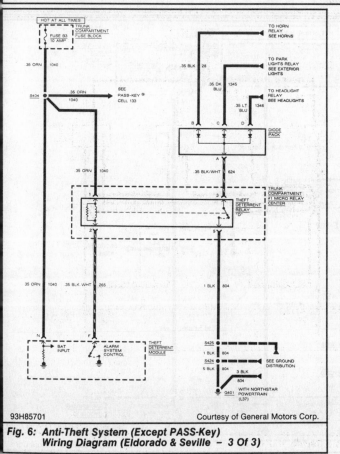

Fig. 6: Anti-Theft System (Except PASS-Key)
Wiring Diagram (Eldorado & Seville — 3 Of 3)

93G85700   Courtesy of General Motors Corp.

93H85701   Courtesy of General Motors Corp.

GM
4-10

1993 ACCESSORIES & EQUIPMENT
Anti-Theft System – "E" & "K" Bodies (Cont.)

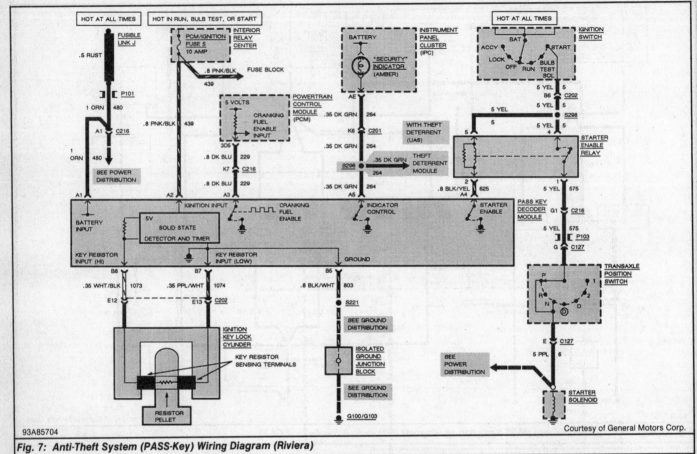

Fig. 7: Anti-Theft System (PASS-Key) Wiring Diagram (Riviera)

93A85704

Courtesy of General Motors Corp.

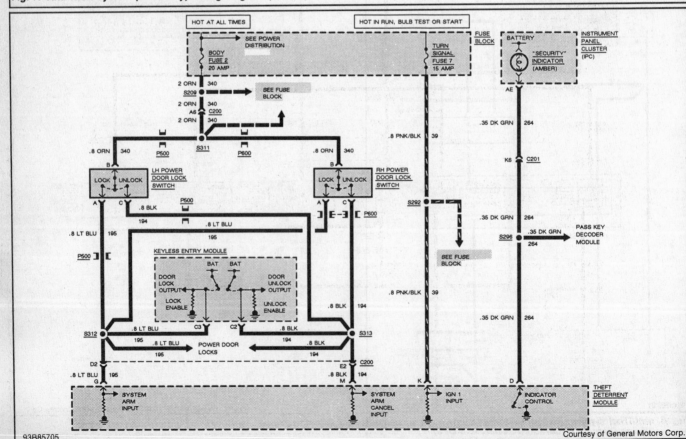

Fig. 8: Anti-Theft System (Except PASS-Key) Wiring Diagram (Riviera – 1 Of 2)

93B85705

Courtesy of General Motors Corp.

1993 ACCESSORIES & EQUIPMENT
Anti-Theft System – "E" & "K" Bodies (Cont.)

GM
4-11

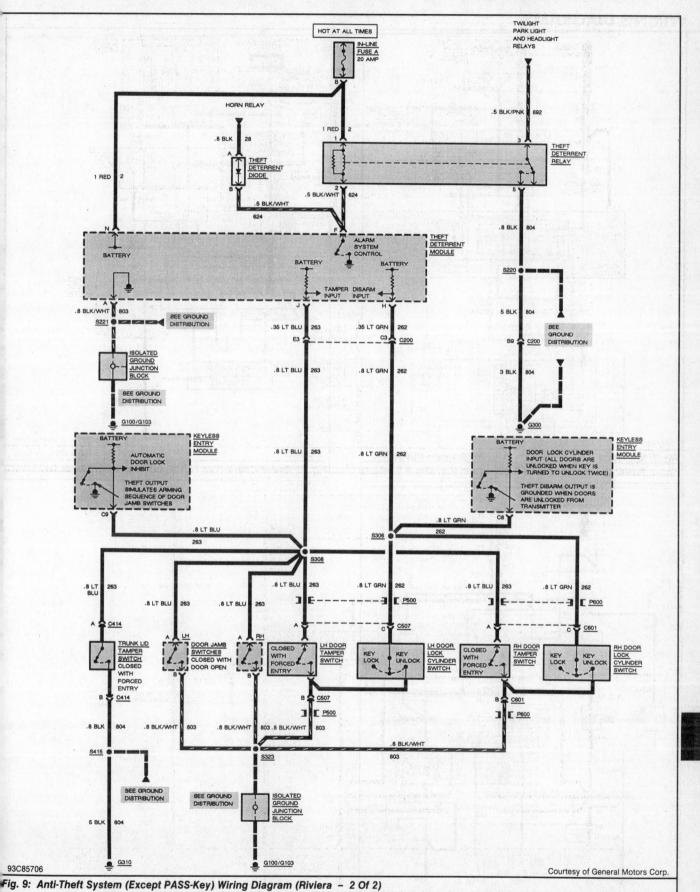

93C85706

Courtesy of General Motors Corp.

Fig. 9: *Anti-Theft System (Except PASS-Key) Wiring Diagram (Riviera – 2 Of 2)*

WIRING DIAGRAMS

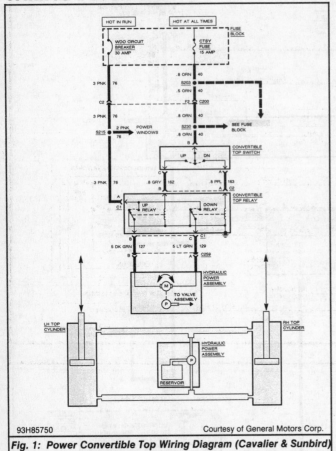

93H85750   Courtesy of General Motors Corp.

Fig. 1: Power Convertible Top Wiring Diagram (Cavalier & Sunbird)

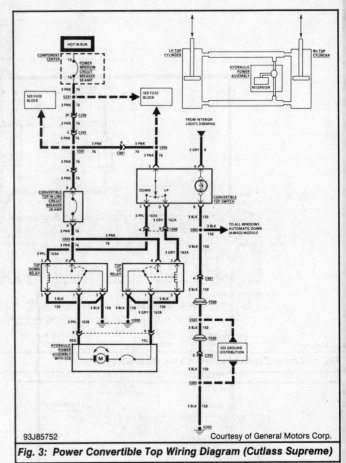

93J85752   Courtesy of General Motors Corp.

Fig. 3: Power Convertible Top Wiring Diagram (Cutlass Supreme)

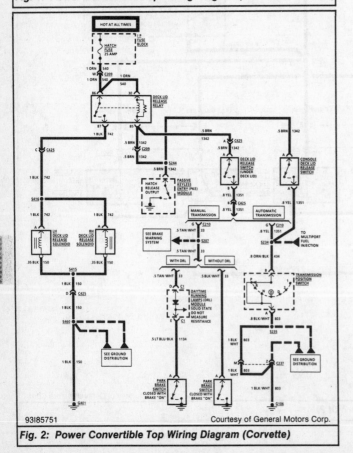

93I85751   Courtesy of General Motors Corp.

Fig. 2: Power Convertible Top Wiring Diagram (Corvette)

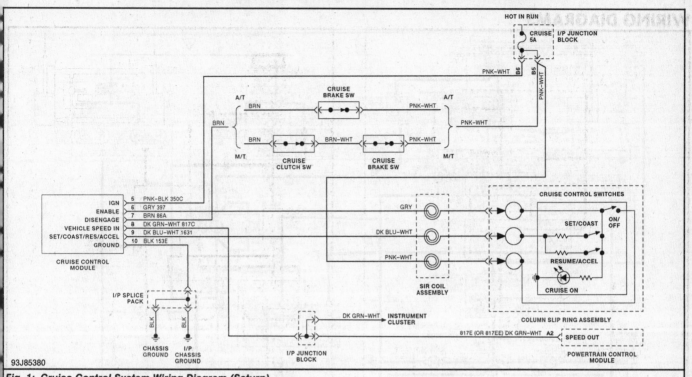

Fig. 1: Cruise Control System Wiring Diagram (Saturn)

93J85380

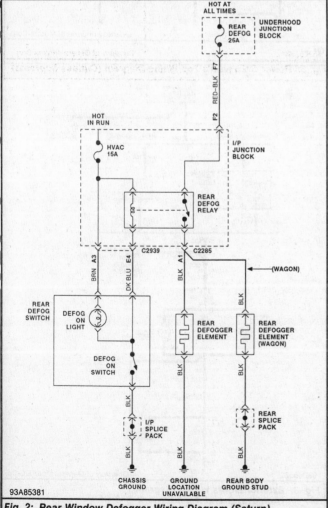

Fig. 2: Rear Window Defogger Wiring Diagram (Saturn)

93A85381

WIRING DIAGRAMS

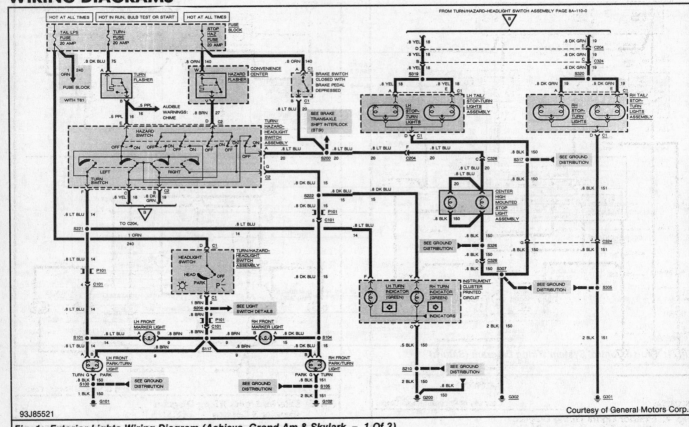

93J85521

Courtesy of General Motors Corp.

Fig. 1: Exterior Lights Wiring Diagram (Achieva, Grand Am & Skylark − 1 Of 3)

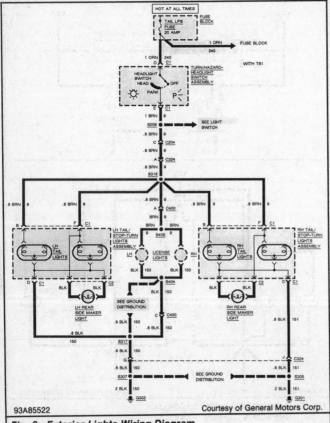

93A85522

Courtesy of General Motors Corp.

Fig. 2: Exterior Lights Wiring Diagram (Achieva, Grand Am & Skylark − 2 Of 3)

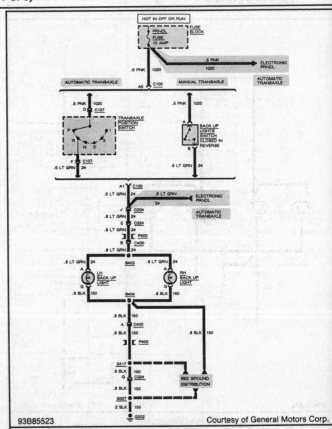

93B85523

Courtesy of General Motors Corp.

Fig. 3: Exterior Lights Wiring Diagram (Achieva, Grand Am & Skylark − 3 Of 3)

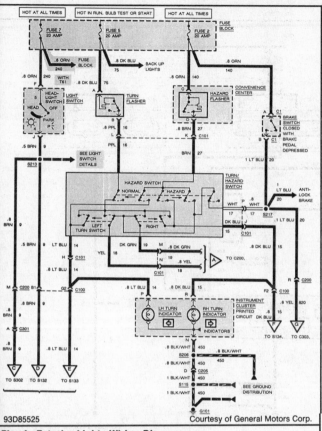

93D85525

Fig. 4: Exterior Lights Wiring Diagram
(Beretta & Corsica – 1 Of 5)

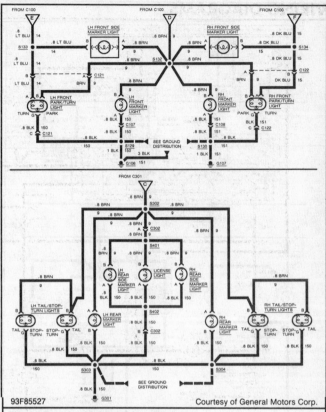

93F85527

Fig. 6: Exterior Lights Wiring Diagram
(Beretta & Corsica – 3 Of 5)

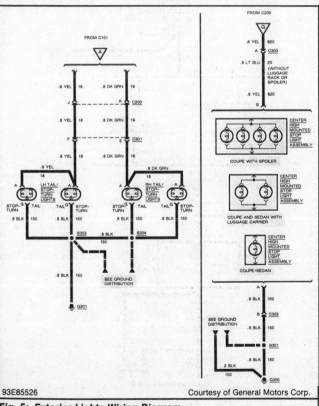

93E85526

Fig. 5: Exterior Lights Wiring Diagram
(Beretta & Corsica – 2 Of 5)

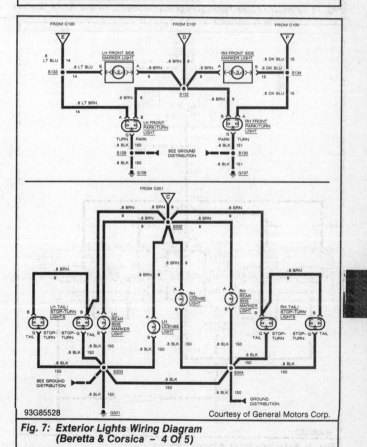

93G85528

Fig. 7: Exterior Lights Wiring Diagram
(Beretta & Corsica – 4 Of 5)

Courtesy of General Motors Corp.

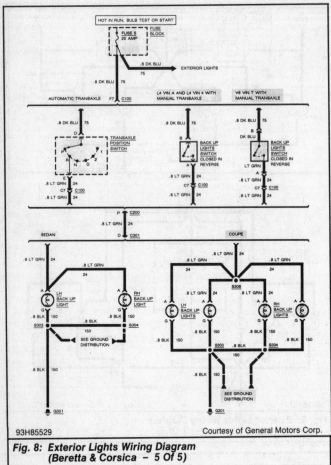

Fig. 8: Exterior Lights Wiring Diagram (Beretta & Corsica – 5 Of 5)

93H85529   Courtesy of General Motors Corp.

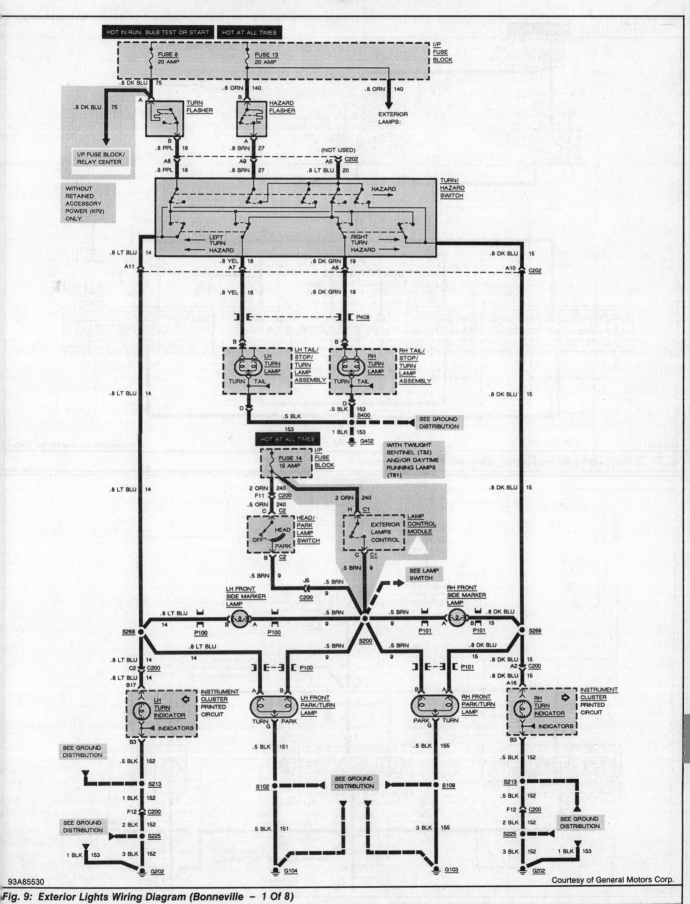

Fig. 9: Exterior Lights Wiring Diagram (Bonneville – 1 Of 8)

93A85530

Courtesy of General Motors Corp.

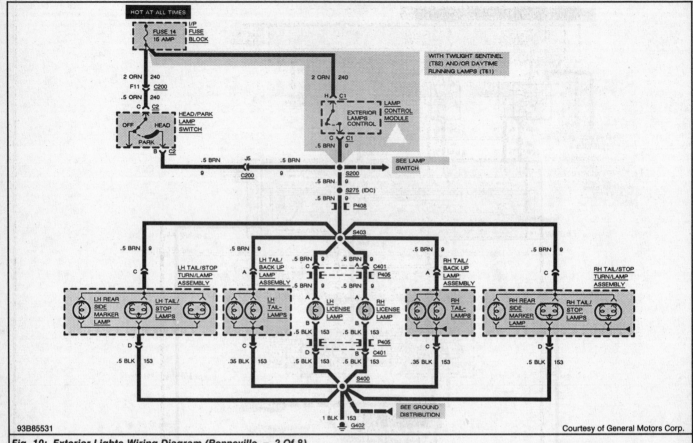

93B85531

Courtesy of General Motors Corp.

Fig. 10: Exterior Lights Wiring Diagram (Bonneville – 2 Of 8)

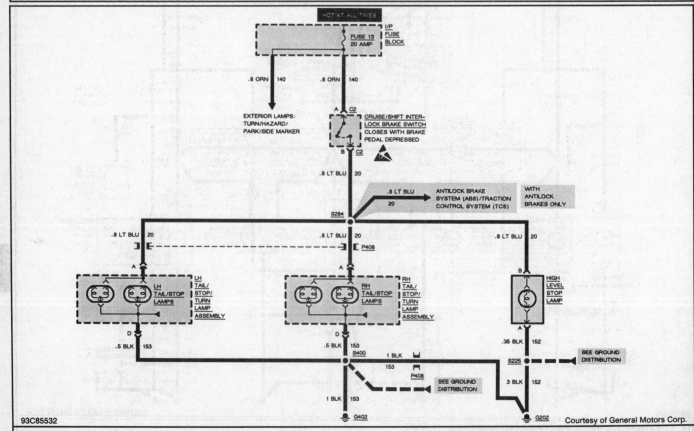

93C85532

Courtesy of General Motors Corp.

Fig. 11: Exterior Lights Wiring Diagram (Bonneville – 3 Of 8)

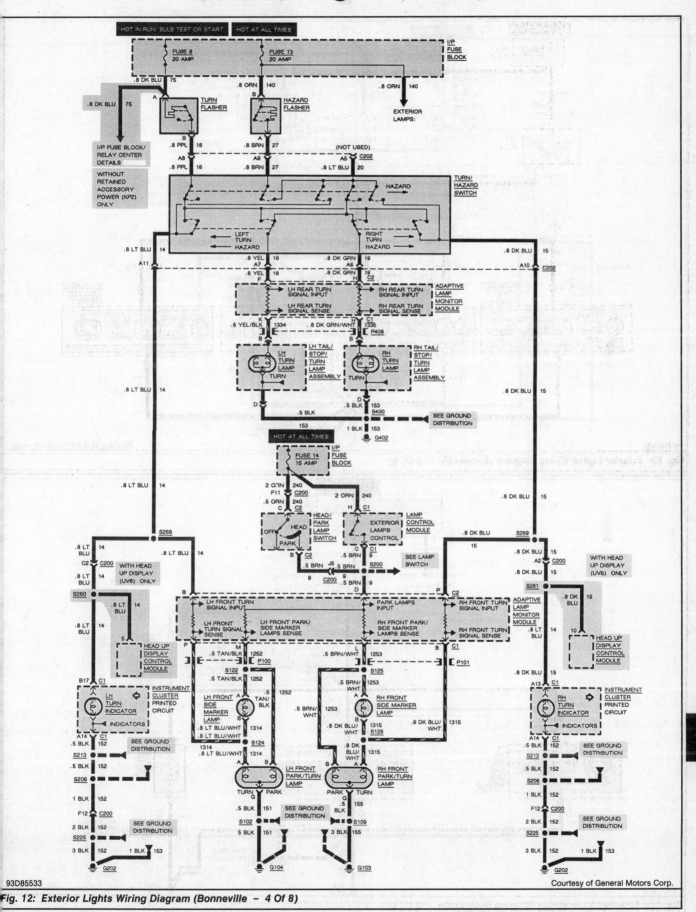

Fig. 12: Exterior Lights Wiring Diagram (Bonneville - 4 Of 8)

93D85533

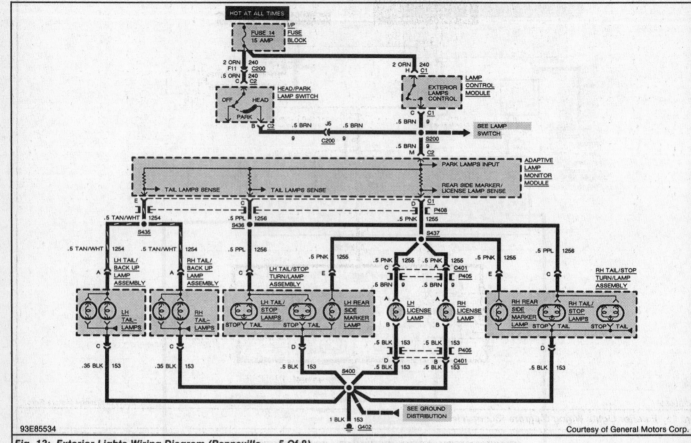

93E85534

Courtesy of General Motors Corp.

Fig. 13: Exterior Lights Wiring Diagram (Bonneville – 5 Of 8)

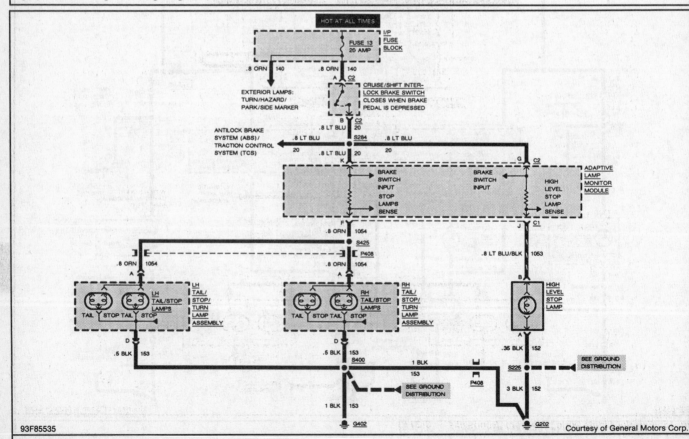

93F85535

Courtesy of General Motors Corp.

Fig. 14: Exterior Lights Wiring Diagram (Bonneville – 6 Of 8)

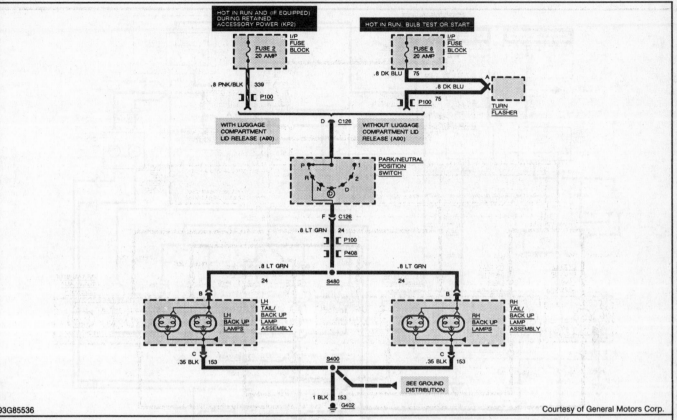

93G85536

Courtesy of General Motors Corp.

Fig. 15: *Exterior Lights Wiring Diagram (Bonneville – 7 Of 8)*

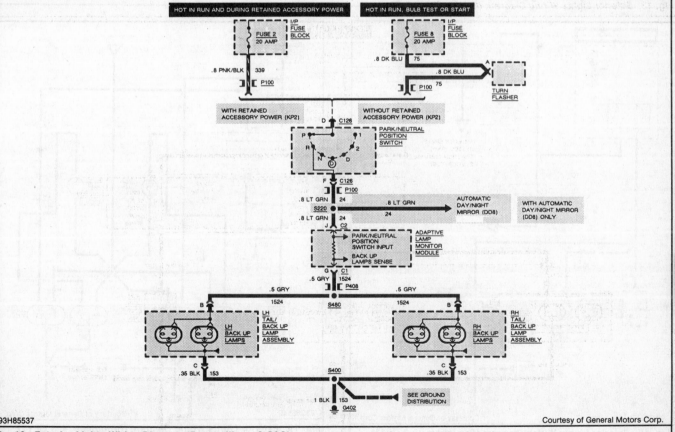

93H85537

Courtesy of General Motors Corp.

Fig. 16: *Exterior Lights Wiring Diagram (Bonneville – 8 Of 8)*

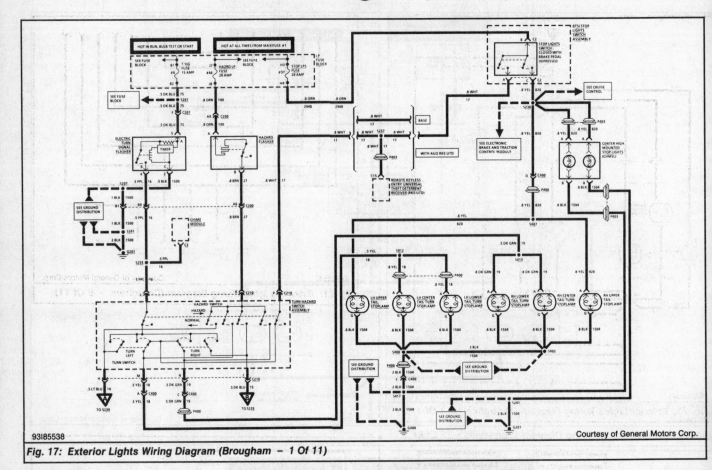

93I85538

Fig. 17: Exterior Lights Wiring Diagram (Brougham – 1 Of 11)

Courtesy of General Motors Corp.

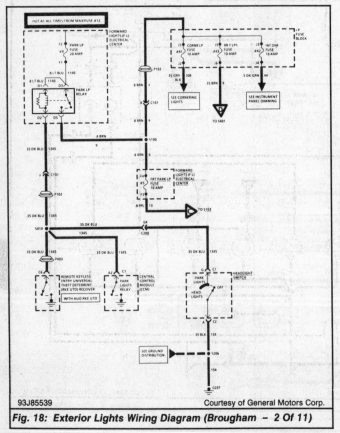

93J85539

Fig. 18: Exterior Lights Wiring Diagram (Brougham – 2 Of 11)

Courtesy of General Motors Corp.

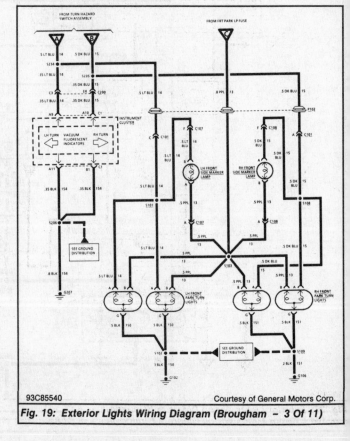

93C85540

Fig. 19: Exterior Lights Wiring Diagram (Brougham – 3 Of 11)

Courtesy of General Motors Corp.

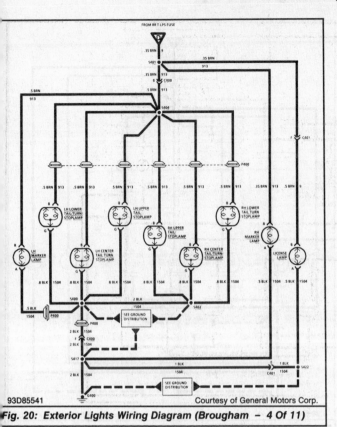

93D85541   Courtesy of General Motors Corp.

Fig. 20: Exterior Lights Wiring Diagram (Brougham – 4 Of 11)

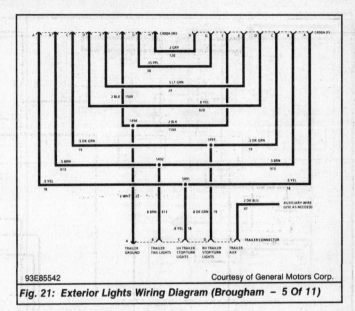

93E85542   Courtesy of General Motors Corp.

Fig. 21: Exterior Lights Wiring Diagram (Brougham – 5 Of 11)

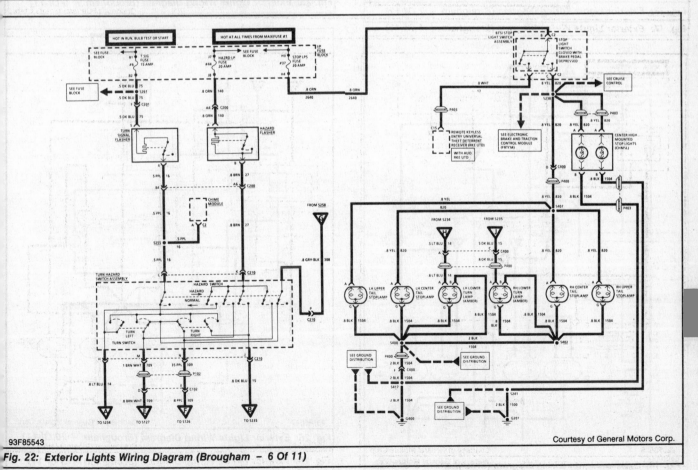

93F85543   Courtesy of General Motors Corp.

Fig. 22: Exterior Lights Wiring Diagram (Brougham – 6 Of 11)

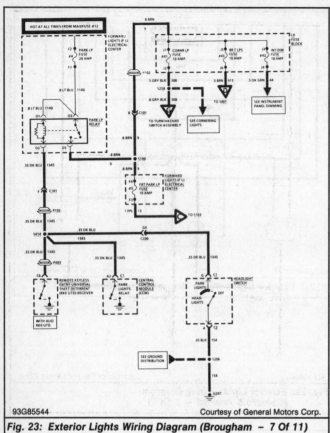

93G85544　　　Courtesy of General Motors Corp.

Fig. 23: Exterior Lights Wiring Diagram (Brougham – 7 Of 11)

93I85546　　　Courtesy of General Motors Corp.

Fig. 25: Exterior Lights Wiring Diagram (Brougham – 9 Of 11)

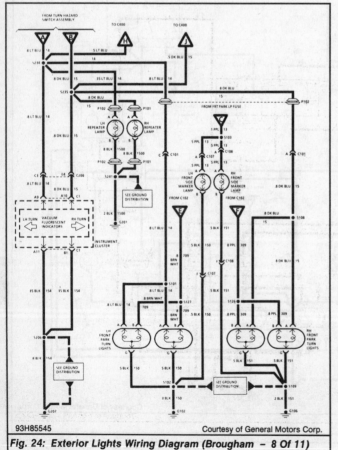

93H85545　　　Courtesy of General Motors Corp.

Fig. 24: Exterior Lights Wiring Diagram (Brougham – 8 Of 11)

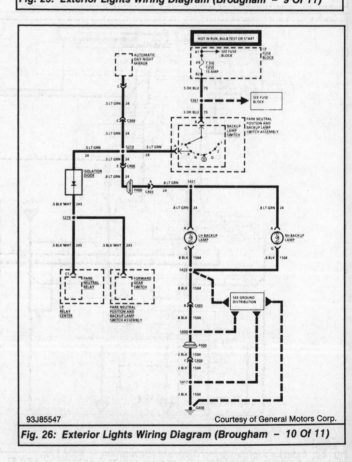

93J85547　　　Courtesy of General Motors Corp.

Fig. 26: Exterior Lights Wiring Diagram (Brougham – 10 Of 11)

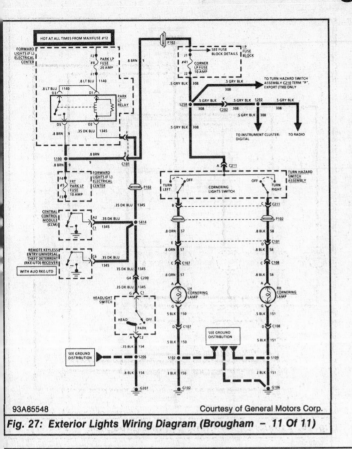

93A85548

Fig. 27: Exterior Lights Wiring Diagram (Brougham – 11 Of 11)

Courtesy of General Motors Corp.

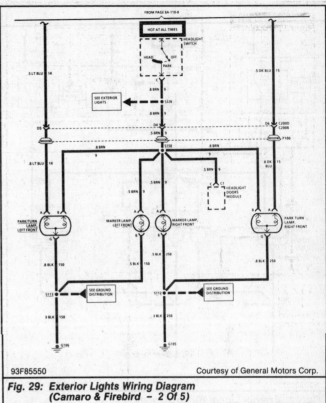

93F85550

Courtesy of General Motors Corp.

**Fig. 29: Exterior Lights Wiring Diagram
(Camaro & Firebird – 2 Of 5)**

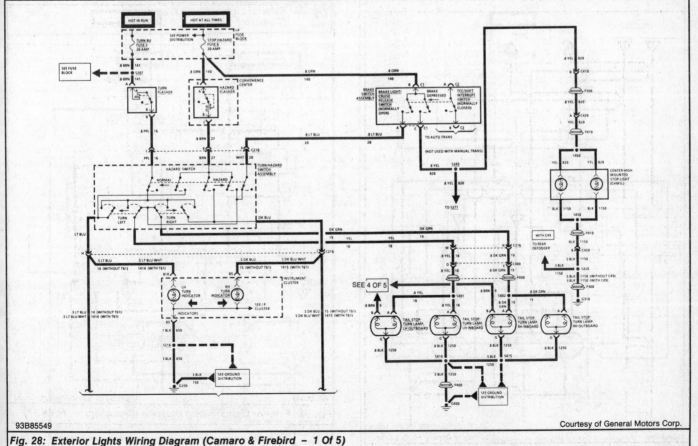

93B85549

Courtesy of General Motors Corp.

Fig. 28: Exterior Lights Wiring Diagram (Camaro & Firebird – 1 Of 5)

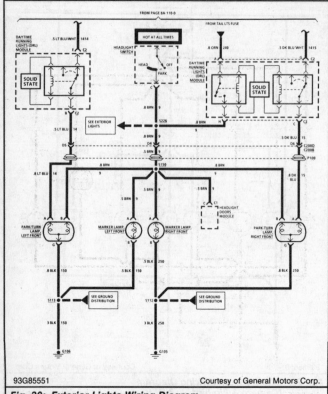

93G85551   Courtesy of General Motors Corp.

Fig. 30: Exterior Lights Wiring Diagram (Camaro & Firebird – 3 Of 5)

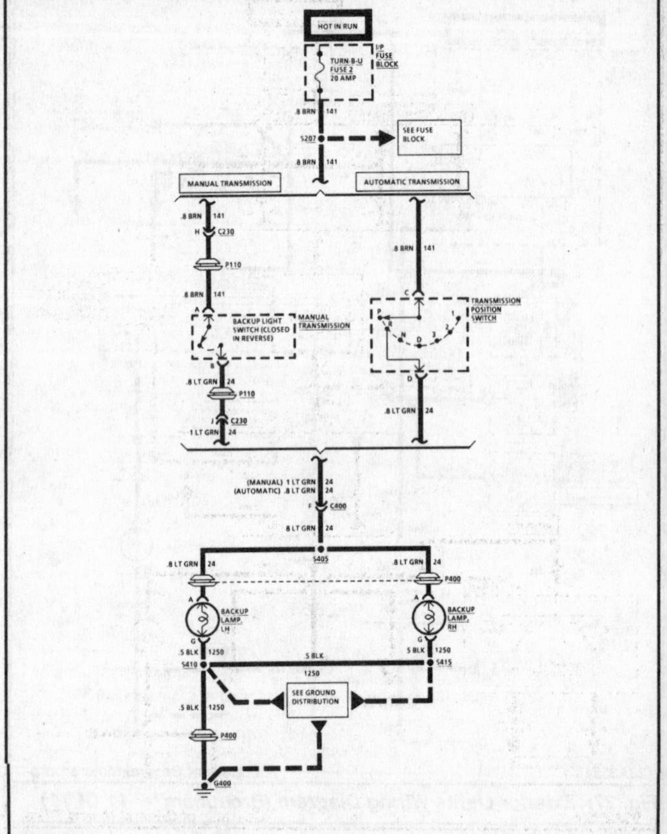

93I85553   Courtesy of General Motors Corp.

Fig. 32: Exterior Lights Wiring Diagram (Camaro & Firebird – 5 Of 5)

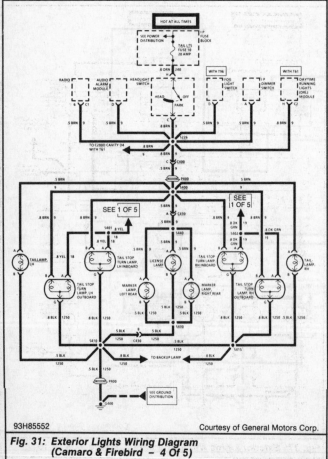

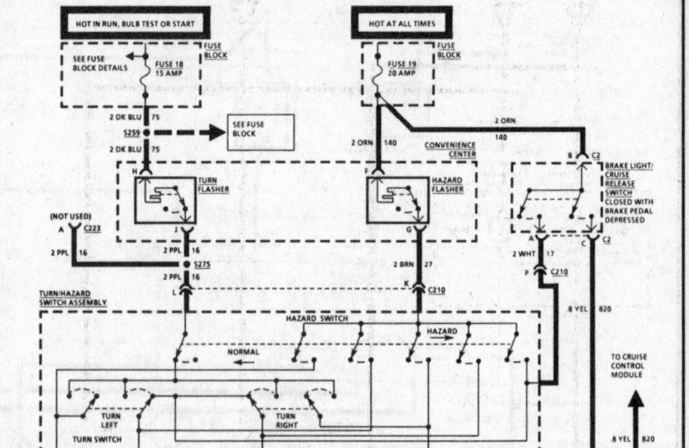

93H85552   Courtesy of General Motors Corp.

Fig. 31: Exterior Lights Wiring Diagram (Camaro & Firebird – 4 Of 5)

93J85554   Courtesy of General Motors Corp.

Fig. 33: Exterior Lights Wiring Diagram (Caprice – 1 Of 10)

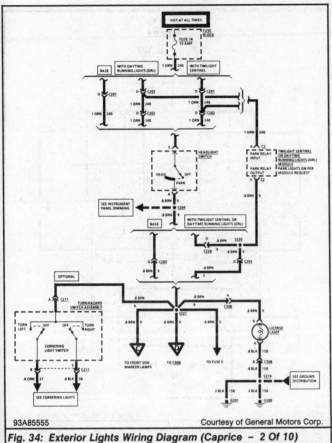

93A85555   Courtesy of General Motors Corp.

Fig. 34: Exterior Lights Wiring Diagram (Caprice – 2 Of 10)

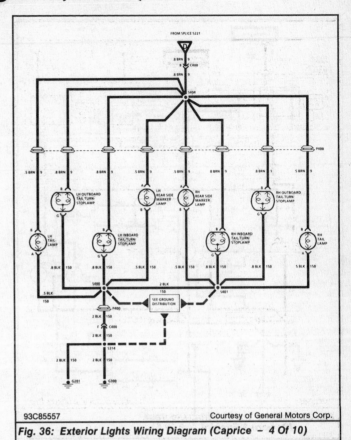

93C85557   Courtesy of General Motors Corp.

Fig. 36: Exterior Lights Wiring Diagram (Caprice – 4 Of 10)

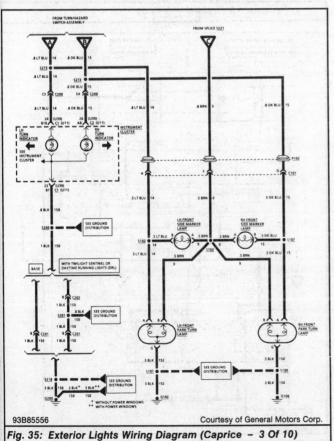

93B85556   Courtesy of General Motors Corp.

Fig. 35: Exterior Lights Wiring Diagram (Caprice – 3 Of 10)

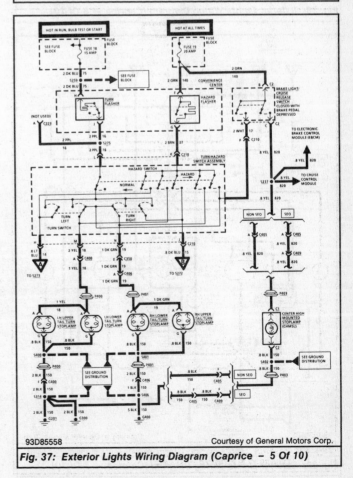

93D85558   Courtesy of General Motors Corp.

Fig. 37: Exterior Lights Wiring Diagram (Caprice – 5 Of 10)

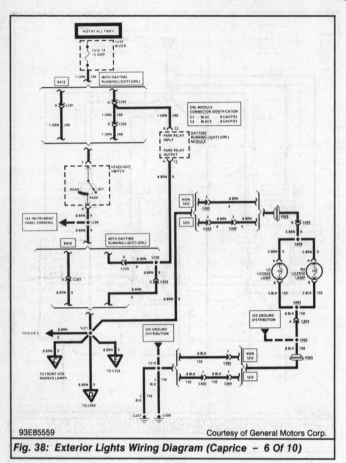

93E85559   Courtesy of General Motors Corp.

Fig. 38: *Exterior Lights Wiring Diagram (Caprice – 6 Of 10)*

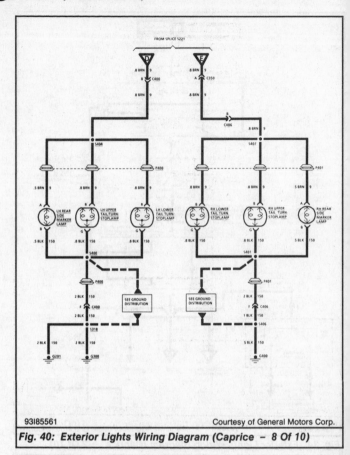

93I85561   Courtesy of General Motors Corp.

Fig. 40: *Exterior Lights Wiring Diagram (Caprice – 8 Of 10)*

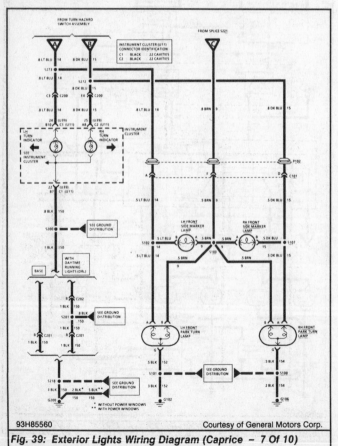

93H85560   Courtesy of General Motors Corp.

Fig. 39: *Exterior Lights Wiring Diagram (Caprice – 7 Of 10)*

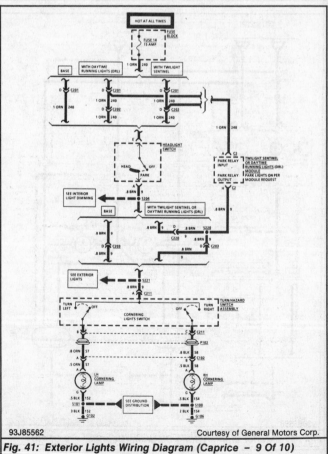

93J85562   Courtesy of General Motors Corp.

Fig. 41: *Exterior Lights Wiring Diagram (Caprice – 9 Of 10)*

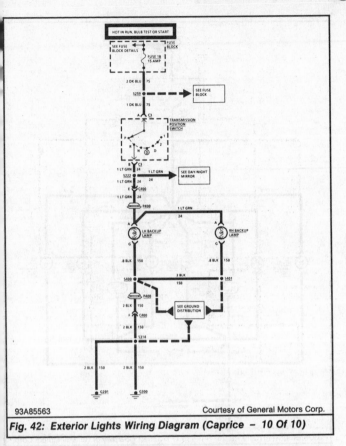

93A85563   Courtesy of General Motors Corp.

Fig. 42: Exterior Lights Wiring Diagram (Caprice – 10 Of 10)

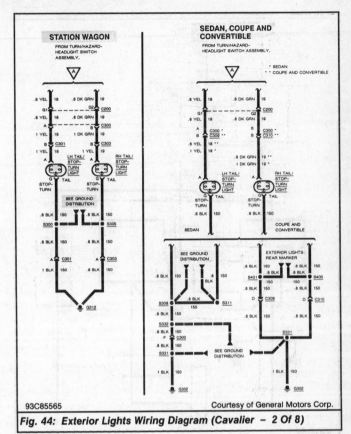

93C85565   Courtesy of General Motors Corp.

Fig. 44: Exterior Lights Wiring Diagram (Cavalier – 2 Of 8)

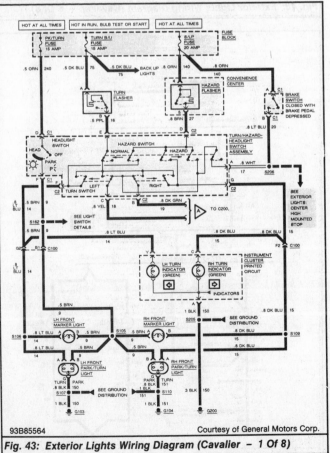

93B85564   Courtesy of General Motors Corp.

Fig. 43: Exterior Lights Wiring Diagram (Cavalier – 1 Of 8)

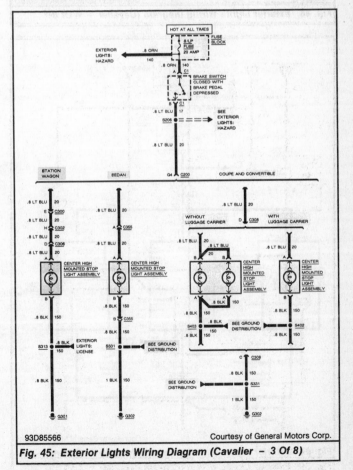

93D85566   Courtesy of General Motors Corp.

Fig. 45: Exterior Lights Wiring Diagram (Cavalier – 3 Of 8)

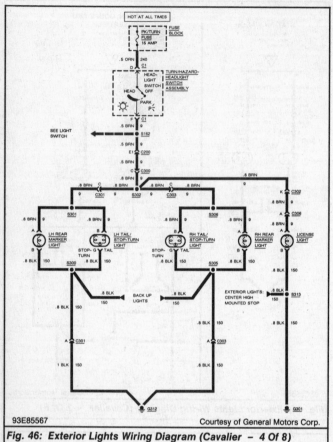

93E85567   Courtesy of General Motors Corp.

Fig. 46: Exterior Lights Wiring Diagram (Cavalier – 4 Of 8)

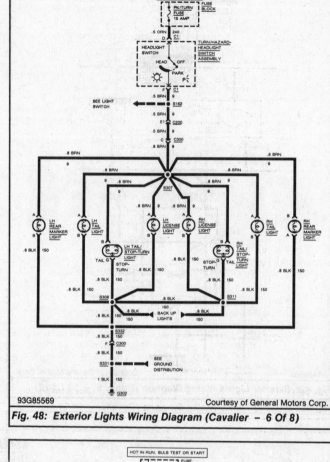

93G85569   Courtesy of General Motors Corp.

Fig. 48: Exterior Lights Wiring Diagram (Cavalier – 6 Of 8)

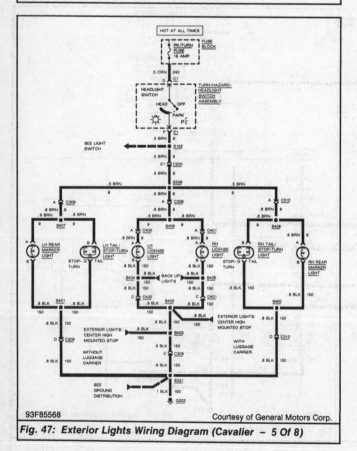

93F85568   Courtesy of General Motors Corp.

Fig. 47: Exterior Lights Wiring Diagram (Cavalier – 5 Of 8)

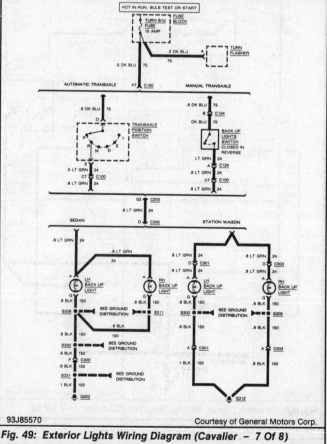

93J85570   Courtesy of General Motors Corp.

Fig. 49: Exterior Lights Wiring Diagram (Cavalier – 7 Of 8)

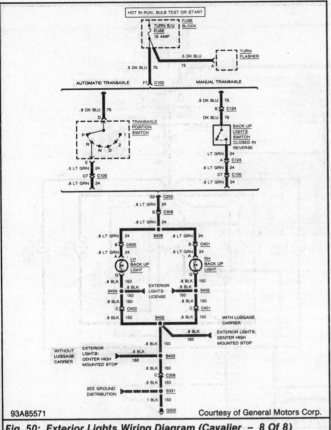

Courtesy of General Motors Corp.

Fig. 50: Exterior Lights Wiring Diagram (Cavalier – 8 Of 8)

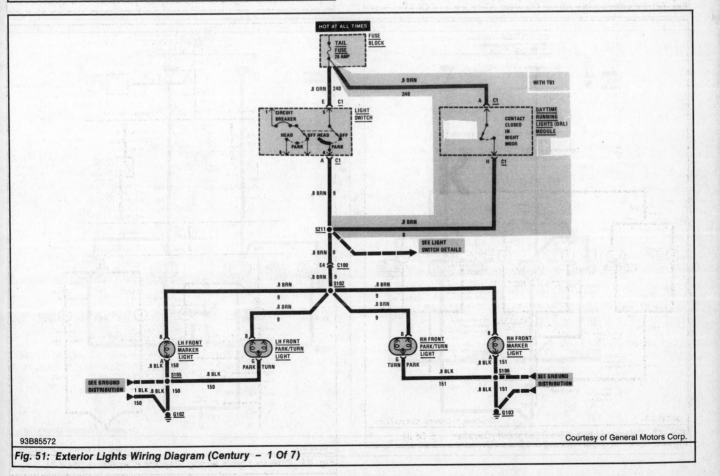

Courtesy of General Motors Corp.

Fig. 51: Exterior Lights Wiring Diagram (Century – 1 Of 7)

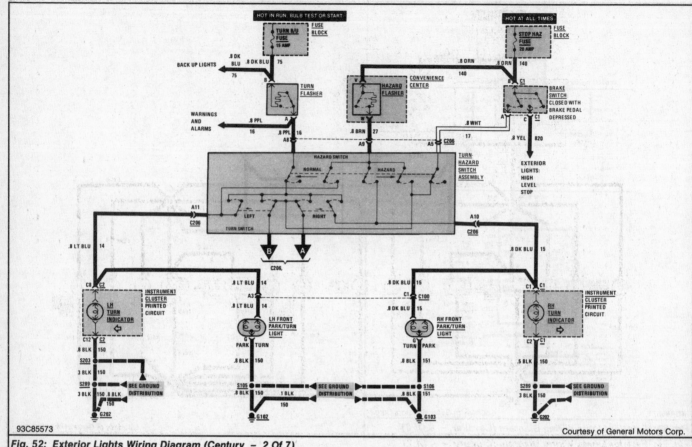

Fig. 52: Exterior Lights Wiring Diagram (Century – 2 Of 7)

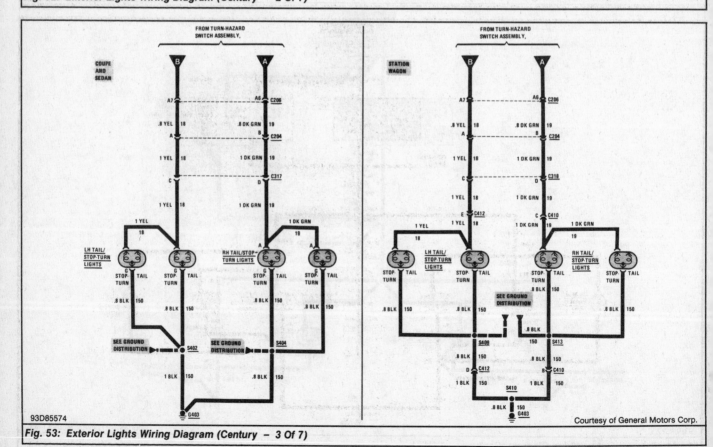

Fig. 53: Exterior Lights Wiring Diagram (Century – 3 Of 7)

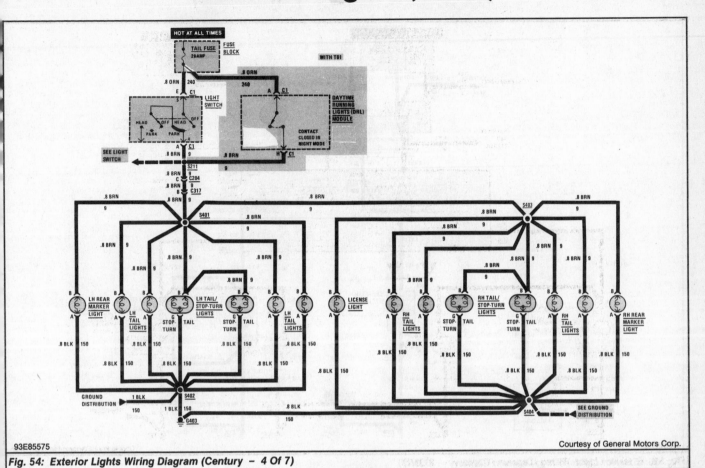

93E85575

Courtesy of General Motors Corp.

Fig. 54: Exterior Lights Wiring Diagram (Century – 4 Of 7)

93F85576

Courtesy of General Motors Corp.

Fig. 55: Exterior Lights Wiring Diagram (Century – 5 Of 7)

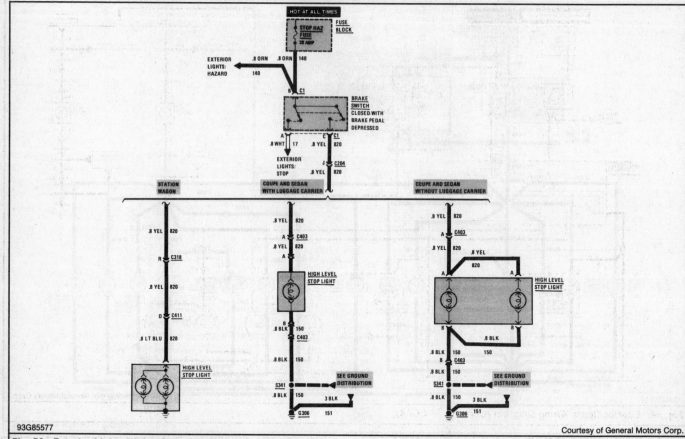

Fig. 56: Exterior Lights Wiring Diagram (Century – 6 Of 7)

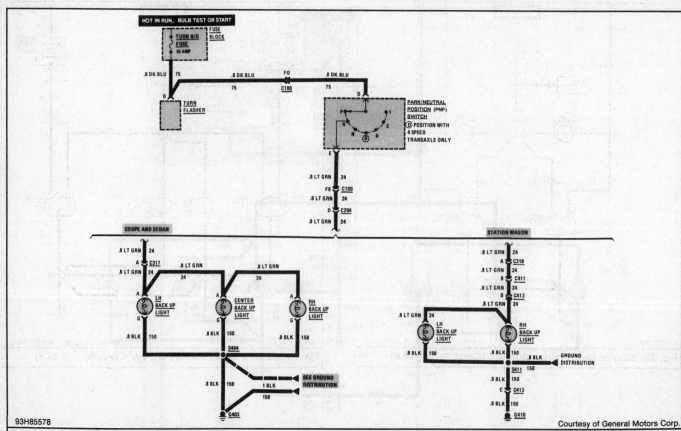

Fig. 57: Exterior Lights Wiring Diagram (Century – 7 Of 7)

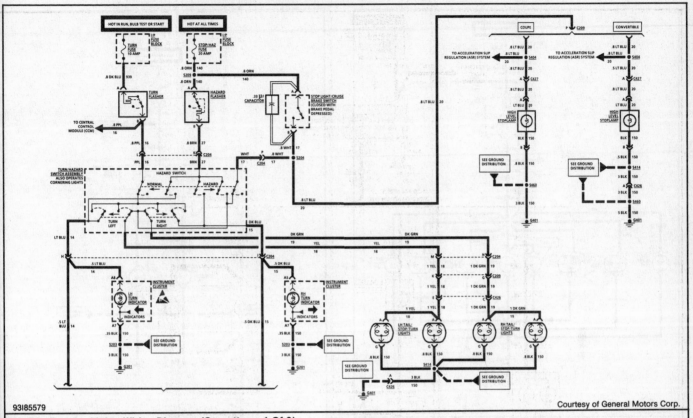

93185579

Courtesy of General Motors Corp.

Fig. 58: Exterior Lights Wiring Diagram (Corvette – 1 Of 6)

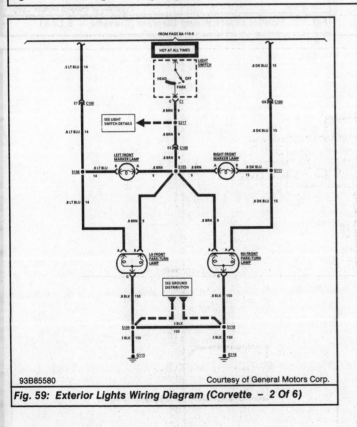

93B85580

Courtesy of General Motors Corp.

Fig. 59: Exterior Lights Wiring Diagram (Corvette – 2 Of 6)

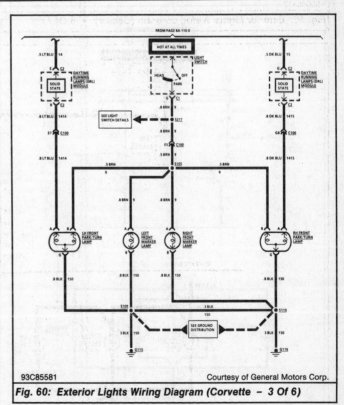

93C85581

Courtesy of General Motors Corp.

Fig. 60: Exterior Lights Wiring Diagram (Corvette – 3 Of 6)

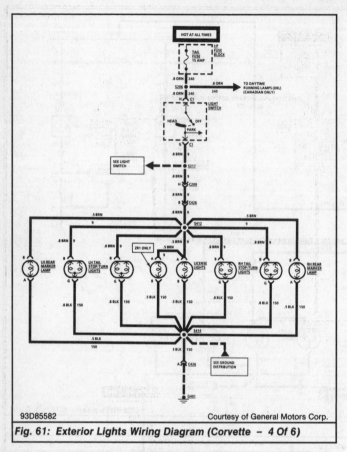

93D85582   Courtesy of General Motors Corp.

Fig. 61: Exterior Lights Wiring Diagram (Corvette – 4 Of 6)

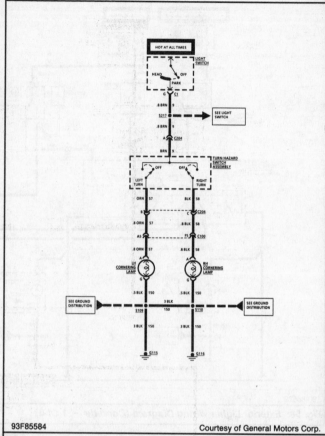

93F85584   Courtesy of General Motors Corp.

Fig. 63: Exterior Lights Wiring Diagram (Corvette – 6 Of 6)

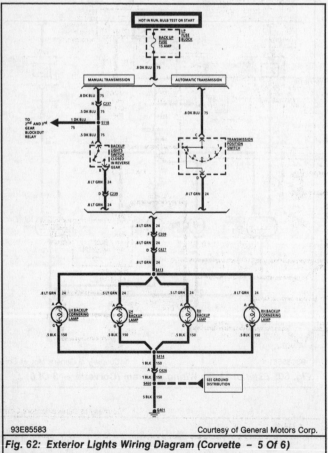

93E85583   Courtesy of General Motors Corp.

Fig. 62: Exterior Lights Wiring Diagram (Corvette – 5 Of 6)

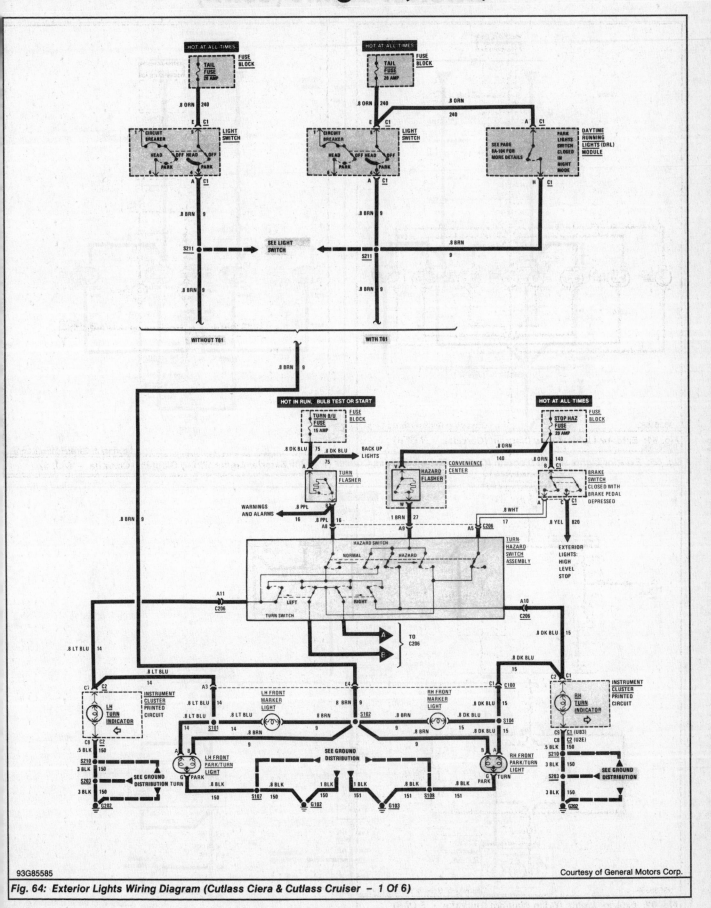

Fig. 64: Exterior Lights Wiring Diagram (Cutlass Ciera & Cutlass Cruiser – 1 Of 6)

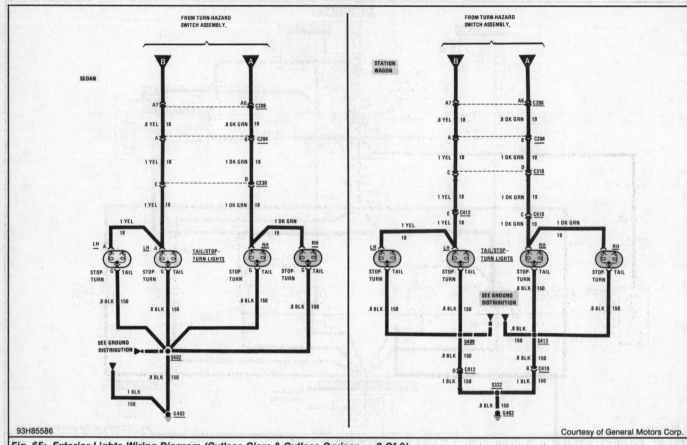

Fig. 65: Exterior Lights Wiring Diagram (Cutlass Ciera & Cutlass Cruiser – 2 Of 6)

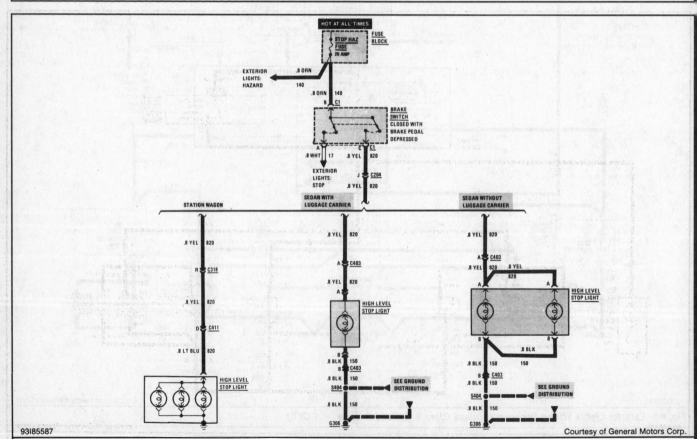

Fig. 66: Exterior Lights Wiring Diagram (Cutlass Ciera & Cutlass Cruiser – 3 Of 6)

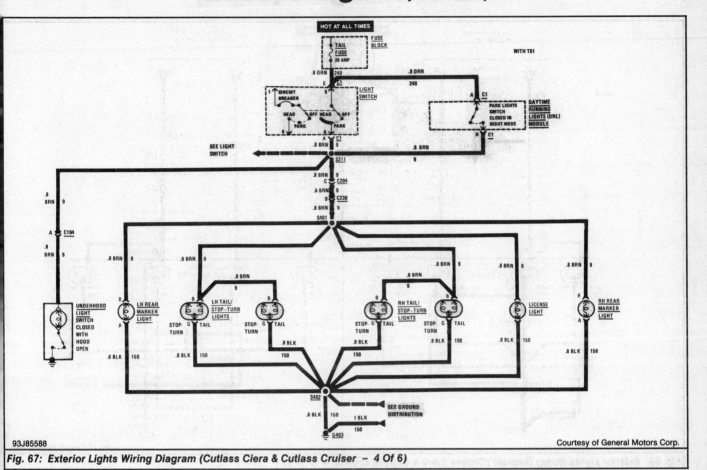

93J85588   Courtesy of General Motors Corp.

Fig. 67: Exterior Lights Wiring Diagram (Cutlass Ciera & Cutlass Cruiser – 4 Of 6)

93A85589   Courtesy of General Motors Corp.

Fig. 68: Exterior Lights Wiring Diagram (Cutlass Ciera & Cutlass Cruiser – 5 Of 6)

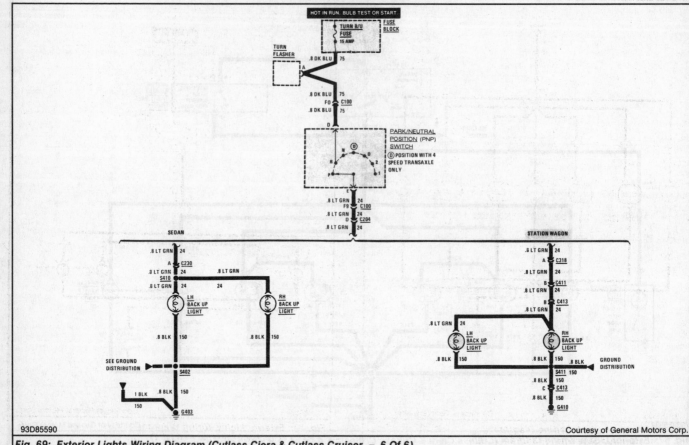

93D85590

Courtesy of General Motors Corp.

Fig. 69: Exterior Lights Wiring Diagram (Cutlass Ciera & Cutlass Cruiser – 6 Of 6)

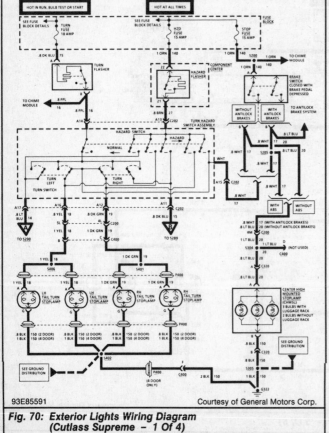

93E85591

Courtesy of General Motors Corp.

Fig. 70: Exterior Lights Wiring Diagram
(Cutlass Supreme – 1 Of 4)

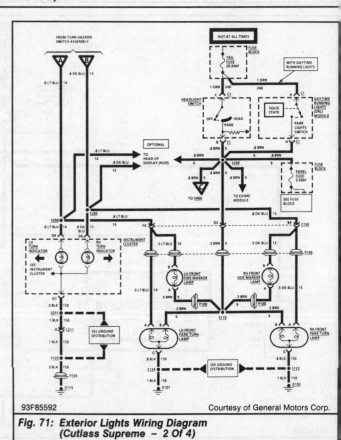

93F85592

Courtesy of General Motors Corp.

Fig. 71: Exterior Lights Wiring Diagram
(Cutlass Supreme – 2 Of 4)

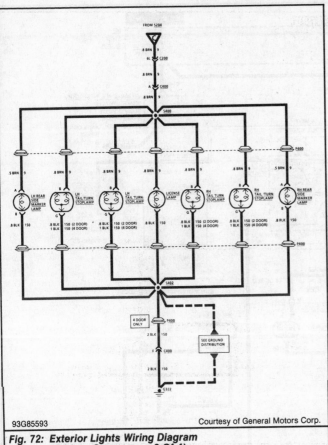

93G85593   Courtesy of General Motors Corp.

*Fig. 72: Exterior Lights Wiring Diagram
(Cutlass Supreme – 3 Of 4)*

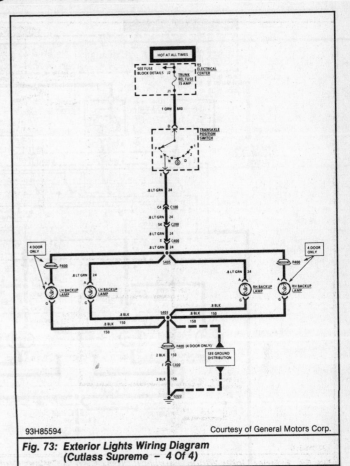

93H85594   Courtesy of General Motors Corp.

*Fig. 73: Exterior Lights Wiring Diagram
(Cutlass Supreme – 4 Of 4)*

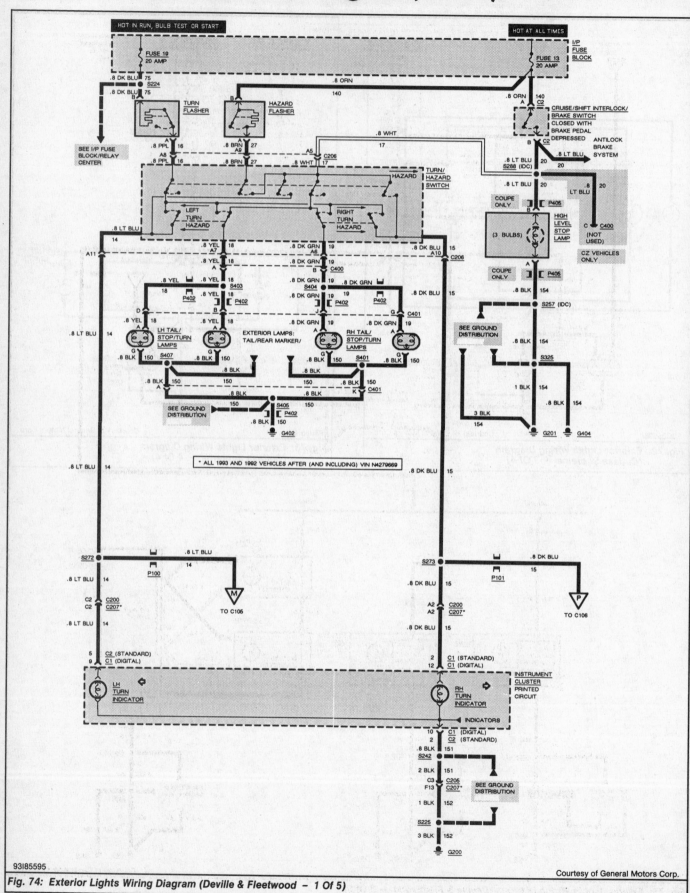

93185595

Fig. 74: Exterior Lights Wiring Diagram (Deville & Fleetwood - 1 Of 5)

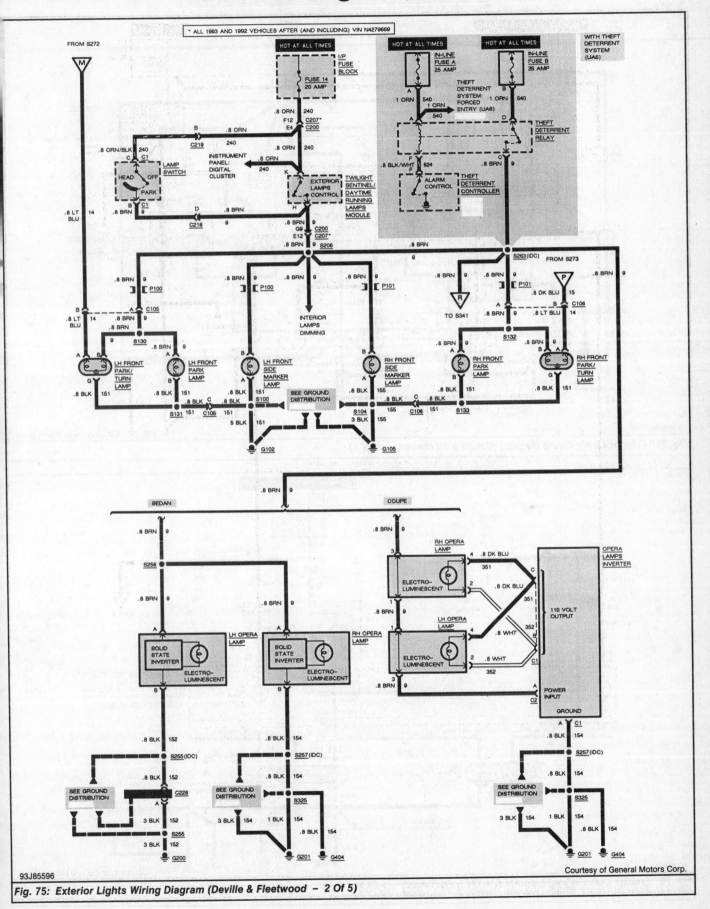

Fig. 75: Exterior Lights Wiring Diagram (Deville & Fleetwood – 2 Of 5)

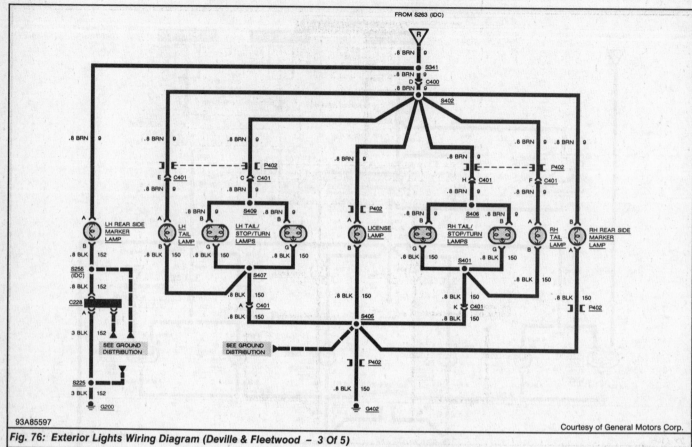

93A85597

Courtesy of General Motors Corp.

Fig. 76: Exterior Lights Wiring Diagram (Deville & Fleetwood – 3 Of 5)

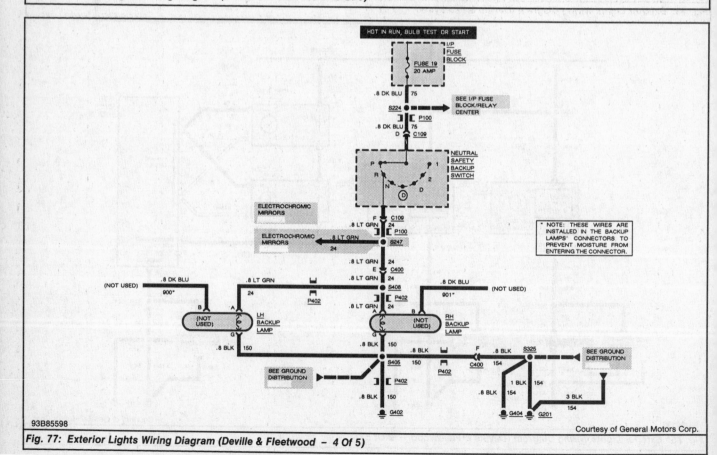

93B85598

Courtesy of General Motors Corp.

Fig. 77: Exterior Lights Wiring Diagram (Deville & Fleetwood – 4 Of 5)

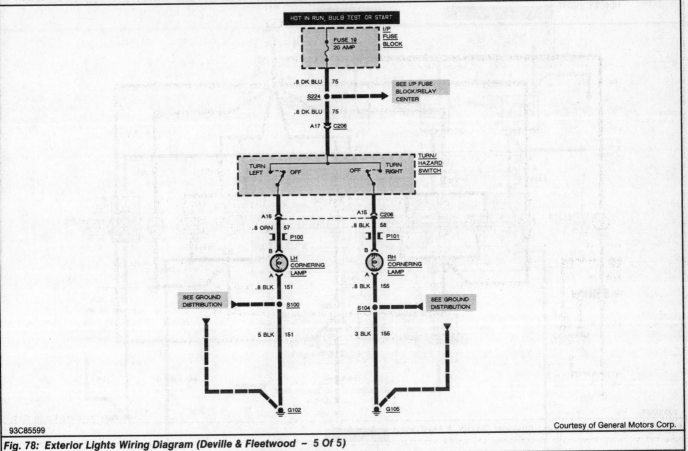

93C85599

Courtesy of General Motors Corp.

Fig. 78: *Exterior Lights Wiring Diagram (Deville & Fleetwood – 5 Of 5)*

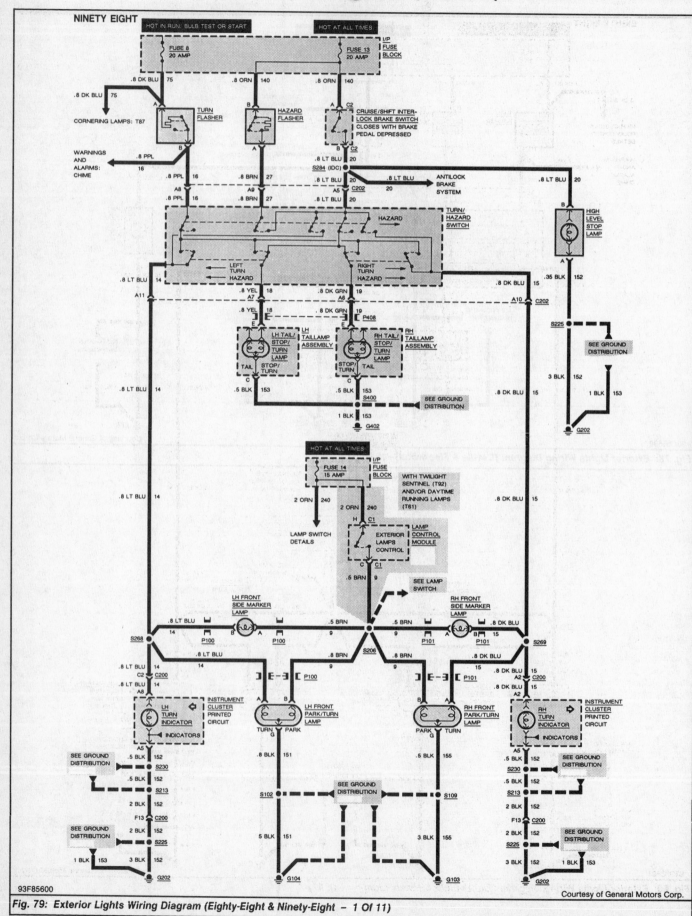

Fig. 79: *Exterior Lights Wiring Diagram (Eighty-Eight & Ninety-Eight – 1 Of 11)*

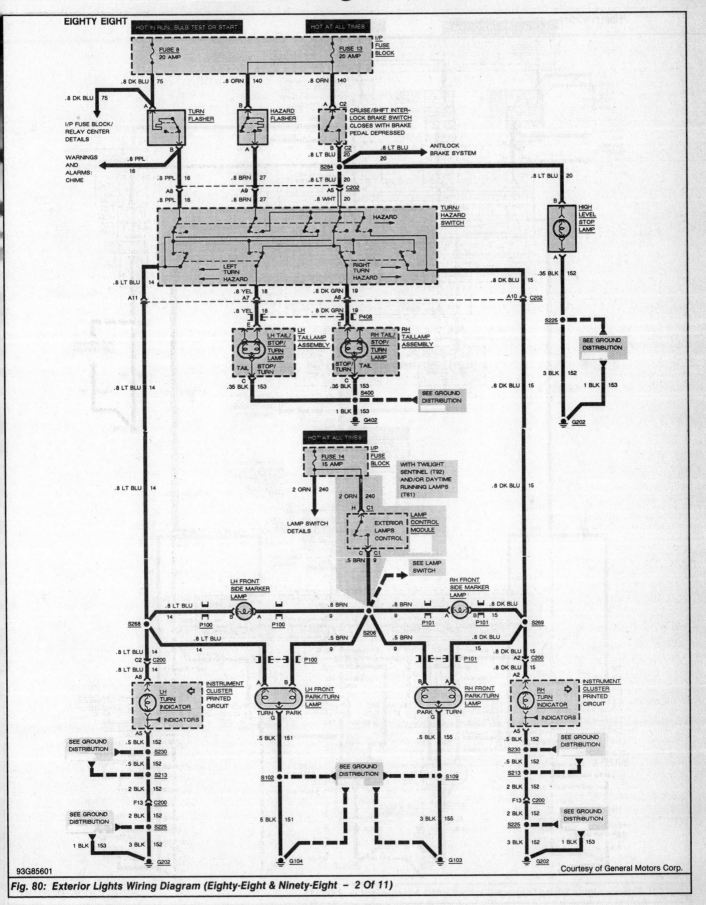

Fig. 80: *Exterior Lights Wiring Diagram (Eighty-Eight & Ninety-Eight – 2 Of 11)*

Courtesy of General Motors Corp.

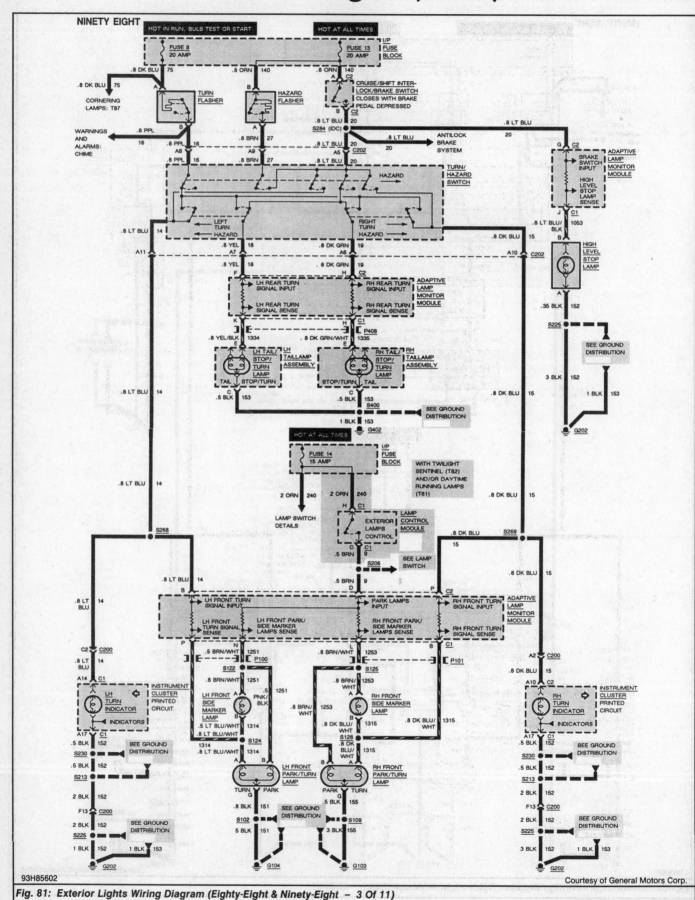

Fig. 81: Exterior Lights Wiring Diagram (Eighty-Eight & Ninety-Eight – 3 Of 11)

Courtesy of General Motors Corp.

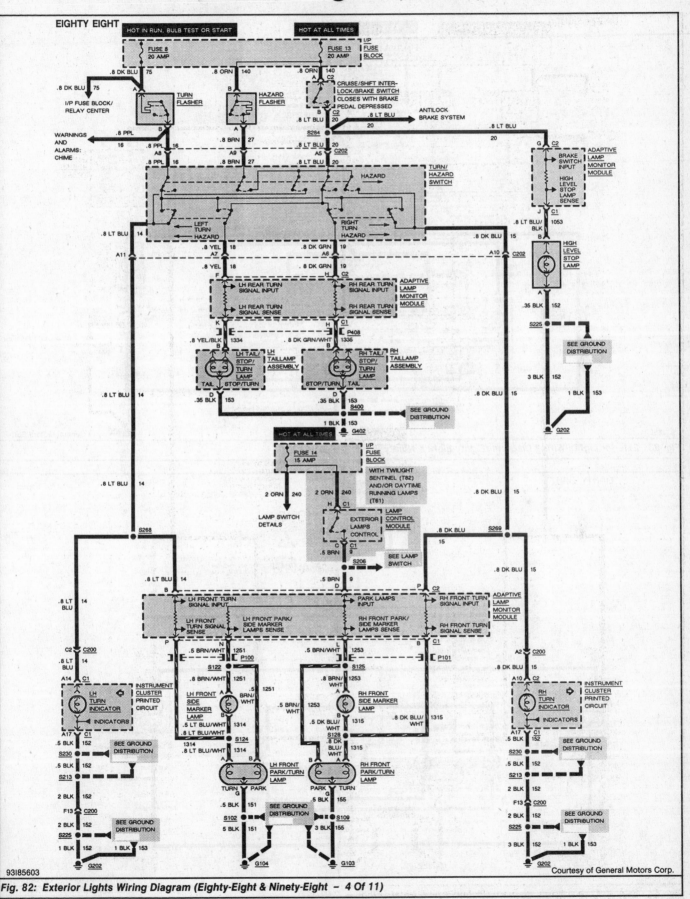

93185603

Courtesy of General Motors Corp.

Fig. 82: Exterior Lights Wiring Diagram (Eighty-Eight & Ninety-Eight - 4 Of 11)

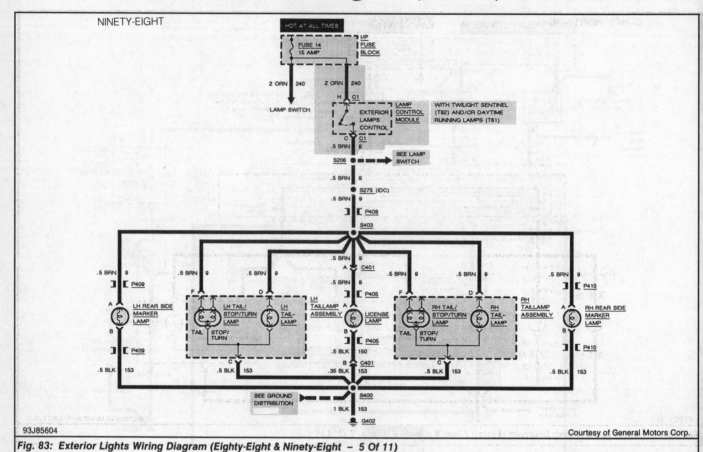

Fig. 83: Exterior Lights Wiring Diagram (Eighty-Eight & Ninety-Eight – 5 Of 11)

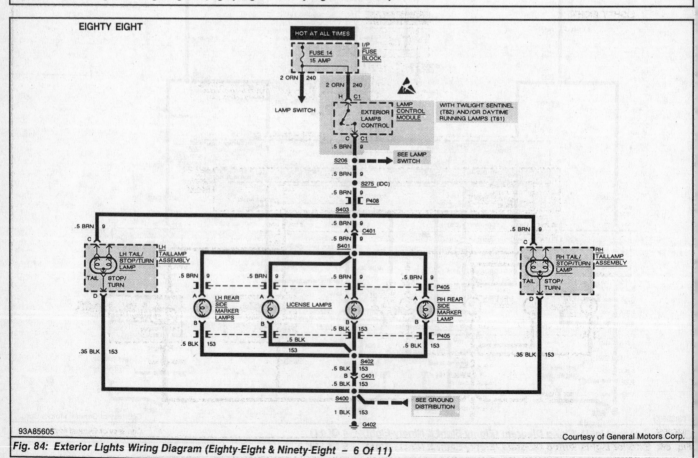

Fig. 84: Exterior Lights Wiring Diagram (Eighty-Eight & Ninety-Eight – 6 Of 11)

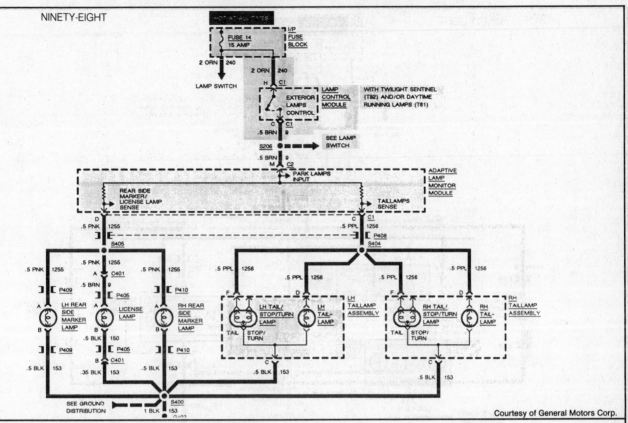

Fig. 85: Exterior Lights Wiring Diagram (Eighty-Eight & Ninety-Eight – 7 Of 11)

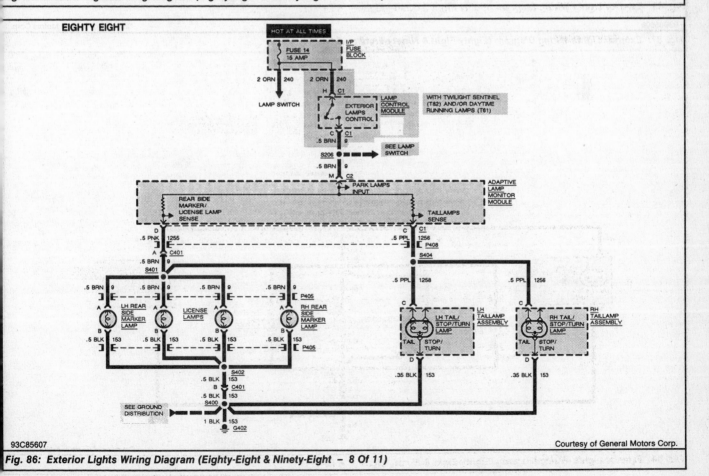

Fig. 86: Exterior Lights Wiring Diagram (Eighty-Eight & Ninety-Eight – 8 Of 11)

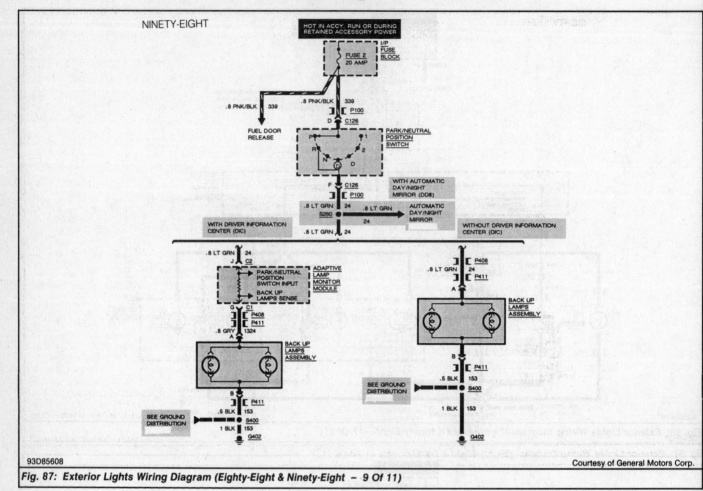

93D85608

Courtesy of General Motors Corp.

Fig. 87: Exterior Lights Wiring Diagram (Eighty-Eight & Ninety-Eight – 9 Of 11)

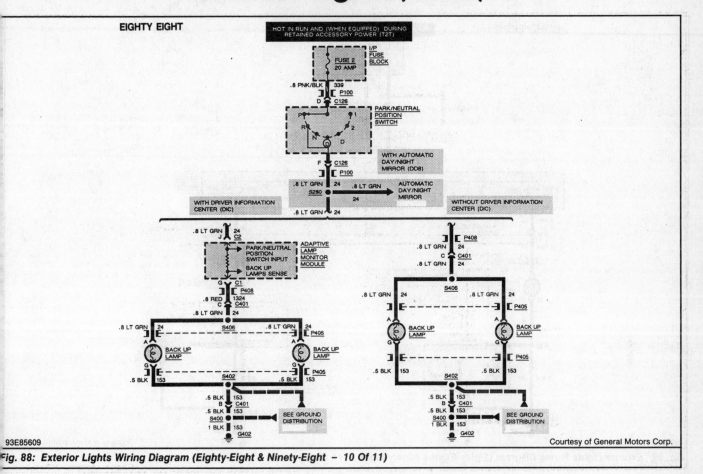

93E85609

Courtesy of General Motors Corp.

Fig. 88: *Exterior Lights Wiring Diagram (Eighty-Eight & Ninety-Eight – 10 Of 11)*

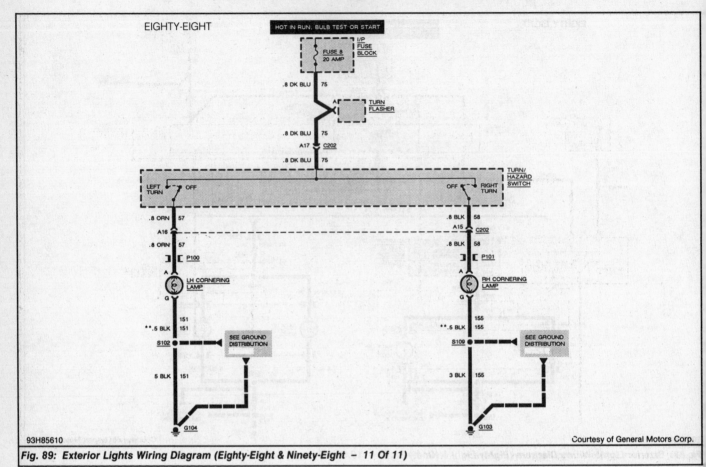

Fig. 89: Exterior Lights Wiring Diagram (Eighty-Eight & Ninety-Eight – 11 Of 11)

93H85610

Courtesy of General Motors Corp.

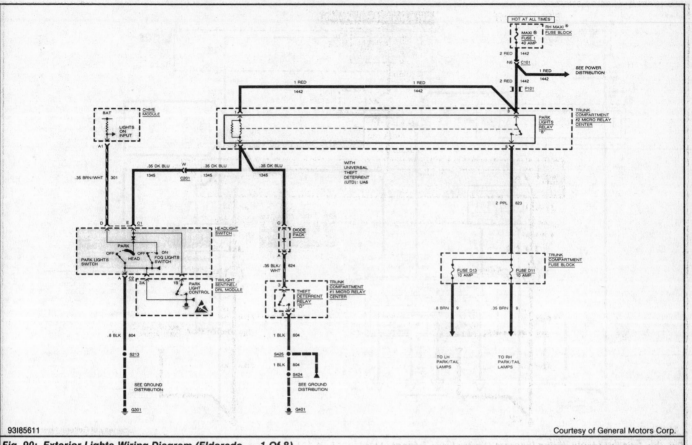

93I85611

Courtesy of General Motors Corp.

Fig. 90: Exterior Lights Wiring Diagram (Eldorado – 1 Of 8)

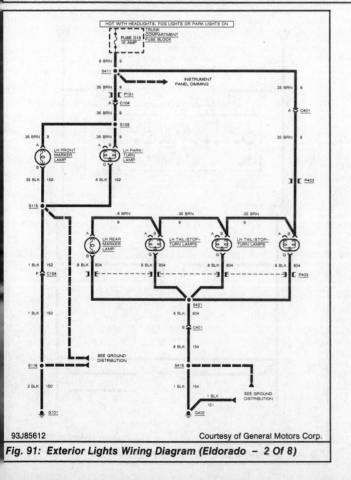

93J85612

Courtesy of General Motors Corp.

Fig. 91: Exterior Lights Wiring Diagram (Eldorado – 2 Of 8)

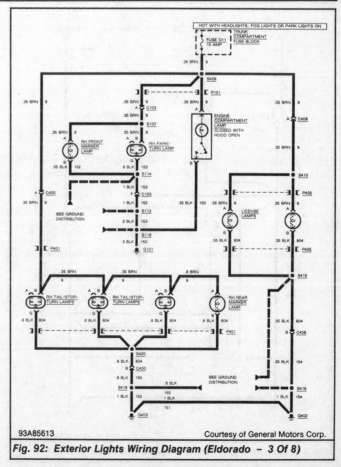

93A85613

Courtesy of General Motors Corp.

Fig. 92: Exterior Lights Wiring Diagram (Eldorado – 3 Of 8)

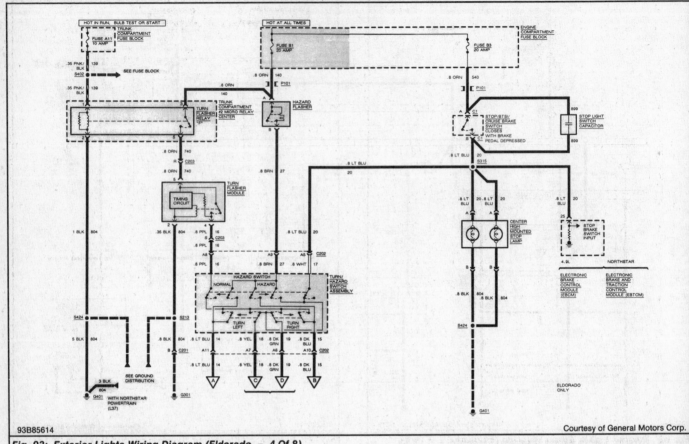

Fig. 93: Exterior Lights Wiring Diagram (Eldorado – 4 Of 8)

93B85614   Courtesy of General Motors Corp.

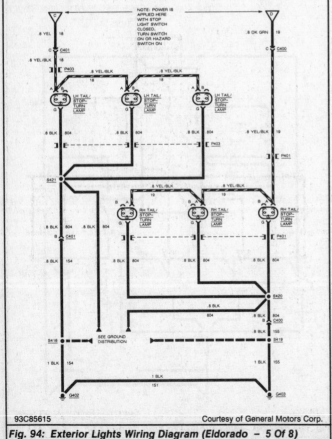

93C85615   Courtesy of General Motors Corp.

Fig. 94: Exterior Lights Wiring Diagram (Eldorado – 5 Of 8)

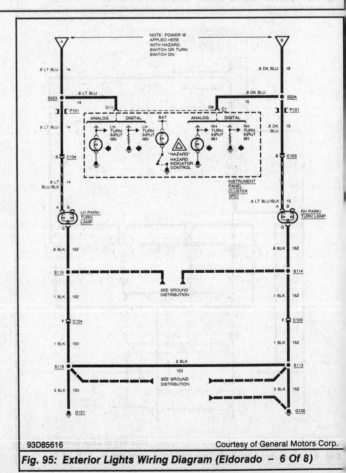

93D85616   Courtesy of General Motors Corp.

Fig. 95: Exterior Lights Wiring Diagram (Eldorado – 6 Of 8)

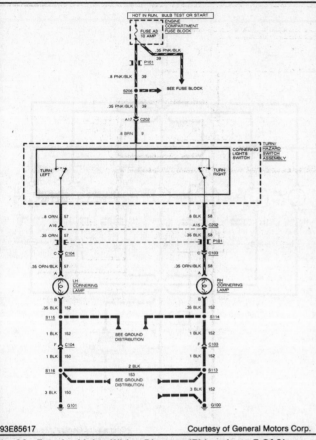

93E85617 Courtesy of General Motors Corp.

Fig. 96: Exterior Lights Wiring Diagram (Eldorado – 7 Of 8)

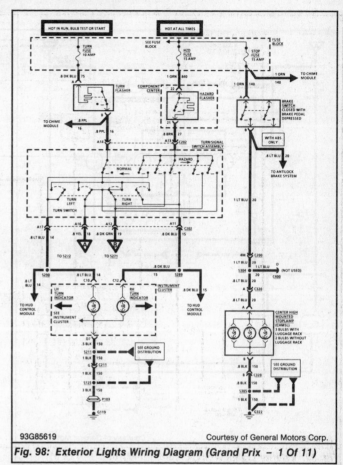

93G85619 Courtesy of General Motors Corp.

Fig. 98: Exterior Lights Wiring Diagram (Grand Prix – 1 Of 11)

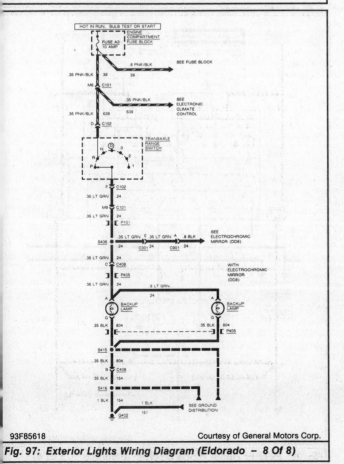

93F85618 Courtesy of General Motors Corp.

Fig. 97: Exterior Lights Wiring Diagram (Eldorado – 8 Of 8)

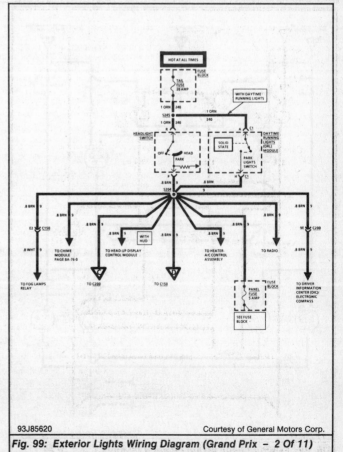

93J85620 Courtesy of General Motors Corp.

Fig. 99: Exterior Lights Wiring Diagram (Grand Prix – 2 Of 11)

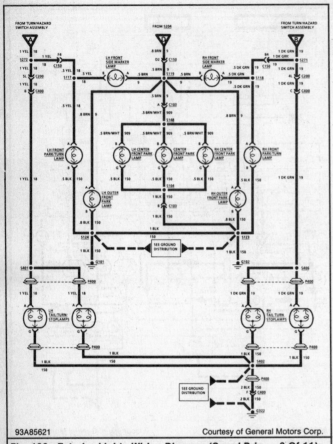

93A85621   Courtesy of General Motors Corp.

Fig. 100: Exterior Lights Wiring Diagram (Grand Prix – 3 Of 11)

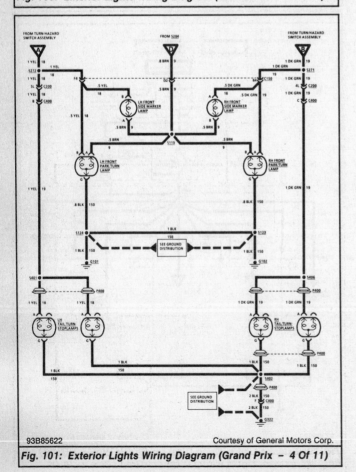

93B85622   Courtesy of General Motors Corp.

Fig. 101: Exterior Lights Wiring Diagram (Grand Prix – 4 Of 11)

93C85623   Courtesy of General Motors Corp.

Fig. 102: Exterior Lights Wiring Diagram (Grand Prix – 5 Of 11)

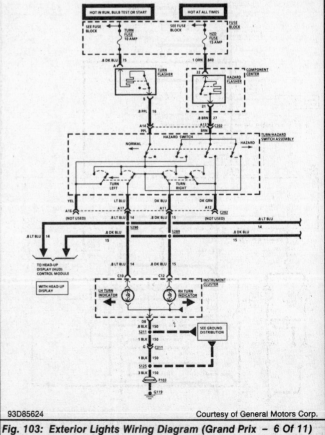

93D85624   Courtesy of General Motors Corp.

Fig. 103: Exterior Lights Wiring Diagram (Grand Prix – 6 Of 11)

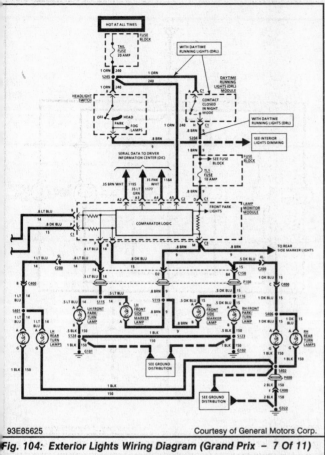

93E85625 Courtesy of General Motors Corp.

Fig. 104: Exterior Lights Wiring Diagram (Grand Prix – 7 Of 11)

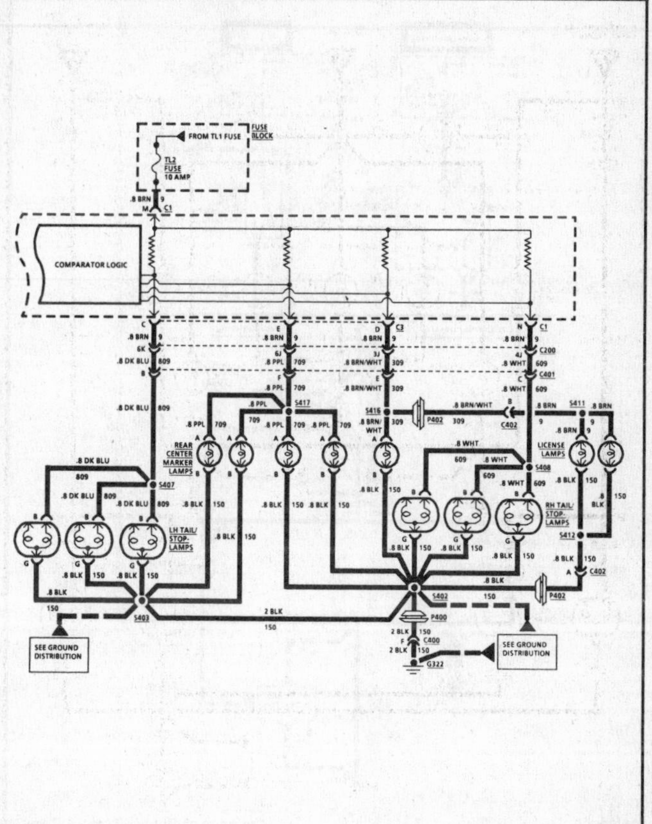

93G85627 Courtesy of General Motors Corp.

Fig. 106: Exterior Lights Wiring Diagram (Grand Prix – 9 Of 11)

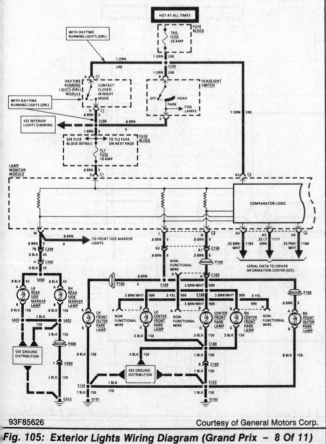

93F85626 Courtesy of General Motors Corp.

Fig. 105: Exterior Lights Wiring Diagram (Grand Prix – 8 Of 11)

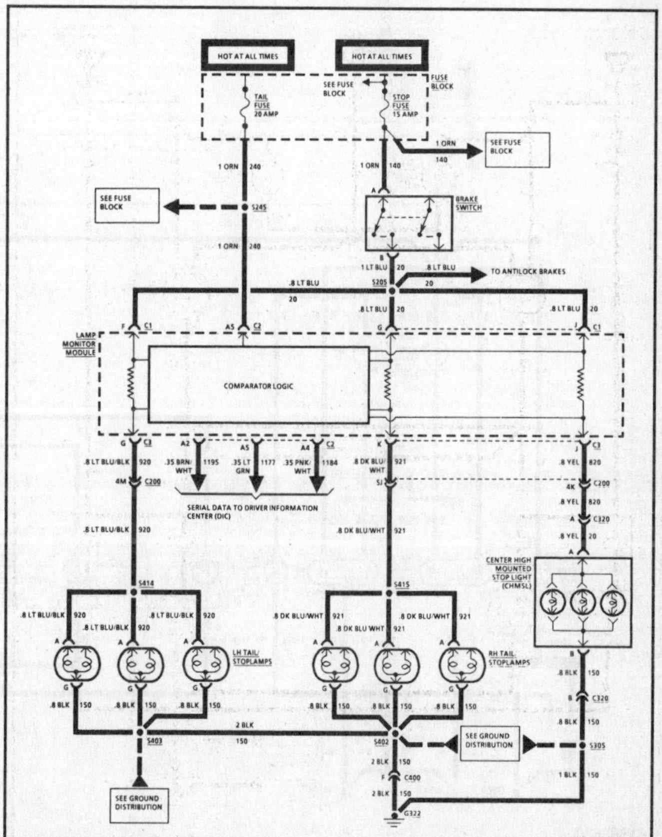

93H85628 Courtesy of General Motors Corp.

Fig. 107: Exterior Lights Wiring Diagram (Grand Prix – 10 Of 11)

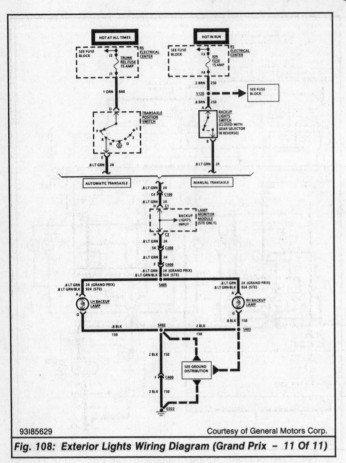

93I85629

Courtesy of General Motors Corp.

Fig. 108: Exterior Lights Wiring Diagram (Grand Prix – 11 Of 11)

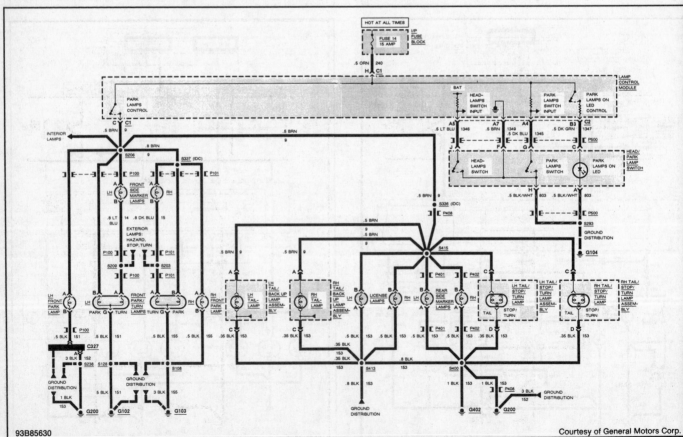

93B85630

Courtesy of General Motors Corp.

Fig. 109: Exterior Lights Wiring Diagram (LeSabre – 1 Of 4)

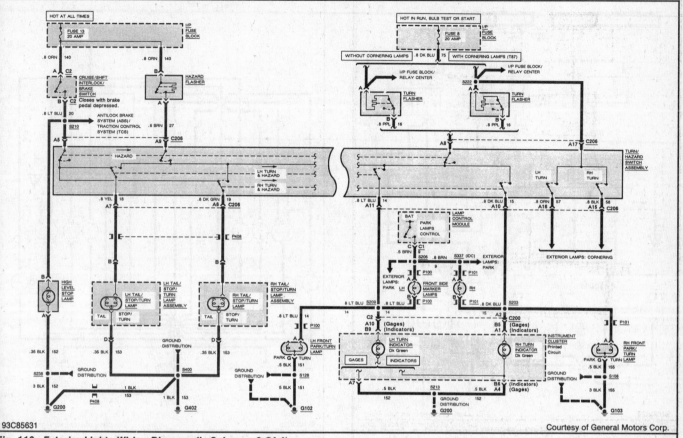

93C85631   Courtesy of General Motors Corp.

Fig. 110: Exterior Lights Wiring Diagram (LeSabre – 2 Of 4)

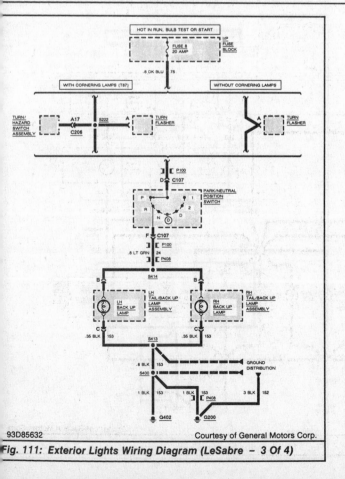

93D85632   Courtesy of General Motors Corp.

Fig. 111: Exterior Lights Wiring Diagram (LeSabre – 3 Of 4)

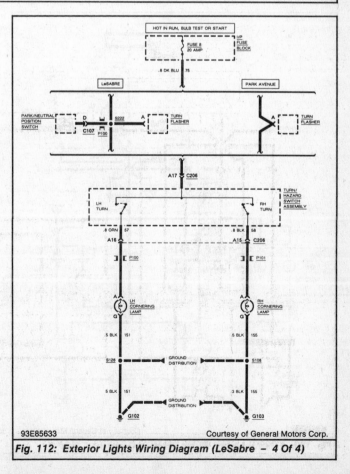

93E85633   Courtesy of General Motors Corp.

Fig. 112: Exterior Lights Wiring Diagram (LeSabre – 4 Of 4)

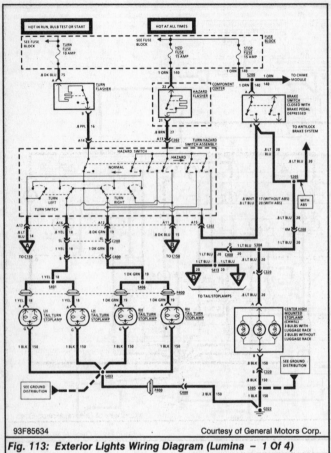

93F85634   Courtesy of General Motors Corp.

Fig. 113: Exterior Lights Wiring Diagram (Lumina – 1 Of 4)

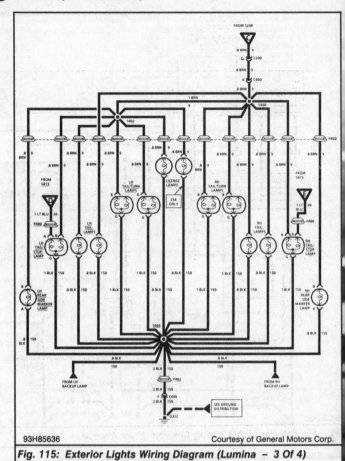

93H85636   Courtesy of General Motors Corp.

Fig. 115: Exterior Lights Wiring Diagram (Lumina – 3 Of 4)

93G85635   Courtesy of General Motors Corp.

Fig. 114: Exterior Lights Wiring Diagram (Lumina – 2 Of 4)

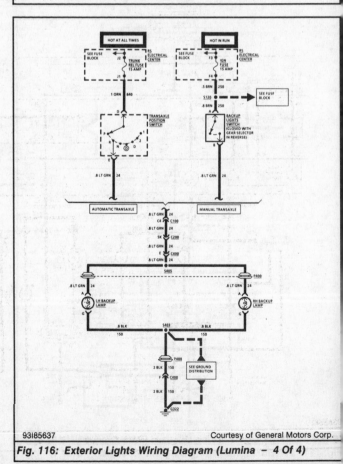

93I85637   Courtesy of General Motors Corp.

Fig. 116: Exterior Lights Wiring Diagram (Lumina – 4 Of 4)

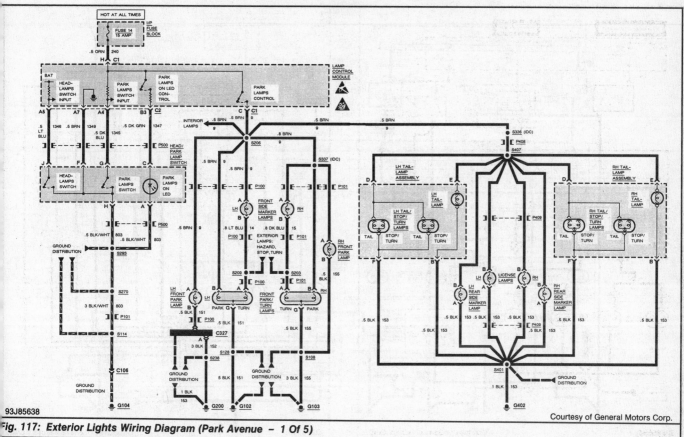

Fig. 117: Exterior Lights Wiring Diagram (Park Avenue – 1 Of 5)

Courtesy of General Motors Corp.

93J85638

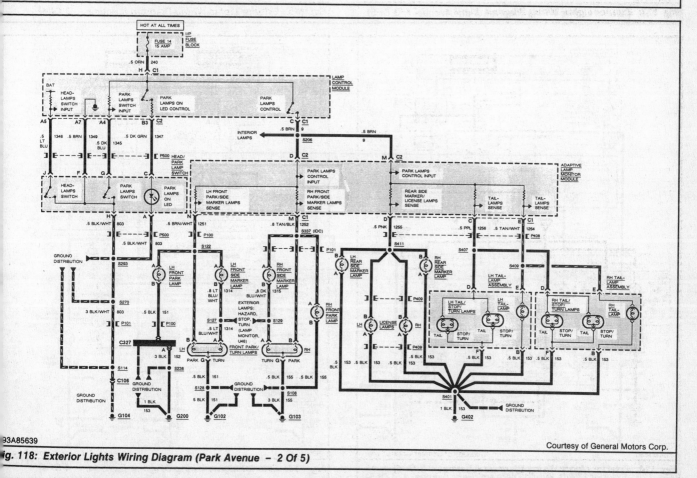

Fig. 118: Exterior Lights Wiring Diagram (Park Avenue – 2 Of 5)

Courtesy of General Motors Corp.

93A85639

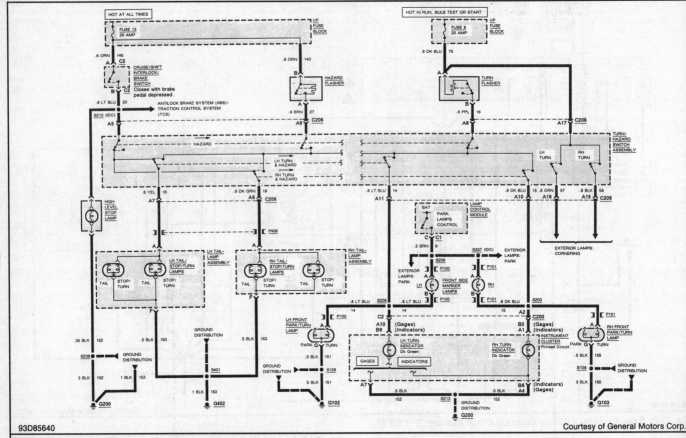

Fig. 119: Exterior Lights Wiring Diagram (Park Avenue – 3 Of 5)

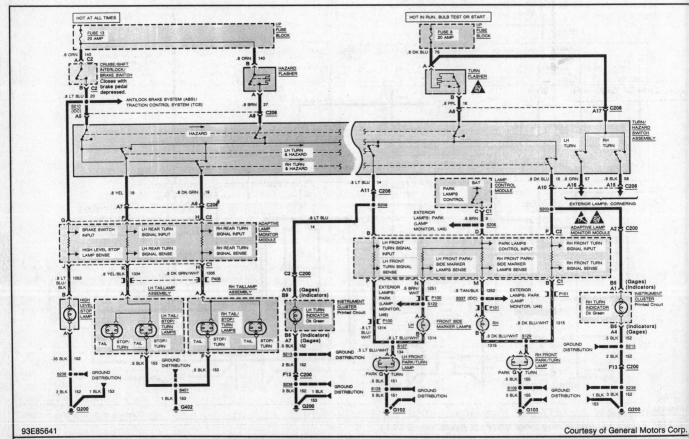

Fig. 120: Exterior Lights Wiring Diagram (Park Avenue – 4 Of 5)

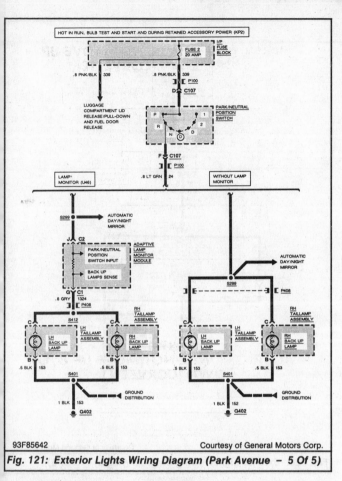

93F85642   Courtesy of General Motors Corp.

Fig. 121: Exterior Lights Wiring Diagram (Park Avenue – 5 Of 5)

93H85644   Courtesy of General Motors Corp.

Fig. 123: Exterior Lights Wiring Diagram (Regal – 2 Of 5)

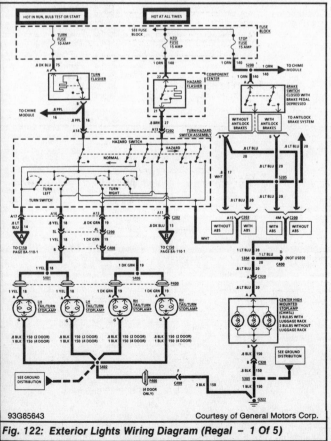

93G85643   Courtesy of General Motors Corp.

Fig. 122: Exterior Lights Wiring Diagram (Regal – 1 Of 5)

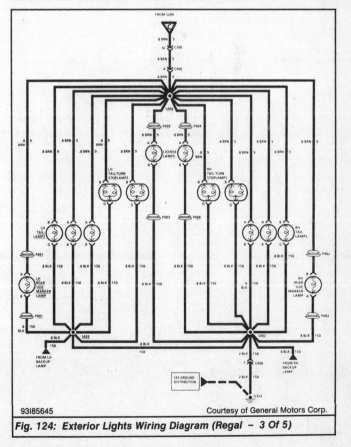

93I85645   Courtesy of General Motors Corp.

Fig. 124: Exterior Lights Wiring Diagram (Regal – 3 Of 5)

1993 ACCESSORIES & EQUIPMENT
Exterior Lights (Cont.)

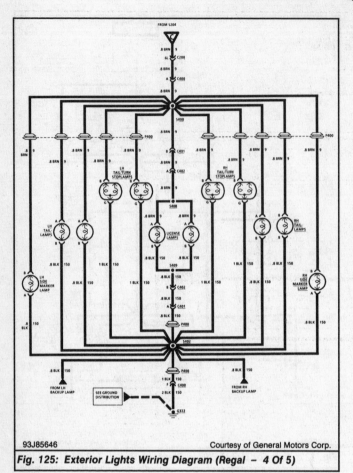

93J85646 Courtesy of General Motors Corp.

Fig. 125: Exterior Lights Wiring Diagram (Regal - 4 Of 5)

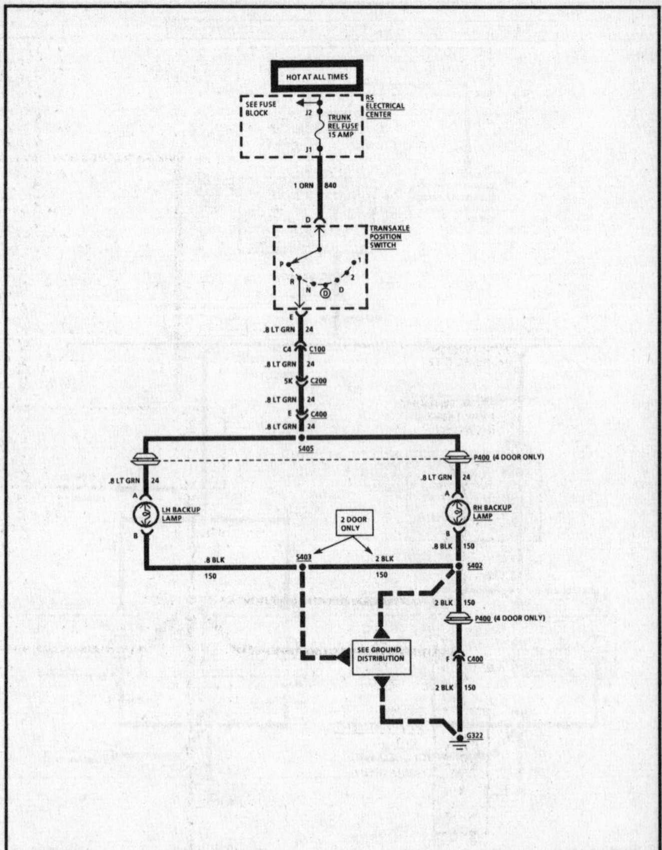

93A85647 Courtesy of General Motors Corp.

Fig. 126: Exterior Lights Wiring Diagram (Regal - 5 Of 5)

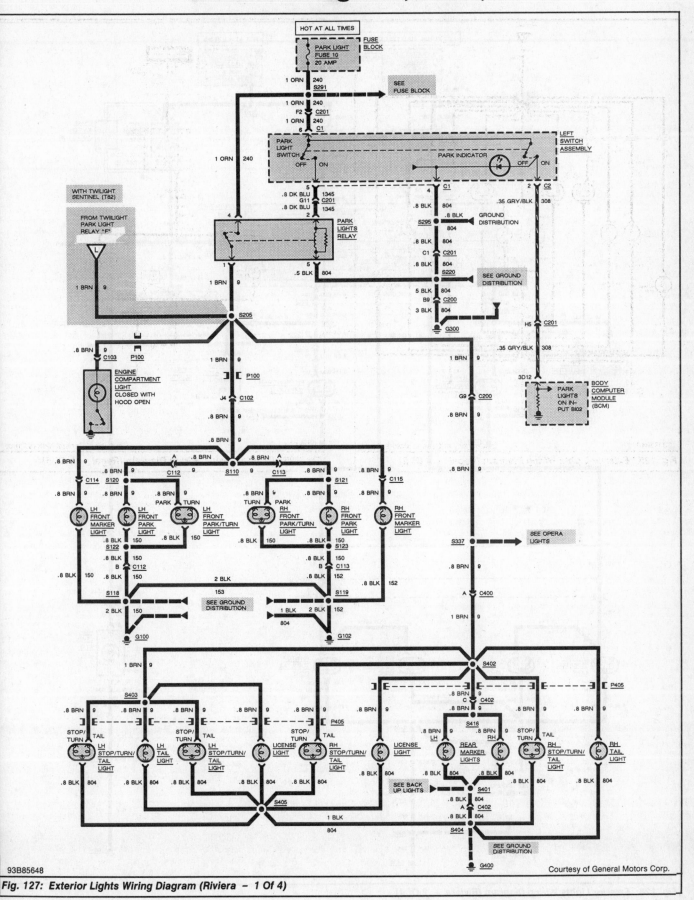

Fig. 127: Exterior Lights Wiring Diagram (Riviera – 1 Of 4)

Courtesy of General Motors Corp.

93B85648

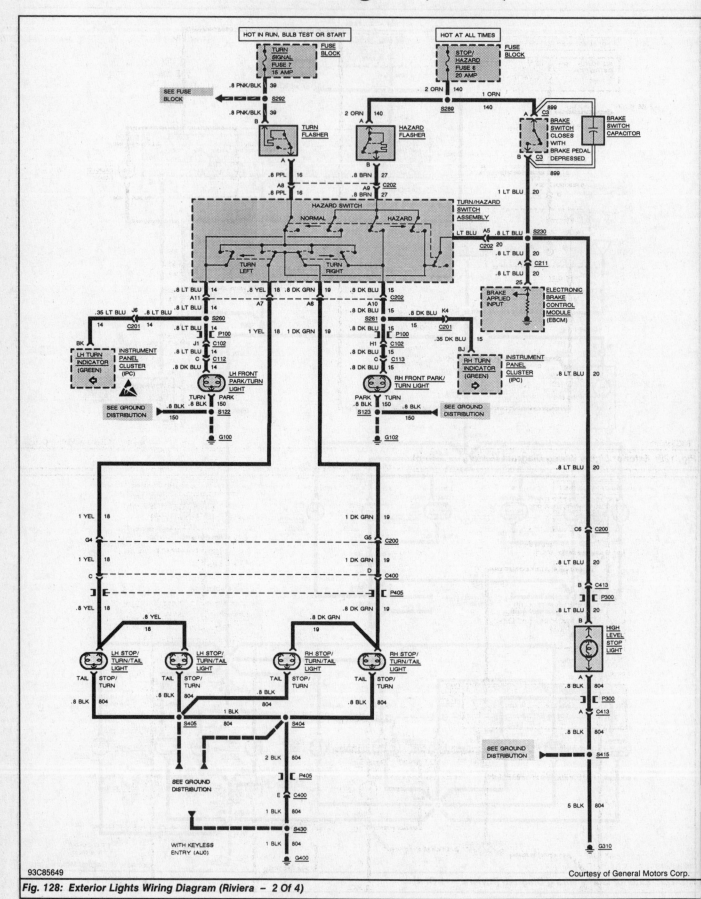

Fig. 128: *Exterior Lights Wiring Diagram (Riviera – 2 Of 4)*

93C85649

Courtesy of General Motors Corp.

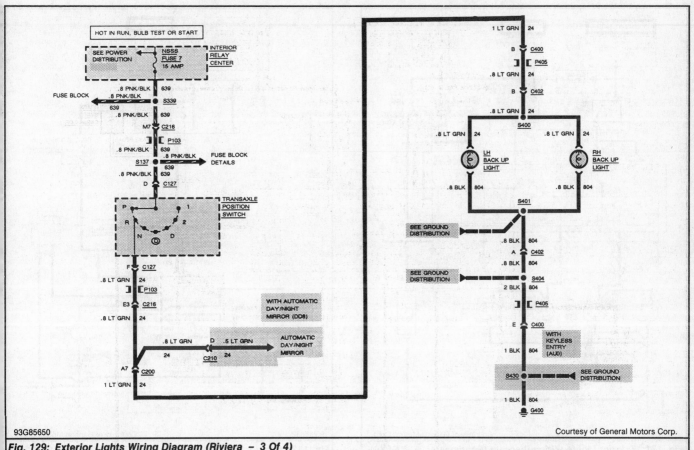

Fig. 129: Exterior Lights Wiring Diagram (Riviera – 3 Of 4)

93G85650

Courtesy of General Motors Corp.

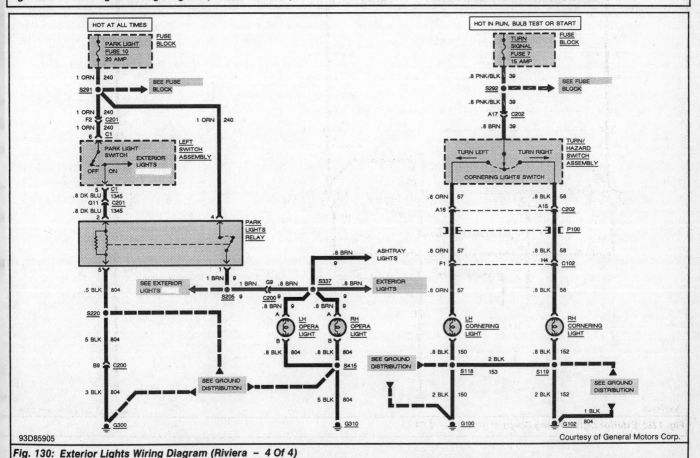

Fig. 130: Exterior Lights Wiring Diagram (Riviera – 4 Of 4)

93D85905

Courtesy of General Motors Corp.

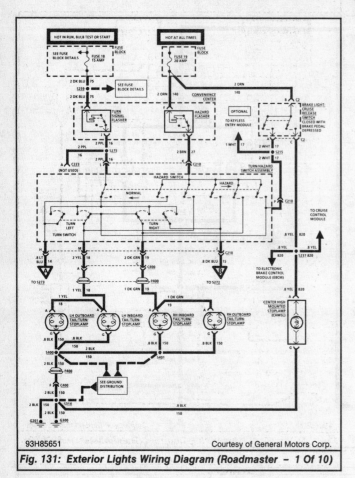

Fig. 131: Exterior Lights Wiring Diagram (Roadmaster – 1 Of 10)

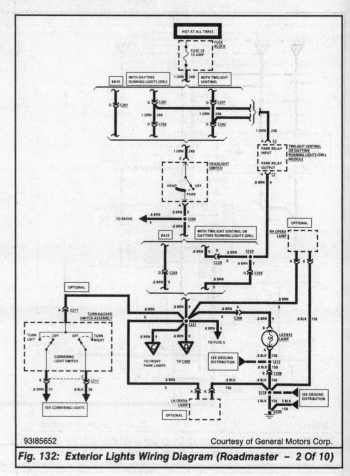

Fig. 132: Exterior Lights Wiring Diagram (Roadmaster – 2 Of 10)

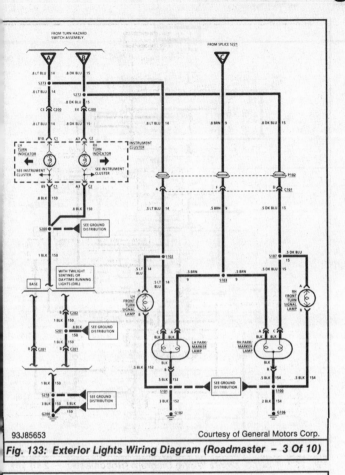

93J85653

Courtesy of General Motors Corp.

Fig. 133: Exterior Lights Wiring Diagram (Roadmaster – 3 Of 10)

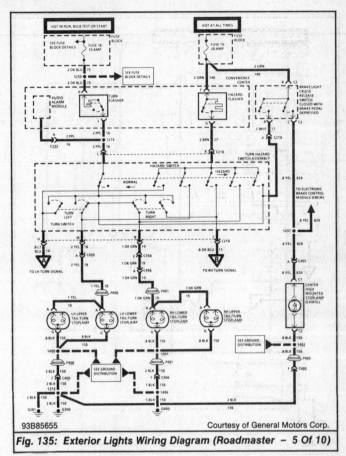

93B85655

Courtesy of General Motors Corp.

Fig. 135: Exterior Lights Wiring Diagram (Roadmaster – 5 Of 10)

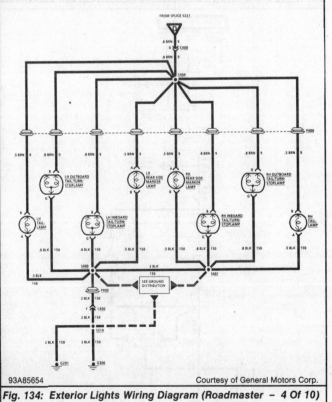

93A85654

Courtesy of General Motors Corp.

Fig. 134: Exterior Lights Wiring Diagram (Roadmaster – 4 Of 10)

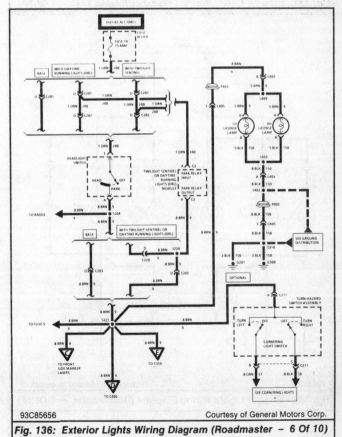

93C85656

Courtesy of General Motors Corp.

Fig. 136: Exterior Lights Wiring Diagram (Roadmaster – 6 Of 10)

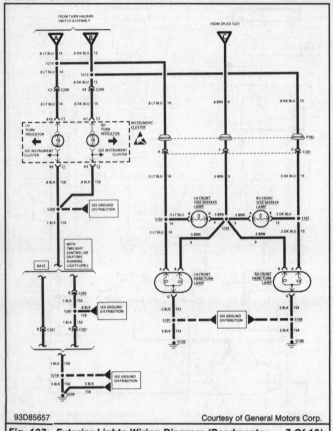

93D85657   Courtesy of General Motors Corp.

Fig. 137: Exterior Lights Wiring Diagram (Roadmaster – 7 Of 10)

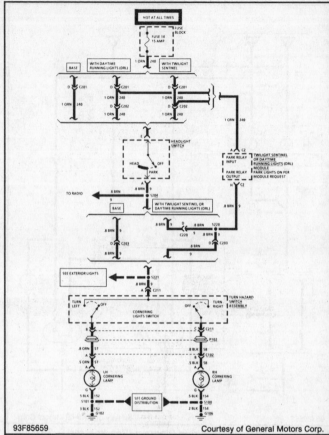

93F85659   Courtesy of General Motors Corp.

Fig. 139: Exterior Lights Wiring Diagram (Roadmaster – 9 Of 10)

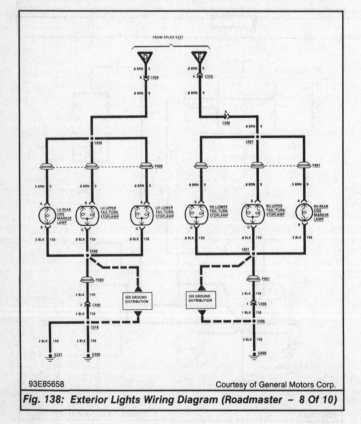

93E85658   Courtesy of General Motors Corp.

Fig. 138: Exterior Lights Wiring Diagram (Roadmaster – 8 Of 10)

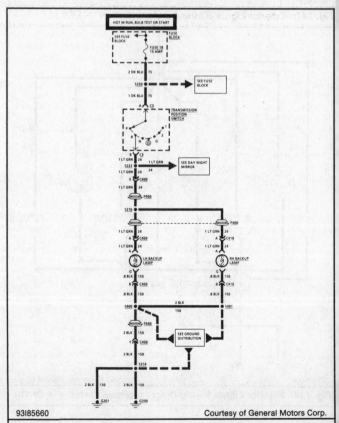

93I85660   Courtesy of General Motors Corp.

Fig. 140: Exterior Lights Wiring Diagram (Roadmaster – 10 Of 10)

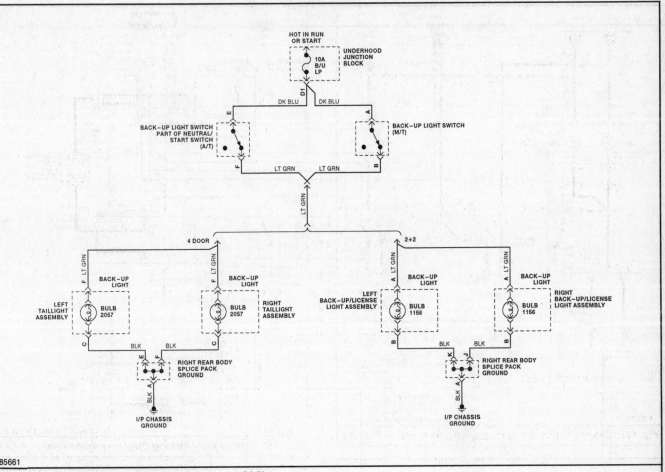

93J85661

Fig. 141: Exterior Lights Wiring Diagram (Saturn – 1 Of 5)

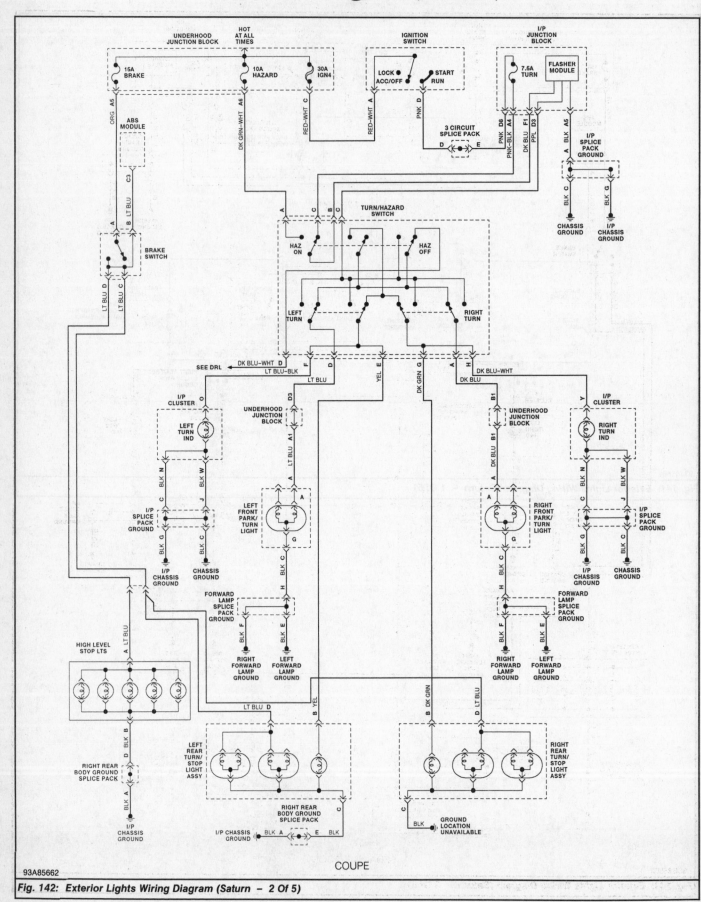

93A85662

COUPE

Fig. 142: Exterior Lights Wiring Diagram (Saturn – 2 Of 5)

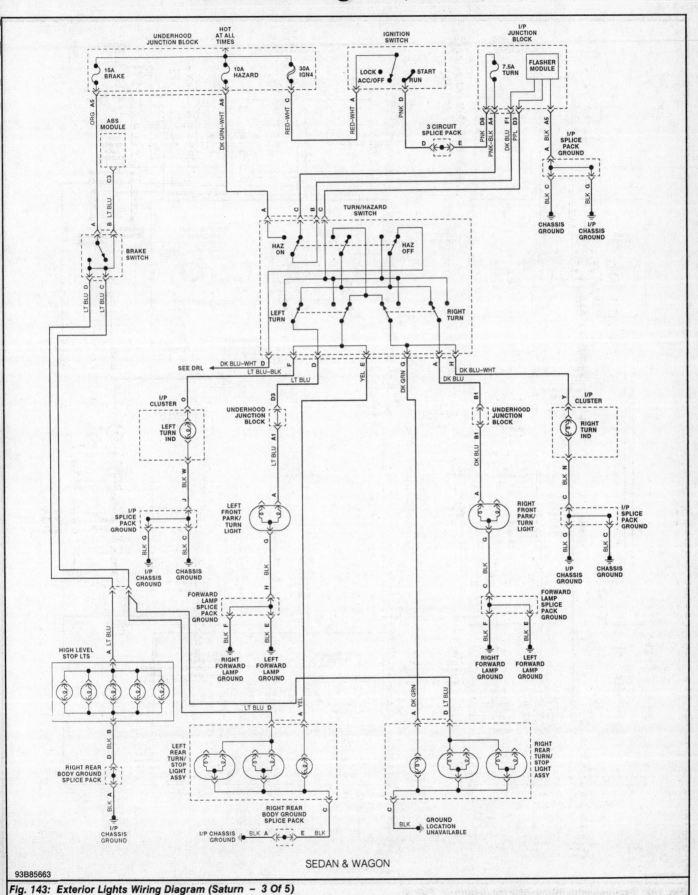

SEDAN & WAGON

93B85663

Fig. 143: Exterior Lights Wiring Diagram (Saturn – 3 Of 5)

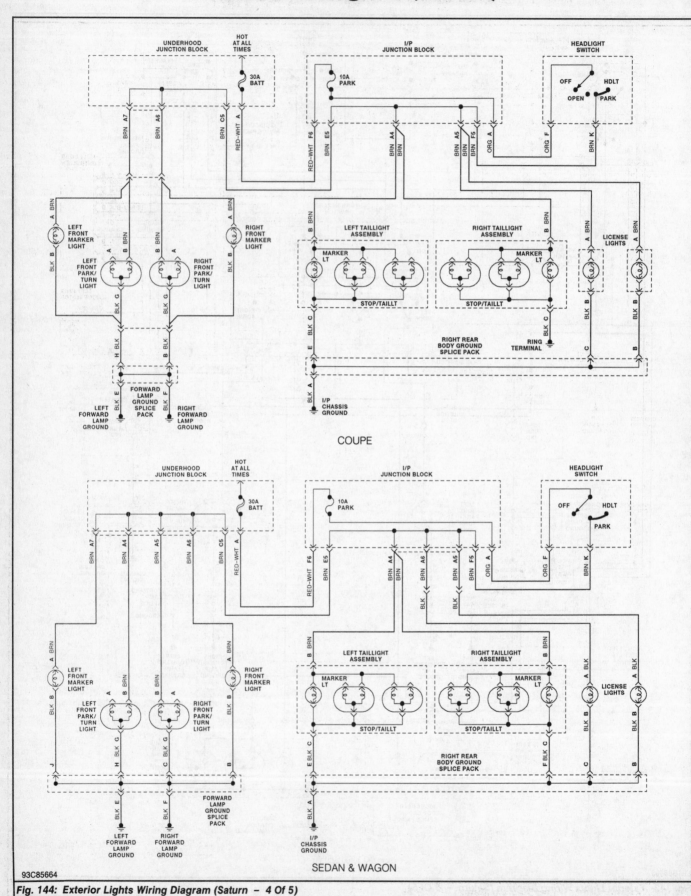

COUPE

SEDAN & WAGON

93C85664

Fig. 144: Exterior Lights Wiring Diagram (Saturn – 4 Of 5)

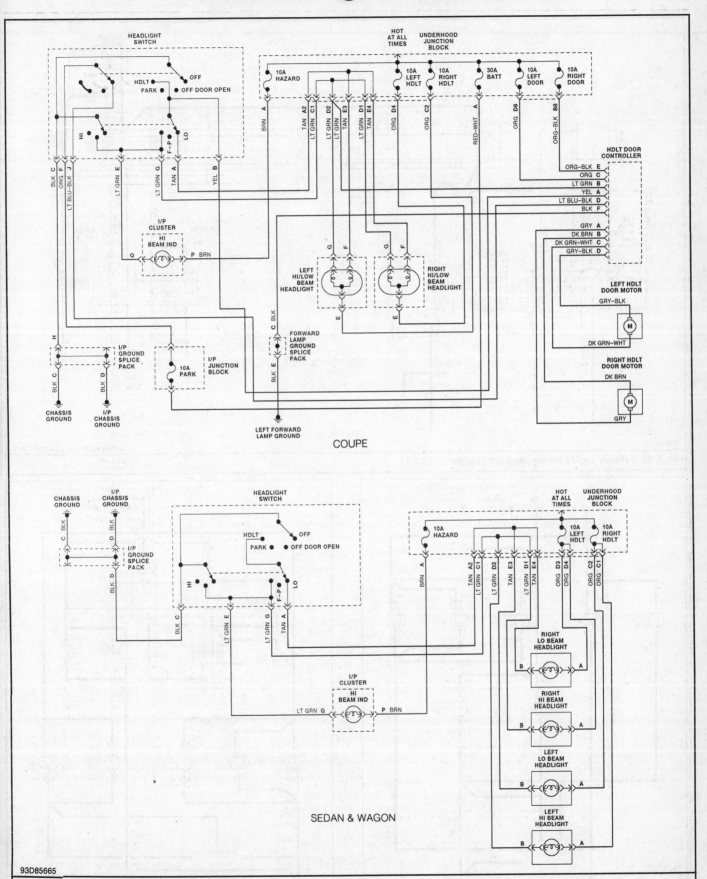

COUPE

SEDAN & WAGON

93D85665

Fig. 145: Exterior Lights Wiring Diagram (Saturn – 5 Of 5)

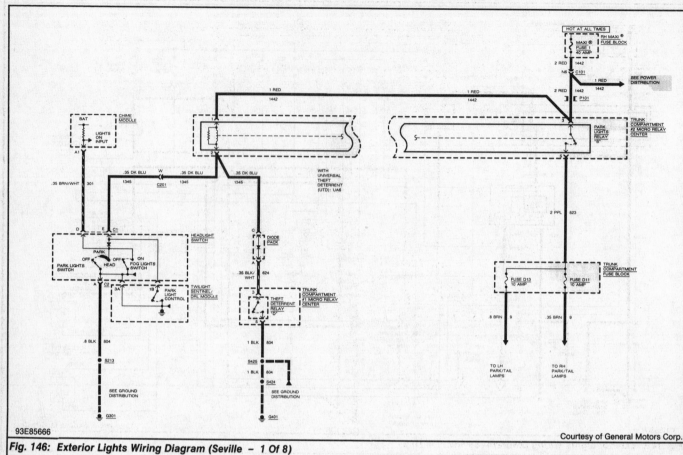

93E85666

Courtesy of General Motors Corp.

Fig. 146: Exterior Lights Wiring Diagram (Seville – 1 Of 8)

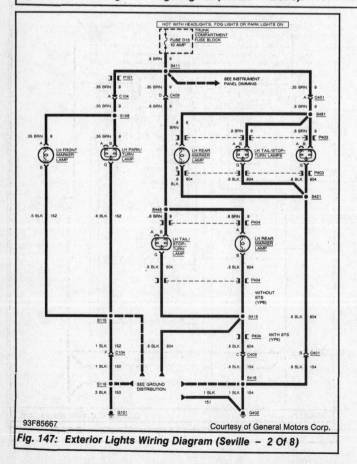

93F85667

Courtesy of General Motors Corp.

Fig. 147: Exterior Lights Wiring Diagram (Seville – 2 Of 8)

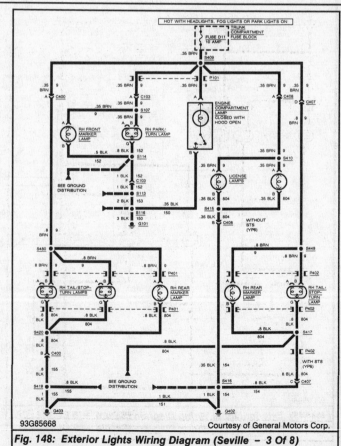

93G85668

Courtesy of General Motors Corp.

Fig. 148: Exterior Lights Wiring Diagram (Seville – 3 Of 8)

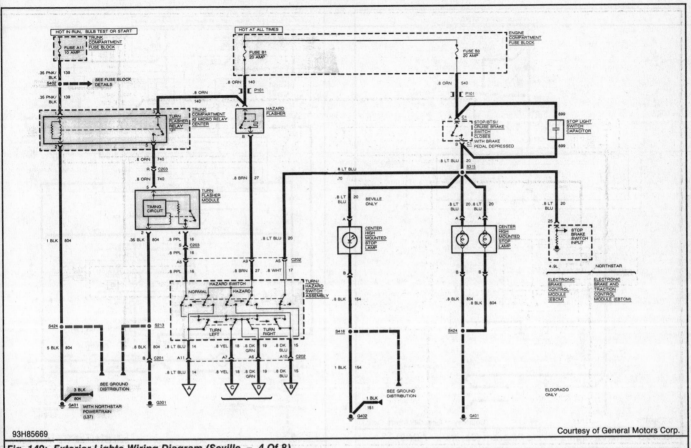

Fig. 149: Exterior Lights Wiring Diagram (Seville – 4 Of 8)

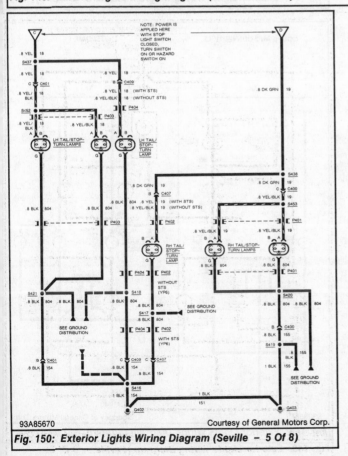

Fig. 150: Exterior Lights Wiring Diagram (Seville – 5 Of 8)

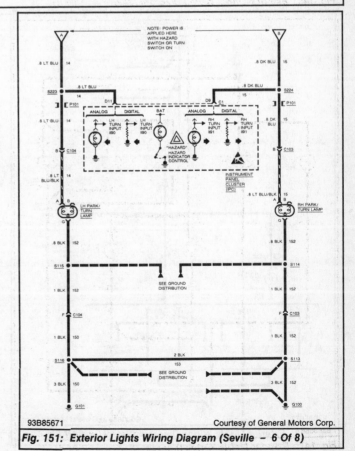

Fig. 151: Exterior Lights Wiring Diagram (Seville – 6 Of 8)

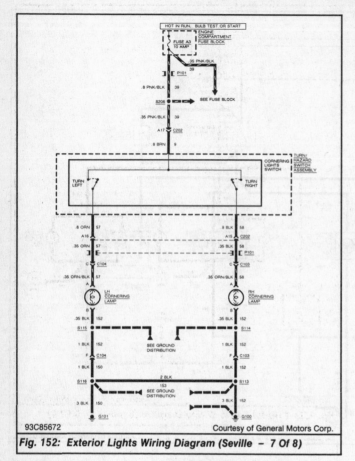

Fig. 152: Exterior Lights Wiring Diagram (Seville – 7 Of 8)

93C85672   Courtesy of General Motors Corp.

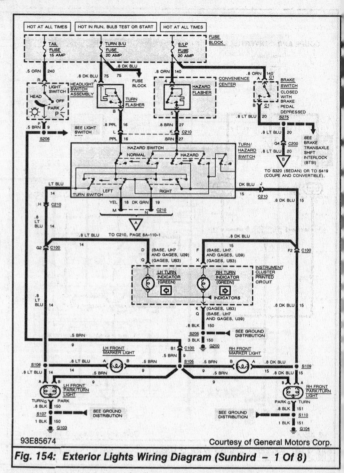

Fig. 154: Exterior Lights Wiring Diagram (Sunbird – 1 Of 8)

93E85674   Courtesy of General Motors Corp.

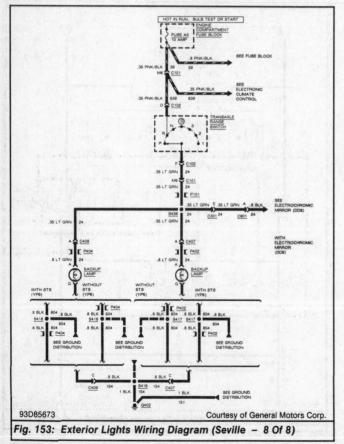

Fig. 153: Exterior Lights Wiring Diagram (Seville – 8 Of 8)

93D85673   Courtesy of General Motors Corp.

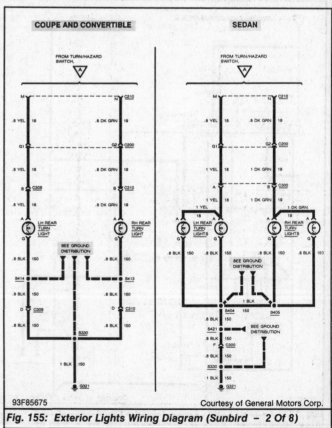

Fig. 155: Exterior Lights Wiring Diagram (Sunbird – 2 Of 8)

93F85675   Courtesy of General Motors Corp.

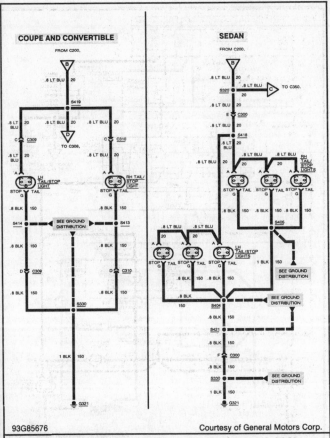

Fig. 156: Exterior Lights Wiring Diagram (Sunbird – 3 Of 8)

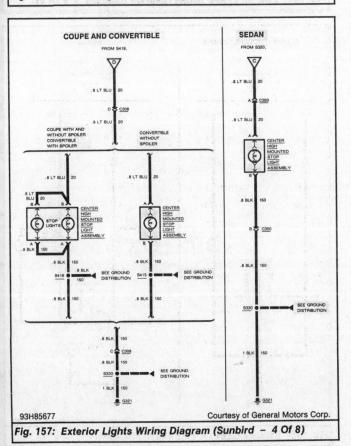

Fig. 157: Exterior Lights Wiring Diagram (Sunbird – 4 Of 8)

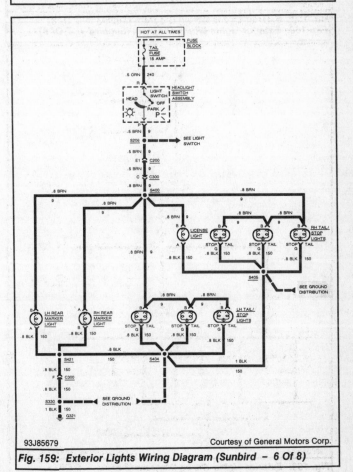

Fig. 158: Exterior Lights Wiring Diagram (Sunbird – 5 Of 8)

Fig. 159: Exterior Lights Wiring Diagram (Sunbird – 6 Of 8)

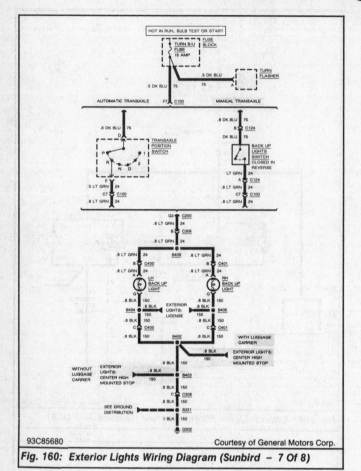

93C85680   Courtesy of General Motors Corp.

Fig. 160: Exterior Lights Wiring Diagram (Sunbird – 7 Of 8)

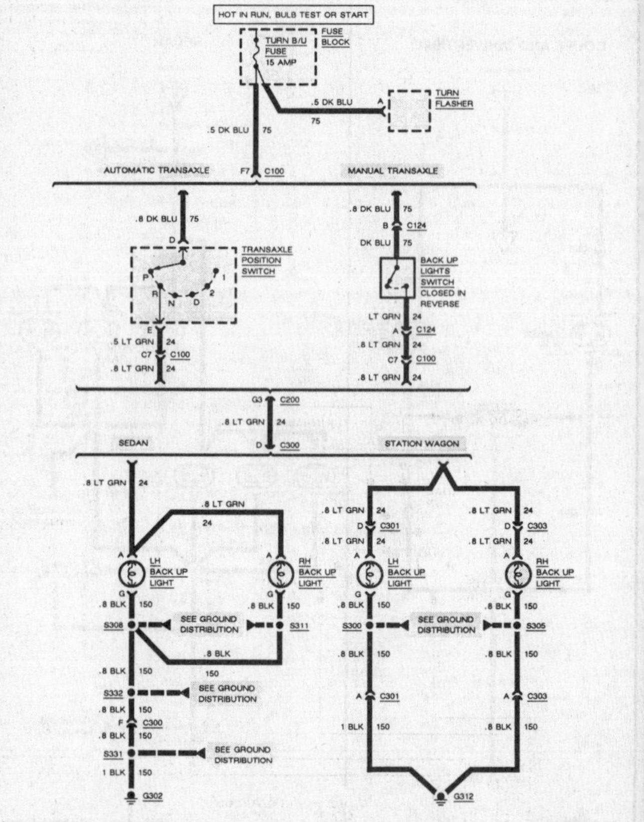

93D85681   Courtesy of General Motors Corp.

Fig. 161: Exterior Lights Wiring Diagram (Sunbird – 8 Of 8)

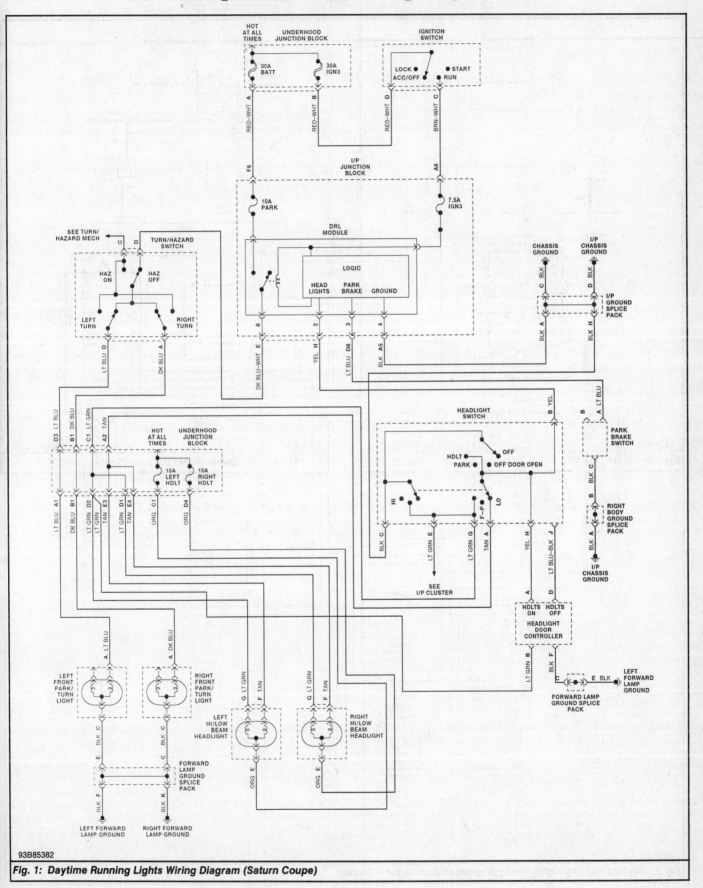

Fig. 1: Daytime Running Lights Wiring Diagram (Saturn Coupe)

93B85382

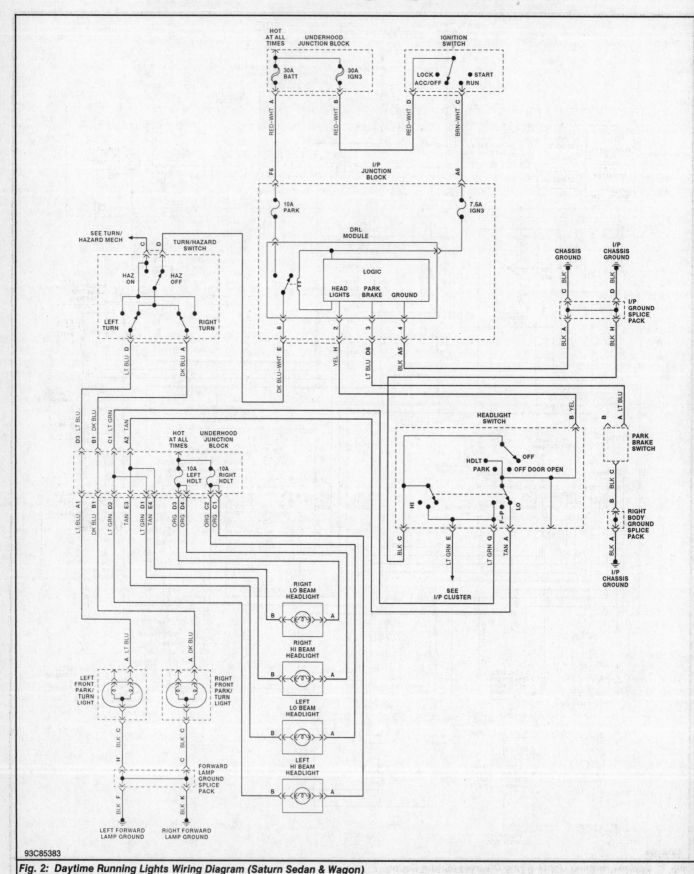

93C85383

Fig. 2: Daytime Running Lights Wiring Diagram (Saturn Sedan & Wagon)

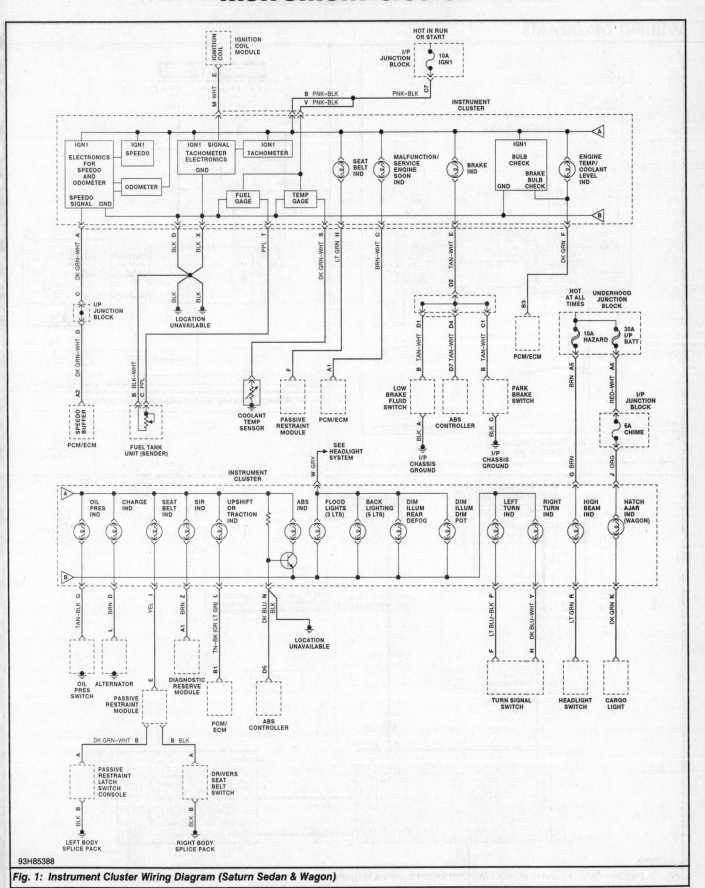

Fig. 1: *Instrument Cluster Wiring Diagram (Saturn Sedan & Wagon)*

93H85388

WIRING DIAGRAMS

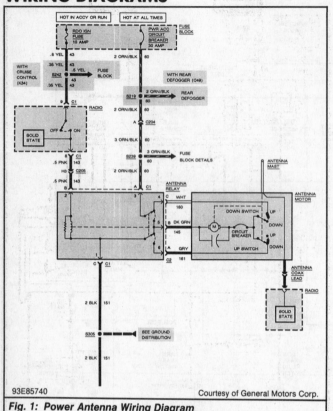

Fig. 1: Power Antenna Wiring Diagram
(Achieva, Grand Am & Skylark)

93E85740   Courtesy of General Motors Corp.

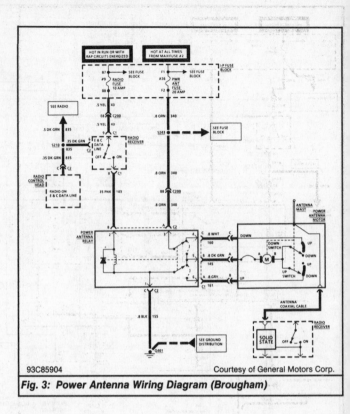

Fig. 3: Power Antenna Wiring Diagram (Brougham)

93C85904   Courtesy of General Motors Corp.

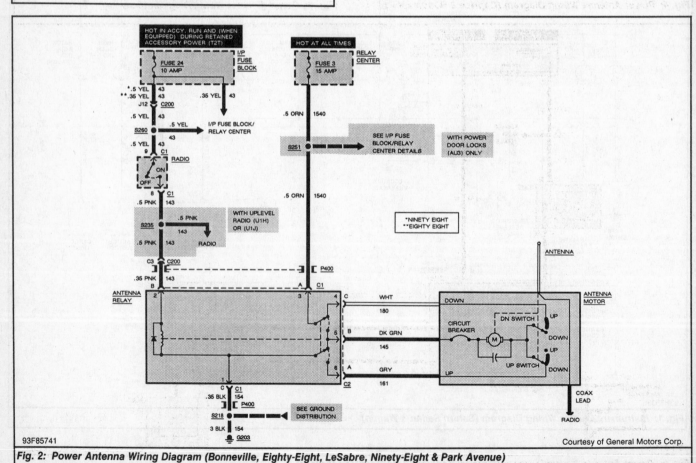

93F85741   Courtesy of General Motors Corp.

Fig. 2: Power Antenna Wiring Diagram (Bonneville, Eighty-Eight, LeSabre, Ninety-Eight & Park Avenue)

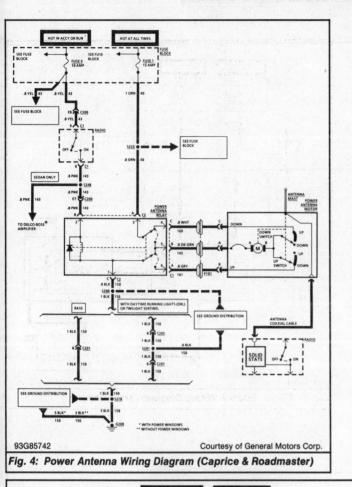

93G85742   Courtesy of General Motors Corp.

Fig. 4: Power Antenna Wiring Diagram (Caprice & Roadmaster)

93I85744   Courtesy of General Motors Corp.

Fig. 6: Power Antenna Wiring Diagram (Corvette)

93H85743   Courtesy of General Motors Corp.

Fig. 5: Power Antenna Wiring Diagram (Century, Cutlass Ciera & Cutlass Cruiser)

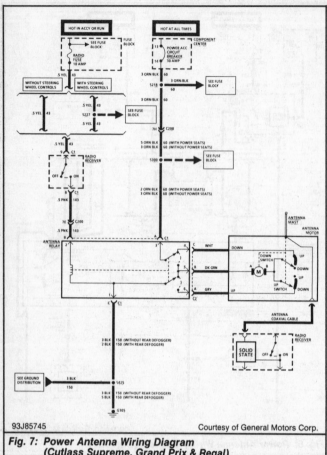

93J85745   Courtesy of General Motors Corp.

*Fig. 7: Power Antenna Wiring Diagram
(Cutlass Supreme, Grand Prix & Regal)*

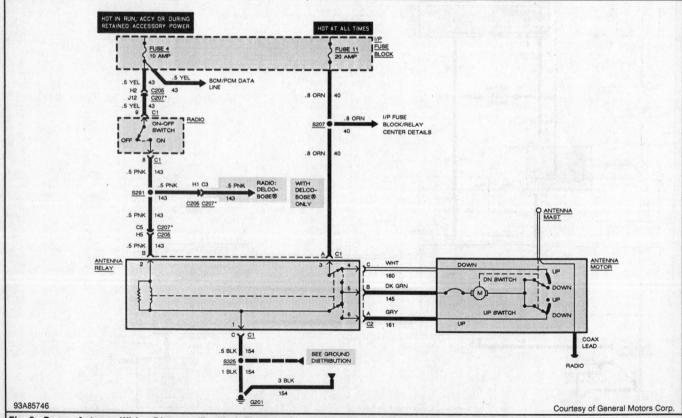

93A85746   Courtesy of General Motors Corp.

Fig. 8: Power Antenna Wiring Diagram (Deville & Fleetwood – Except Commercial CZ Chassis)

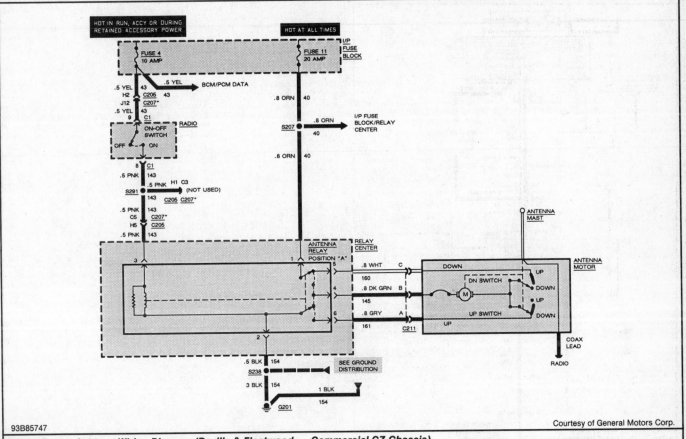

Fig. 9: Power Antenna Wiring Diagram (Deville & Fleetwood – Commercial CZ Chassis)

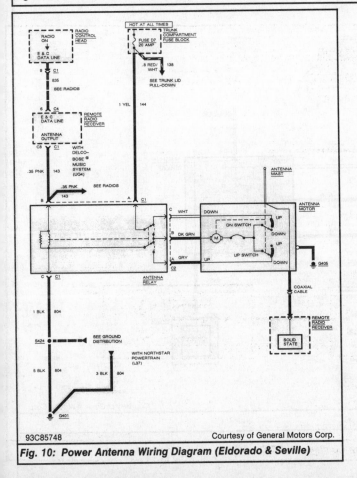

Fig. 10: Power Antenna Wiring Diagram (Eldorado & Seville)

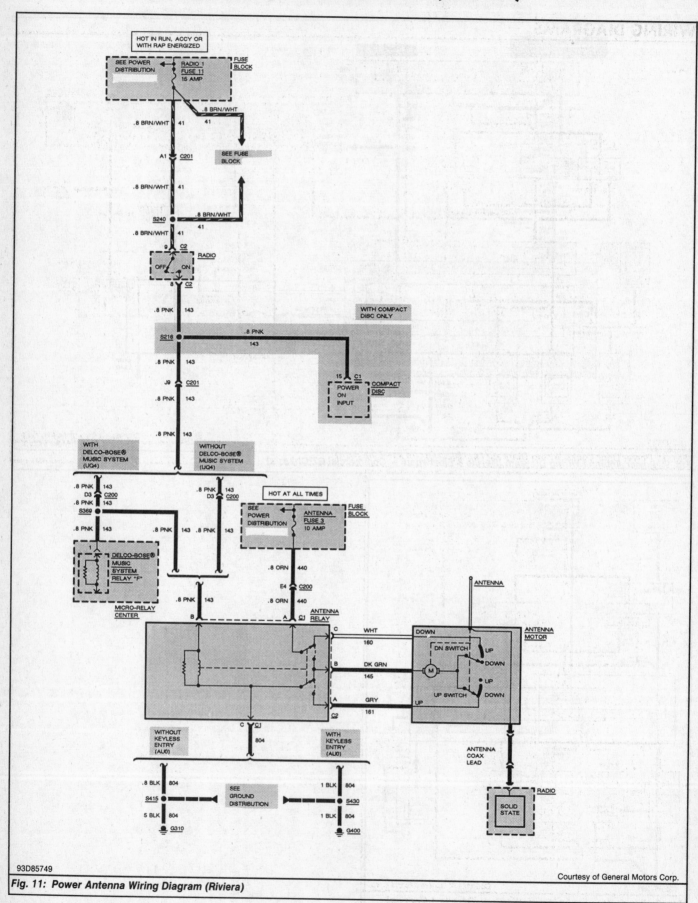

93D85749

Fig. 11: Power Antenna Wiring Diagram (Riviera)

Courtesy of General Motors Corp.

WIRING DIAGRAMS

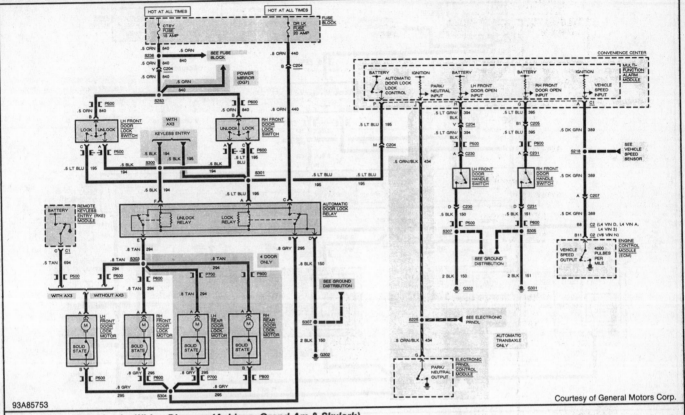

93A85753

Fig. 1: Power Door Locks Wiring Diagram (Achieva, Grand Am & Skylark)

Courtesy of General Motors Corp.

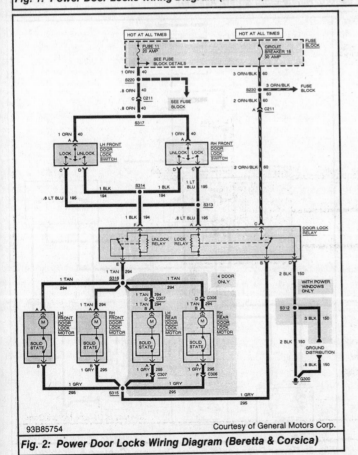

93B85754

Courtesy of General Motors Corp.

Fig. 2: Power Door Locks Wiring Diagram (Beretta & Corsica)

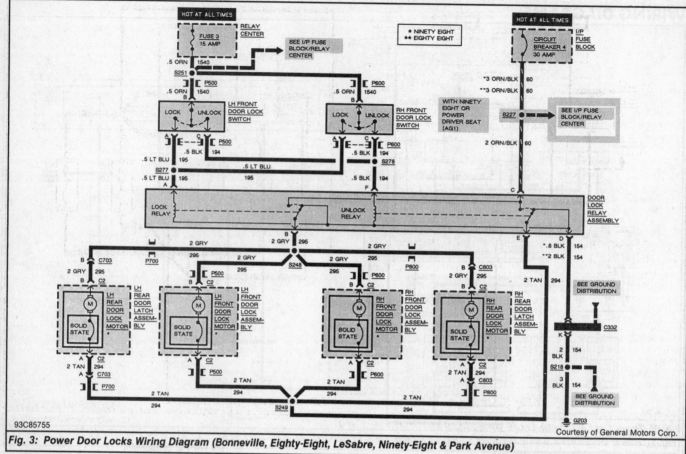

Fig. 3: Power Door Locks Wiring Diagram (Bonneville, Eighty-Eight, LeSabre, Ninety-Eight & Park Avenue)

Courtesy of General Motors Corp.

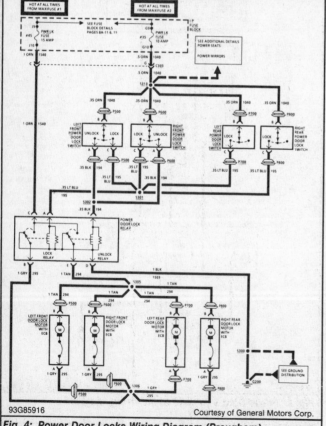

Fig. 4: Power Door Locks Wiring Diagram (Brougham)

Courtesy of General Motors Corp.

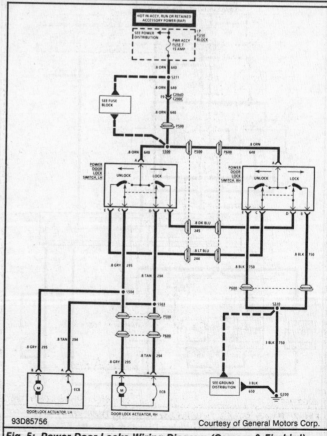

Fig. 5: Power Door Locks Wiring Diagram (Camaro & Firebird)

Courtesy of General Motors Corp.

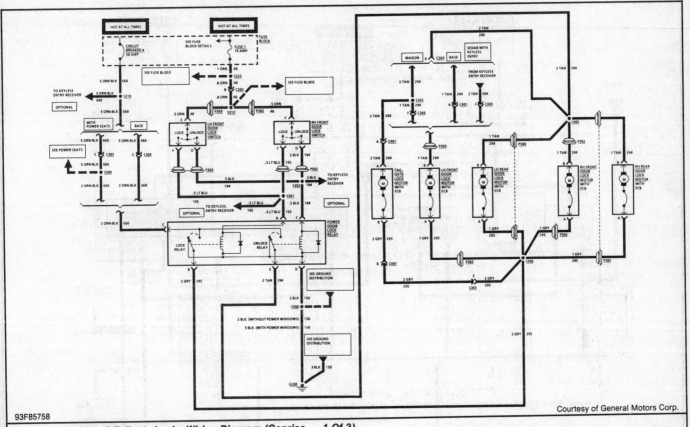

93F85758

Fig. 6: Power Door & Tailgate Locks Wiring Diagram (Caprice – 1 Of 3)

Courtesy of General Motors Corp.

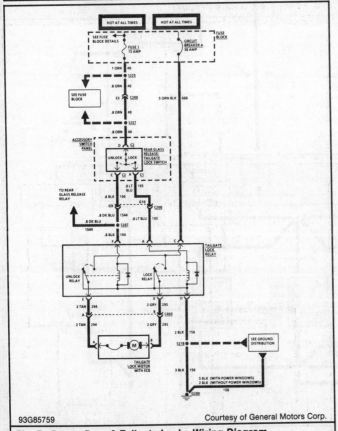

93G85759

Fig. 7: Power Door & Tailgate Locks Wiring Diagram (Caprice – 2 Of 3)

Courtesy of General Motors Corp.

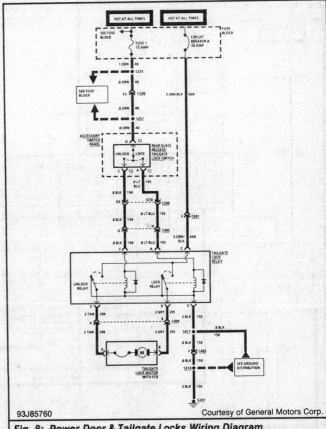

93J85760

Fig. 8: Power Door & Tailgate Locks Wiring Diagram (Caprice – 3 Of 3)

Courtesy of General Motors Corp.

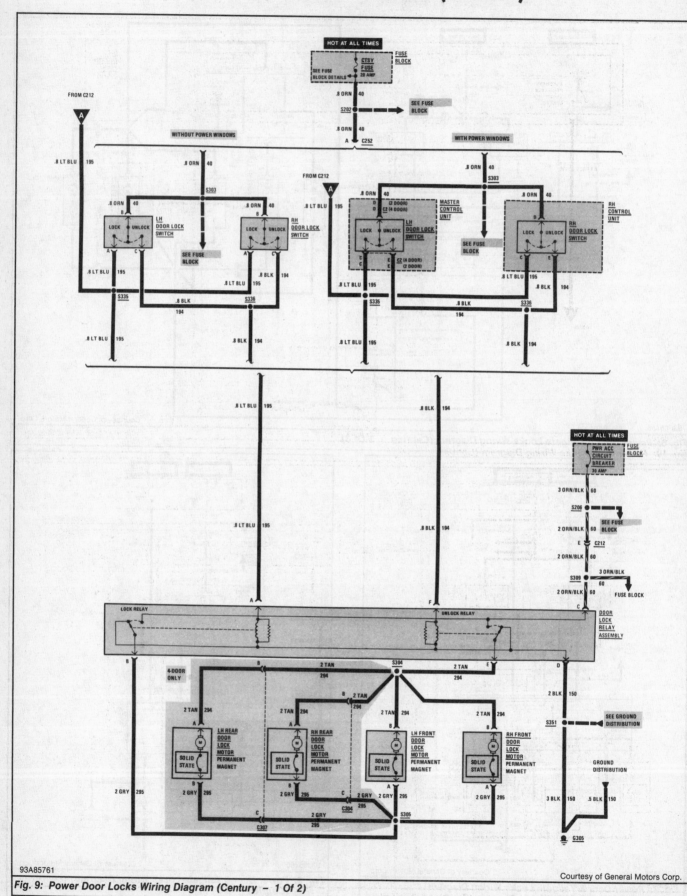

Fig. 9: Power Door Locks Wiring Diagram (Century – 1 Of 2)

93A85761

Courtesy of General Motors Corp.

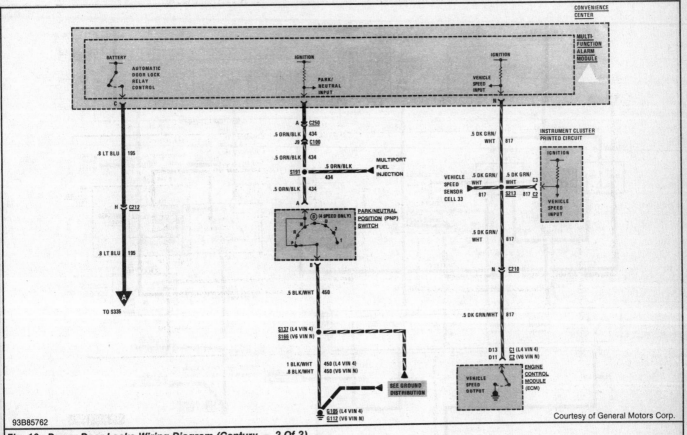

Fig. 10: Power Door Locks Wiring Diagram (Century – 2 Of 2)

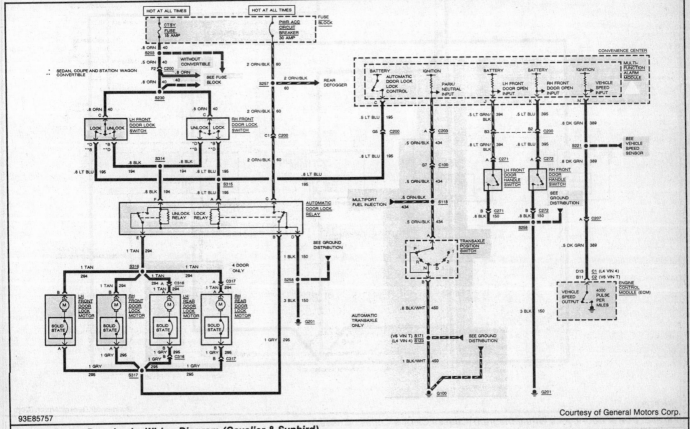

Fig. 11: Power Door Locks Wiring Diagram (Cavalier & Sunbird)

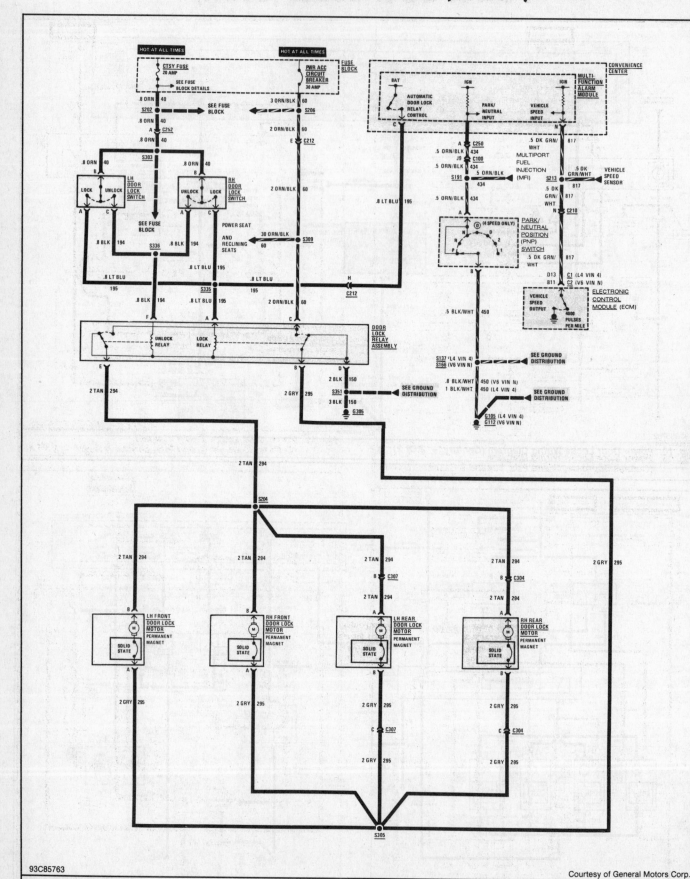

Fig. 12: Power Door Locks Wiring Diagram (Cutlass Ciera & Cutlass Cruiser)

93C85763

Courtesy of General Motors Corp.

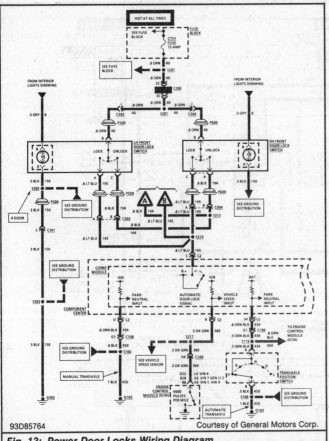

93D85764

Courtesy of General Motors Corp.

Fig. 13: Power Door Locks Wiring Diagram (Cutlass Supreme, Grand Prix, Lumina & Regal – 1 Of 4)

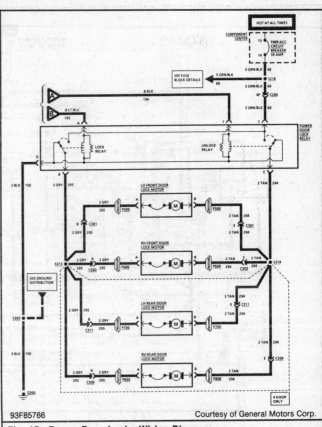

93F85766

Courtesy of General Motors Corp.

Fig. 15: Power Door Locks Wiring Diagram (Cutlass Supreme, Grand Prix, Lumina & Regal – 3 Of 4)

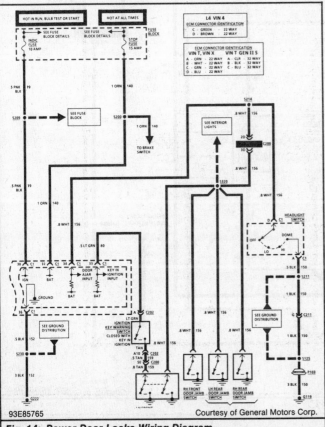

93E85765

Courtesy of General Motors Corp.

Fig. 14: Power Door Locks Wiring Diagram (Cutlass Supreme, Grand Prix, Lumina & Regal – 2 Of 4)

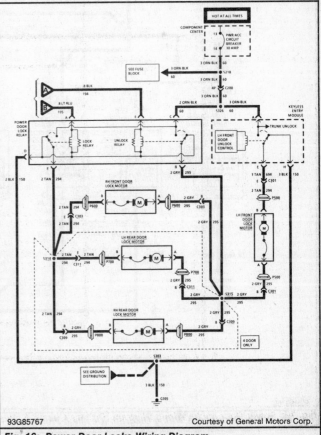

93G85767

Courtesy of General Motors Corp.

Fig. 16: Power Door Locks Wiring Diagram (Cutlass Supreme, Grand Prix, Lumina & Regal – 4 Of 4)

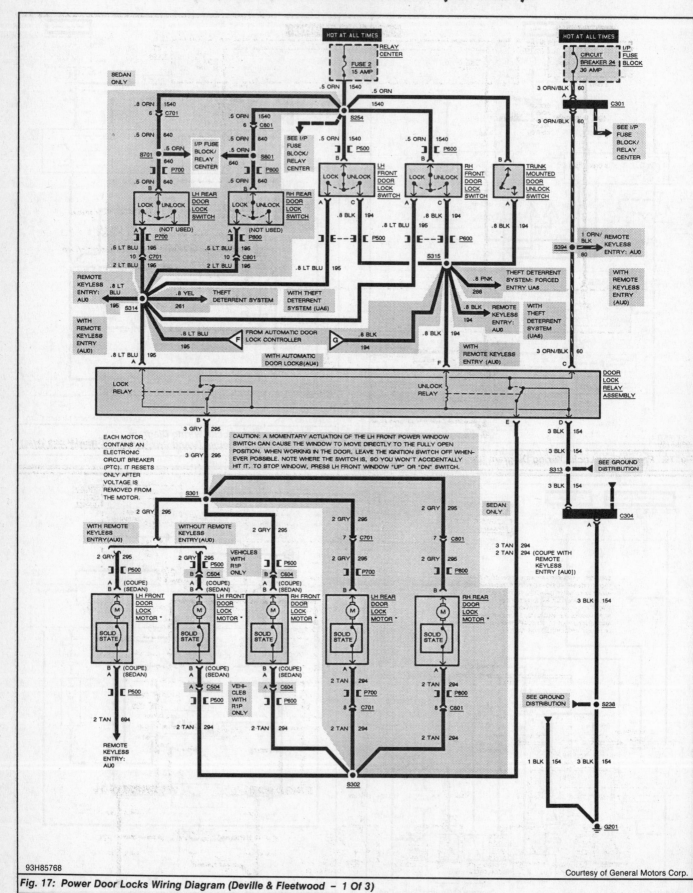

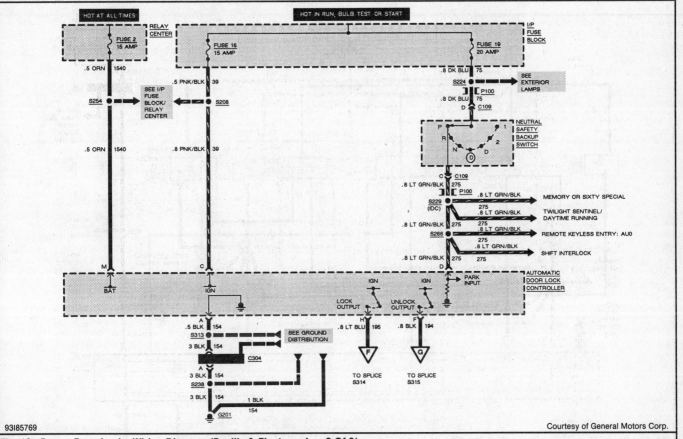

Fig. 18: Power Door Locks Wiring Diagram (Deville & Fleetwood – 2 Of 3)

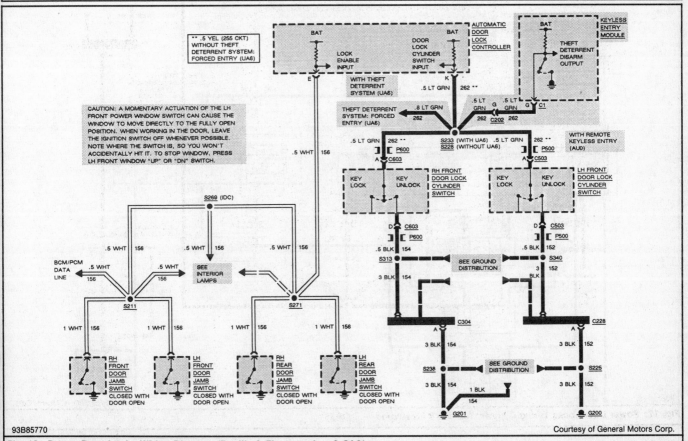

Fig. 19: Power Door Locks Wiring Diagram (Deville & Fleetwood – 3 Of 3)

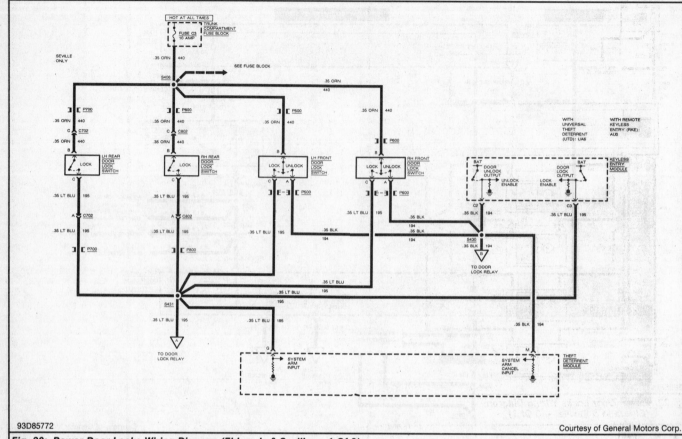

93D85772

Courtesy of General Motors Corp.

Fig. 20: Power Door Locks Wiring Diagram (Eldorado & Seville – 1 Of 3)

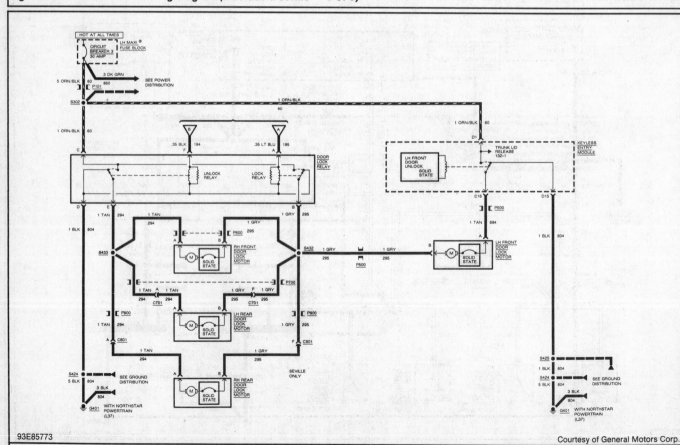

93E85773

Courtesy of General Motors Corp.

Fig. 21: Power Door Locks Wiring Diagram (Eldorado & Seville – 2 Of 3)

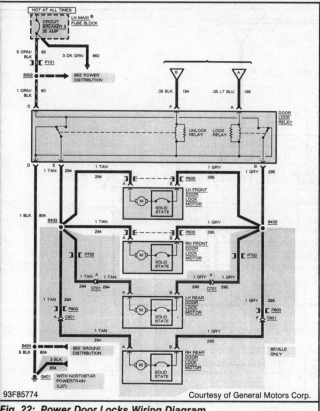

93F85774   Courtesy of General Motors Corp.

*Fig. 22: Power Door Locks Wiring Diagram
(Eldorado & Seville – 3 Of 3)*

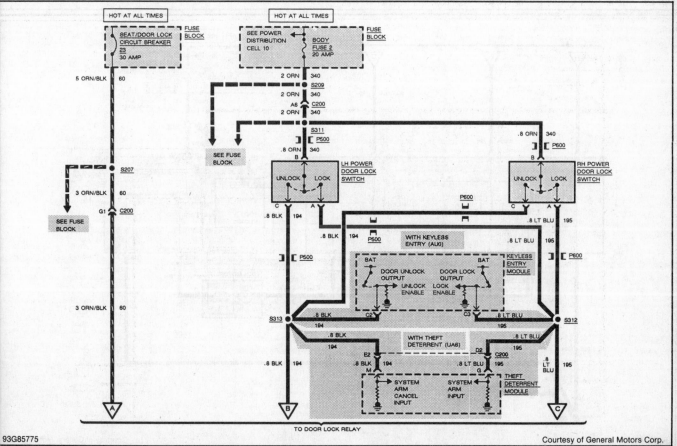

93G85775   Courtesy of General Motors Corp.

Fig. 23: Power Door Locks Wiring Diagram (Riviera – 1 Of 3)

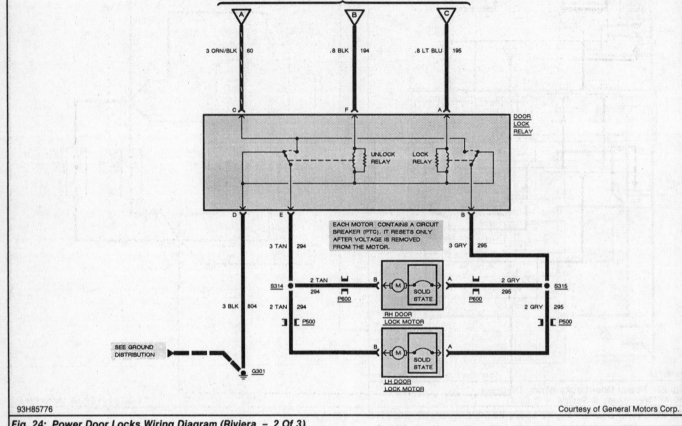

93H85776   Courtesy of General Motors Corp.

Fig. 24: Power Door Locks Wiring Diagram (Riviera – 2 Of 3)

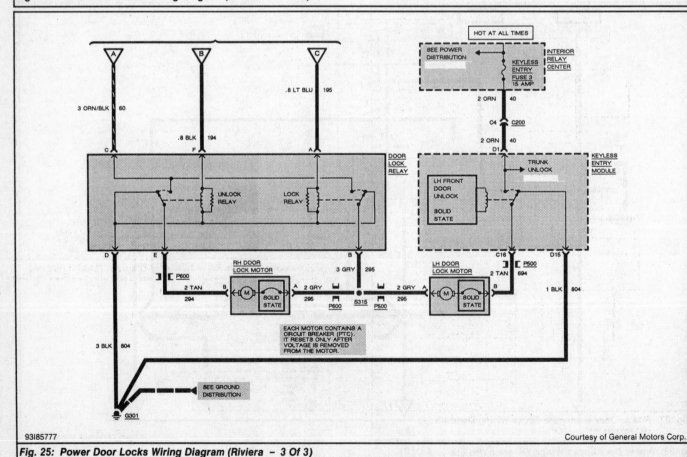

93I85777   Courtesy of General Motors Corp.

Fig. 25: Power Door Locks Wiring Diagram (Riviera – 3 Of 3)

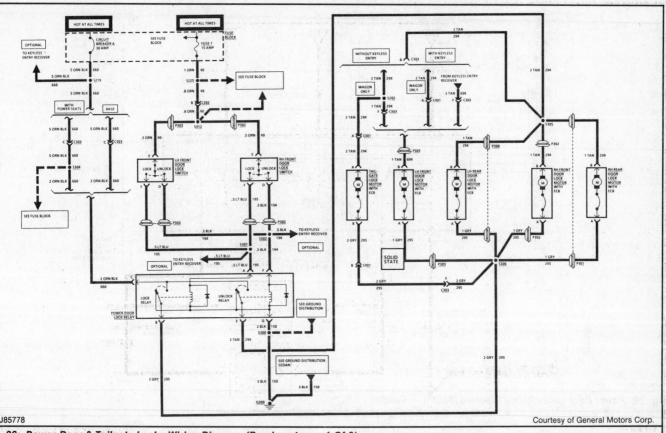

93J85778

Courtesy of General Motors Corp.

Fig. 26: Power Door & Tailgate Locks Wiring Diagram (Roadmaster – 1 Of 2)

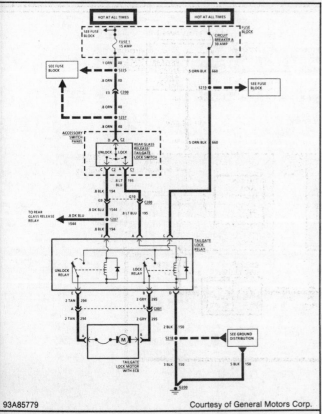

93A85779

Courtesy of General Motors Corp.

Fig. 27: Power Door & Tailgate Locks Wiring Diagram (Roadmaster – 2 Of 2)

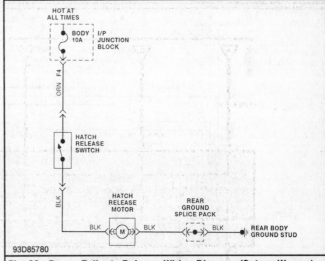

93D85780

Fig. 28: Power Tailgate Release Wiring Diagram (Saturn Wagon)

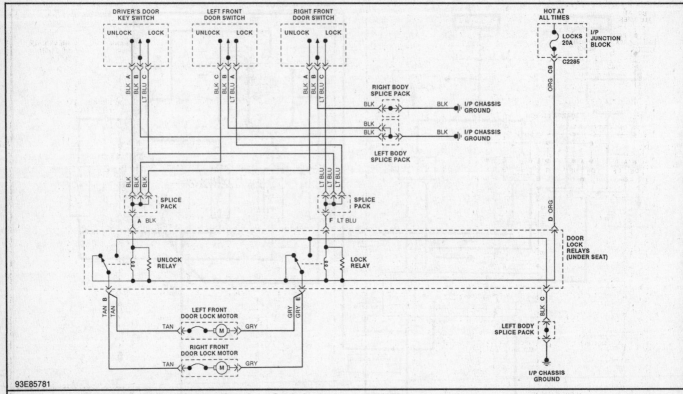

Fig. 29: Power Door Locks Wiring Diagram (Saturn – Coupe)

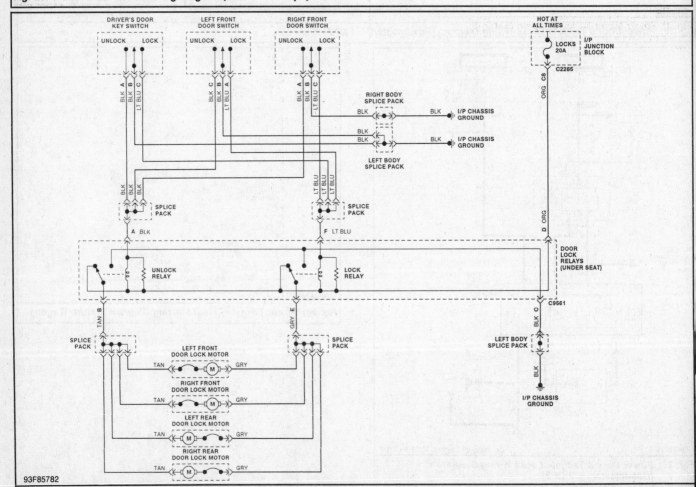

Fig. 30: Power Door Locks Wiring Diagram (Saturn – Sedan & Wagon)

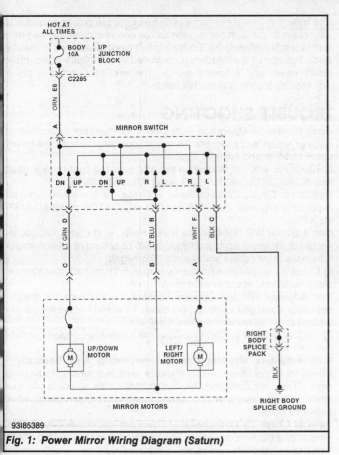

Fig. 1: Power Mirror Wiring Diagram (Saturn)

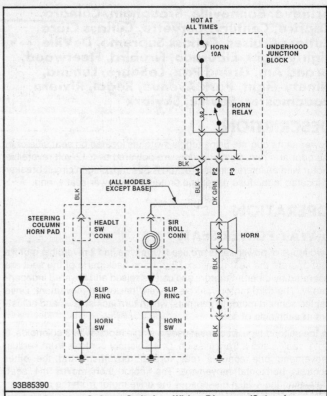

Fig. 2: Steering Column Switches Wiring Diagram (Saturn)

Achieva, Bonneville, Brougham, Camaro, Caprice, Century, Corvette, Cutlass Ciera, Cutlass Cruiser, Cutlass Supreme, DeVille, Eighty-Eight, Eldorado, Firebird, Fleetwood, Grand Am, Grand Prix, LeSabre, Lumina, Ninety-Eight, Park Avenue, Regal, Riviera, Roadmaster, Seville, Skylark

DESCRIPTION

Power seats operate using toggle switches located on seat side or in the door arm rest. Seat adjusters are powered by a 12-volt reversible motor with an interal circuit breaker. A 30-amp, plug-in circuit breaker is located in the fuse panel and protects the power seat wiring.

OPERATION

6-WAY POWER SEATS

Two types of power seats are used. One type has 3 reversible motors that operate the seat functions. Front and back parts of the seat are operated by different motors and can be raised and lowered independently. The third motor controls forward/backward movement. Drive cables connect motor to gearnuts, which turn jack screws and adjusters at each side of seat.

In the second type, each seat uses a single motor with 3 solenoids, 6 drive cables and a transmission. One solenoid controls front vertical movement, one controls rear vertical movement and the other controls horizontal movement. The motor then moves the seat. Releasing the switch disengages the drive motor from the cables.

POWER RECLINING SEAT BACK

Power reclining seat back is an option on some models. The system includes a motor under the seat, drive cable, actuator and control switch. The switch is on the seat edge or the armrest. Power seat back recliners operate independently of other power seat adjustments.

SPORT LUMBAR SEATS

The sport lumbar seats are an option on some models. It is used on either the driver's seat only, or on both front seats. Power is supplied by a 30-amp circuit breaker in the fuse block. Adjustments are made by a solenoid valve assembly located under the seat(s). Operation is controlled by a switch located on the seat side, or in the center console.

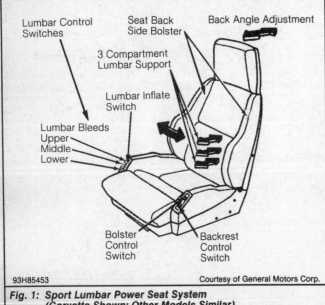

93H85453   Courtesy of General Motors Corp.

Fig. 1: Sport Lumbar Power Seat System (Corvette Shown; Other Models Similar)

The backrest lateral restraints (side bolsters) are power adjusted 15 degress in or out. Lumbar support can be pneumatically adjusted from soft to firm by inflating the 3 compartment bladders located in the seat back. Inflation of the bladders is controlled by a pressure pump, bleed down valves and a control switch. The seat back angle is power adjusted by a control in the left bolster.

TROUBLE SHOOTING

Jerky Horizontal Operation – 1) Check for improper lubrication of adjuster shoes and channels. To correct operation, lubricate adjuster upper channel and adjuster shoes.
2) Check for adjuster horizontal actuator gear too tight to rack gear. See HORIZONTAL ACTUATOR under ADJUSTMENTS.
Horizontal Chuck Or Looseness – Check for horizontal actuator improperly adjusted. See HORIZONTAL ACTUATOR under ADJUSTMENTS.
One Adjuster Will Not Operate Horizontally – 1) Check for disconnected or damaged horizontal drive cable. To correct operation, check horizontal drive cables and replace if damaged.
2) Check for inoperative horizontal actuator. To correct operation, replace horizontal actuator assembly.
One Adjuster Will Not Operate Vertically – 1) Check for disconnected or damaged vertical drive cable. To correct operation, check vertical drive cables and replace if damaged.
2) Vertical gearnut inoperative. To correct operation, replace vertical actuator assembly.
Both Adjusters Will Not Operate Horizontally &/Or Vertically – Check for inoperative horizontal and/or vertical solenoid in transmission. Check for damaged, broken or inoperable solenoid plunger, shaft, gear or drive gear. To correct operation, replace damaged or defective parts.
Vertical Chuck Or Looseness – Check for excessive clearance at vertical gearnut tension spring. To correct looseness, grind top of vertical gearnut shoulder until slack is removed.
Power Seat Back Motor Operates, But Seat Back Does Not Move –

Check for disconnected or broken drive cable. Check for damaged or broken reclining actuator gearnut. Ensure reclining actuator is not disconnected from arm of seat back lock or support. Check for incorrect application of seat back lock or support.
Power Seat Back Operation Jerky – Check for kink or damage to drive cable. Check for bind in reclining hinge arm. Check for damaged or bent jack screw. Check for damaged actuator gearnut. Ensure there is sufficient lubrication. Check for loose jack screw lock nut.

ELECTRICAL

Inoperative Adjuster Motor – Check for shorted or open circuit between power source, switch or motor. Check for a defective adjuster motor.
Motor Operates But Adjuster Will Not Operate – Check for a shorted or open circuit between switch and solenoid. Check solenoid for defects.
Motor Operates, But Adjusters Or Recliner Only Operates In One Direction – Check for a shorted or open circuit between one of the motor fields and control switch. Check for a defective field coil.

ADJUSTMENTS

HORIZONTAL ACTUATOR

1) Chucking can be corrected by adjusting horizontal actuator and pinion gear to fully mesh with lower adjuster track rack gear. Operate seat to full up position and about 3/4 forward. Loosen horizontal actuator screws.
2) Using a large screwdriver, apply outward pressure on horizontal actuator (about 15-25 ft. lbs.) and energize horizontal switch to move seat slightly fore and aft. This keeps seat horizontal actuator pinion gear teeth in close contact with lower track rack gear teeth and eliminates free play between gear teeth. Tighten screws while maintaining ouward pressure against horizontal actuators.

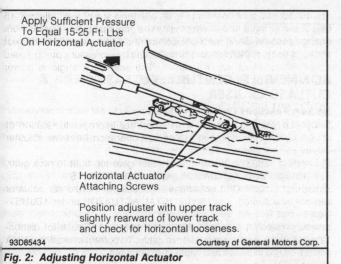

Apply Sufficient Pressure
To Equal 15-25 Ft. Lbs
On Horizontal Actuator

Horizontal Actuator
Attaching Screws

Position adjuster with upper track
slightly rearward of lower track
and check for horizontal looseness.

93D85434   Courtesy of General Motors Corp.

Fig. 2: Adjusting Horizontal Actuator

SEAT ADJUSTER PHASING

When installing power seat adjusters (except at back recliner), ensure each pair of adjusters is in phase with each other. When adjusters are out of phase, one adjuster will reach its maximum travel limit before the other, resulting in improper seat travel.

Horizontal Travel – Operate seat until one adjuster reaches full forward position. Detach horizontal drive cable from adjuster which has reached its travel limit. Operate seat forward until other adjuster reaches its full forward position. Reconnect drive cable of first adjuster. Adjusters are now in phase.

Vertical Travel (Front Or Rear) – 1) Operate seat until one adjuster has reached fully raised position at both front and rear vertical travel limits. Disconnect both front and rear vertical drive cables from adjuster which has reached its travel limit.

2) Operate seat until other adjuster reaches fully raised position. Now reconnect previously disconnected front and rear vertical drive cables. Seat should now be in phase. If not, repeat procedure.

REMOVAL & INSTALLATION

CAUTION: When battery is disconnected, vehicle computer and memory systems may lose memory data. Driveability problems may exist until computer systems have completed a relearn cycle. See COMPUTER RELEARN PROCEDURES article in GENERAL INFORMATION before disconnecting battery.

BASIC SEAT ASSEMBLY

Removal & Installation – 1) Remove seatbelt-to-floor anchor plate attaching bolts. Where required, remove door sill plates and turn back carpet to gain access to adjuster-to-floor attaching bolts. Operate seat to full forward and upward position. At rear of adjusters, remove adjuster-to-floor rear attaching bolts.

2) Operate seat to full rearward and full rear tilt position. Remove front adjuster-to-floor pan attaching nuts. Disconnect electrical connector under seat and remove seat. To install, reverse removal procedure.

SEAT ADJUSTER ASSEMBLY

1) Remove seat as previously described. Place seat upside-down on a clean bench. Disconnect drive cables at adjuster being removed. Squeeze oblong connector to remove. On bucket seats, remove motor support-to-adjuster bolt.

2) Remove adjuster-to-seat bottom attaching bolts and remove seat adjuster. Note locations of spacers (if equipped). To install, reverse removal procedure and ensure seats are in phase.

SEAT BACK RECLINING ACTUATOR

Removal & Installation – Remove seat and place upside-down on clean bench. Remove trim on outside of seat for access to actuator. Unscrew reclining back drive cable from reclining actuator and detach cable from actuator. Remove pin securing reclining actuator coupling-to-hinge arm. Remove actuator. To install, reverse removal procedure.

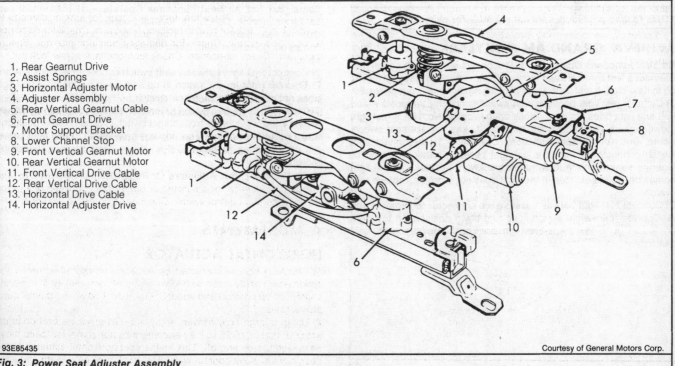

1. Rear Gearnut Drive
2. Assist Springs
3. Horizontal Adjuster Motor
4. Adjuster Assembly
5. Rear Vertical Gearnut Cable
6. Front Gearnut Drive
7. Motor Support Bracket
8. Lower Channel Stop
9. Front Vertical Gearnut Motor
10. Rear Vertical Gearnut Motor
11. Front Vertical Drive Cable
12. Rear Vertical Drive Cable
13. Horizontal Drive Cable
14. Horizontal Adjuster Drive

93E85435   Courtesy of General Motors Corp.

Fig. 3: Power Seat Adjuster Assembly

DRIVE MOTOR

Removal & Installation – **1)** Remove seat and place upside-down on clean bench. Disconnect wiring. On single motor seats, remove transmission-to-support screws and cable ends plates on transmission ends. Separate motor and transmission and disengage rubber coupling.

2) On 3-motor seats, remove motor support-to-motor mounting bracket screw. Disconnect drive cables from adjusters, remove nut from motor retaining rod and remove motor. To install, reverse removal procedure and check phasing

BACK ANGLE OR BOLSTER SWITCH

Removal & Installation – Disconnect battery ground cable. Remove seat cushion. Remove 2 screws retaining left side control panel trim plate. Pull face plate with switches attached out of armrest to gain access to electrical connector. Remove defective switch. To install, reverse removal procedure.

LUMBAR CONTROL OR VALVE BODY

Removal & Installation – **1)** Disconnect battery ground cable. Remove seat cushion and release bail clip from from frame panel. Disconnect pneumatic tubing and electrical connector to lumbar control assembly. Remove hog ring at underside of seat to gain access.

2) Remove face plate and remove control assembly through bottom of seat cushion. If necessary, valve body can also be replaced at this time. To install, reverse removal procedure.

LUMBAR MOTOR & PUMP ASSEMBLY

Removal & Installation – **1)** Disconnect battery ground cable. Remove seat cushion. Remove 4 bolts retaining cushion frame panel to adjuster. Disconnect electrical connector and remove seat from vehicle.

2) Disconnect electrical and pneumatic harness connectors at motor. Remove motor and pump assembly to frame attaching parts. Remove motor from seat cushion frame. To install, reverse removal procedure. Check operation of motor and pump.

TESTING

NOTE: Testing procedures are not available for all models.

ACHIEVA, GRAND AM & SKYLARK

No Seat Functions Operate – **1)** Disconnect seat switch connector. Connect a test light between terminal F and ground. If test light glows, go to next step. If test light does not glow, repair open in circuit No. 60.

2) Connect test light between seat switch connector terminals A and F. If test light does not glow, repair open in circuit No. 150. If test light glows, ensure switch is mated correctly. If okay, replace seat switch.

Some, But Not All Seat Functions Operate – **1)** Disconnect seat switch connector. Connect a test light between terminals E and D. Operate seat switch in forward and backward positions. If test light comes on, go to next step. If test light does not come on, replace seat switch.

2) Connect test light between seat switch connector terminals A and B. Operate rear height switch in up and down positions. if test light comes on, go to next step. If test light does not come on, replace seat switch.

3) Connect test light between switch terminals G and H. Operate front height switch in up and down positions. If test light does not come on, replace seat switch. If test light comes on, check wiring to motors. If wiring is okay, replace inoperable motor(s).

BONNEVILLE, CENTURY, CUTLASS CIERA & CUTLASS CRUISER

No Seat Functions Operate – **1)** Disconnect seat switch connector. Connect a test light between terminal F and ground. If test light comes on, go to next step. If test light does not come on, repair open in circuit No. 60.

2) Connect test light between seat switch connector terminals C and F. If test light does not come on, repair open in circuit No. 151 or 152. If test light comes on, ensure switch is mated correctly. If okay, replace seat switch.

Some, But Not All Seat Functions Operate – **1)** Disconnect seat switch connector. Connect a test light between terminals C and D. Operate rear height switch in up and down positions. If test light comes on, go to next step. If test light does not come on, replace seat switch.

2) Connect test light between seat switch connector terminals A and B. Operate front height switch in up and down positions. If test light comes on, go to next step. If test light does not come on, replace seat switch.

3) Connect test light between switch terminals E and F. Operate front height switch in up and down positions. If test light does not come on, replace seat switch. If test light comes on, check wiring to motors. If wiring is okay, replace inoperable motor(s).

EIGHTY-EIGHT & NINETY-EIGHT

No Seat Functions Operate – **1)** Disconnect seat switch connector. Connect a test light between terminal F and ground on Eighty-Eight, or terminal L and ground on Ninety Eight. If test light comes on, go to next step. If test light does not come on, repair open in circuit No. 60.

2) Connect test light between seat switch connector terminals C and F on Eighty Eight, or terminals A and L on Ninety Eight. If test light does not come on, repair open in circuit No. 152 or 154. If test light comes on, check that switch is mated correctly. If okay, replace seat switch.

Some, But Not All Seat Functions Operate – **1)** Disconnect seat switch connector. Connect a test light between terminals C and D. Operate rear height switch in up and down positions. If test light comes on, go to next step. If test light does not come on, replace seat switch.

2) Connect test light between seat switch connector terminals A and B. Operate front height switch in up and down positions. If test light does not come on, replace seat switch.

3) If test light came on in step **2)**, Connect test light between switch terminals E and F. Operate front height switch in up and down positions. If test light does not come on, replace seat switch. If test light comes on, check wiring to motors. If wiring is okay, replace inoperable motor(s).

CHART 1,
ALL POSITIONS DO NOT OPERATE (BROUGHAM)

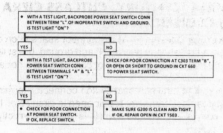

CHART 2,
ENTIRE SEAT WILL NOT MOVE FORWARD &/OR BACK (BROUGHAM)

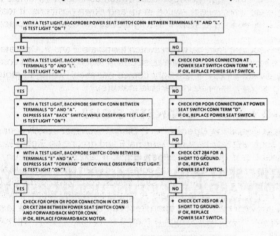

CHART 3,
FRONT HEIGHT WILL NOT MOVE UP &/OR DOWN (BROUGHAM)

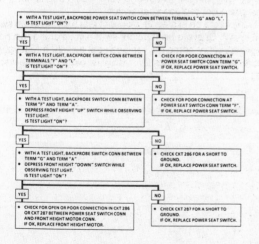

CHART 4,
REAR HEIGHT WILL NOT MOVE UP &/OR DOWN (BROUGHAM)

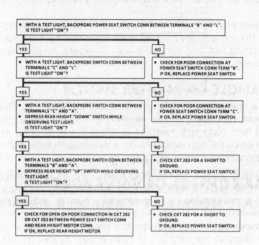

CHART 5,
RECLINER INOPERATIVE (BROUGHAM)

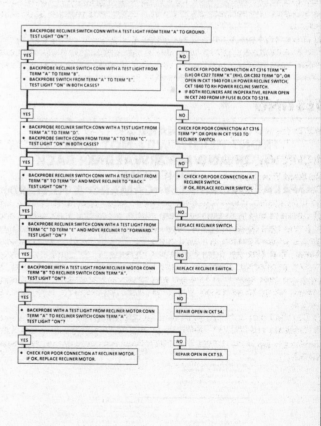

93B85473 93C85474 93D85475 93E85476 93F85477

CHART 1,
ALL POWER SEAT FUNCTIONS INOPERATIVE
(CAMARO & FIREBIRD)

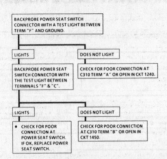

- BACKPROBE POWER SEAT SWITCH CONNECTOR WITH A TEST LIGHT BETWEEN TERM "F" AND GROUND.

LIGHTS — BACKPROBE POWER SEAT SWITCH CONNECTOR WITH THE TEST LIGHT BETWEEN TERMINALS "F" & "C".

DOES NOT LIGHT — CHECK FOR POOR CONNECTION AT C310 TERM "A" OR OPEN IN CKT 1240.

LIGHTS — • CHECK FOR POOR CONNECTION AT POWER SEAT SWITCH. IF OK, REPLACE POWER SEAT SWITCH.

DOES NOT LIGHT — CHECK FOR POOR CONNECTION AT C310 TERM "B" OR OPEN IN CKT 1450.

CHART 2,
ENTIRE SEAT WILL NOT MOVE FORWARD
&/OR BACK UP OR DOWN FUNCTIONS
OPERATE NORMALLY (CAMARO & FIREBIRD)

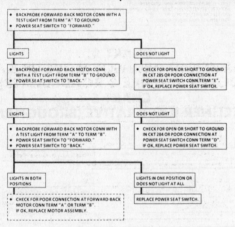

- BACKPROBE FORWARD BACK MOTOR CONN WITH A TEST LIGHT FROM TERM "A" TO GROUND
- POWER SEAT SWITCH TO "FORWARD."

LIGHTS — • BACKPROBE FORWARD BACK MOTOR CONN WITH A TEST LIGHT FROM TERM "B" TO GROUND. • POWER SEAT SWITCH TO "BACK."

DOES NOT LIGHT — • CHECK FOR OPEN OR SHORT TO GROUND IN CKT 285 OR POOR CONNECTION AT POWER SEAT SWITCH CONN TERM "E". IF OK, REPLACE POWER SEAT SWITCH.

LIGHTS — • BACKPROBE FORWARD BACK MOTOR CONN WITH A TEST LIGHT FROM TERM "A" TO TERM "B". • POWER SEAT SWITCH TO "FORWARD." • POWER SEAT SWITCH TO "BACK."

DOES NOT LIGHT — • CHECK FOR OPEN OR SHORT TO GROUND IN CKT 284 OR POOR CONNECTION AT POWER SEAT SWITCH CONN TERM "D". IF OK, REPLACE POWER SEAT SWITCH.

LIGHTS IN BOTH POSITIONS — • CHECK FOR POOR CONNECTION AT FORWARD BACK MOTOR CONN TERM "A" OR TERM "B". IF OK, REPLACE MOTOR ASSEMBLY.

LIGHTS IN ONE POSITION OR DOES NOT LIGHT AT ALL — REPLACE POWER SEAT SWITCH.

CHART 3,
FRONT HEIGHT WILL NOT MOVE UP
&/OR DOWN FORWARD OR BACK
FUNCTIONS
OPERATE NORMALLY (CAMARO & FIREBIRD)

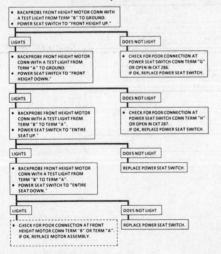

- BACKPROBE FRONT HEIGHT MOTOR CONN WITH A TEST LIGHT FROM TERM "B" TO GROUND.
- POWER SEAT SWITCH TO "FRONT HEIGHT UP."

LIGHTS — • BACKPROBE FRONT HEIGHT MOTOR CONN WITH A TEST LIGHT FROM TERM "A" TO GROUND. • POWER SEAT SWITCH TO "FRONT HEIGHT DOWN."

DOES NOT LIGHT — • CHECK FOR POOR CONNECTION AT POWER SEAT SWITCH CONN TERM "G" OR OPEN IN CKT 286. IF OK, REPLACE POWER SEAT SWITCH.

LIGHTS — • BACKPROBE FRONT HEIGHT MOTOR CONN WITH A TEST LIGHT FROM TERM "B" TO TERM "A". • POWER SEAT SWITCH TO "ENTIRE SEAT UP."

DOES NOT LIGHT — • CHECK FOR POOR CONNECTION AT POWER SEAT SWITCH CONN TERM "H" OR OPEN IN CKT 287. IF OK, REPLACE POWER SEAT SWITCH.

LIGHTS — • BACKPROBE FRONT HEIGHT MOTOR CONN WITH A TEST LIGHT FROM TERM "B" TO TERM "A". • POWER SEAT SWITCH TO "ENTIRE SEAT DOWN."

DOES NOT LIGHT — REPLACE POWER SEAT SWITCH.

LIGHTS — • CHECK FOR POOR CONNECTION AT FRONT HEIGHT MOTOR CONN TERM "B" OR TERM "A". IF OK, REPLACE MOTOR ASSEMBLY.

DOES NOT LIGHT — REPLACE POWER SEAT SWITCH.

CHART 4,
REAR HEIGHT WILL NOT MOVE UP &/OR
DOWN FORWARD OR BACK FUNCTIONS
OPERATE NORMALLY (CAMARO & FIREBIRD)

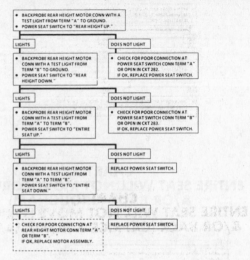

- BACKPROBE REAR HEIGHT MOTOR CONN WITH A TEST LIGHT FROM TERM "A" TO GROUND.
- POWER SEAT SWITCH TO "REAR HEIGHT UP."

LIGHTS — • BACKPROBE REAR HEIGHT MOTOR CONN WITH A TEST LIGHT FROM TERM "B" TO GROUND. • POWER SEAT SWITCH TO "REAR HEIGHT DOWN."

DOES NOT LIGHT — • CHECK FOR POOR CONNECTION AT POWER SEAT SWITCH CONN TERM "A" OR OPEN IN CKT 282. IF OK, REPLACE POWER SEAT SWITCH.

LIGHTS — • BACKPROBE REAR HEIGHT MOTOR CONN WITH A TEST LIGHT FROM TERM "A" TO TERM "B". • POWER SEAT SWITCH TO "ENTIRE SEAT UP."

DOES NOT LIGHT — • CHECK FOR POOR CONNECTION AT POWER SEAT SWITCH CONN TERM "B" OR OPEN IN CKT 283. IF OK, REPLACE POWER SEAT SWITCH.

LIGHTS — • BACKPROBE REAR HEIGHT MOTOR CONN WITH A TEST LIGHT FROM TERM "A" TO TERM "B". • POWER SEAT SWITCH TO "ENTIRE SEAT DOWN."

DOES NOT LIGHT — REPLACE POWER SEAT SWITCH.

LIGHTS — • CHECK FOR POOR CONNECTION AT REAR HEIGHT MOTOR CONN TERM "A" OR TERM "B". IF OK, REPLACE MOTOR ASSEMBLY.

DOES NOT LIGHT — REPLACE POWER SEAT SWITCH.

CHART 5,
ENTIRE SEAT WILL NOT MOVE UP OR DOWN
FORWARD & BACK FUNCTIONS OPERATE
NORMALLY (CAMARO & FIREBIRD)

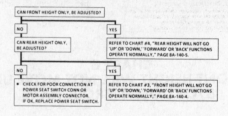

- CAN FRONT HEIGHT ONLY, BE ADJUSTED?

NO — CAN REAR HEIGHT ONLY, BE ADJUSTED?

YES — REFER TO CHART #4, "REAR HEIGHT WILL NOT GO 'UP' OR 'DOWN', 'FORWARD' OR 'BACK' FUNCTIONS OPERATE NORMALLY," PAGE 8A-140-5.

NO — • CHECK FOR POOR CONNECTION AT POWER SEAT SWITCH CONN OR MOTOR ASSEMBLY CONNECTOR. IF OK, REPLACE POWER SEAT SWITCH.

YES — REFER TO CHART #3, "FRONT HEIGHT WILL NOT GO 'UP' OR 'DOWN,' 'FORWARD' OR 'BACK' FUNCTIONS OPERATE NORMALLY," PAGE 8A-140-4.

CHART 1,
ALL POSITIONS DO NOT OPERATE
(CAPRICE & ROADMASTER)

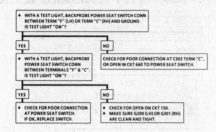

CHART 2,
ENTIRE SEAT WILL NOT MOVE FORWARD
&/OR BACK (CAPRICE & ROADMASTER)

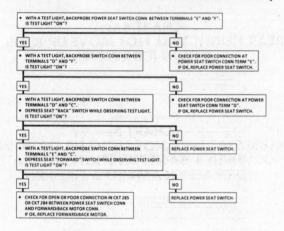

CHART 3,
FRONT HEIGHT WILL NOT MOVE UP
&/OR DOWN (CAPRICE & ROADMASTER)

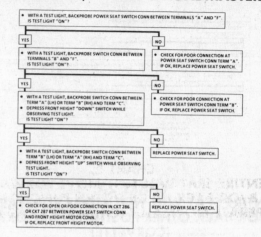

CHART 4,
REAR HEIGHT WILL NOT MOVE UP &/OR
DOWN (CAPRICE & ROADMASTER)

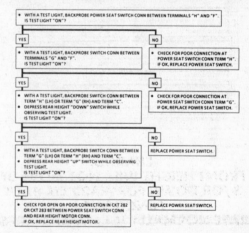

93C85490 93D85491 93E85492 93F85493

Courtesy of General Motors Corp.

CHART 1A,
ALL POSITIONS DO NOT OPERATE
(CORVETTE)

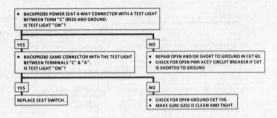

CHART 2A,
ENTIRE SEAT WILL NOT MOVE FORWARD
&/OR BACK OTHER POSITIONS ARE OKAY
(CORVETTE)

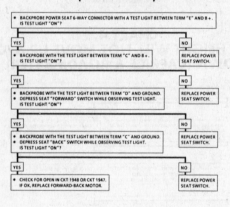

CHART 3A,
FRONT HEIGHT WILL NOT MOVE UP
&/OR DOWN (CORVETTE)

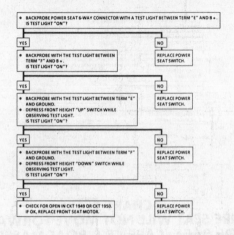

CHART 4A,
REAR HEIGHT WILL NOT MOVE UP &/OR
DOWN (CORVETTE)

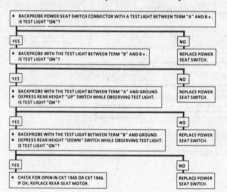

93G85494 93H85495 93I85496 93J85497

CHART 1B,
BACKREST CONTROL DOES NOT MOVE FORWARD &/OR BACK (CORVETTE)

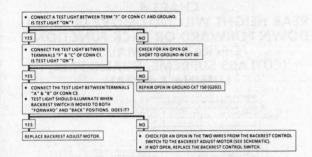

- CONNECT A TEST LIGHT BETWEEN TERM "F" OF CONN C1 AND GROUND.
  IS TEST LIGHT "ON"?

YES ↓   NO → CHECK FOR AN OPEN OR SHORT TO GROUND IN CKT 60.

- CONNECT THE TEST LIGHT BETWEEN TERMINALS "F" & "C" OF CONN C1.
  IS TEST LIGHT "ON"?

YES ↓   NO → REPAIR OPEN IN GROUND CKT 150 (G202).

- CONNECT THE TEST LIGHT BETWEEN TERMINALS "A" & "B" OF CONN C3.
- TEST LIGHT SHOULD ILLUMINATE WHEN BACKREST SWITCH IS MOVED TO BOTH "FORWARD" AND "BACK" POSITIONS. DOES IT?

YES ↓   NO →
- REPLACE BACKREST ADJUST MOTOR.
- CHECK FOR AN OPEN IN THE TWO WIRES FROM THE BACKREST CONTROL SWITCH TO THE BACKREST ADJUST MOTOR (SEE SCHEMATIC).
- IF NOT OPEN, REPLACE THE BACKREST CONTROL SWITCH.

CHART 2B,
BOLSTER CONTROL DOES NOT MOVE IN &/OR OUT (CORVETTE)

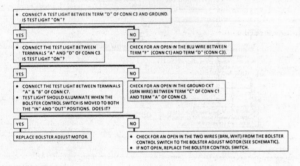

- CONNECT A TEST LIGHT BETWEEN TERM "D" OF CONN C3 AND GROUND.
  IS TEST LIGHT "ON"?

YES ↓   NO → CHECK FOR AN OPEN IN THE BLU WIRE BETWEEN TERM "F" (CONN C1) AND TERM "D" (CONN C3).

- CONNECT THE TEST LIGHT BETWEEN TERMINALS "A" AND "D" OF CONN C3.
  IS TEST LIGHT "ON"?

YES ↓   NO → CHECK FOR AN OPEN IN THE GROUND CKT (GRN WIRE) BETWEEN TERM "C" OF CONN C1 AND TERM "A" OF CONN C3.

- CONNECT THE TEST LIGHT BETWEEN TERMINALS "A" & "B" OF CONN C7.
- TEST LIGHT SHOULD ILLUMINATE WHEN THE BOLSTER CONTROL SWITCH IS MOVED TO BOTH THE "IN" AND "OUT" POSITIONS. DOES IT?

YES ↓   NO →
- REPLACE BOLSTER ADJUST MOTOR.
- CHECK FOR AN OPEN IN THE TWO WIRES (BRN, WHT) FROM THE BOLSTER CONTROL SWITCH TO THE BOLSTER ADJUST MOTOR (SEE SCHEMATIC).
- IF NOT OPEN, REPLACE THE BOLSTER CONTROL SWITCH.

CHART 3B,
ALL LUMBAR SUPPORT BLADDERS WILL NOT INFLATE (CORVETTE)

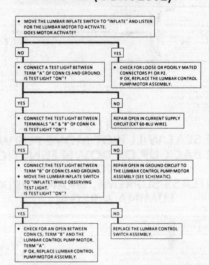

- MOVE THE LUMBAR INFLATE SWITCH TO "INFLATE" AND LISTEN FOR THE LUMBAR MOTOR TO ACTIVATE.
  DOES MOTOR ACTIVATE?

NO ↓   YES → CHECK FOR LOOSE OR POORLY MATED CONNECTORS P1 OR P2.
IF OK, REPLACE THE LUMBAR CONTROL PUMP/MOTOR ASSEMBLY.

- CONNECT A TEST LIGHT BETWEEN TERM "A" OF CONN C5 AND GROUND.
  IS TEST LIGHT "ON"?

YES ↓   NO → REPAIR OPEN IN CURRENT SUPPLY CIRCUIT (CKT 60-BLU WIRE).

- CONNECT THE TEST LIGHT BETWEEN TERMINALS "A" & "B" OF CONN C4.
  IS TEST LIGHT "ON"?

YES ↓   NO → REPAIR OPEN IN GROUND CIRCUIT TO THE LUMBAR CONTROL PUMP/MOTOR ASSEMBLY (SEE SCHEMATIC).

- CONNECT THE TEST LIGHT BETWEEN TERM "B" OF CONN C5 AND GROUND.
- MOVE THE LUMBAR INFLATE SWITCH TO "INFLATE" WHILE OBSERVING TEST LIGHT.
  IS TEST LIGHT "ON"?

YES ↓   NO → REPLACE THE LUMBAR CONTROL SWITCH ASSEMBLY.

- CHECK FOR AN OPEN BETWEEN CONN C5, TERM "B" AND THE LUMBAR CONTROL PUMP MOTOR, TERM "A".
  IF OK, REPLACE LUMBAR CONTROL PUMP/MOTOR ASSEMBLY.

1993 ACCESSORIES & EQUIPMENT
Power Seats (Cont.)

CHART 1,
ALL POSITIONS DO NOT OPERATE
ON ONE SEAT ONLY
(CUTLASS SUPREME, GRAND PRIX, LUMINA & REGAL)

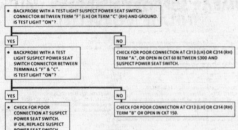

CHART 2,
ENTIRE SEAT WILL NOT MOVE FORWARD
&/OR BACK UP OR DOWN FUNCTIONS
OPERATE NORMALLY
(CUTLASS SUPREME, GRAND PRIX, LUMINA & REGAL)

CHART 3,
FRONT HEIGHT WILL NOT MOVE UP &/OR
DOWN FORWARD OR BACK FUNCTIONS
OPERATE NORMALLY
(CUTLASS SUPREME, GRAND PRIX, LUMINA & REGAL)

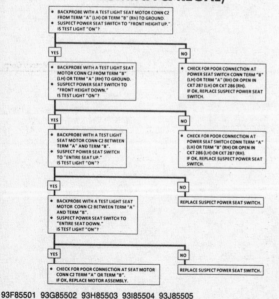

CHART 4,
REAR HEIGHT WILL NOT MOVE UP &/OR
DOWN FORWARD OR BACK FUNCTIONS
OPERATE NORMALLY
(CUTLASS SUPREME, GRAND PRIX, LUMINA & REGAL)

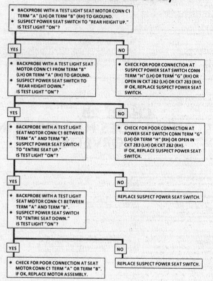

CHART 5,
ENTIRE SEAT WILL NOT MOVE UP OR DOWN
FORWARD & BACK FUNCTIONS OPERATE
NORMALLY
(CUTLASS SUPREME, GRAND PRIX, LUMINA & REGAL)

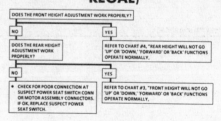

93F85501 93G85502 93H85503 93I85504 93J85505

Courtesy of General Motors Corp.

CHART 1,
BOTH SEATS INOPERATIVE & PUMP DOES NOT RUN (FIREBIRD)

CHART 2,
LUMBAR BLADDER INOPERATIVE, BUT LATERAL BLADDERS OPERATE NORMALLY WITHIN SAME SEAT (FIREBIRD)

CHART 3,
LATERAL BLADDERS INOPERATIVE, BUT LUMBAR BLADDER OPERATE NORMALLY WITHIN SAME SEAT (FIREBIRD)

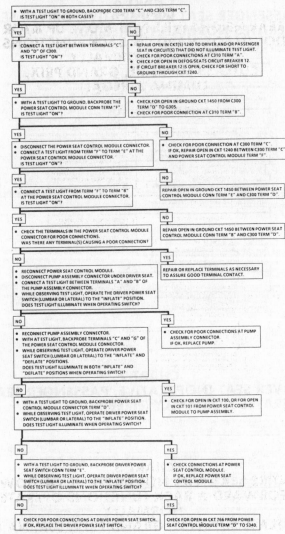

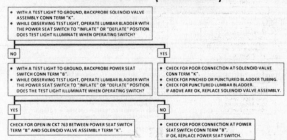

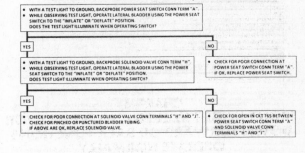

93G85478 93H85479 93A85480

Courtesy of General Motors Corp.

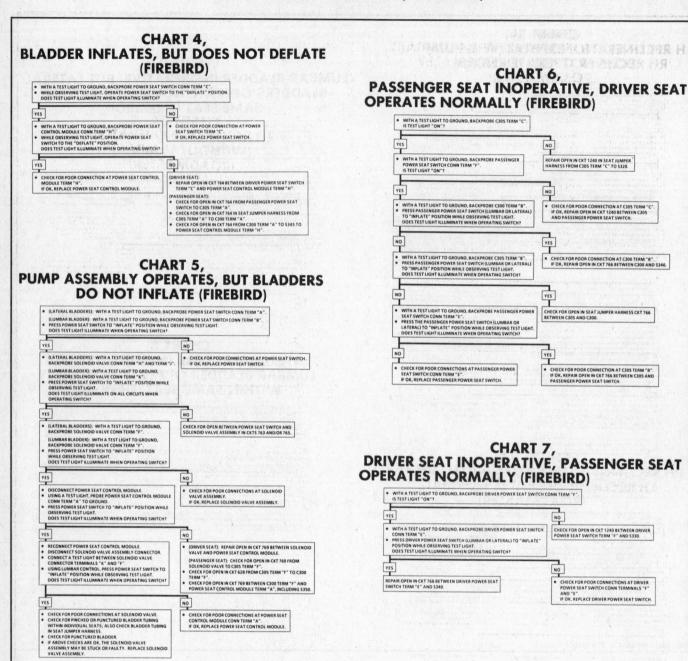

CHART 4,
BLADDER INFLATES, BUT DOES NOT DEFLATE (FIREBIRD)

- WITH A TEST LIGHT TO GROUND, BACKPROBE POWER SEAT SWITCH CONN TERM "C".
- WHILE OBSERVING TEST LIGHT, OPERATE POWER SEAT SWITCH TO THE "DEFLATE" POSITION. DOES TEST LIGHT ILLUMINATE WHEN OPERATING SWITCH?

YES

- WITH A TEST LIGHT TO GROUND, BACKPROBE POWER SEAT CONTROL MODULE CONN TERM "H".
- WHILE OBSERVING TEST LIGHT, OPERATE POWER SEAT SWITCH TO THE "DEFLATE" POSITION. DOES TEST LIGHT ILLUMINATE WHEN OPERATING SWITCH?

NO

- CHECK FOR POOR CONNECTION AT POWER SEAT SWITCH TERM "C". IF OK, REPLACE POWER SEAT SWITCH.

YES

- CHECK FOR POOR CONNECTION AT POWER SEAT CONTROL MODULE TERM "H". IF OK, REPLACE POWER SEAT CONTROL MODULE.

NO

- (DRIVER SEAT):
  - REPAIR OPEN IN CKT 764 BETWEEN DRIVER POWER SEAT SWITCH TERM "C" AND POWER SEAT CONTROL MODULE TERM "H".
- (PASSENGER SEAT):
  - CHECK FOR OPEN IN CKT 764 FROM PASSENGER POWER SEAT SWITCH TO C305 TERM "A".
  - CHECK FOR OPEN IN CKT 764 IN SEAT JUMPER HARNESS FROM C305 TERM "A" TO C300 TERM "A".
  - CHECK FOR OPEN IN CKT 764 FROM C300 TERM "A" TO S345 TO POWER SEAT CONTROL MODULE TERM "H".

CHART 5,
PUMP ASSEMBLY OPERATES, BUT BLADDERS DO NOT INFLATE (FIREBIRD)

- (LATERAL BLADDERS): WITH A TEST LIGHT TO GROUND, BACKPROBE POWER SEAT SWITCH CONN TERM "A".
- (LUMBAR BLADDER): WITH A TEST LIGHT TO GROUND, BACKPROBE POWER SEAT SWITCH CONN TERM "B".
- PRESS POWER SEAT SWITCH TO "INFLATE" POSITION WHILE OBSERVING TEST LIGHT. DOES TEST LIGHT ILLUMINATE WHEN OPERATING SWITCH?

YES

- (LATERAL BLADDERS): WITH A TEST LIGHT TO GROUND, BACKPROBE SOLENOID VALVE CONN TERM "H" AND TERM "J".
- (LUMBAR BLADDER): WITH A TEST LIGHT TO GROUND, BACKPROBE SOLENOID VALVE CONN TERM "K".
- PRESS POWER SEAT SWITCH TO "INFLATE" POSITION WHILE OBSERVING TEST LIGHT. DOES TEST LIGHT ILLUMINATE ON ALL CIRCUITS WHEN OPERATING SWITCH?

NO

- CHECK FOR POOR CONNECTIONS AT POWER SEAT SWITCH. IF OK, REPLACE POWER SEAT SWITCH.

YES

- (LATERAL BLADDERS): WITH A TEST LIGHT TO GROUND, BACKPROBE SOLENOID VALVE CONN TERM "F".
- (LUMBAR BLADDER): WITH A TEST LIGHT TO GROUND, BACKPROBE SOLENOID VALVE CONN TERM "F".
- PRESS POWER SEAT SWITCH TO "INFLATE" POSITION WHILE OBSERVING TEST LIGHT. DOES TEST LIGHT ILLUMINATE WHEN OPERATING SWITCH?

NO

CHECK FOR OPEN BETWEEN POWER SEAT SWITCH AND SOLENOID VALVE ASSEMBLY IN CKTS 763 AND/OR 765.

YES

- DISCONNECT POWER SEAT CONTROL MODULE.
- USING A TEST LIGHT, PROBE POWER SEAT CONTROL MODULE CONN TERM "A" TO GROUND.
- PRESS POWER SEAT SWITCH TO "INFLATE" POSITION WHILE OBSERVING TEST LIGHT. DOES TEST LIGHT ILLUMINATE WHEN OPERATING SWITCH?

NO

- CHECK FOR POOR CONNECTIONS AT SOLENOID VALVE ASSEMBLY. IF OK, REPLACE SOLENOID VALVE ASSEMBLY.

YES

- RECONNECT POWER SEAT CONTROL MODULE.
- DISCONNECT SOLENOID VALVE ASSEMBLY CONNECTOR.
- CONNECT A TEST LIGHT BETWEEN SOLENOID VALVE CONNECTOR TERMINALS "K" AND "F".
- USING LUMBAR CONTROL, PRESS POWER SEAT SWITCH TO "INFLATE" POSITION WHILE OBSERVING TEST LIGHT. DOES TEST LIGHT ILLUMINATE WHEN OPERATING SWITCH?

NO

- (DRIVER SEAT): REPAIR OPEN IN CKT 769 BETWEEN SOLENOID VALVE AND POWER SEAT CONTROL MODULE.
- (PASSENGER SEAT): CHECK FOR OPEN IN CKT 769 FROM SOLENOID VALVE TO C305 TERM "F".
- CHECK FOR OPEN IN CKT 628 FROM C305 TERM "F" TO C300 TERM "F".
- CHECK FOR OPEN IN CKT 769 BETWEEN C300 TERM "F" AND POWER SEAT CONTROL MODULE TERM "A", INCLUDING S350.

YES

- CHECK FOR POOR CONNECTIONS AT SOLENOID VALVE.
- CHECK FOR PINCHED OR PUNCTURED BLADDER TUBING WITHIN INDIVIDUAL SEATS; ALSO CHECK BLADDER TUBING IN SEAT JUMPER HARNESS.
- CHECK FOR PUNCTURED BLADDER.
- IF ABOVE CHECKS ARE OK, THE SOLENOID VALVE ASSEMBLY MAY BE STUCK OR FAULTY. REPLACE SOLENOID VALVE ASSEMBLY.

NO

- CHECK FOR POOR CONNECTIONS AT POWER SEAT CONTROL MODULE CONN TERM "A". IF OK, REPLACE POWER SEAT CONTROL MODULE.

CHART 6,
PASSENGER SEAT INOPERATIVE, DRIVER SEAT OPERATES NORMALLY (FIREBIRD)

- WITH A TEST LIGHT TO GROUND, BACKPROBE C305 TERM "C". IS TEST LIGHT "ON"?

YES

- WITH A TEST LIGHT TO GROUND, BACKPROBE PASSENGER POWER SEAT SWITCH CONN TERM "F". IS TEST LIGHT "ON"?

NO

REPAIR OPEN IN CKT 1240 IN SEAT JUMPER HARNESS FROM C305 TERM "C" TO S320.

YES

- WITH A TEST LIGHT TO GROUND, BACKPROBE C300 TERM "B".
- PRESS PASSENGER POWER SEAT SWITCH (LUMBAR OR LATERAL) TO "INFLATE" POSITION WHILE OBSERVING TEST LIGHT. DOES TEST LIGHT ILLUMINATE WHEN OPERATING SWITCH?

NO

- CHECK FOR POOR CONNECTION AT C305 TERM "C". IF OK, REPAIR OPEN IN CKT 1240 BETWEEN C305 AND PASSENGER POWER SEAT SWITCH.

NO

- WITH A TEST LIGHT TO GROUND, BACKPROBE C305 TERM "B".
- PRESS PASSENGER POWER SEAT SWITCH (LUMBAR OR LATERAL) TO "INFLATE" POSITION WHILE OBSERVING TEST LIGHT. DOES TEST LIGHT ILLUMINATE WHEN OPERATING SWITCH?

YES

- CHECK FOR POOR CONNECTION AT C300 TERM "B". IF OK, REPAIR OPEN IN CKT 766 BETWEEN C300 AND S340.

NO

- WITH A TEST LIGHT TO GROUND, BACKPROBE PASSENGER POWER SEAT SWITCH CONN TERM "E".
- PRESS THE PASSENGER POWER SEAT SWITCH (LUMBAR OR LATERAL) TO "INFLATE" POSITION WHILE OBSERVING TEST LIGHT. DOES TEST LIGHT ILLUMINATE WHEN OPERATING SWITCH?

YES

CHECK FOR OPEN IN SEAT JUMPER HARNESS CKT 766 BETWEEN C305 AND C300.

NO

- CHECK FOR POOR CONNECTIONS AT PASSENGER POWER SEAT SWITCH CONN TERM "E". IF OK, REPLACE PASSENGER POWER SEAT SWITCH.

YES

- CHECK FOR POOR CONNECTION AT C305 TERM "B". IF OK, REPAIR OPEN IN CKT 766 BETWEEN C305 AND PASSENGER POWER SEAT SWITCH.

CHART 7,
DRIVER SEAT INOPERATIVE, PASSENGER SEAT OPERATES NORMALLY (FIREBIRD)

- WITH A TEST LIGHT TO GROUND, BACKPROBE DRIVER POWER SEAT SWITCH CONN TERM "F". IS TEST LIGHT "ON"?

YES

- WITH A TEST LIGHT TO GROUND, BACKPROBE DRIVER POWER SEAT SWITCH CONN TERM "E".
- PRESS DRIVER POWER SEAT SWITCH (LUMBAR OR LATERAL) TO "INFLATE" POSITION WHILE OBSERVING TEST LIGHT. DOES TEST LIGHT ILLUMINATE WHEN OPERATING SWITCH?

NO

CHECK FOR OPEN IN CKT 1240 BETWEEN DRIVER POWER SEAT SWITCH TERM "F" AND S330.

YES

REPAIR OPEN IN CKT 766 BETWEEN DRIVER POWER SEAT SWITCH TERM "E" AND S340.

NO

- CHECK FOR POOR CONNECTIONS AT DRIVER POWER SEAT SWITCH CONN TERMINALS "F" AND "E". IF OK, REPLACE DRIVER POWER SEAT SWITCH.

CHART 1A,
LH RECLINER INOPERATIVE (WITH LUMBAR)
RH RECLINER OPERATES NORMALLY
(ROADMASTER)

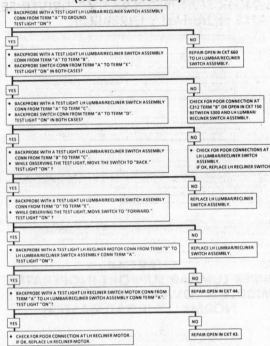

CHART 3A,
RH RECLINER INOPERATIVE
(WITHOUT LUMBAR)
(ROADMASTER)

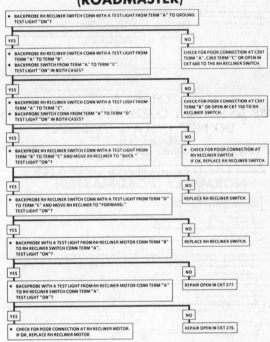

CHART 2A,
RH RECLINER INOPERATIVE (WITH LUMBAR)
LH RECLINER OPERATES NORMALLY
(ROADMASTER)

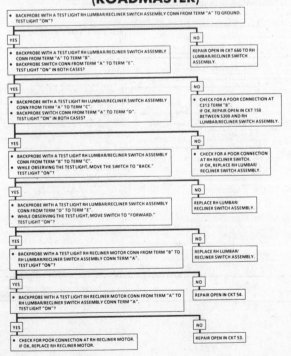

93A85506   93B85507   93C85508

Courtesy of General Motors Corp.

CHART 1B,
ALL LUMBAR SUPPORTS INOPERATIVE
(ROADMASTER)

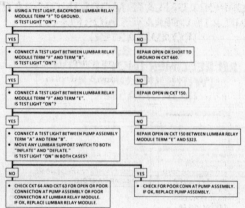

CHART 2B,
ALL LUMBAR SUPPORTS: INFLATE MODE
INOPERATIVE, DEFLATE OPERATES
NORMALLY (ROADMASTER)

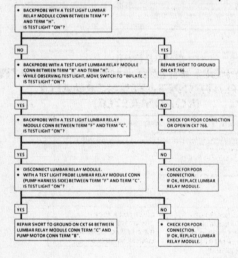

CHART 3B,
ALL LUMBAR SUPPORTS: DEFLATE MODE
INOPERATIVE, INFLATE OPERATES
NORMALLY (ROADMASTER)

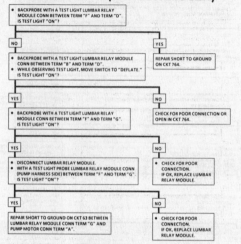

CHART 4B,
UPPER LUMBAR SUPPORT INOPERATIVE
MIDDLE & LOWER SUPPORTS OPERATE
NORMALLY (ROADMASTER)

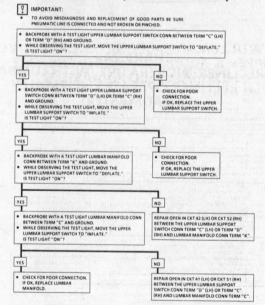

CHART 5B,
MIDDLE LUMBAR SUPPORT INOPERATIVE UPPER & LOWER SUPPORTS OPERATE NORMALLY (ROADMASTER)

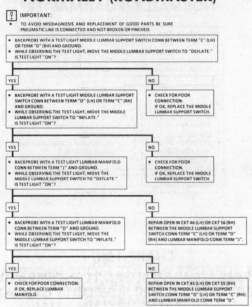

IMPORTANT:
TO AVOID MISDIAGNOSIS AND REPLACEMENT OF GOOD PARTS BE SURE PNEUMATIC LINE IS CONNECTED AND NOT BROKEN OR PINCHED.

- BACKPROBE WITH A TEST LIGHT MIDDLE LUMBAR SUPPORT SWITCH CONN BETWEEN TERM "C" (LH) OR TERM "D" (RH) AND GROUND.
- WHILE OBSERVING THE TEST LIGHT, MOVE THE MIDDLE LUMBAR SUPPORT SWITCH TO "DEFLATE." IS TEST LIGHT "ON"?

YES
- BACKPROBE WITH A TEST LIGHT MIDDLE LUMBAR SUPPORT SWITCH CONN BETWEEN TERM "D" (LH) OR TERM "C" (RH) AND GROUND.
- WHILE OBSERVING THE TEST LIGHT, MOVE THE MIDDLE LUMBAR SUPPORT SWITCH TO "INFLATE." IS TEST LIGHT "ON"?

NO
- CHECK FOR POOR CONNECTION. IF OK, REPLACE THE MIDDLE LUMBAR SUPPORT SWITCH.

YES
- BACKPROBE WITH A TEST LIGHT LUMBAR MANIFOLD CONN BETWEEN TERM "J" AND GROUND.
- WHILE OBSERVING THE TEST LIGHT, MOVE THE MIDDLE LUMBAR SUPPORT SWITCH TO "DEFLATE." IS TEST LIGHT "ON"?

NO
- CHECK FOR POOR CONNECTION. IF OK, REPLACE THE MIDDLE LUMBAR SUPPORT SWITCH.

YES
- BACKPROBE WITH A TEST LIGHT LUMBAR MANIFOLD CONN BETWEEN TERM "D" AND GROUND.
- WHILE OBSERVING THE TEST LIGHT, MOVE THE MIDDLE LUMBAR SUPPORT SWITCH TO "INFLATE." IS TEST LIGHT "ON"?

NO
REPAIR OPEN IN CKT 46 (LH) OR CKT 56 (RH) BETWEEN THE MIDDLE LUMBAR SUPPORT SWITCH CONN TERM "C" (LH) OR TERM "D" (RH) AND LUMBAR MANIFOLD CONN TERM "J".

YES
- CHECK FOR POOR CONNECTION. IF OK, REPLACE LUMBAR MANIFOLD.

NO
REPAIR OPEN IN CKT 45 (LH) OR CKT 55 (RH) BETWEEN THE MIDDLE LUMBAR SUPPORT SWITCH CONN TERM "D" (LH) OR TERM "C" (RH) AND LUMBAR MANIFOLD CONN TERM "D".

CHART 7B,
UPPER SUPPORT DEFLATE MODE INOPERATIVE INFLATE OPERATES NORMALLY (ROADMASTER)

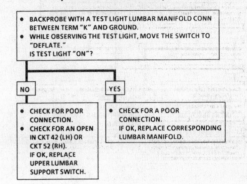

- BACKPROBE WITH A TEST LIGHT LUMBAR MANIFOLD CONN BETWEEN TERM "K" AND GROUND.
- WHILE OBSERVING THE TEST LIGHT, MOVE THE SWITCH TO "DEFLATE." IS TEST LIGHT "ON"?

NO
- CHECK FOR POOR CONNECTION.
- CHECK FOR AN OPEN IN CKT 42 (LH) OR CKT 52 (RH). IF OK, REPLACE UPPER LUMBAR SUPPORT SWITCH.

YES
- CHECK FOR A POOR CONNECTION. IF OK, REPLACE CORRESPONDING LUMBAR MANIFOLD.

CHART 6B,
LOWER LUMBAR SUPPORT INOPERATIVE UPPER & MIDDLE SUPPORTS OPERATE NORMALLY (ROADMASTER)

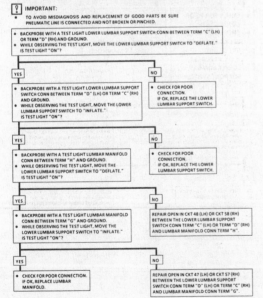

IMPORTANT:
TO AVOID MISDIAGNOSIS AND REPLACEMENT OF GOOD PARTS BE SURE PNEUMATIC LINE IS CONNECTED AND NOT BROKEN OR PINCHED.

- BACKPROBE WITH A TEST LIGHT LOWER LUMBAR SUPPORT SWITCH CONN BETWEEN TERM "C" (LH) OR TERM "D" (RH) AND GROUND.
- WHILE OBSERVING THE TEST LIGHT, MOVE THE LOWER LUMBAR SUPPORT SWITCH TO "DEFLATE." IS TEST LIGHT "ON"?

YES
- BACKPROBE WITH A TEST LIGHT LOWER LUMBAR SUPPORT SWITCH CONN BETWEEN TERM "D" (LH) OR TERM "C" (RH) AND GROUND.
- WHILE OBSERVING THE TEST LIGHT, MOVE THE LOWER LUMBAR SUPPORT SWITCH TO "INFLATE." IS TEST LIGHT "ON"?

NO
- CHECK FOR POOR CONNECTION. IF OK, REPLACE THE LOWER LUMBAR SUPPORT SWITCH.

YES
- BACKPROBE WITH A TEST LIGHT LUMBAR MANIFOLD CONN BETWEEN TERM "H" AND GROUND.
- WHILE OBSERVING THE TEST LIGHT, MOVE THE LOWER LUMBAR SUPPORT SWITCH TO "DEFLATE." IS TEST LIGHT "ON"?

NO
- CHECK FOR POOR CONNECTION. IF OK, REPLACE THE LOWER LUMBAR SUPPORT SWITCH.

YES
- BACKPROBE WITH A TEST LIGHT LUMBAR MANIFOLD CONN BETWEEN TERM "G" AND GROUND.
- WHILE OBSERVING THE TEST LIGHT, MOVE THE LOWER LUMBAR SUPPORT SWITCH TO "INFLATE." IS TEST LIGHT "ON"?

NO
REPAIR OPEN IN CKT 48 (LH) OR CKT 58 (RH) BETWEEN THE LOWER LUMBAR SUPPORT SWITCH CONN TERM "C" (LH) OR TERM "D" (RH) AND LUMBAR MANIFOLD CONN TERM "H".

YES
- CHECK FOR POOR CONNECTION. IF OK, REPLACE LUMBAR MANIFOLD.

NO
REPAIR OPEN IN CKT 47 (LH) OR CKT 57 (RH) BETWEEN THE LOWER LUMBAR SUPPORT SWITCH CONN TERM "D" (LH) OR TERM "C" (RH) AND LUMBAR MANIFOLD CONN TERM "G".

CHART 8B,
UPPER SUPPORT INFLATE MODE INOPERATIVE DEFLATE OPERATES NORMALLY (ROADMASTER)

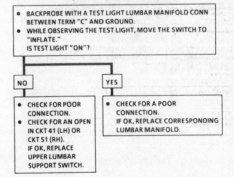

- BACKPROBE WITH A TEST LIGHT LUMBAR MANIFOLD CONN BETWEEN TERM "C" AND GROUND.
- WHILE OBSERVING THE TEST LIGHT, MOVE THE SWITCH TO "INFLATE." IS TEST LIGHT "ON"?

NO
- CHECK FOR POOR CONNECTION.
- CHECK FOR AN OPEN IN CKT 41 (LH) OR CKT 51 (RH). IF OK, REPLACE UPPER LUMBAR SUPPORT SWITCH.

YES
- CHECK FOR A POOR CONNECTION. IF OK, REPLACE CORRESPONDING LUMBAR MANIFOLD.

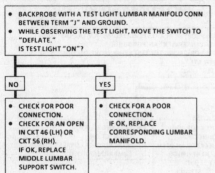

CHART 9B,
MIDDLE SUPPORT DEFLATE MODE
INOPERATIVE INFLATE OPERATES
NORMALLY (ROADMASTER)

- BACKPROBE WITH A TEST LIGHT LUMBAR MANIFOLD CONN BETWEEN TERM "J" AND GROUND.
- WHILE OBSERVING THE TEST LIGHT, MOVE THE SWITCH TO "DEFLATE."
  IS TEST LIGHT "ON"?

NO
- CHECK FOR POOR CONNECTION.
- CHECK FOR AN OPEN IN CKT 46 (LH) OR CKT 56 (RH).
  IF OK, REPLACE MIDDLE LUMBAR SUPPORT SWITCH.

YES
- CHECK FOR A POOR CONNECTION.
  IF OK, REPLACE CORRESPONDING LUMBAR MANIFOLD.

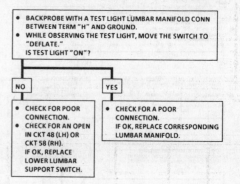

CHART 11B,
LOWER SUPPORT DEFLATE MODE
INOPERATIVE INFLATE OPERATES
NORMALLY (ROADMASTER)

- BACKPROBE WITH A TEST LIGHT LUMBAR MANIFOLD CONN BETWEEN TERM "H" AND GROUND.
- WHILE OBSERVING THE TEST LIGHT, MOVE THE SWITCH TO "DEFLATE."
  IS TEST LIGHT "ON"?

NO
- CHECK FOR POOR CONNECTION.
- CHECK FOR AN OPEN IN CKT 48 (LH) OR CKT 58 (RH).
  IF OK, REPLACE LOWER LUMBAR SUPPORT SWITCH.

YES
- CHECK FOR A POOR CONNECTION.
  IF OK, REPLACE CORRESPONDING LUMBAR MANIFOLD.

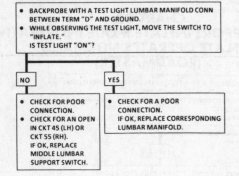

CHART 10B,
MIDDLE SUPPORT INFLATE MODE
INOPERATIVE DEFLATE OPERATES
NORMALLY (ROADMASTER)

- BACKPROBE WITH A TEST LIGHT LUMBAR MANIFOLD CONN BETWEEN TERM "D" AND GROUND.
- WHILE OBSERVING THE TEST LIGHT, MOVE THE SWITCH TO "INFLATE."
  IS TEST LIGHT "ON"?

NO
- CHECK FOR POOR CONNECTION.
- CHECK FOR AN OPEN IN CKT 45 (LH) OR CKT 55 (RH).
  IF OK, REPLACE MIDDLE LUMBAR SUPPORT SWITCH.

YES
- CHECK FOR A POOR CONNECTION.
  IF OK, REPLACE CORRESPONDING LUMBAR MANIFOLD.

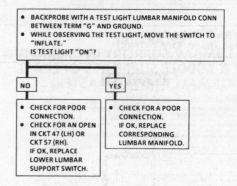

CHART 12B,
LOWER SUPPORT INFLATE MODE INOPERATIVE
DEFLATE OPERATES NORMALLY
(ROADMASTER)

- BACKPROBE WITH A TEST LIGHT LUMBAR MANIFOLD CONN BETWEEN TERM "G" AND GROUND.
- WHILE OBSERVING THE TEST LIGHT, MOVE THE SWITCH TO "INFLATE."
  IS TEST LIGHT "ON"?

NO
- CHECK FOR POOR CONNECTION.
- CHECK FOR AN OPEN IN CKT 47 (LH) OR CKT 57 (RH).
  IF OK, REPLACE LOWER LUMBAR SUPPORT SWITCH.

YES
- CHECK FOR A POOR CONNECTION.
  IF OK, REPLACE CORRESPONDING LUMBAR MANIFOLD.

93D85517 93E85518 93F85519 93I85520

WIRING DIAGRAMS

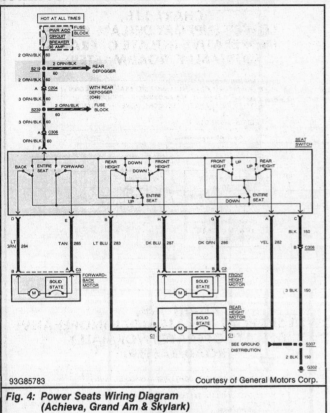

93G85783   Courtesy of General Motors Corp.

Fig. 4: Power Seats Wiring Diagram (Achieva, Grand Am & Skylark)

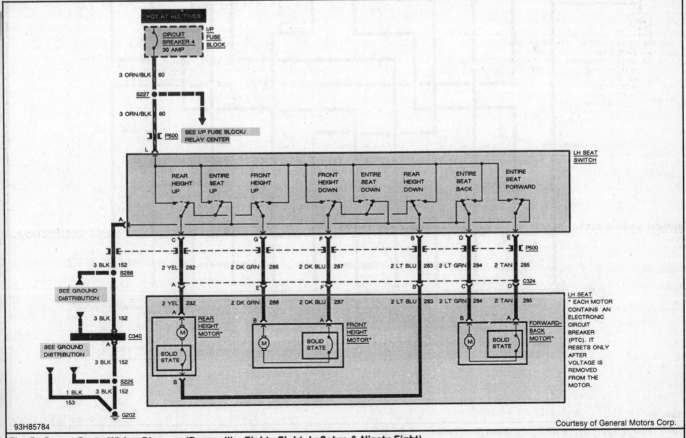

93H85784   Courtesy of General Motors Corp.

Fig. 5: Power Seats Wiring Diagram (Bonneville, Eighty-Eight, LeSabre & Ninety-Eight)

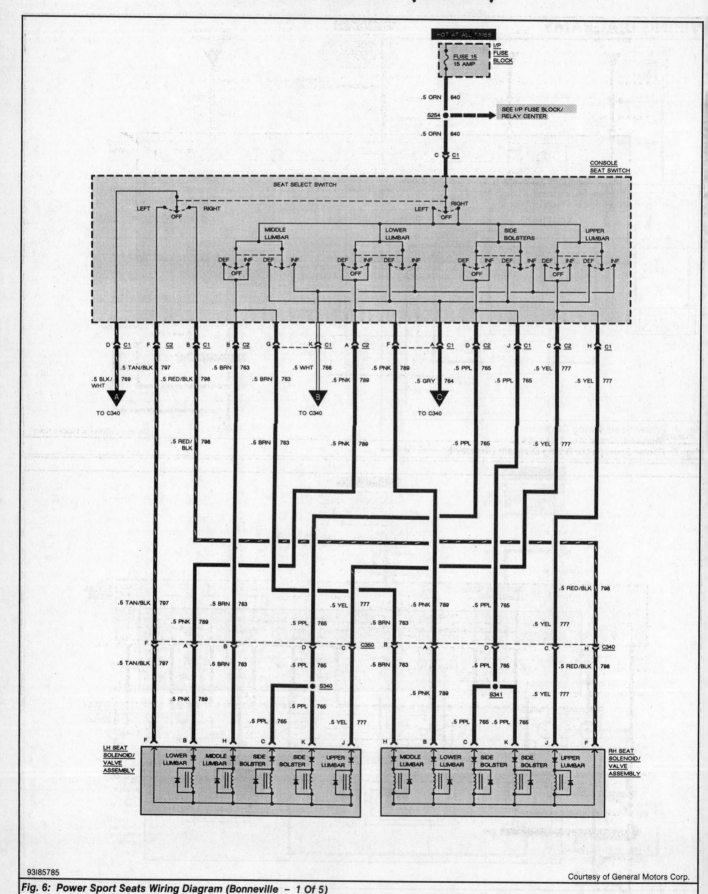

93I85785

Courtesy of General Motors Corp.

Fig. 6: Power Sport Seats Wiring Diagram (Bonneville – 1 Of 5)

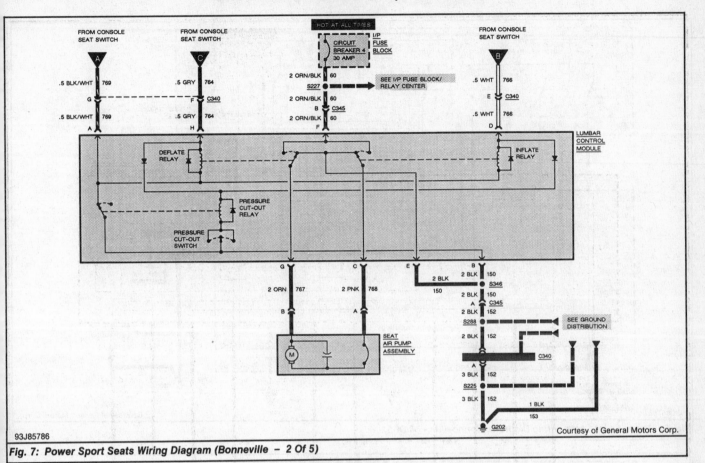

Fig. 7: Power Sport Seats Wiring Diagram (Bonneville – 2 Of 5)

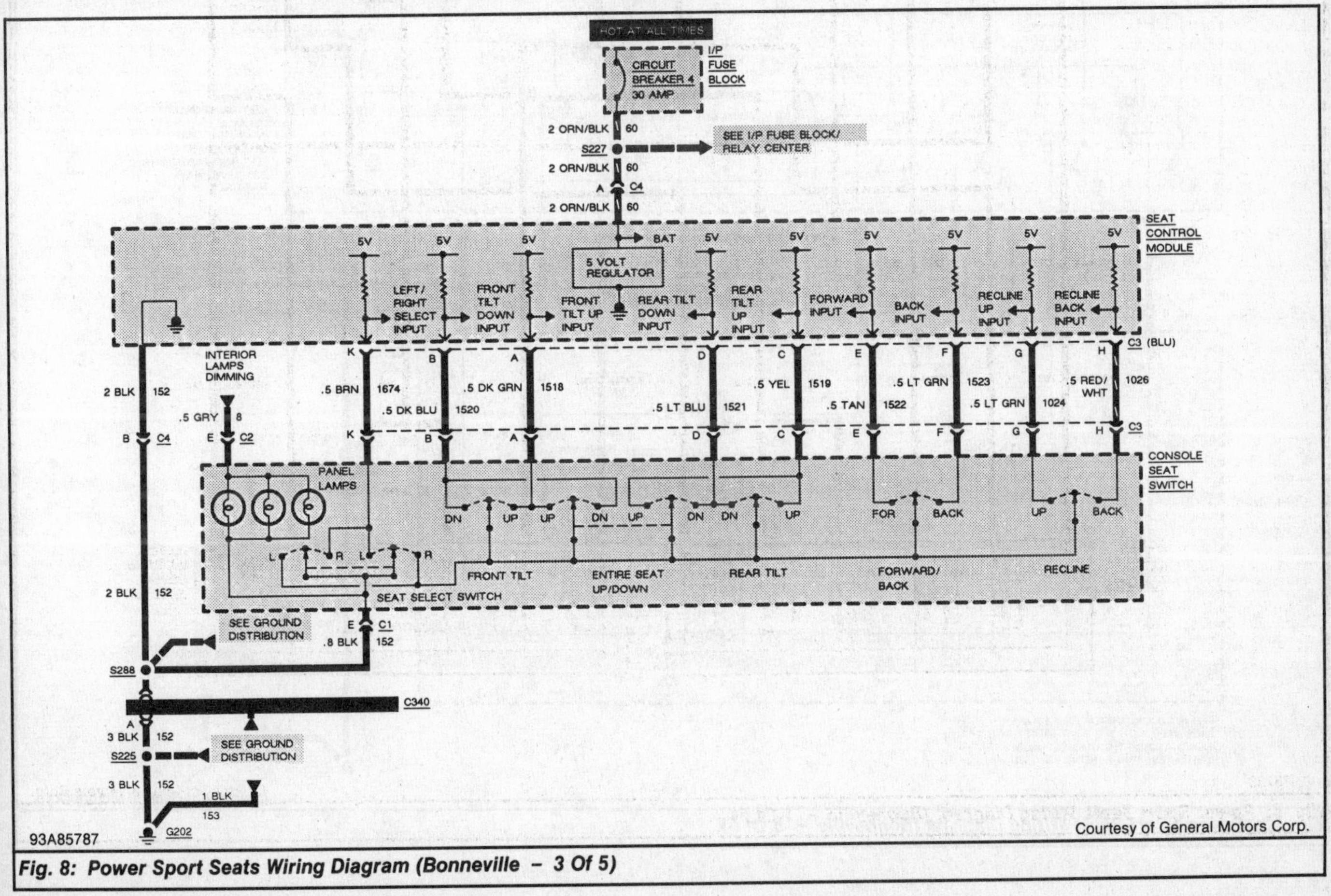

93J85786

Courtesy of General Motors Corp.

Fig. 8: Power Sport Seats Wiring Diagram (Bonneville – 3 Of 5)

93A85787

Courtesy of General Motors Corp.

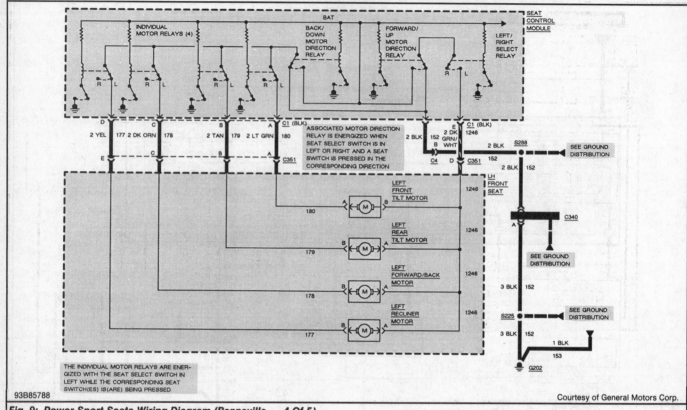

Fig. 9: *Power Sport Seats Wiring Diagram (Bonneville – 4 Of 5)*

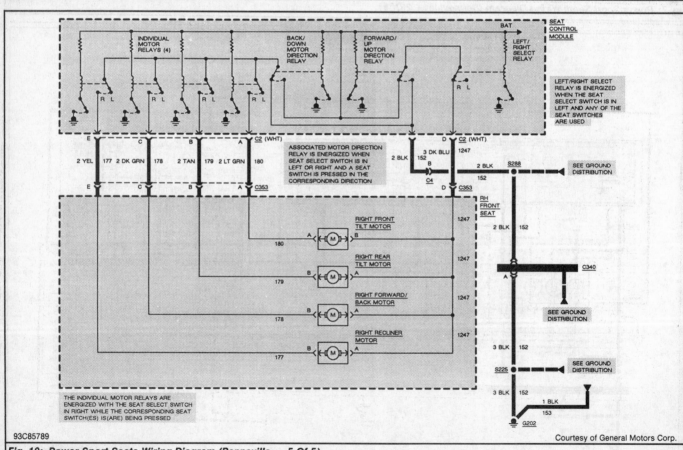

Fig. 10: *Power Sport Seats Wiring Diagram (Bonneville – 5 Of 5)*

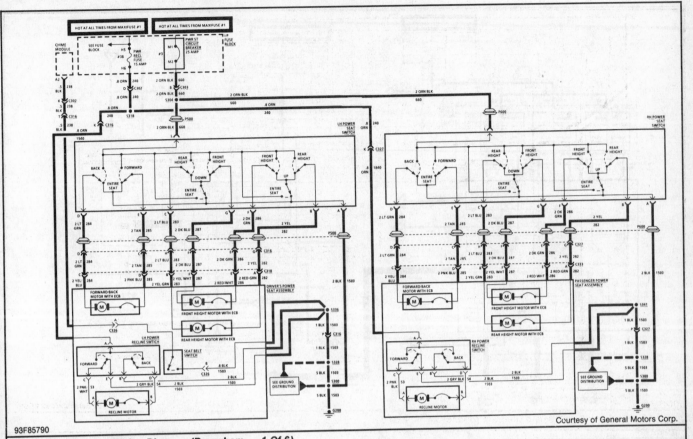

Fig. 11: Power Seats Wiring Diagram (Brougham – 1 Of 6)

93F85790

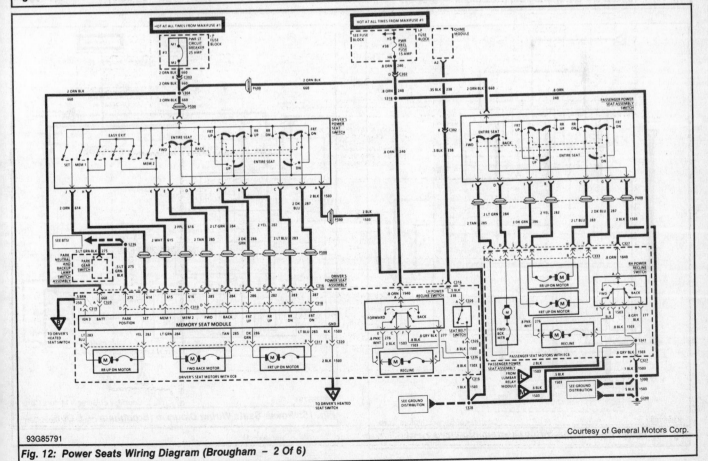

Fig. 12: Power Seats Wiring Diagram (Brougham – 2 Of 6)

93G85791

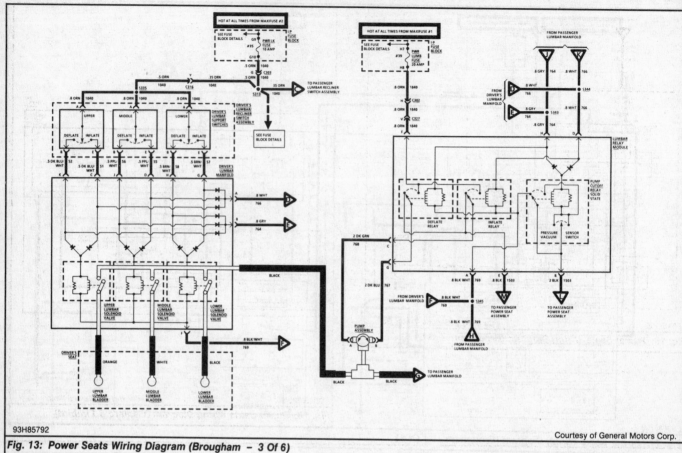

93H85792

Courtesy of General Motors Corp.

Fig. 13: Power Seats Wiring Diagram (Brougham – 3 Of 6)

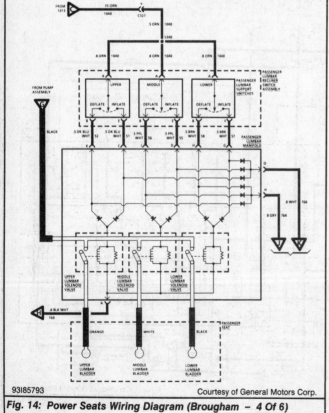

93I85793

Courtesy of General Motors Corp.

Fig. 14: Power Seats Wiring Diagram (Brougham – 4 Of 6)

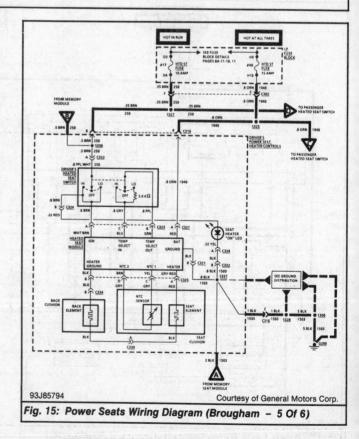

93J85794

Courtesy of General Motors Corp.

Fig. 15: Power Seats Wiring Diagram (Brougham – 5 Of 6)

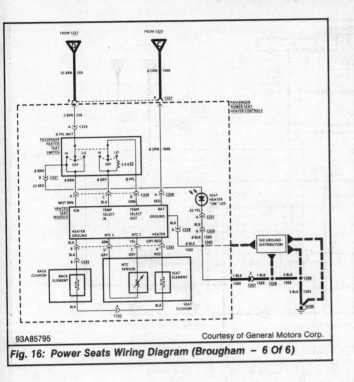

Fig. 16: Power Seats Wiring Diagram (Brougham – 6 Of 6)

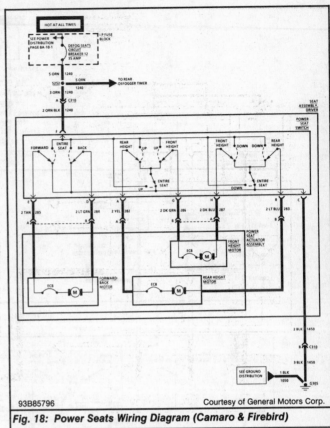

Fig. 18: Power Seats Wiring Diagram (Camaro & Firebird)

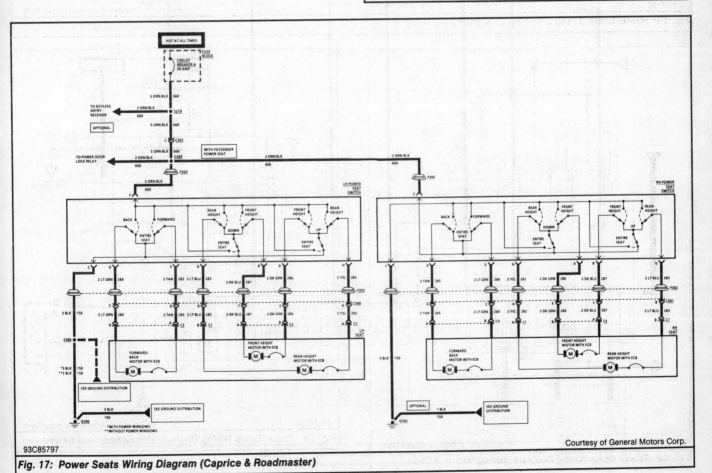

Fig. 17: Power Seats Wiring Diagram (Caprice & Roadmaster)

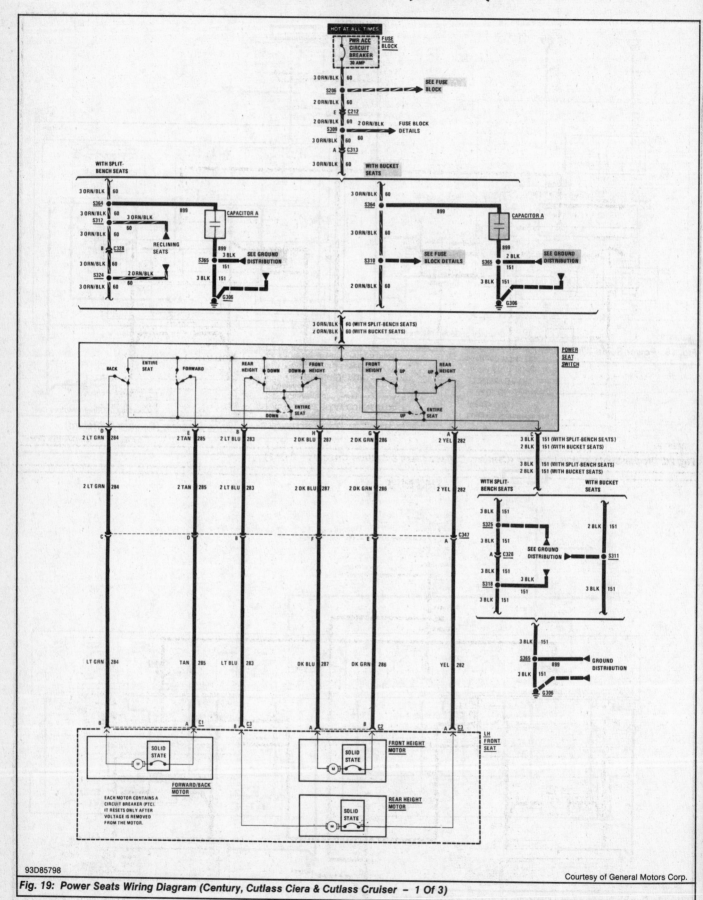

93D85798

Fig. 19: Power Seats Wiring Diagram (Century, Cutlass Ciera & Cutlass Cruiser – 1 Of 3)

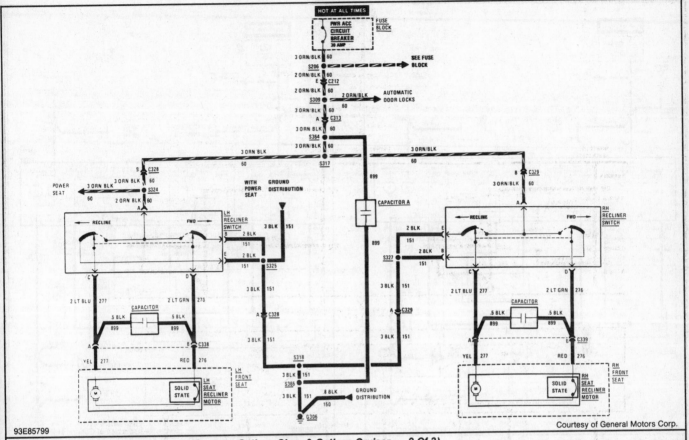

93E85799

Fig. 20: *Power Seats Wiring Diagram (Century, Cutlass Ciera & Cutlass Cruiser – 2 Of 3)*

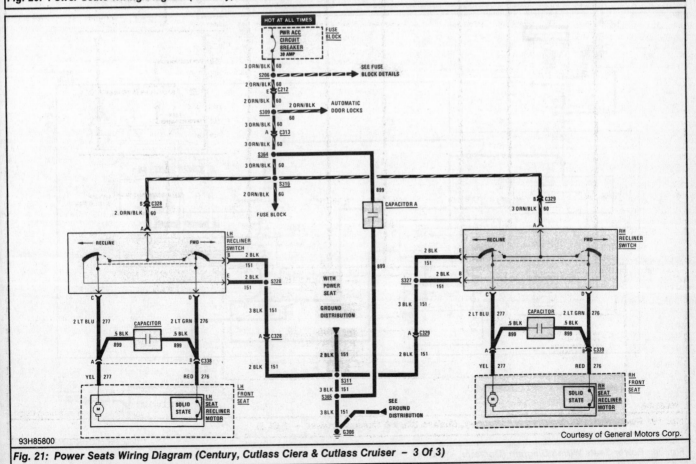

93H85800

Fig. 21: *Power Seats Wiring Diagram (Century, Cutlass Ciera & Cutlass Cruiser – 3 Of 3)*

1993 ACCESSORIES & EQUIPMENT
Power Seats (Cont.)

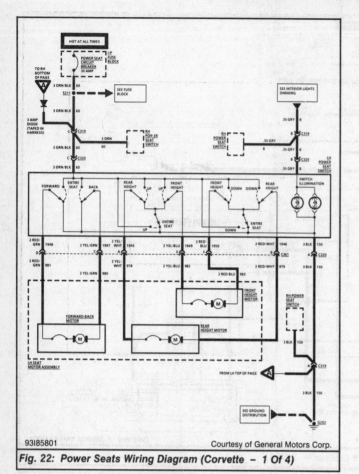

93I85801 Courtesy of General Motors Corp.

Fig. 22: Power Seats Wiring Diagram (Corvette – 1 Of 4)

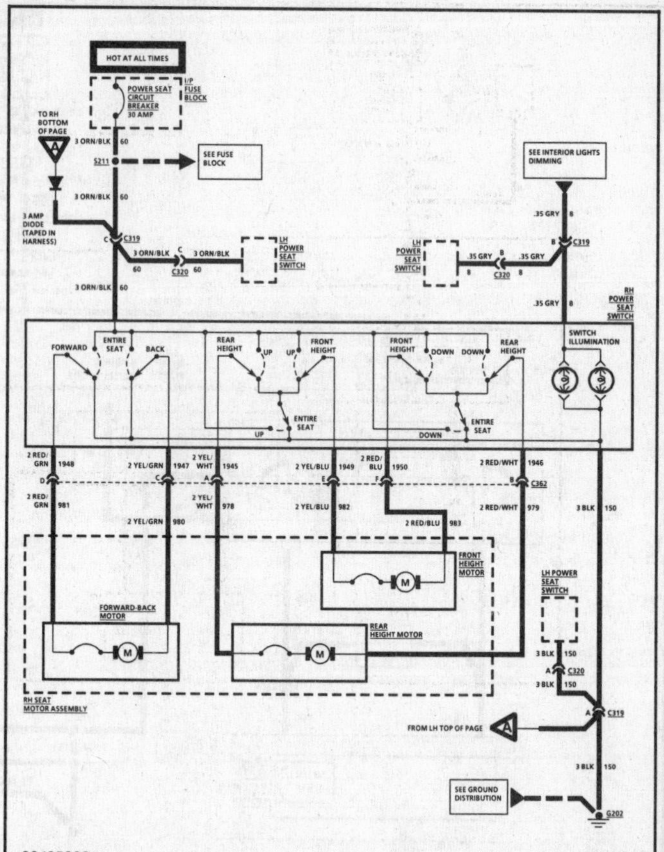

93J85802 Courtesy of General Motors Corp.

Fig. 23: Power Seats Wiring Diagram (Corvette – 2 Of 4)

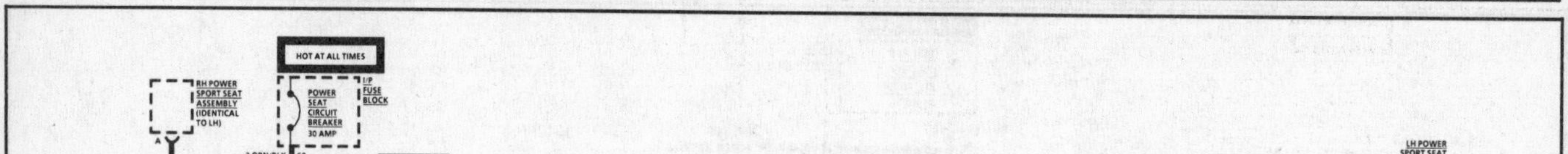

93A85803 Courtesy of General Motors Corp.

Fig. 24: Power Seats Wiring Diagram (Corvette – 3 Of 4)

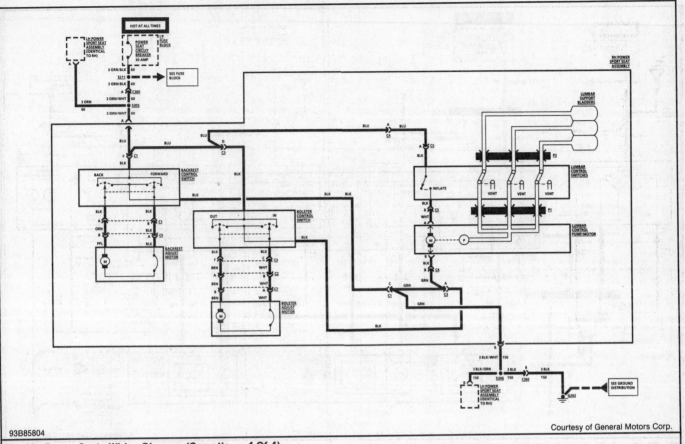

93B85804

Fig. 25: Power Seats Wiring Diagram (Corvette – 4 Of 4)

Courtesy of General Motors Corp.

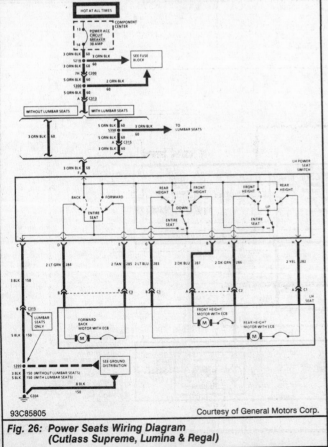

93C85805

Courtesy of General Motors Corp.

Fig. 26: Power Seats Wiring Diagram
(Cutlass Supreme, Lumina & Regal)

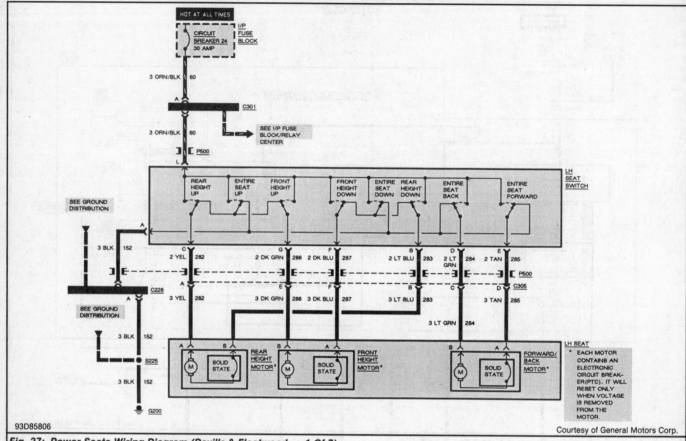

Fig. 27: Power Seats Wiring Diagram (Deville & Fleetwood – 1 Of 7)

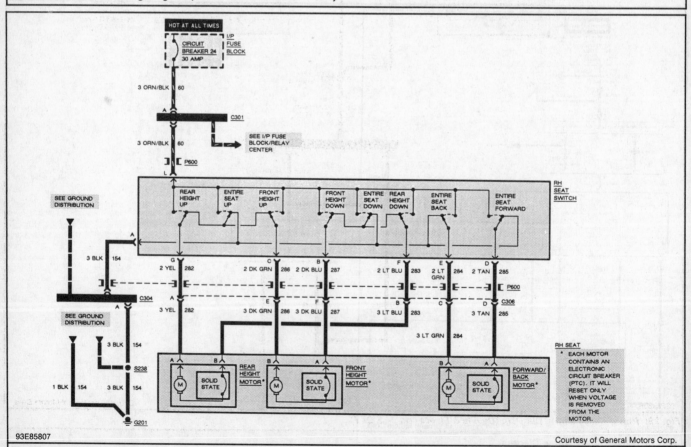

Fig. 28: Power Seats Wiring Diagram (Deville & Fleetwood – 2 Of 7)

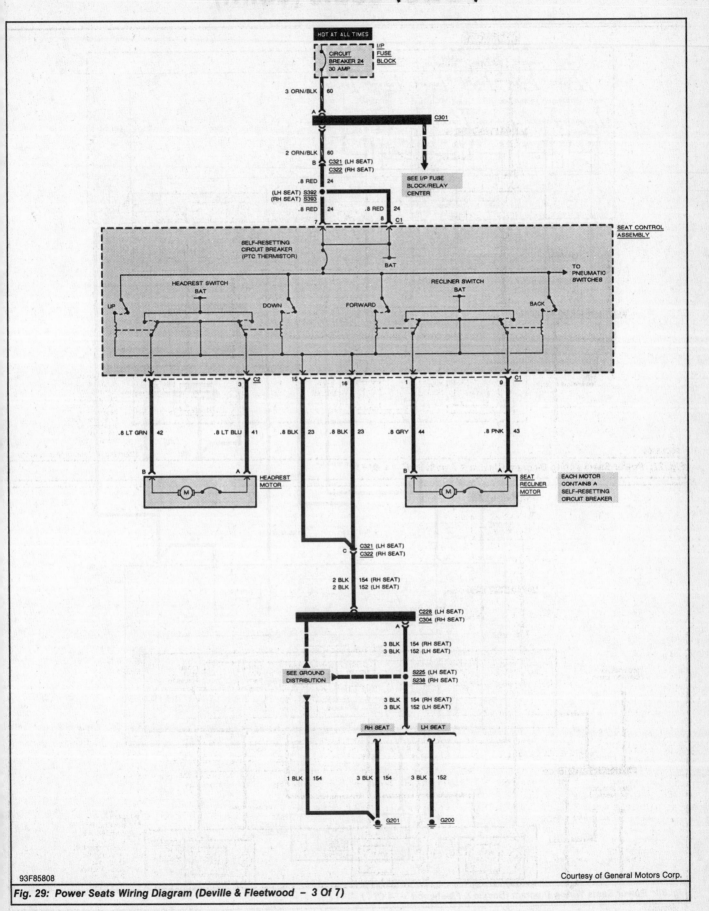

93F85808

Courtesy of General Motors Corp.

Fig. 29: Power Seats Wiring Diagram (Deville & Fleetwood – 3 Of 7)

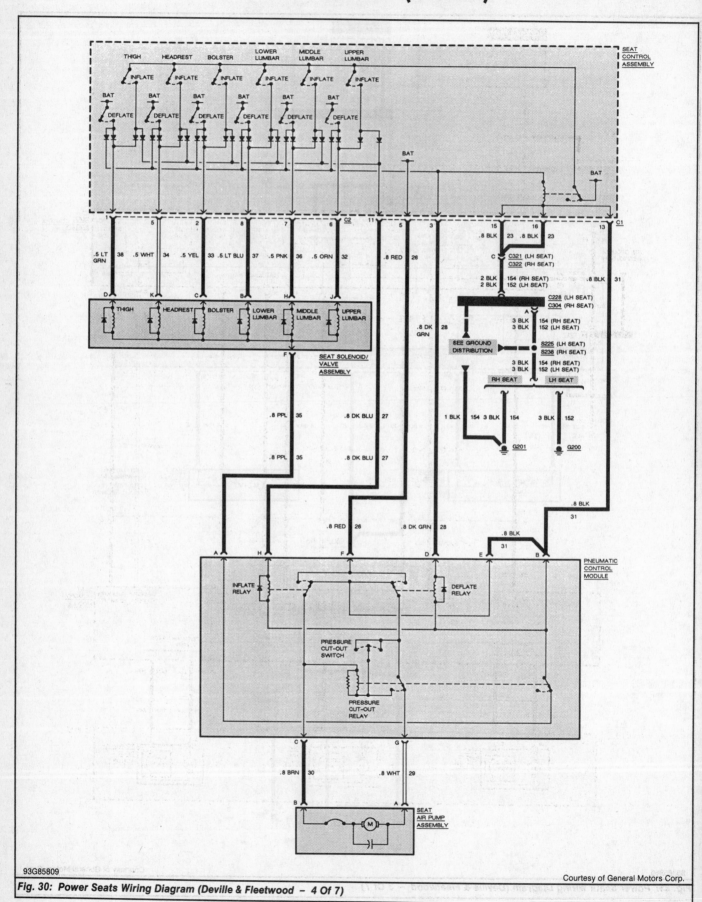

Fig. 30: Power Seats Wiring Diagram (Deville & Fleetwood – 4 Of 7)

Courtesy of General Motors Corp.

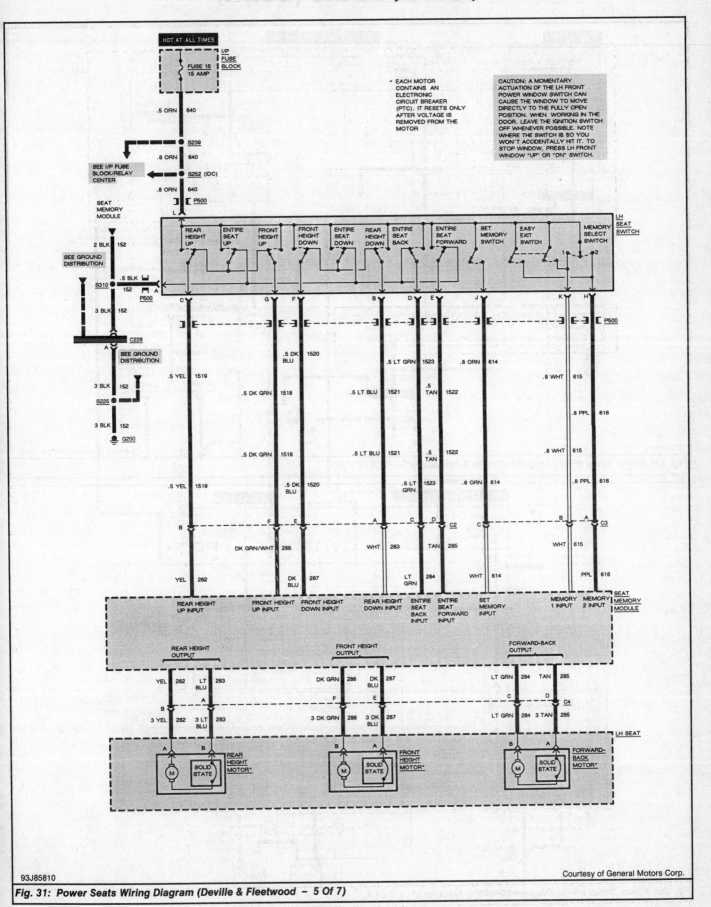

Fig. 31: Power Seats Wiring Diagram (Deville & Fleetwood — 5 Of 7)

93J85810

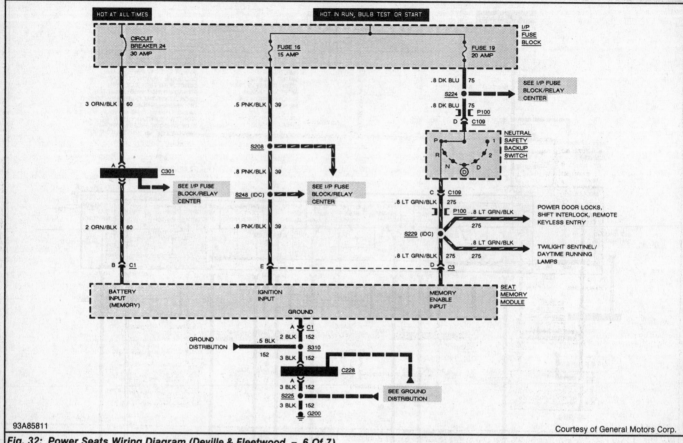

93A85811

Courtesy of General Motors Corp.

Fig. 32: Power Seats Wiring Diagram (Deville & Fleetwood – 6 Of 7)

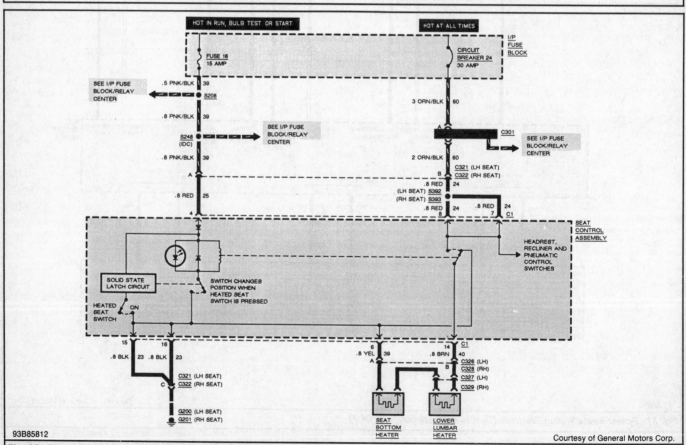

93B85812

Courtesy of General Motors Corp.

Fig. 33: Power Seats Wiring Diagram (Deville & Fleetwood – 7 Of 7)

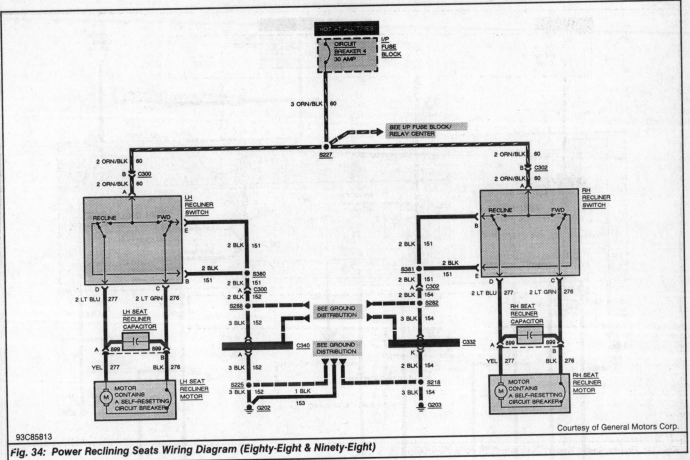

93C85813

Fig. 34: Power Reclining Seats Wiring Diagram (Eighty-Eight & Ninety-Eight)

Courtesy of General Motors Corp.

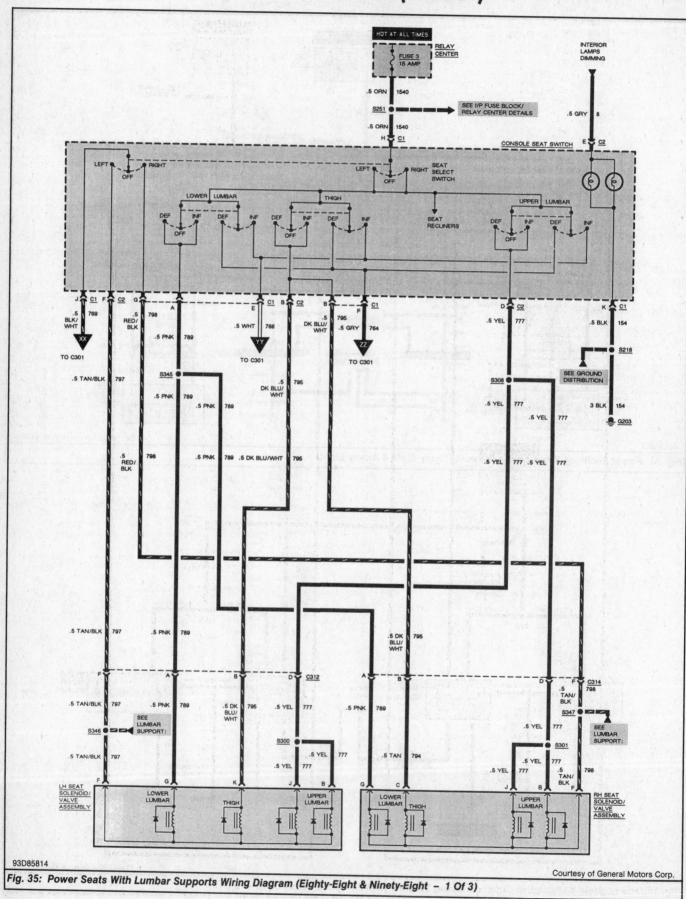

93D85814

Fig. 35: Power Seats With Lumbar Supports Wiring Diagram (Eighty-Eight & Ninety-Eight – 1 Of 3)

Courtesy of General Motors Corp.

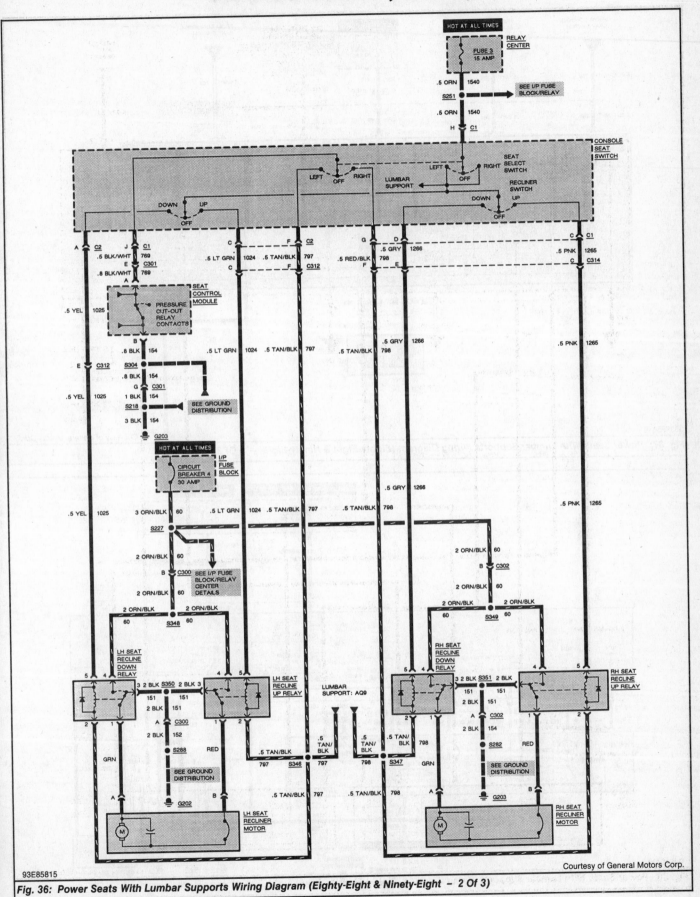

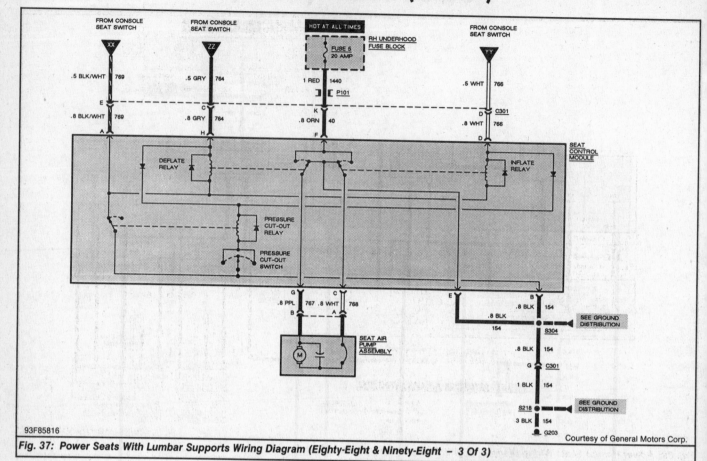

93F85816

Fig. 37: Power Seats With Lumbar Supports Wiring Diagram (Eighty-Eight & Ninety-Eight – 3 Of 3)

Courtesy of General Motors Corp.

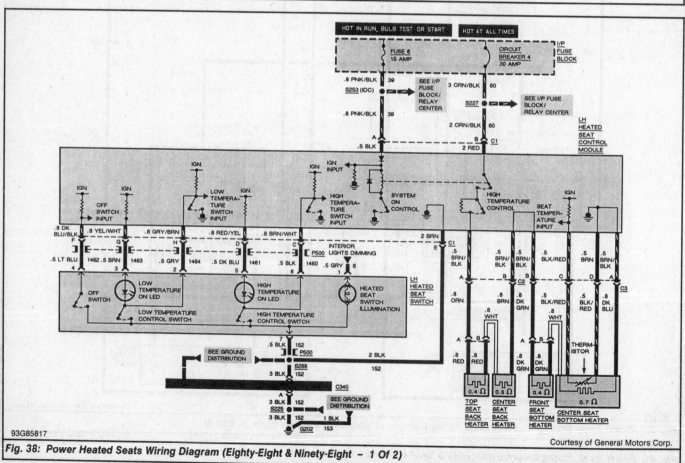

93G85817

Fig. 38: Power Heated Seats Wiring Diagram (Eighty-Eight & Ninety-Eight – 1 Of 2)

Courtesy of General Motors Corp.

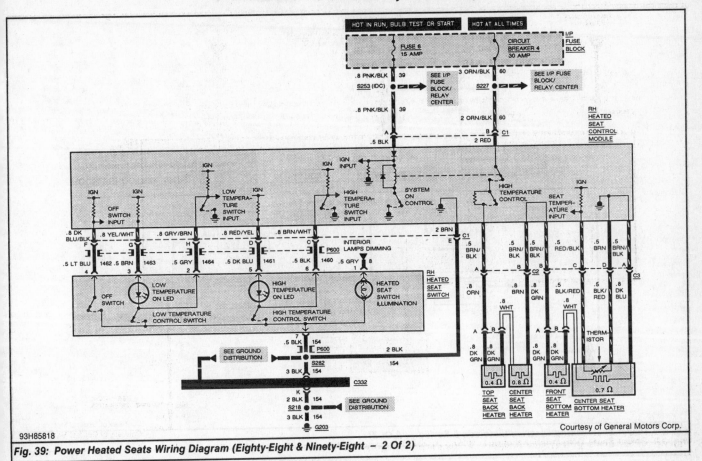

Fig. 39: Power Heated Seats Wiring Diagram (Eighty-Eight & Ninety-Eight – 2 Of 2)

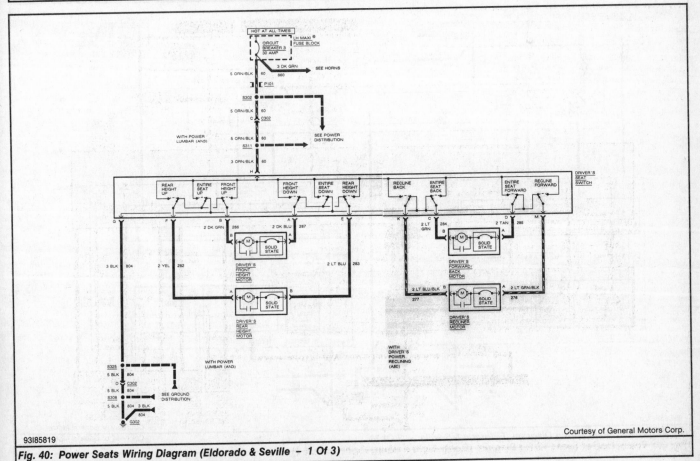

Fig. 40: Power Seats Wiring Diagram (Eldorado & Seville – 1 Of 3)

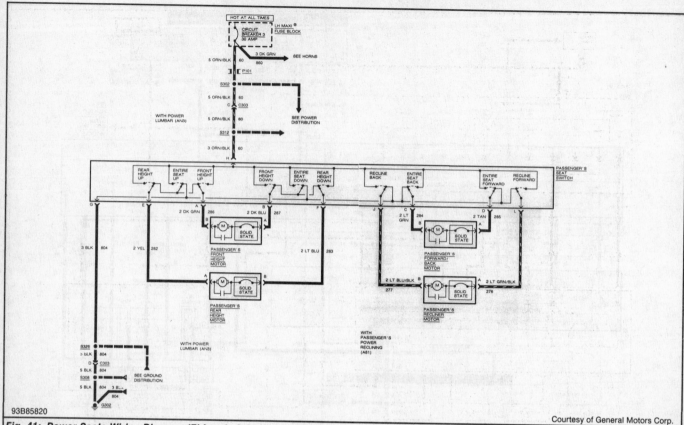

Fig. 41: **Power Seats Wiring Diagram (Eldorado & Seville – 2 Of 3)**

93B85820

Courtesy of General Motors Corp.

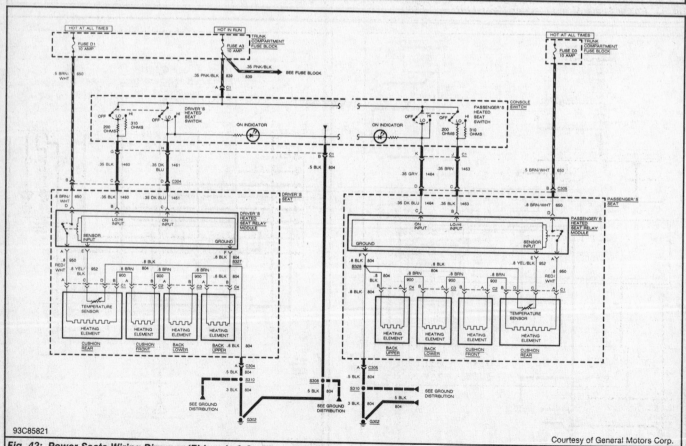

Fig. 42: **Power Seats Wiring Diagram (Eldorado & Seville – 3 Of 3)**

93C85821

Courtesy of General Motors Corp.

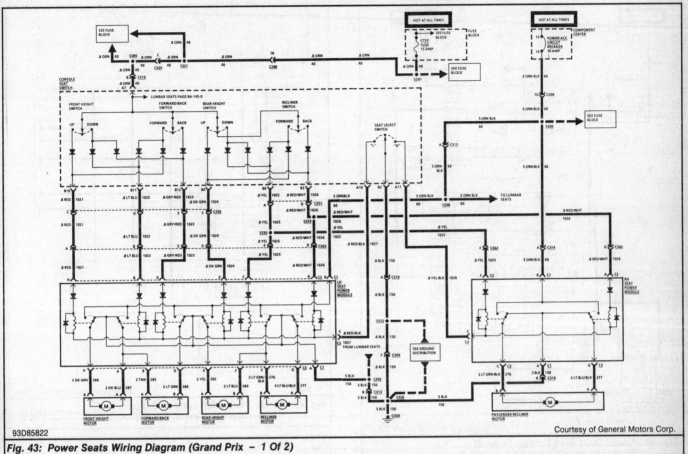

93D85822

Fig. 43: Power Seats Wiring Diagram (Grand Prix − 1 Of 2)

Courtesy of General Motors Corp.

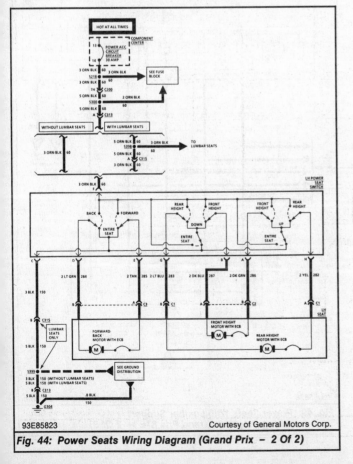

93E85823

Fig. 44: Power Seats Wiring Diagram (Grand Prix − 2 Of 2)

Courtesy of General Motors Corp.

93F85824

Fig. 45: Power Seats With Lumbar Support Wiring Diagram (Grand Prix − 1 Of 3)

Courtesy of General Motors Corp.

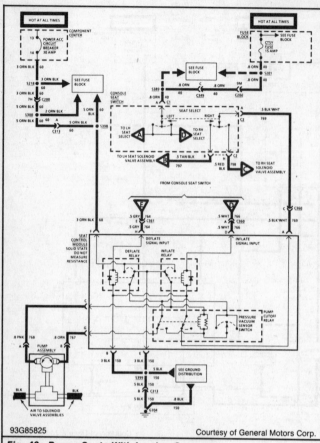

93G85825

Courtesy of General Motors Corp.

**Fig. 46: Power Seats With Lumbar Support
Wiring Diagram (Grand Prix – 2 Of 3)**

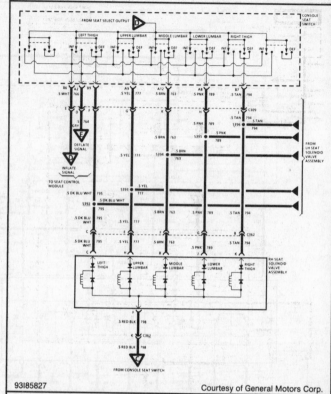

93I85827

Courtesy of General Motors Corp.

**Fig. 48: Power Seats With Lumbar Support
Wiring Diagram (Grand Prix STE – 1 Of 3)**

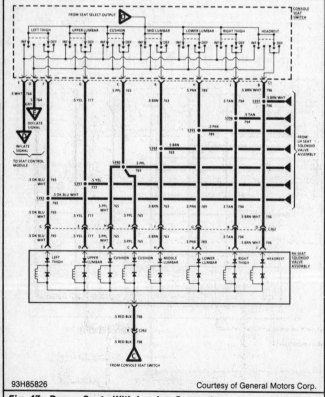

93H85826

Courtesy of General Motors Corp.

**Fig. 47: Power Seats With Lumbar Support
Wiring Diagram (Grand Prix – 3 Of 3)**

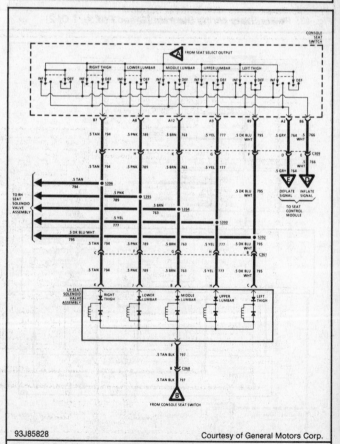

93J85828

Courtesy of General Motors Corp.

**Fig. 49: Power Seats With Lumbar Support
Wiring Diagram (Grand Prix STE – 2 Of 3)**

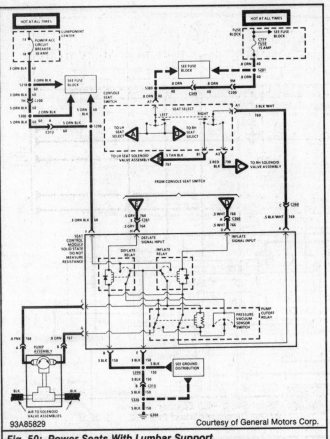

93A85829

Courtesy of General Motors Corp.

Fig. 50: Power Seats With Lumbar Support Wiring Diagram (Grand Prix STE – 3 Of 3)

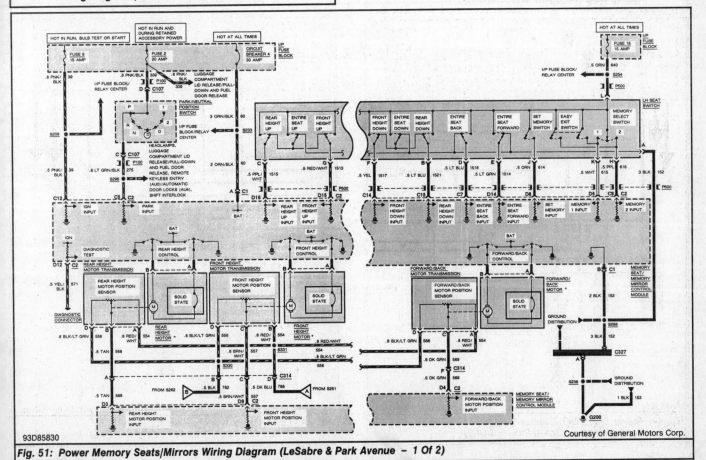

93D85830

Courtesy of General Motors Corp.

Fig. 51: Power Memory Seats/Mirrors Wiring Diagram (LeSabre & Park Avenue – 1 Of 2)

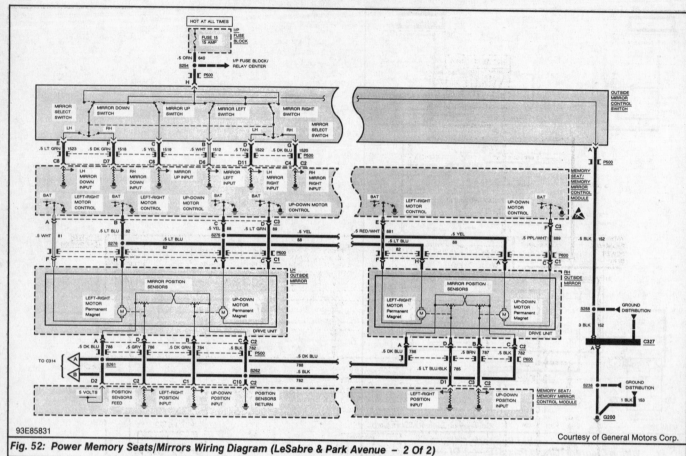

93E85831

Courtesy of General Motors Corp.

Fig. 52: Power Memory Seats/Mirrors Wiring Diagram (LeSabre & Park Avenue – 2 Of 2)

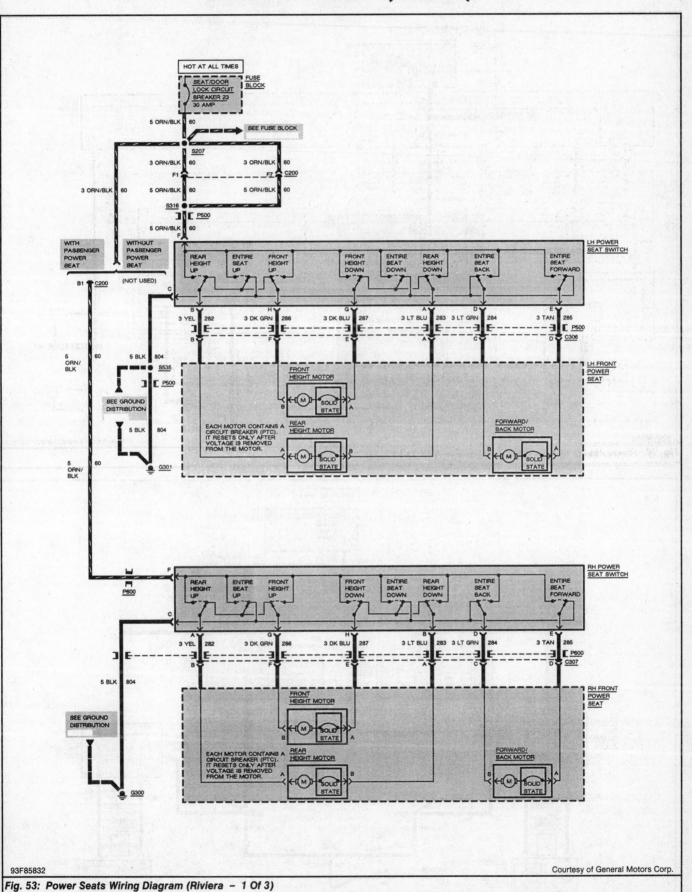

93F85832

Fig. 53: Power Seats Wiring Diagram (Riviera - 1 Of 3)

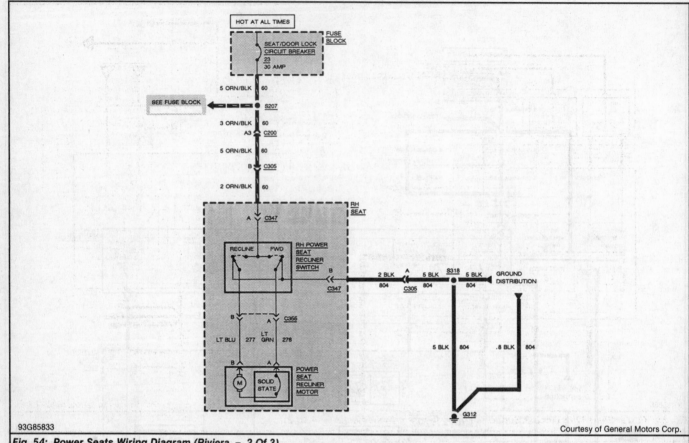

Fig. 54: Power Seats Wiring Diagram (Riviera – 2 Of 3)

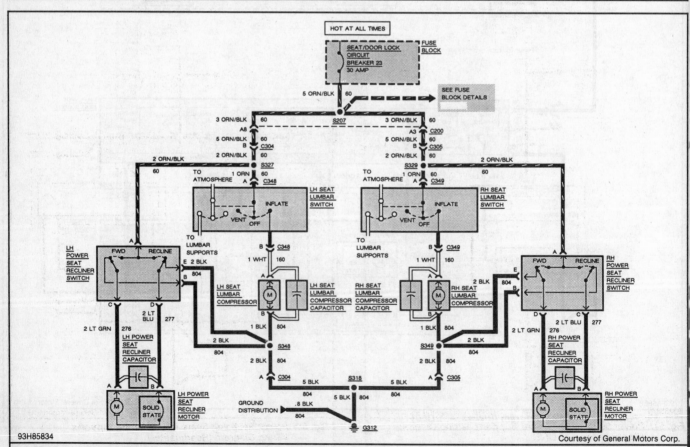

Fig. 55: Power Seats Wiring Diagram (Riviera – 3 Of 3)

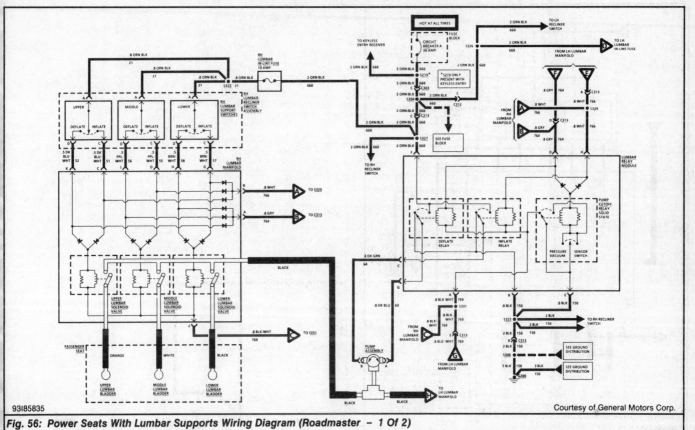

Fig. 56: Power Seats With Lumbar Supports Wiring Diagram (Roadmaster – 1 Of 2)

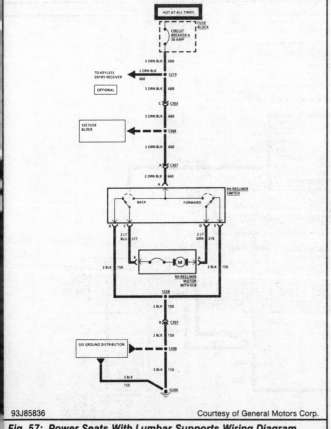

Fig. 57: Power Seats With Lumbar Supports Wiring Diagram (Roadmaster – 2 Of 2)

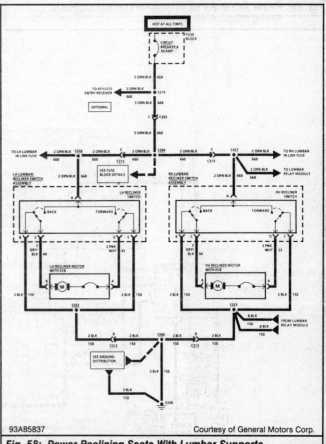

Fig. 58: Power Reclining Seats With Lumbar Supports Wiring Diagram (Roadmaster)

Courtesy of General Motors Corp.

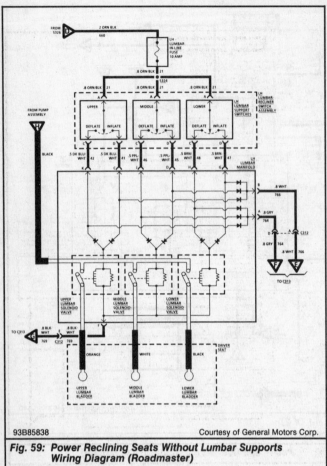

93B85838

Courtesy of General Motors Corp.

Fig. 59: Power Reclining Seats Without Lumbar Supports Wiring Diagram (Roadmaster)

WIRING DIAGRAMS

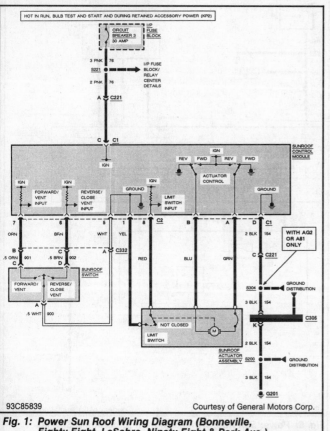

93C85839
Courtesy of General Motors Corp.

Fig. 1: Power Sun Roof Wiring Diagram (Bonneville, Eighty-Eight, LeSabre, Ninety-Eight & Park Ave.)

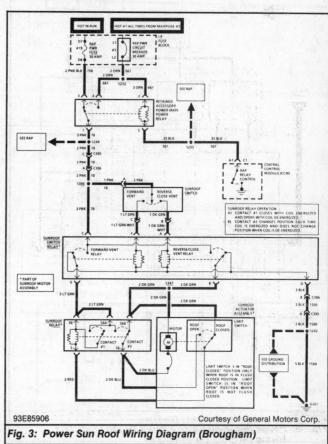

93E85906
Courtesy of General Motors Corp.

Fig. 3: Power Sun Roof Wiring Diagram (Brougham)

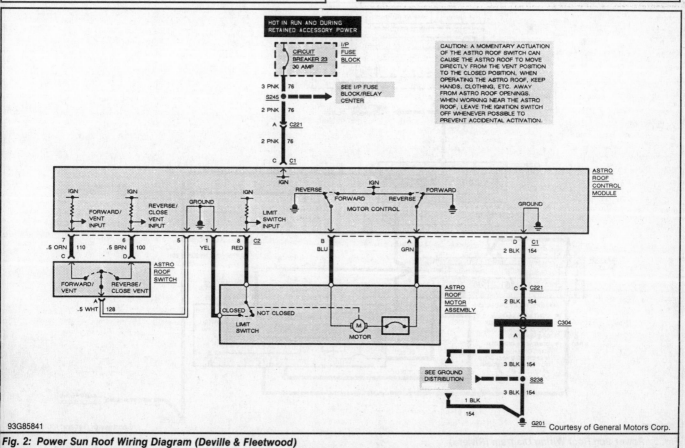

93G85841
Courtesy of General Motors Corp.

Fig. 2: Power Sun Roof Wiring Diagram (Deville & Fleetwood)

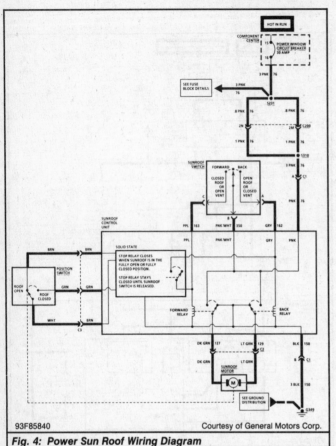

93F85840
Courtesy of General Motors Corp.

Fig. 4: Power Sun Roof Wiring Diagram (Cutlass Supreme, Grand Prix & Regal)

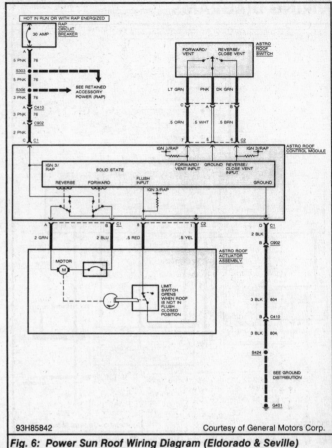

93H85842
Courtesy of General Motors Corp.

Fig. 6: Power Sun Roof Wiring Diagram (Eldorado & Seville)

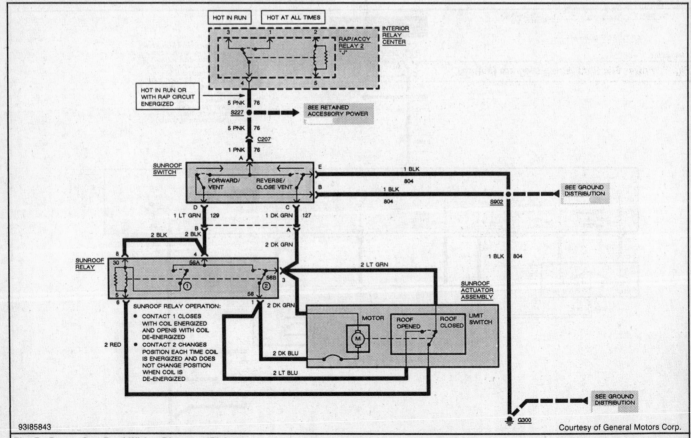

93I85843
Courtesy of General Motors Corp.

Fig. 5: Power Sun Roof Wiring Diagram (Riviera)

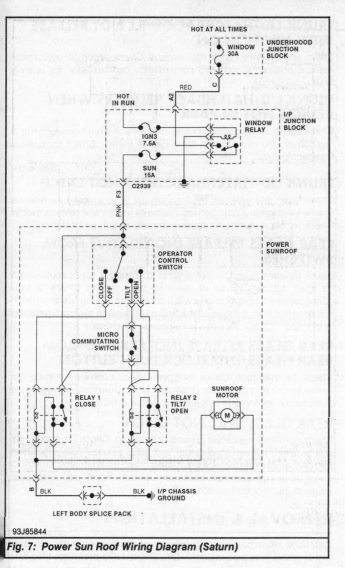

Fig. 7: Power Sun Roof Wiring Diagram (Saturn)

1993 ACCESSORIES & EQUIPMENT
Power Trunk/Hatchback Release

Beretta, Bonneville, Brougham, Camaro, Caprice, Century, Corsica, Corvette, Cutlass Ciera, Cutlass Cruiser, Cutlass Supreme, Deville, Eighty-Eight, Eldorado, Firebird, Fleetwood, Grand Prix, LeSabre, Lumina, Ninety-Eight, Park Avenue, Regal, Riviera, Roadmaster, Seville

DESCRIPTION

The trunk lid or hatchback release system allows the trunk lid or hatchback to be opened using a remote release switch. The release switch is located in the glove box, on the instrument panel or on the console. On models with remote keyless entry systems, the lid/hatchback can also be opened using the remote transmitter.

Some station wagon models also have a rear window glass release that allows the rear window to be opened using the remote release switch or remote keyless entry system.

OPERATION

Trunk Lid/Hatchback Release – The trunk lid and hatchback release system consists of a release switch, release solenoid, release relay, connectors and necessary wiring. The wiring harness is routed from the switch to the trunk/hatchback lid and solenoid. When the switch is pressed the release solenoid coil is energized. The release is pulled back, unlatching the trunk/hatchback lid lock and the lid is opened.

On models with remote keyless entry, the same action takes place except the solenoid is energized by the remote transmitter. The release solenoid is part of the trunk lid on sedan models, and at the latch assembly in hatchback models. Some models with automatic transmission also use a transmission position switch that allows the trunk/lid/hatchback to only be opened with the transmission in Park or Neutral. On some manual transmission models, the parking brake must be applied before release will operate.

Rear Window Glass Release – The rear window glass release switch in located in the accessory panel in the instrument panel or the glove box. When the switch is pressed the release relay is energized, and voltage is applied to the release solenoid. The solenoid then releases the glass latch and the glass is opened. On models with remote keyless entry the same action takes place except the remote transmitter energizes the solenoid. The solenoid is located at the inside center of the tailgate. Some models with automatic transmission also use a transmission position switch that allows the rear glass to only be opened in Park or Neutral.

TESTING

NOTE: On models with remote/keyless entry systems, see appropriate KEYLESS ENTRY article in MITCHELL'S DOMESTIC CAR ELECTRICAL SERVICE & REPAIR manual for specific testing of trunk/hatchback release system.

Always check the following items for possible causes of system malfunction before performing any test on the trunk lid/hatchback or rear glass release system.
- Faulty fuses or circuit breakers
- Loose or corroded connectors
- Low battery charge
- Poor ground connections
- Inoperative lock or latch mechanism.

TROUBLE SHOOTING

TRUNK LID/HATCHBACK WILL NOT RELEASE

Check lock and relase mechanism for mechanical interference. Check solenoid connectors. Check release relay and circuits. Check for fuse block open. Check security switch connections. Check system grounds. Check release switch connections.

TRUNK LID/HATCHBACK WILL NOT RELEASE WITH IGNITION ON

Check convenience center connections. Check circuit between transmission position switch and convenience center.Check for open in fuse block circuit.

TRUNK LID/HATCHBACK RELEASES WHEN VEHICLE NOT IN PARK

Check convenience center connections. Check circuit between transmission position switch and convenience center. Check for open in fuse block circuit.

TRUNK LID/HATCHBACK DOES NOT LATCH

Check lock and release mechanism for mechanical interference. Check for short in circuit between security switch and release switch. Check for short in circuit between security switch and solenoid.

REAR GLASS RELEASE INOPERATIVE FROM SWITCHES

Check for open fuse. Check for short to ground in fuse circuit. Check for open in ground circuit or check for poor ground. Check for poor connections at transmission switch connector. Check for open in circuit between convenience center and transmission switch. Check isolation diode. Check for open in release relay circuit.

REAR GLASS RELEASE INOPERATIVE FROM REAR GLASS/INTERLOCK PUSH BUTTON

Check for open fuse. Check for open in circuit between tailgate lock sense switch and convenience center. Check for poor connections at push button switch and tailgate lock sense switch.

REAR GLASS WILL NOT LATCH

Check convenience center ground connection. Check for short in circuit between convenience center and glass release solenoid. Check for mechanical interference preventing glass from latching. Check for short in circuit between accessory switch panel and rear glass interlock/push button switch.

REMOVAL & INSTALLATION

CAUTION: When battery is disconnected, vehicle computer and memory systems may lose memory data. Driveability problems may exist until computer systems have completed a relearn cycle. See COMPUTER RELEARN PROCEDURES article in GENERAL INFORMATION before disconnecting battery.

TRUNK/HATCHBACK RELEASE SWITCH

Removal & Installation – Remove switch trim cover or filler panel, if equipped. Gently pry switch mounting assembly from instrument panel or console. Disconnect electrical connector and remove switch. To install, reverse removal procedure.

TRUNK LID RELEASE SOLENOID

Removal & Installation – Open trunk lid. Disconnect electrical connector from release solenoid. Remove solenoid attaching screws. Lift solenoid tab from notch in lock assembly and remove solenoid. To install, reverse removal procedure.

HATCHBACK RELEASE SOLENOID

Removal & Installation – Open hatchback. Remove inside rear compartment trim assembly. Remove lock retainer from release solenoid. Disconnect electrical connector from solenoid. Remove solenoid attaching screws and remove solenoid from latch assembly. To install, reverse removal procedure.

GLASS RELEASE SOLENOID

Removal & Installation – Open rear glass and tailgate. Remove tailgate lock cylinder. Remove release solenoid bumper, if equipped. Disconnect electrical connectors. Loosen nuts on striker locator and move it aside. Remove solenoid attaching nuts and remove solenoid. To install, reverse removal procedure.

WIRING DIAGRAMS

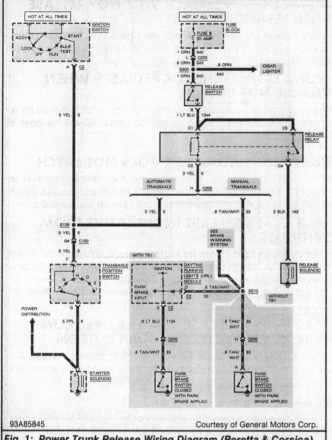

93A85845   Courtesy of General Motors Corp.

Fig. 1: Power Trunk Release Wiring Diagram (Beretta & Corsica)

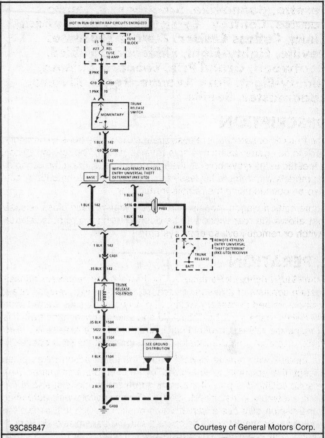

93C85847   Courtesy of General Motors Corp.

Fig. 3: Power Trunk Release Wiring Diagram (Brougham)

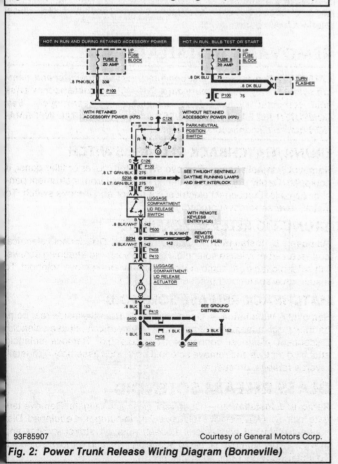

93F85907   Courtesy of General Motors Corp.

Fig. 2: Power Trunk Release Wiring Diagram (Bonneville)

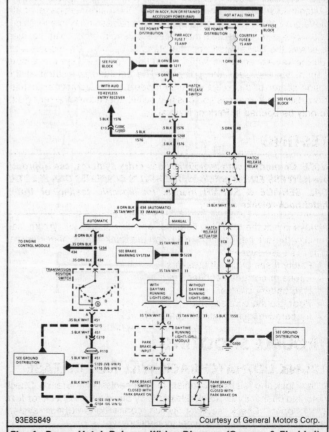

93E85849   Courtesy of General Motors Corp.

Fig. 4: Power Hatch Release Wiring Diagram (Camaro & Firebird)

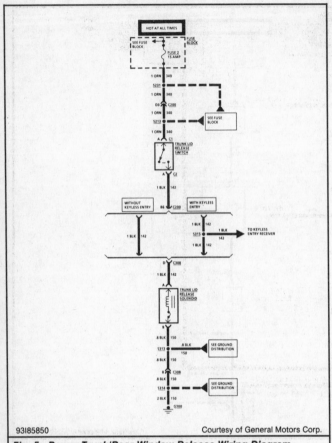

93I85850   Courtesy of General Motors Corp.

Fig. 5: Power Trunk/Rear Window Release Wiring Diagram (Caprice – 1 Of 3)

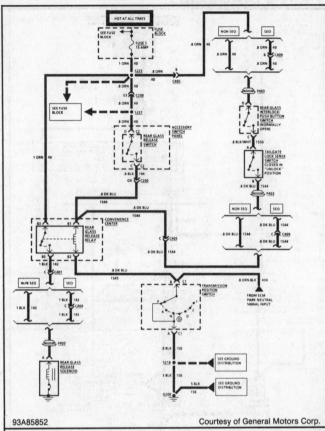

93A85852   Courtesy of General Motors Corp.

Fig. 7: Power Trunk/Rear Window Release Wiring Diagram (Caprice – 3 Of 3)

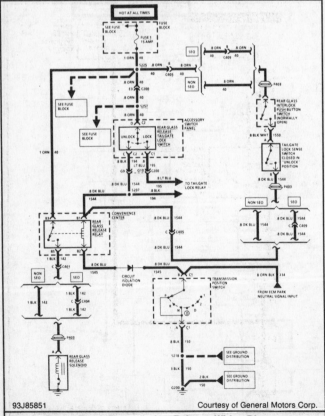

93J85851   Courtesy of General Motors Corp.

Fig. 6: Power Trunk/Rear Window Release Wiring Diagram (Caprice – 2 Of 3)

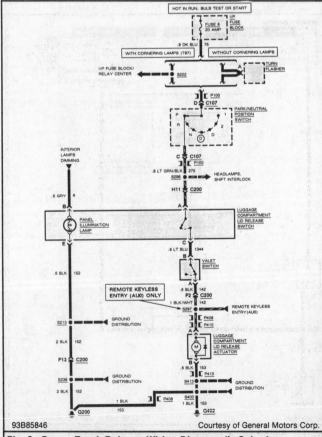

93B85846   Courtesy of General Motors Corp.

Fig. 8: Power Trunk Release Wiring Diagram (LeSabre)

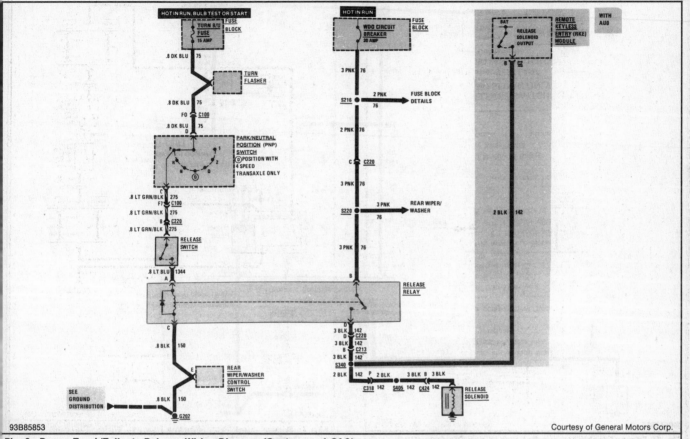

93B85853

Courtesy of General Motors Corp.

Fig. 9: Power Trunk/Tailgate Release Wiring Diagram (Century – 1 Of 2)

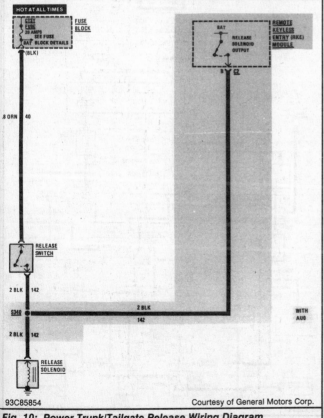

93C85854

Courtesy of General Motors Corp.

Fig. 10: Power Trunk/Tailgate Release Wiring Diagram (Century – 2 Of 2)

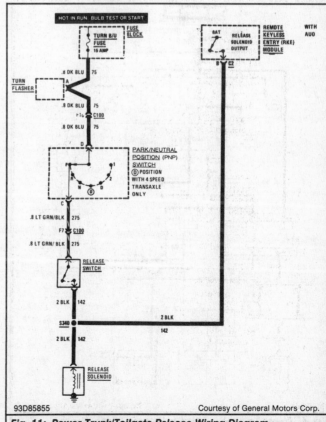

93D85855

Courtesy of General Motors Corp.

Fig. 11: Power Trunk/Tailgate Release Wiring Diagram (Cutlass Ciera & Cutlass Cruiser – 1 Of 2)

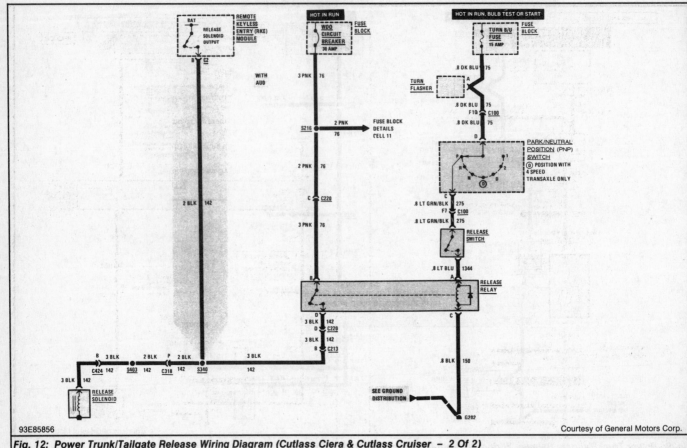

Fig. 12: Power Trunk/Tailgate Release Wiring Diagram (Cutlass Ciera & Cutlass Cruiser – 2 Of 2)

93E85856   Courtesy of General Motors Corp.

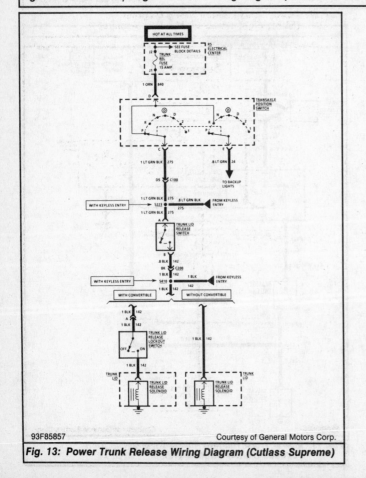

Fig. 13: Power Trunk Release Wiring Diagram (Cutlass Supreme)

93F85857   Courtesy of General Motors Corp.

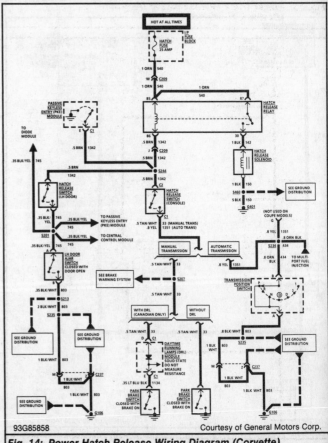

Fig. 14: Power Hatch Release Wiring Diagram (Corvette)

93G85858   Courtesy of General Motors Corp.

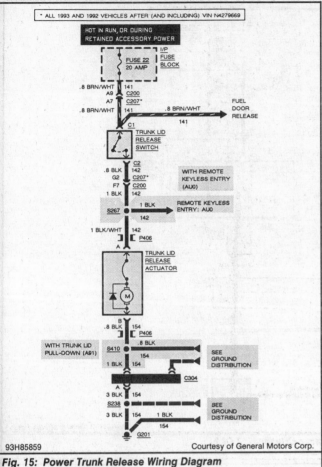

Fig. 15: Power Trunk Release Wiring Diagram (Deville & Fleetwood)

93H85859 — Courtesy of General Motors Corp.

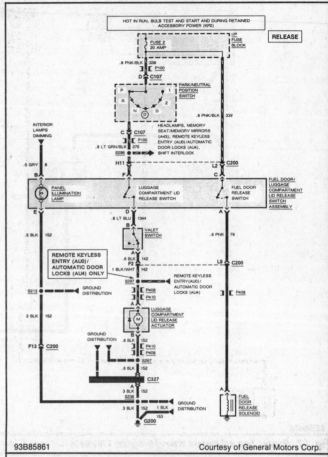

Fig. 17: Power Trunk Release Wiring Diagram (Eighty-Eight, Ninety-Eight & Park Avenue)

93B85861 — Courtesy of General Motors Corp.

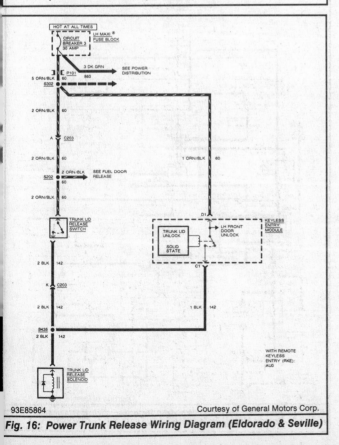

Fig. 16: Power Trunk Release Wiring Diagram (Eldorado & Seville)

93E85864 — Courtesy of General Motors Corp.

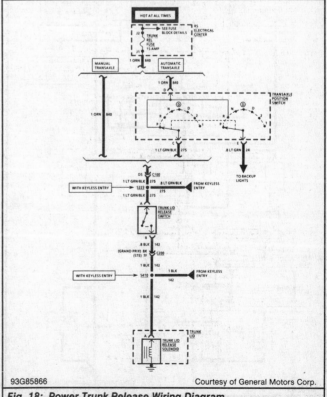

Fig. 18: Power Trunk Release Wiring Diagram (Grand Prix, Lumina & Regal)

93G85866 — Courtesy of General Motors Corp.

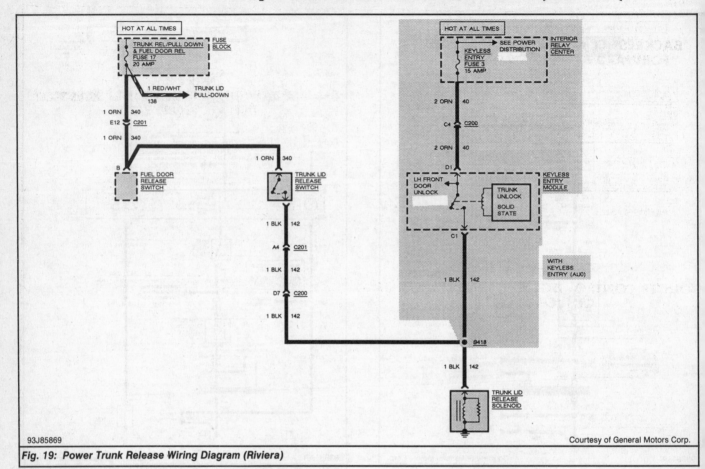

93J85869

Courtesy of General Motors Corp.

Fig. 19: Power Trunk Release Wiring Diagram (Riviera)

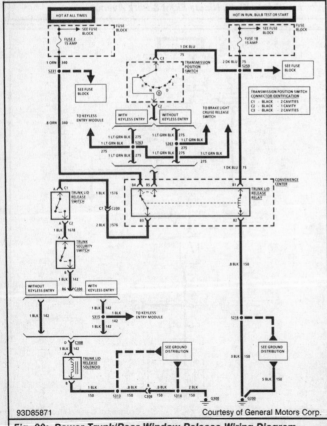

93D85871

Courtesy of General Motors Corp.

Fig. 20: Power Trunk/Rear Window Release Wiring Diagram (Roadmaster – 1 Of 4)

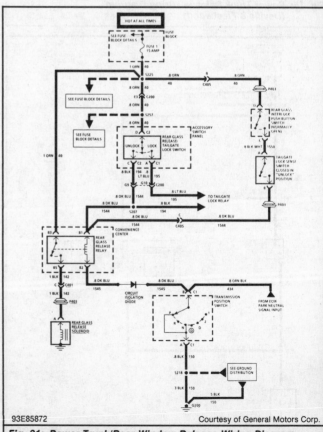

93E85872

Courtesy of General Motors Corp.

Fig. 21: Power Trunk/Rear Window Release Wiring Diagram (Roadmaster – 2 Of 4)

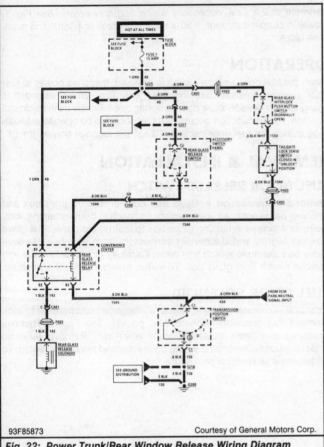

93F85873   Courtesy of General Motors Corp.

Fig. 22: Power Trunk/Rear Window Release Wiring Diagram (Roadmaster – 3 Of 4)

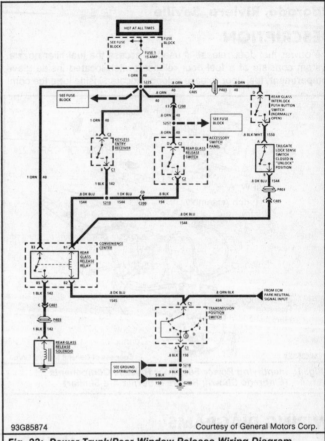

93G85874   Courtesy of General Motors Corp.

Fig. 23: Power Trunk/Rear Window Release Wiring Diagram (Roadmaster – 4 Of 4)

Eldorado, Riviera, Seville

DESCRIPTION

The power fuel door release is used to access the fuel filler nozzle. System consists of a fuel door release switch located inside glove compartment, fuel door release solenoid located inside luggage com-partment at left side, necessary wiring and connectors. See Fig. 1. Power is supplied through a 30-amp circuit breaker in left-hand maxi-fuse block.

OPERATION

When the fuel door release switch is pressed, it applies power to fuel door release solenoid causing it to energize. When solenoid is energized it moves to allow door to spring open slightly from its closed position. If a malfunction occurs, the fuel door can be opened manual-ly by pulling the fuel door cable handle in the luggage compartment.

REMOVAL & INSTALLATION

FUEL DOOR RELEASE SWITCH

Removal & Installation – Open trap door in rear of glove box and remove passenger air bag wiring connector from retaining clip. Remove 4 screws attaching glove box to instrument panel. Pull glove box out slightly and disconnect connectors from switches. Remove glove box. Remove switch trim plate. Carefully pinch switch tabs and remove switch from glove box. To install, reverse removal procedure.

FUEL DOOR SOLENOID

Removal & Installation – Remove luggage compartment trim. Remove nut retaining latch to fuel pocket. See Fig. 1. Remove grommet and latch assembly from wheelwell. Remove solenoid attaching bolts. Disconnect wiring connector and remove solenoid. To install, reverse removal procedure.

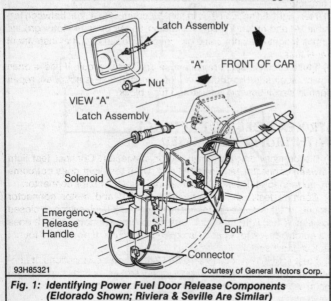

93H85321   Courtesy of General Motors Corp.

Fig. 1: Identifying Power Fuel Door Release Components (Eldorado Shown; Riviera & Seville Are Similar)

WIRING DIAGRAMS

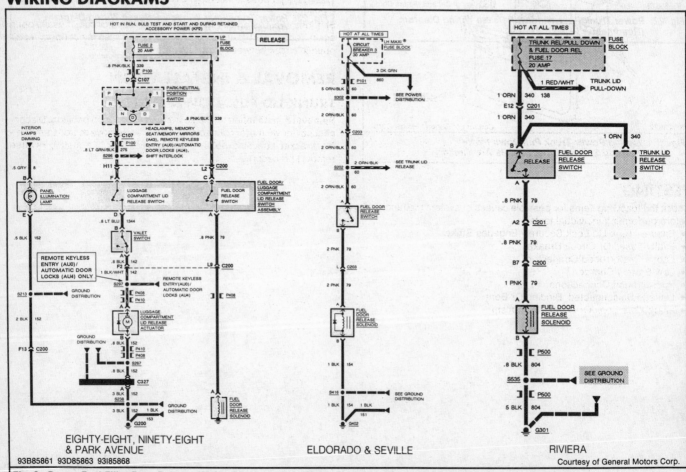

93B85861   93D85863   93I85868   Courtesy of General Motors Corp.

Fig. 2: Power Fuel Filler Door Release Wiring Diagram (Eight-Eight, Eldorado, Ninety-Eight, Park Ave., Riviera & Seville)

Brougham, Caprice, Eldorado, Riviera, Roadmaster, Seville

DESCRIPTION & OPERATION

All models use a power trunk pull-down system that pulls down and latches the trunk lid during the last 1" (25 mm) of travel. A combination latch/release mechanism is located in the trunk lid. A permanent magnet pull-down motor is located in the trunk lid opening lower panel. *See Fig. 1.*

When the trunk lid is closed, very light pressure is required to cause the latch to grab the extended striker on the motor. The motor will then run, taking the lid to its completely closed position. The key lock frame then depresses the plunger switch breaking the circuit to the motor. The motor will then shut off.

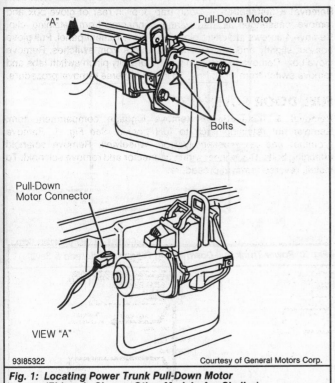

93185322   Courtesy of General Motors Corp.

***Fig. 1: Locating Power Trunk Pull-Down Motor
(Eldorado Shown; Other Models Are Similar)***

TESTING

Check the following items for possible causes of system malfunctions before performing individual tests.
- Ensure Trunk Lid Lock Securely Engages Striker
- Faulty Fuses Or Circuit Breaker
- Loose Or Corroded Connectors
- Low Battery Charge
- Poor Ground Connections
- Linkage Disconnected, Binding Or Bent
- Inoperative Lock Or Latch Mechanism

STRIKER DOES NOT EXTEND WITH TRUNK LID UNLATCHED

1) Disconnect trunk pull-down motor connector. Connect test light between connector terminals "A" and "D". If test light comes on, install a known good striker switch and check that striker extends. If striker does not extend, replace pull-down motor. If striker extends, repair is complete.

2) If test light did not come on in step **1)**, connect test light between terminal "A" and ground. If light comes on, repair open in motor ground circuit. If light does not come on, check for open circuit at instrument panel fuse.

3) If fuse circuit is open, replace fuse and retest circuit. If use is open again, repair short-to-ground in fuse circuit. If fuse is not open, repair open in circuit between motor and fuse block.

STRIKER DOES NOT RETRACT WITH TRUNK LID CLOSED

1) Disconnect trunk pull-down motor connector. Connect test light between connector terminals "A" and "D". If test light does not come on, go to step **4)**. If test light comes on, reinstall motor connector.

2) Connect test light between terminal "B" and motor connector ground. If light comes on, manually move trunk latch switch to closed position. If test light goes out, replace pull-down motor. If light does not go out, check for open in latch switch circuits. If no open is found, replace latch switch.

3) If test light was not on in step **2)**, Check motor connections. If connections are okay, install known good striker switch. If pull-down motor works, repair is complete. If motor does not work, replace pull-down motor.

4) If test light did not come on in step **1)**, connect test light between terminal "A" and ground. If light comes on, repair open in motor ground circuit. If light does not come on, check for open circuit at instrument panel fuse.

5) If fuse circuit is open, replace fuse and retest circuit. If use is open again, repair short-to-ground in fuse circuit. If fuse is not open, repair open in circuit between motor and fuse block.

REMOVAL & INSTALLATION

TRUNK LID PULL-DOWN MOTOR

Removal & Installation – Raise trunk lid to full open position. Disconnect pull-down motor connector. *See Fig. 1.* Remove motor-to-mounting bracket attaching bolts and remove motor. To install, reverse removal procedure.

WIRING DIAGRAMS

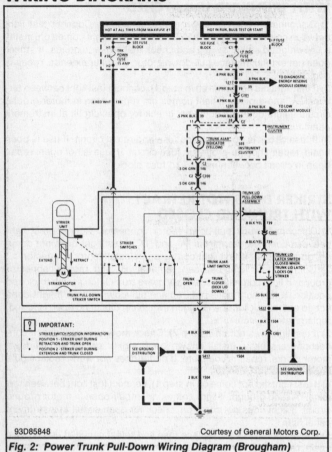

93D85848   Courtesy of General Motors Corp.

Fig. 2: Power Trunk Pull-Down Wiring Diagram (Brougham)

93F85865   Courtesy of General Motors Corp.

Fig. 3: Power Trunk Pull-Down Wiring Diagram (Eldorado & Seville)

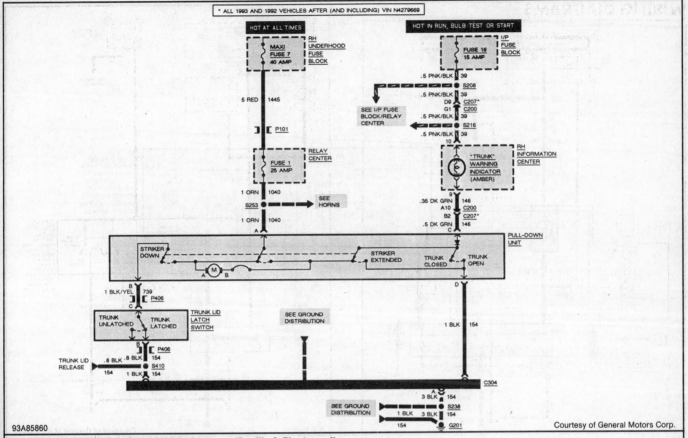

Fig. 4: Power Trunk Pull-Down Wiring Diagram (Deville & Fleetwood)

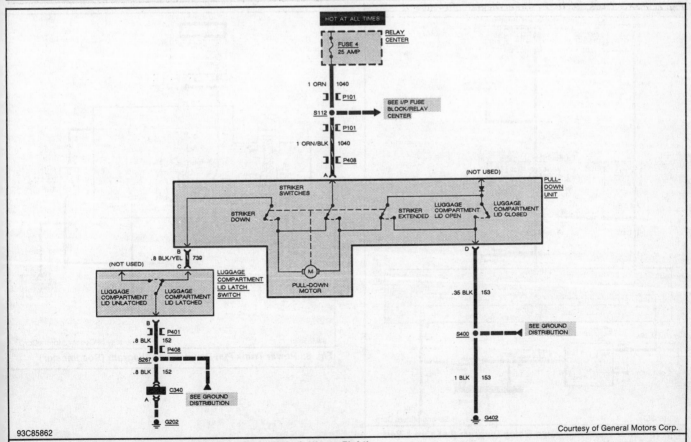

Fig. 5: Power Trunk Pull-Down Wiring Diagram (Eight-Eight & Ninety-Eight)

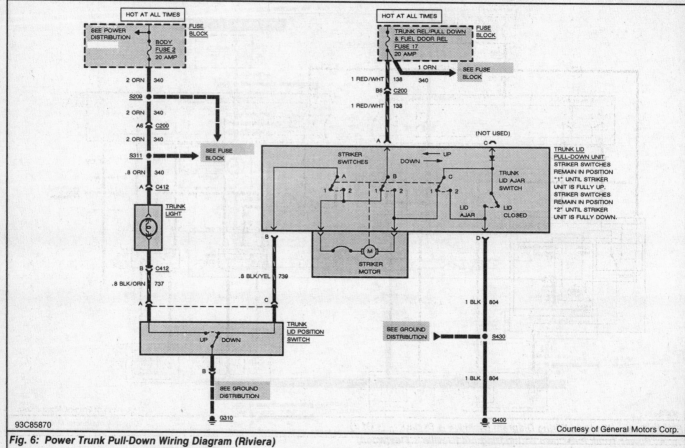

93C85870   Courtesy of General Motors Corp.

Fig. 6: Power Trunk Pull-Down Wiring Diagram (Riviera)

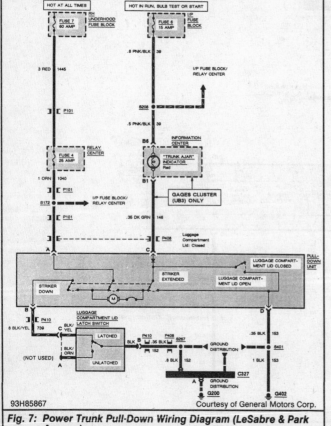

93H85867   Courtesy of General Motors Corp.

Fig. 7: Power Trunk Pull-Down Wiring Diagram (LeSabre & Park Avenue)

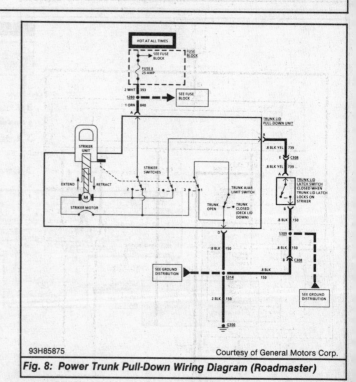

93H85875   Courtesy of General Motors Corp.

Fig. 8: Power Trunk Pull-Down Wiring Diagram (Roadmaster)

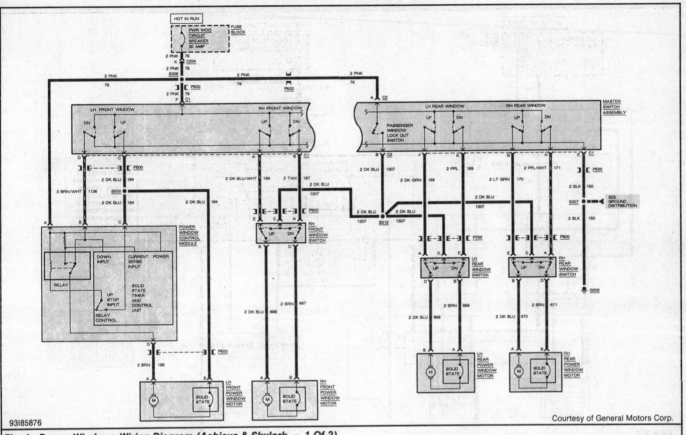

93I85876

Courtesy of General Motors Corp.

Fig. 1: Power Windows Wiring Diagram (Achieva & Skylark – 1 Of 2)

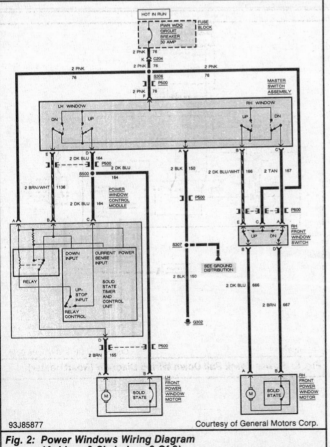

93J85877

Courtesy of General Motors Corp.

Fig. 2: Power Windows Wiring Diagram
(Achieva & Skylark – 2 Of 2)

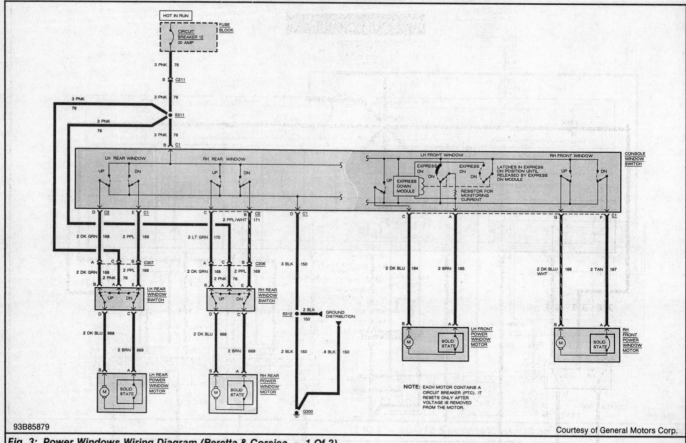

93B85879

Courtesy of General Motors Corp.

Fig. 3: Power Windows Wiring Diagram (Beretta & Corsica – 1 Of 2)

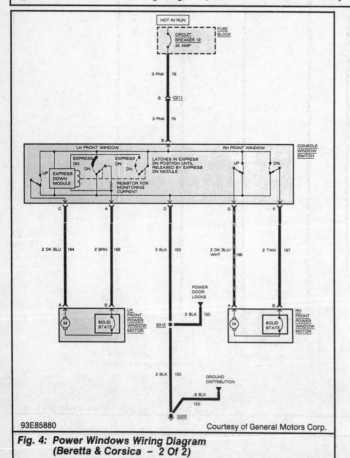

93E85880   Courtesy of General Motors Corp.

Fig. 4: Power Windows Wiring Diagram (Beretta & Corsica – 2 Of 2)

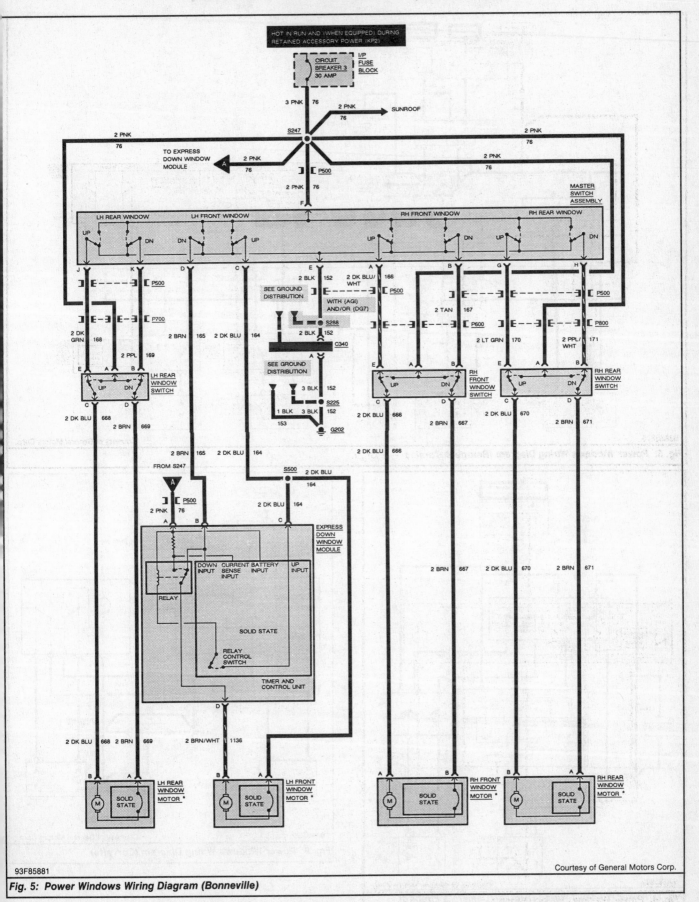

93F85881

Courtesy of General Motors Corp.

Fig. 5: Power Windows Wiring Diagram (Bonneville)

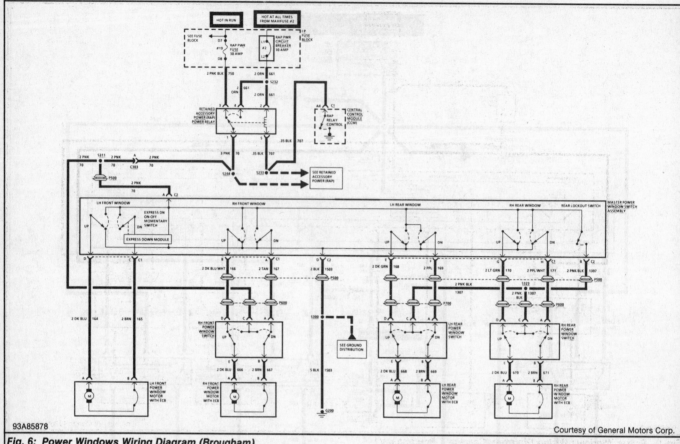

Fig. 6: Power Windows Wiring Diagram (Brougham)

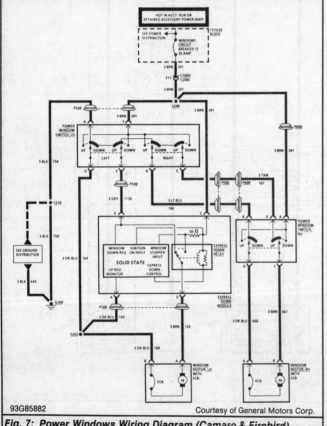

Fig. 7: Power Windows Wiring Diagram (Camaro & Firebird)

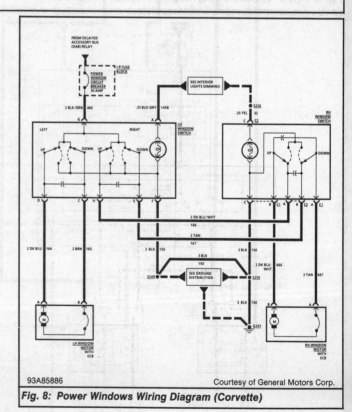

Fig. 8: Power Windows Wiring Diagram (Corvette)

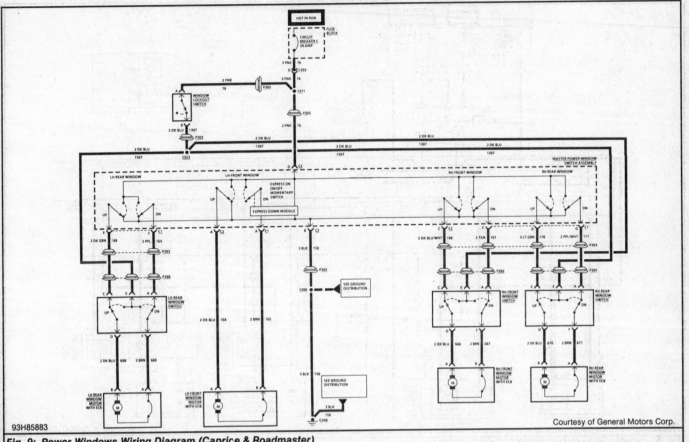

Fig. 9: Power Windows Wiring Diagram (Caprice & Roadmaster)

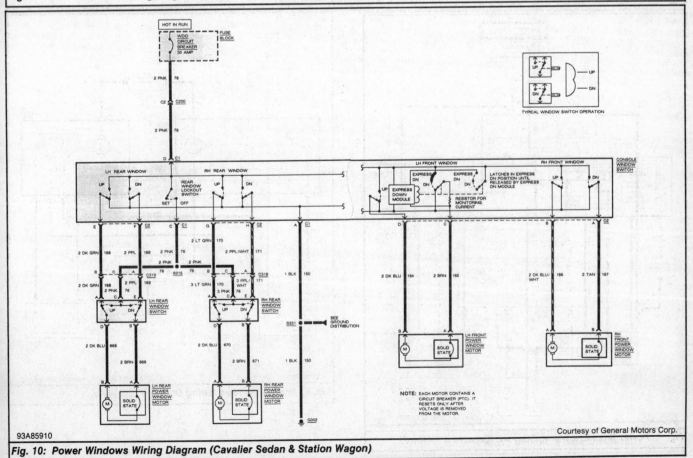

Fig. 10: Power Windows Wiring Diagram (Cavalier Sedan & Station Wagon)

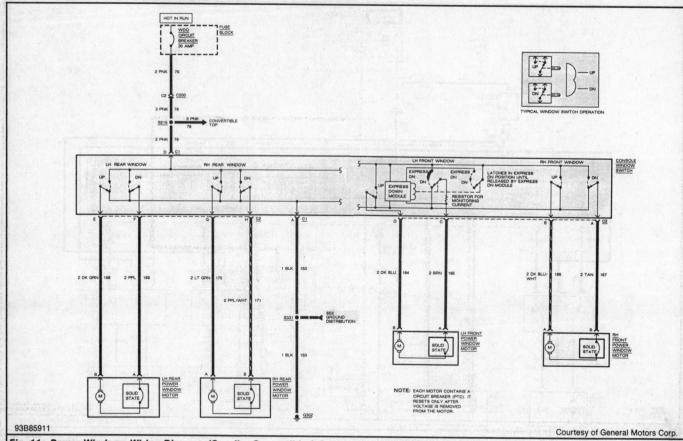

93B85911   Courtesy of General Motors Corp.

Fig. 11: Power Windows Wiring Diagram (Cavalier Convertible & Sunbird Convertible)

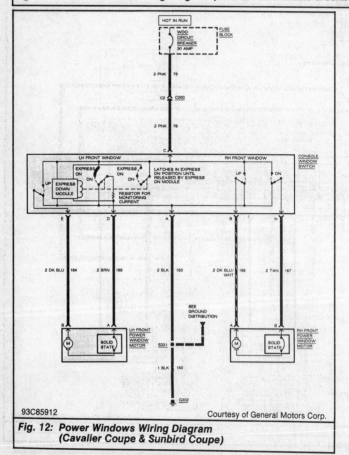

93C85912   Courtesy of General Motors Corp.

**Fig. 12: Power Windows Wiring Diagram
(Cavalier Coupe & Sunbird Coupe)**

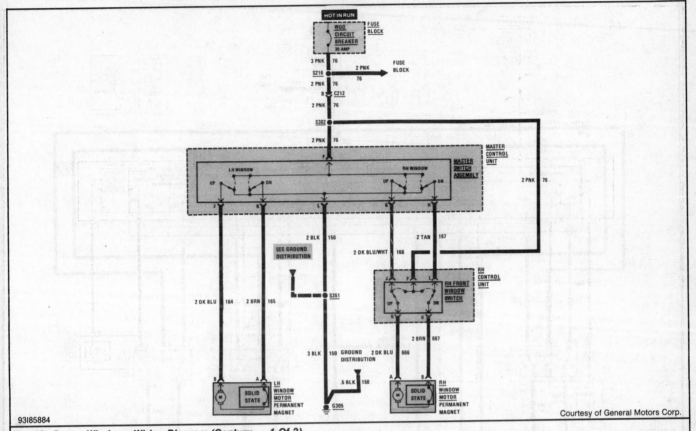

Fig. 13: Power Windows Wiring Diagram (Century – 1 Of 2)

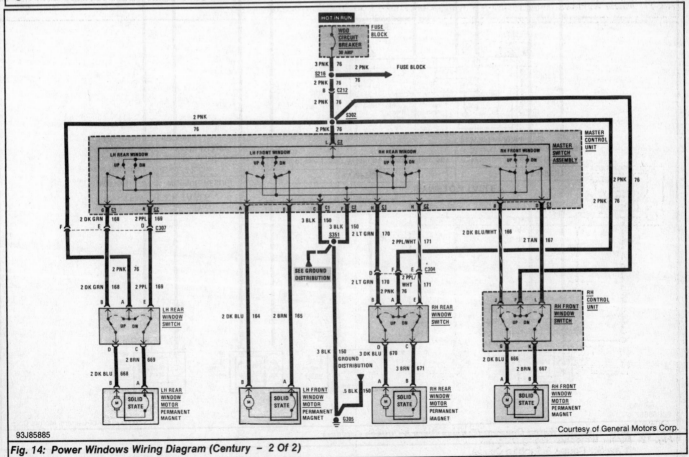

Fig. 14: Power Windows Wiring Diagram (Century – 2 Of 2)

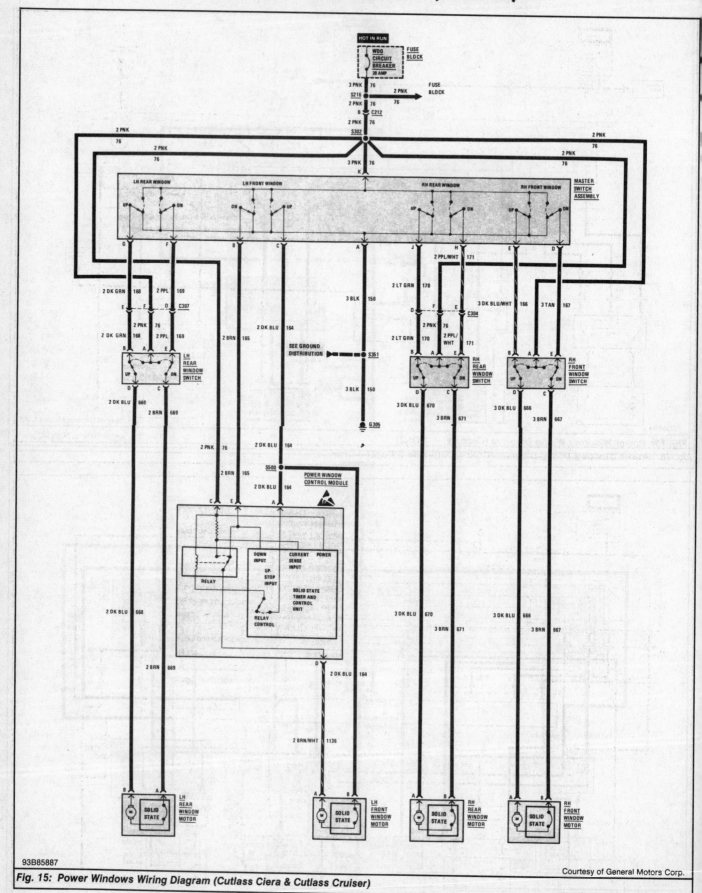

Fig. 15: Power Windows Wiring Diagram (Cutlass Ciera & Cutlass Cruiser)

93B85887

Courtesy of General Motors Corp.

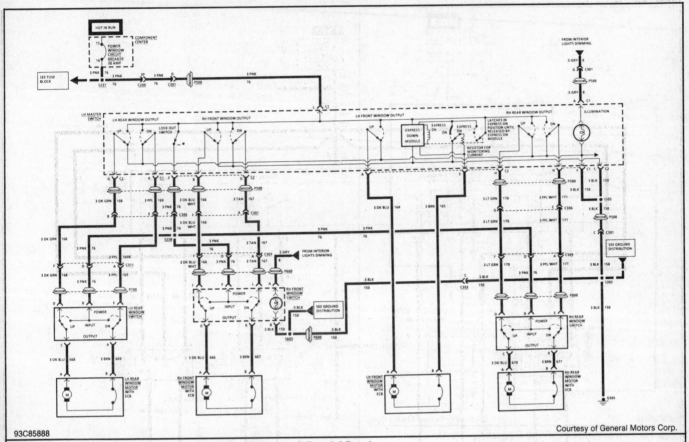

Fig. 16: Power Windows Wiring Diagram (Cutlass Supreme & Regal 4-Door)

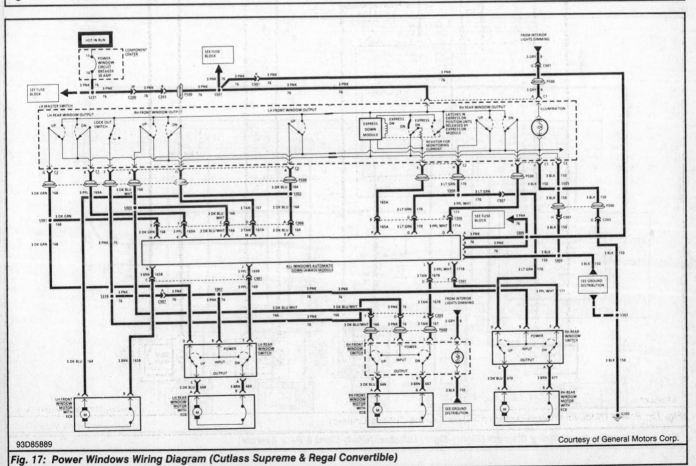

Fig. 17: Power Windows Wiring Diagram (Cutlass Supreme & Regal Convertible)

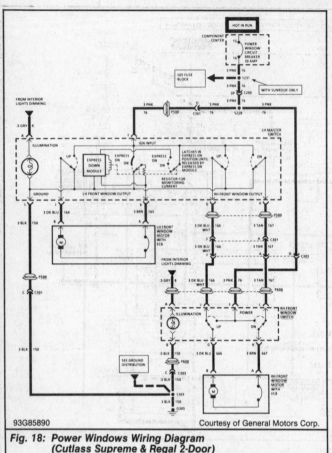

Fig. 18: Power Windows Wiring Diagram
(Cutlass Supreme & Regal 2-Door)

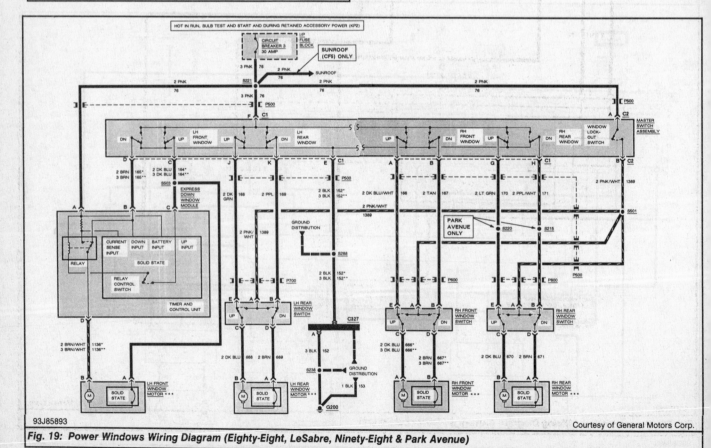

Fig. 19: Power Windows Wiring Diagram (Eighty-Eight, LeSabre, Ninety-Eight & Park Avenue)

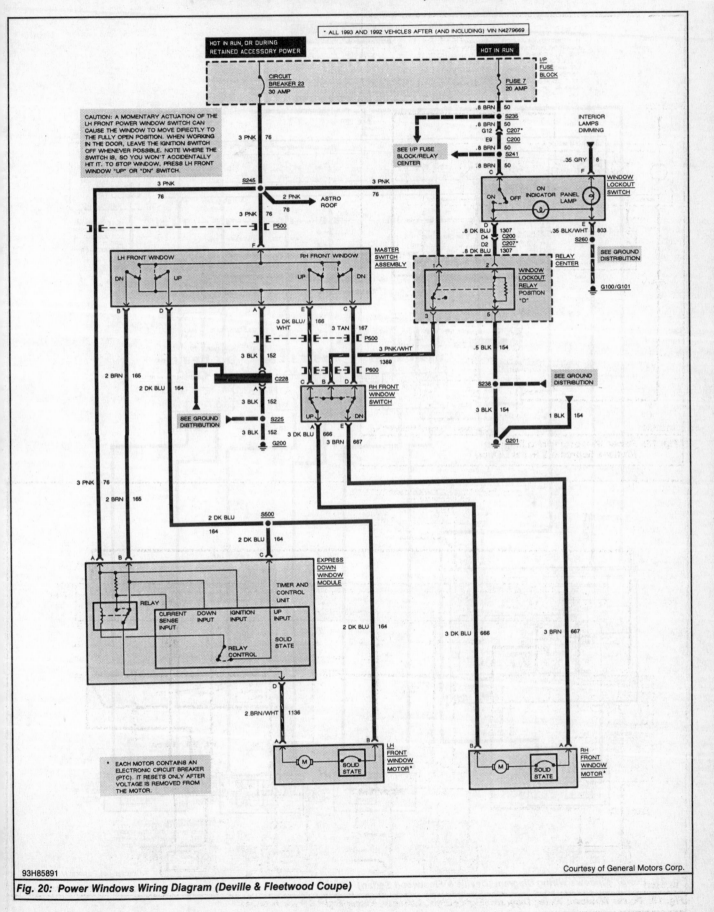

93H85891

Fig. 20: Power Windows Wiring Diagram (Deville & Fleetwood Coupe)

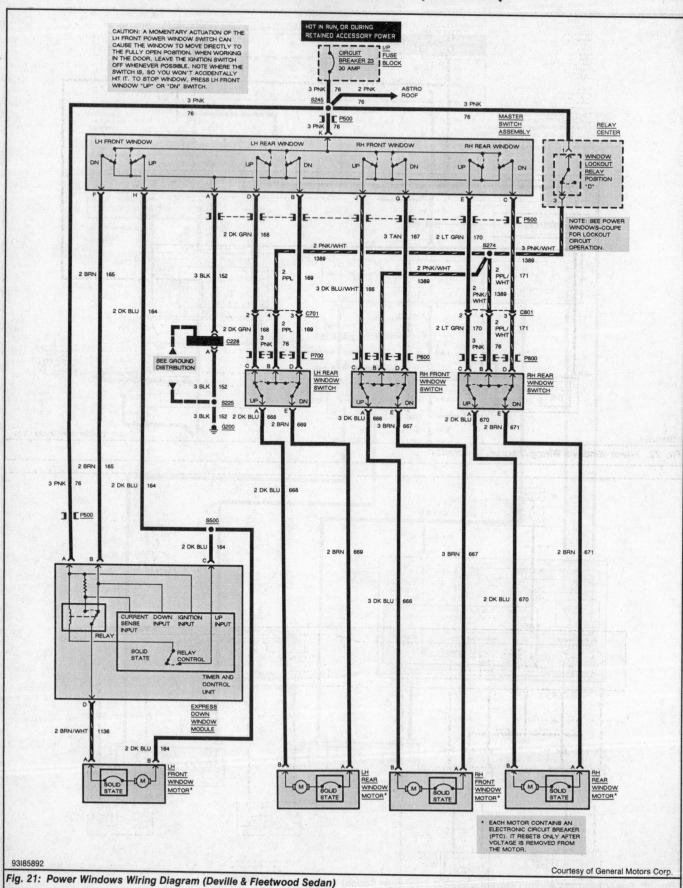

Fig. 21: *Power Windows Wiring Diagram (Deville & Fleetwood Sedan)*

93I85892

Courtesy of General Motors Corp.

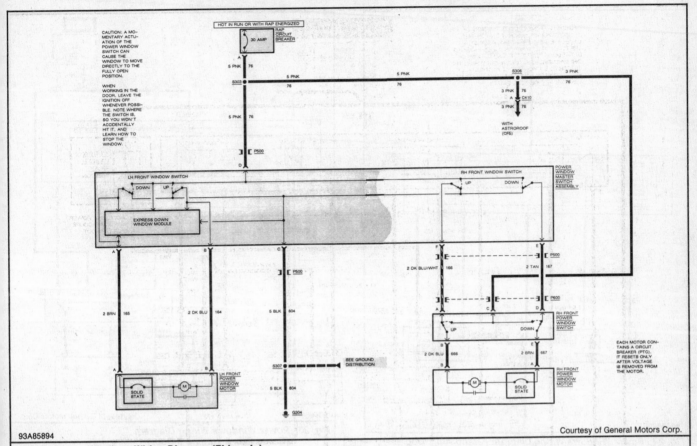

Fig. 22: Power Windows Wiring Diagram (Eldorado)

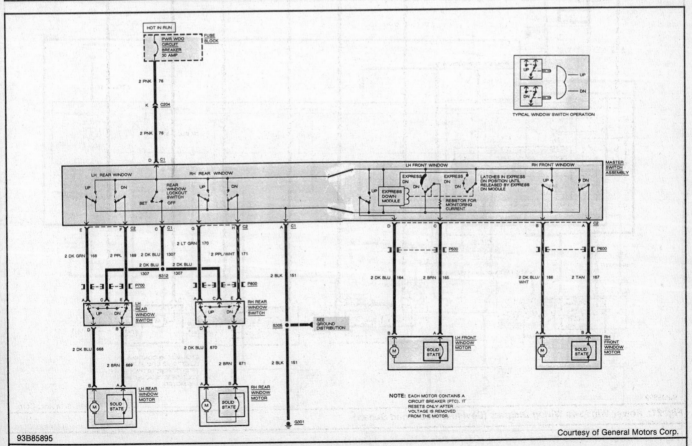

Fig. 23: Power Windows Wiring Diagram (Grand Am 4-Door)

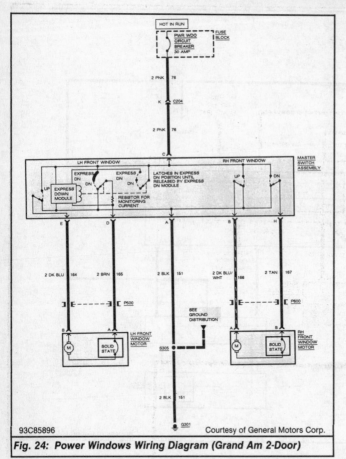

93C85896

Fig. 24: Power Windows Wiring Diagram (Grand Am 2-Door)

Courtesy of General Motors Corp.

93F85899

Fig. 26: Power Windows Wiring Diagram (Grand Prix & Lumina 2-Door)

Courtesy of General Motors Corp.

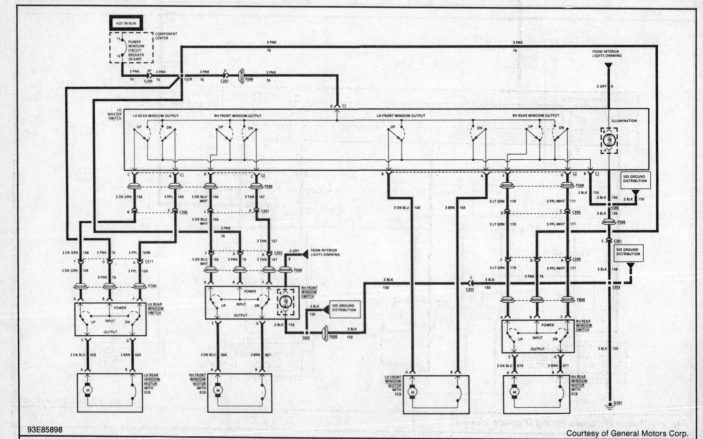

93E85898

Fig. 25: Power Windows Wiring Diagram (Grand Prix & Lumina 4-Door)

Courtesy of General Motors Corp.

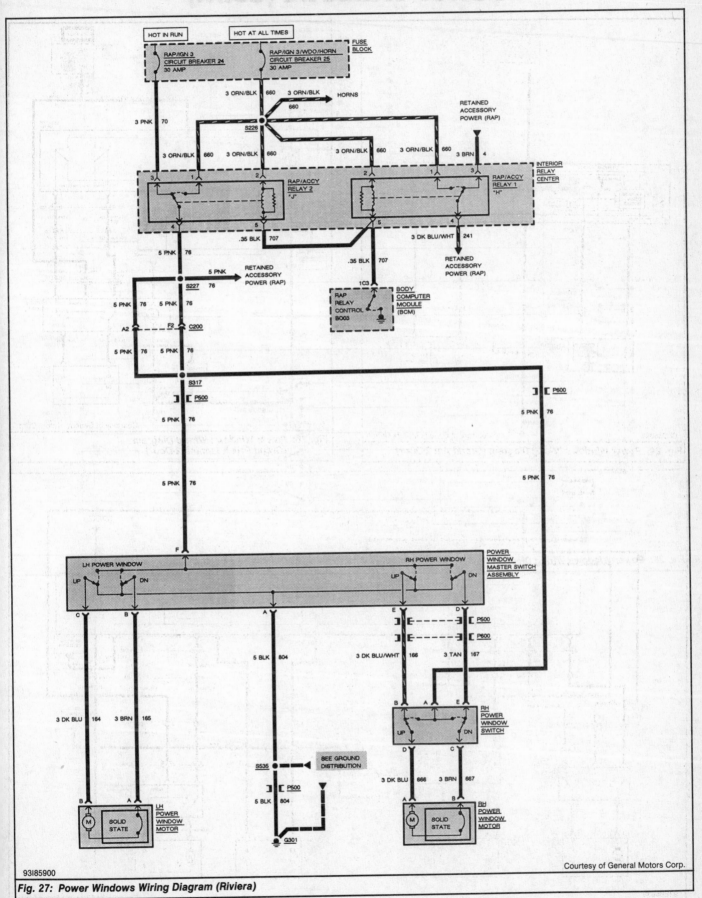

Fig. 27: Power Windows Wiring Diagram (Riviera)

Courtesy of General Motors Corp.

93185900

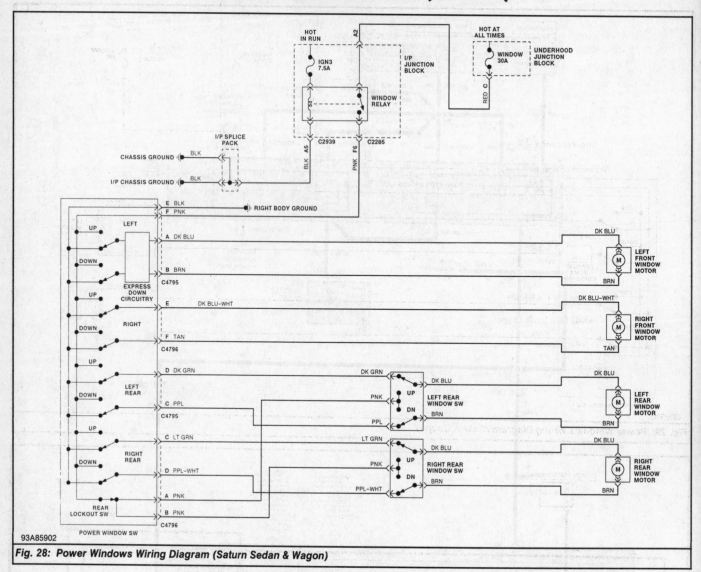

Fig. 28: Power Windows Wiring Diagram (Saturn Sedan & Wagon)

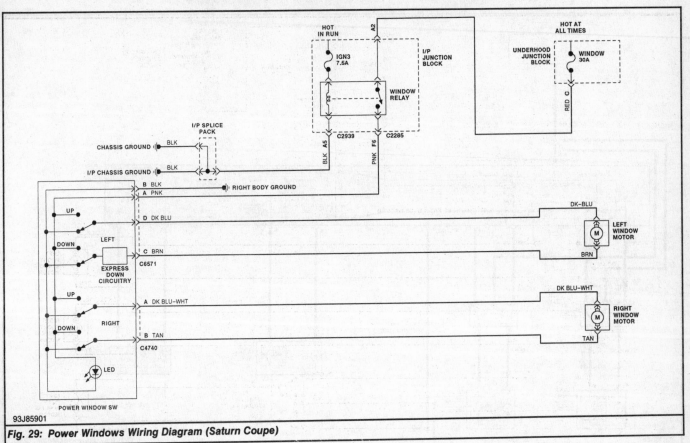

Fig. 29: Power Windows Wiring Diagram (Saturn Coupe)

93J85901

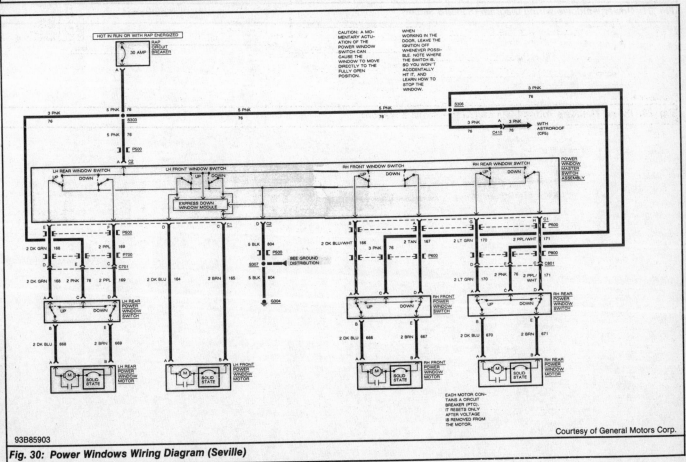

Courtesy of General Motors Corp.

93B85903

Fig. 30: Power Windows Wiring Diagram (Seville)

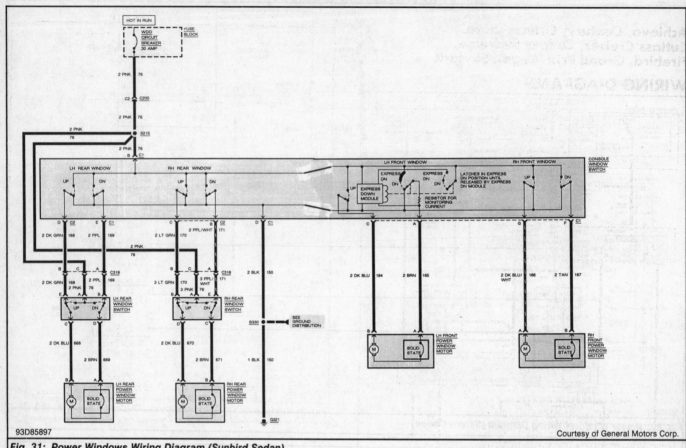

Fig. 31: Power Windows Wiring Diagram (Sunbird Sedan)

93D85897

Courtesy of General Motors Corp.

GM
4-185

1993 ACCESSORIES & EQUIPMENT
Remote Keyless Entry System – "A", "F", "N" & "W" Bodies (Cont.)

Achieva, Century, Cutlass Ciera, Cutlass Cruiser, Cutlass Supreme, Firebird, Grand Prix, Regal, Skylark

WIRING DIAGRAMS

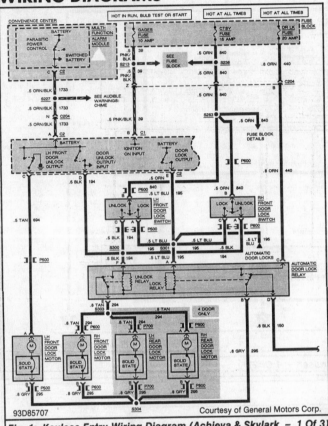

93D85707   Courtesy of General Motors Corp.

Fig. 1: Keyless Entry Wiring Diagram (Achieva & Skylark – 1 Of 3)

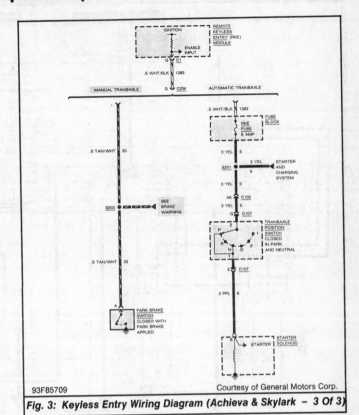

93F85709   Courtesy of General Motors Corp.

Fig. 3: Keyless Entry Wiring Diagram (Achieva & Skylark – 3 Of 3)

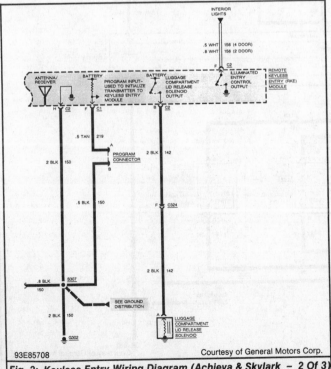

93E85708   Courtesy of General Motors Corp.

Fig. 2: Keyless Entry Wiring Diagram (Achieva & Skylark – 2 Of 3)

GM
4-186

1993 ACCESSORIES & EQUIPMENT
Remote Keyless Entry System – "A", "F", "N" & "W" Bodies (Cont.)

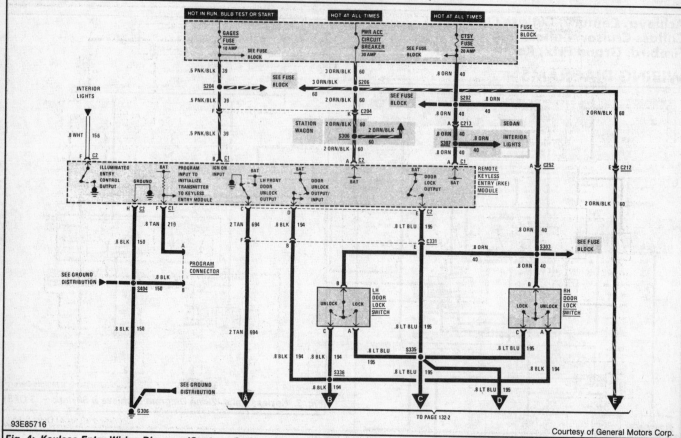

Fig. 4: Keyless Entry Wiring Diagram (Century, Cutlass Ciera & Cutlass Cruiser – 1 Of 2)

93E85716

Courtesy of General Motors Corp.

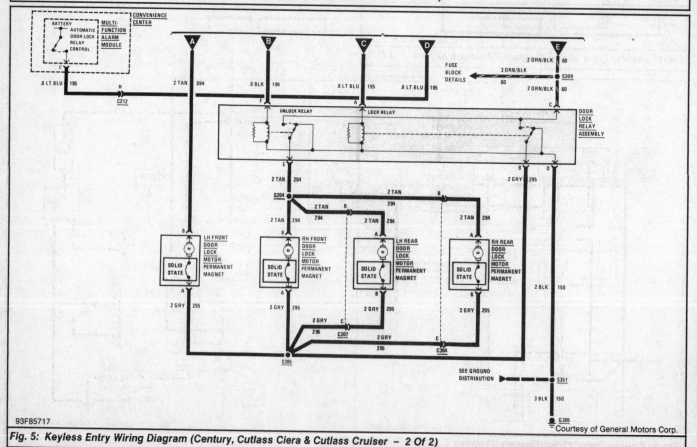

Fig. 5: Keyless Entry Wiring Diagram (Century, Cutlass Ciera & Cutlass Cruiser – 2 Of 2)

93F85717

Courtesy of General Motors Corp.

1993 ACCESSORIES & EQUIPMENT
Remote Keyless Entry System – "A", "F", "N" & "W" Bodies (Cont.)

GM
4-187

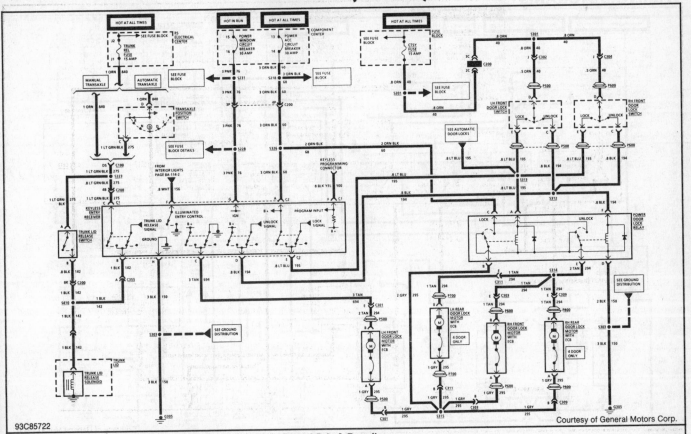

Fig. 6: Keyless Entry Wiring Diagram (Cutlass Supreme, Grand Prix & Regal)

93C85722

Courtesy of General Motors Corp.

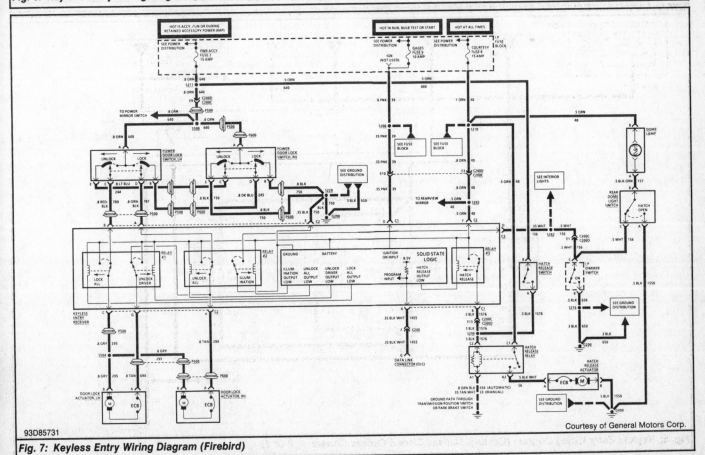

Fig. 7: Keyless Entry Wiring Diagram (Firebird)

93D85731

Courtesy of General Motors Corp.

WIRING DIAGRAMS

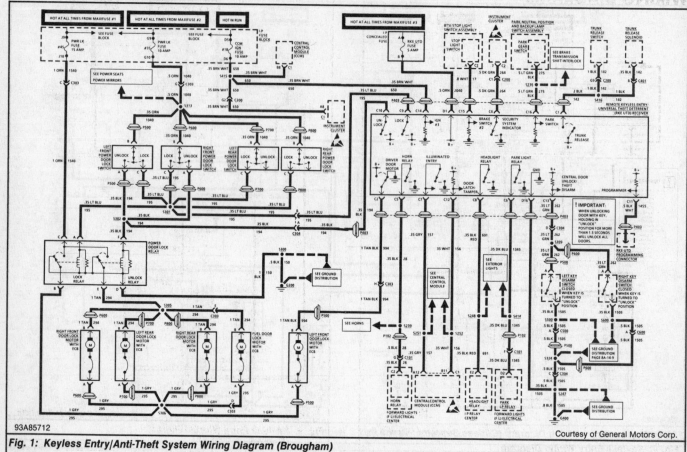

93A85712

Courtesy of General Motors Corp.

Fig. 1: Keyless Entry/Anti-Theft System Wiring Diagram (Brougham)

WIRING DIAGRAMS

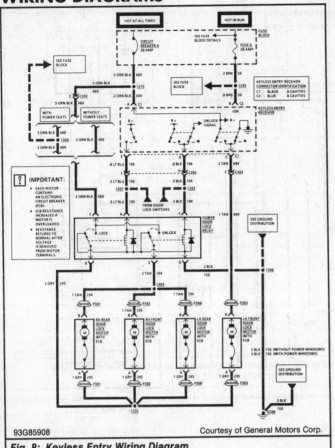

Fig. 8: Keyless Entry Wiring Diagram (Caprice – 1 Of 2)

93G85908

Courtesy of General Motors Corp.

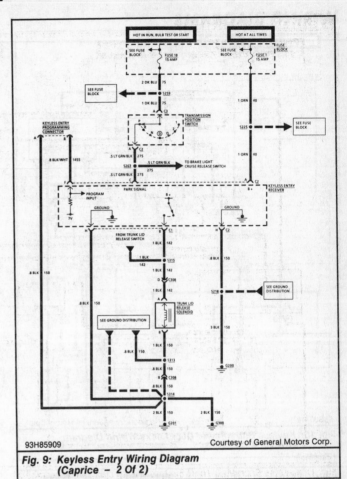

Fig. 9: Keyless Entry Wiring Diagram (Caprice – 2 Of 2)

93H85909

Courtesy of General Motors Corp.

WIRING DIAGRAMS

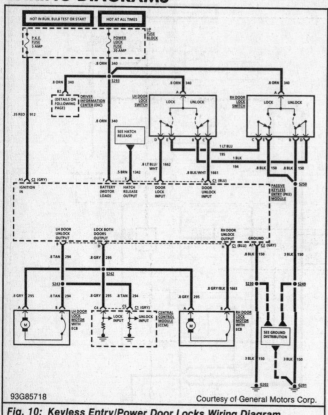

93G85718

Courtesy of General Motors Corp.

Fig. 10: *Keyless Entry/Power Door Locks Wiring Diagram (Corvette – 1 Of 4)*

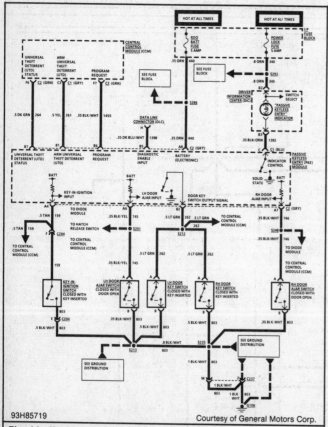

93H85719

Courtesy of General Motors Corp.

Fig. 11: *Keyless Entry/Power Door Locks Wiring Diagram (Corvette – 2 Of 4)*

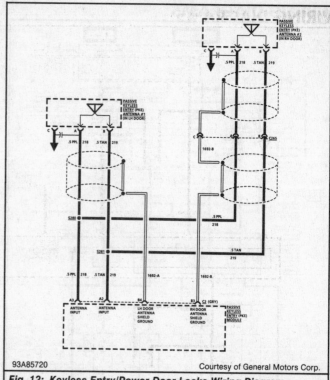

93A85720

Courtesy of General Motors Corp.

Fig. 12: *Keyless Entry/Power Door Locks Wiring Diagram (Corvette – 3 Of 4)*

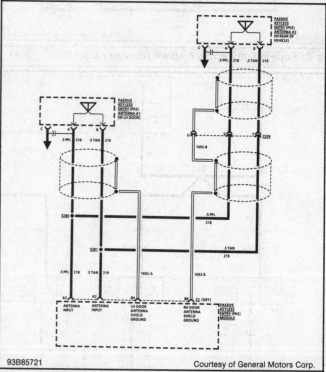

93B85721

Courtesy of General Motors Corp.

Fig. 13: *Keyless Entry/Power Door Locks Wiring Diagram (Corvette – 4 Of 4)*

1993 ACCESSORIES & EQUIPMENT
Remote Keyless Entry System – "E" & "K" Bodies (Cont.)

GM
4-191

WIRING DIAGRAMS

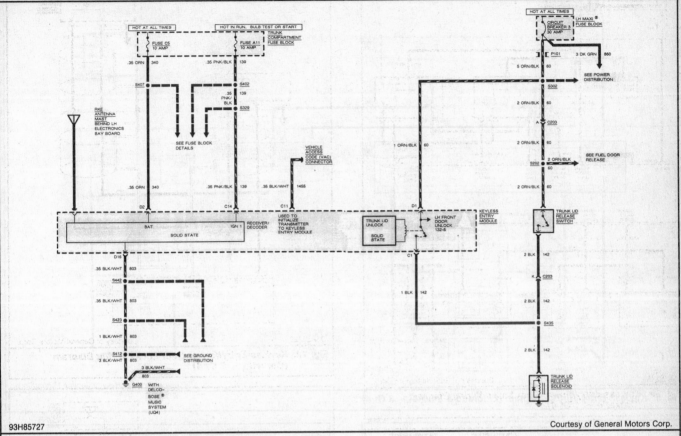

93H85727

Courtesy of General Motors Corp.

Fig. 3: Keyless Entry Wiring Diagram (Eldorado & Seville – 1 Of 4)

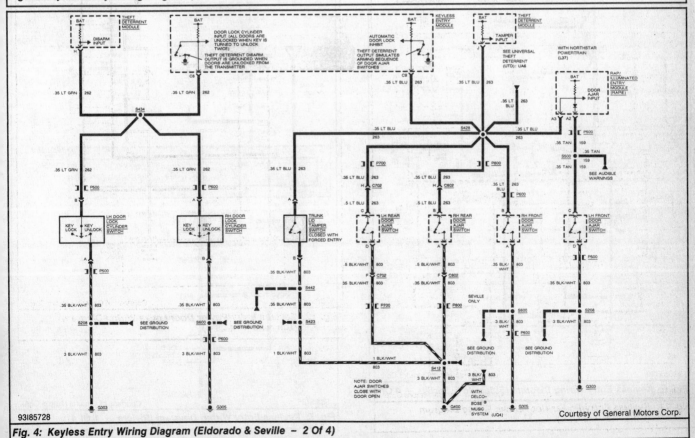

93I85728

Courtesy of General Motors Corp.

Fig. 4: Keyless Entry Wiring Diagram (Eldorado & Seville – 2 Of 4)

GM
4-192

1993 ACCESSORIES & EQUIPMENT
Remote Keyless Entry System – "E" & "K" Bodies (Cont.)

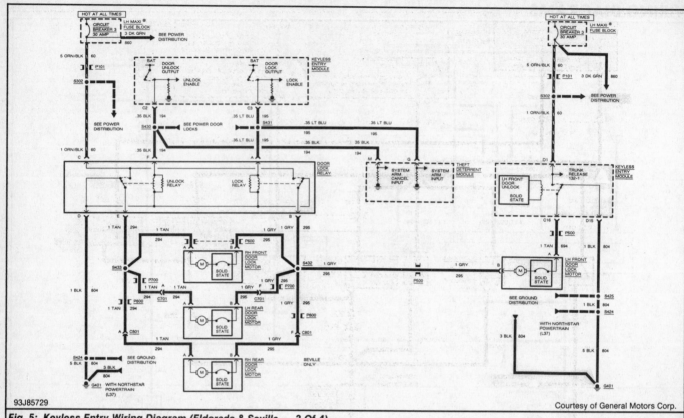

Fig. 5: Keyless Entry Wiring Diagram (Eldorado & Seville – 3 Of 4)

93J85729

Courtesy of General Motors Corp.

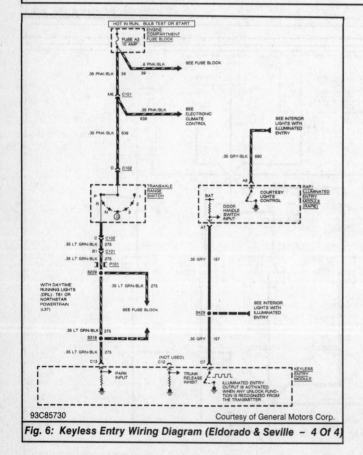

Fig. 6: Keyless Entry Wiring Diagram (Eldorado & Seville – 4 Of 4)

93C85730

Courtesy of General Motors Corp.

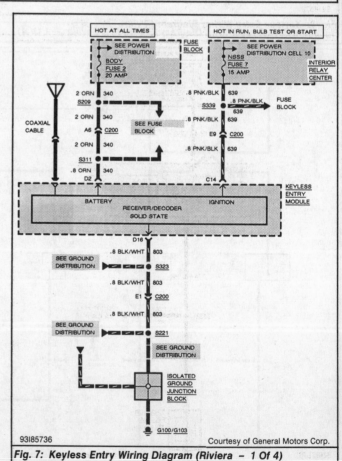

93I85736

Courtesy of General Motors Corp.

Fig. 7: Keyless Entry Wiring Diagram (Riviera – 1 Of 4)

1993 ACCESSORIES & EQUIPMENT
Remote Keyless Entry System – "E" & "K" Bodies (Cont.)

GM
4-193

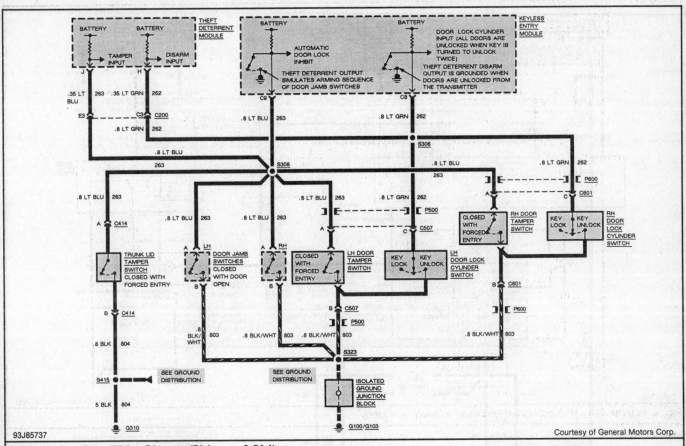

93J85737

Courtesy of General Motors Corp.

Fig. 8: Keyless Entry Wiring Diagram (Riviera – 2 Of 4)

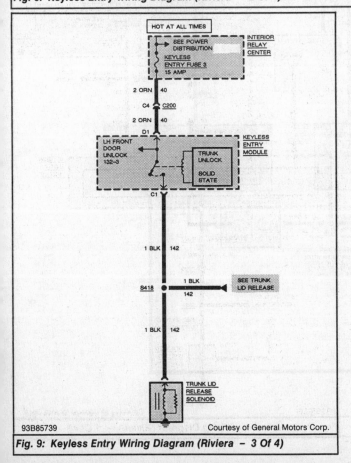

93B85739

Courtesy of General Motors Corp.

Fig. 9: Keyless Entry Wiring Diagram (Riviera – 3 Of 4)

GM
4-194

1993 ACCESSORIES & EQUIPMENT
Remote Keyless Entry System – "E" & "K" Bodies (Cont.)

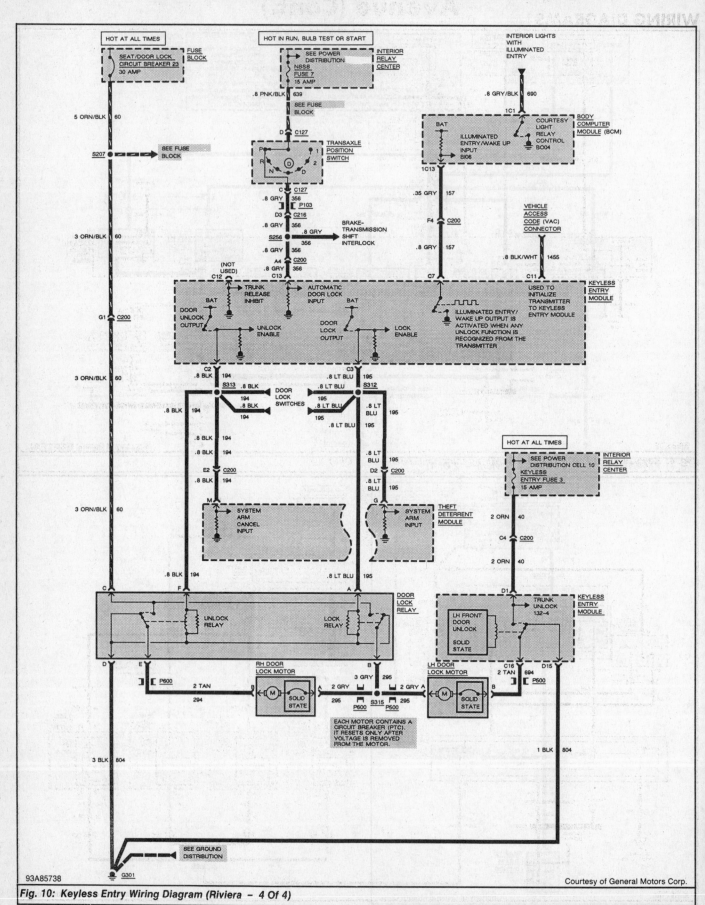

1993 ACCESSORIES & EQUIPMENT
Remote Keyless Entry System – LeSabre & Park Avenue (Cont.)

GM
4-195

WIRING DIAGRAMS

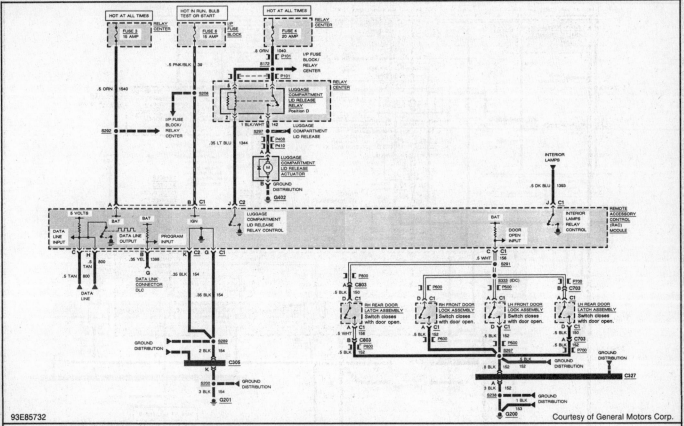

93E85732

Courtesy of General Motors Corp.

Fig. 4: Keyless Entry/Power Door Locks Wiring Diagram (LeSabre – 1 Of 2)

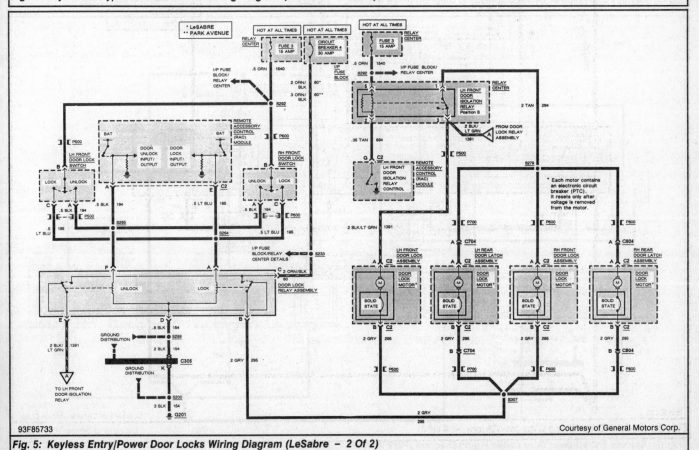

93F85733

Courtesy of General Motors Corp.

Fig. 5: Keyless Entry/Power Door Locks Wiring Diagram (LeSabre – 2 Of 2)

GM
4-196

1993 ACCESSORIES & EQUIPMENT
Remote Keyless Entry System – LeSabre & Park Avenue (Cont.)

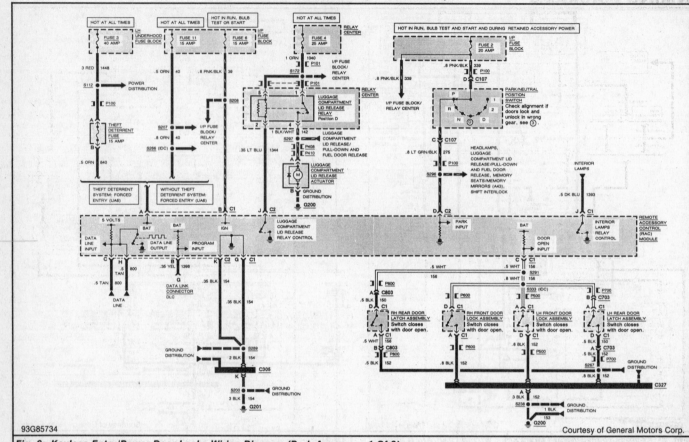

93G85734

Courtesy of General Motors Corp.

Fig. 6: Keyless Entry/Power Door Locks Wiring Diagram (Park Avenue – 1 Of 2)

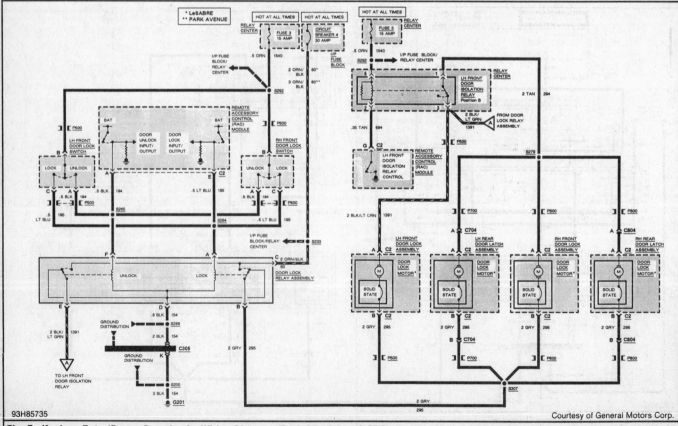

93H85735

Courtesy of General Motors Corp.

Fig. 7: Keyless Entry/Power Door Locks Wiring Diagram (Park Avenue – 2 Of 2)

WIRING DIAGRAMS

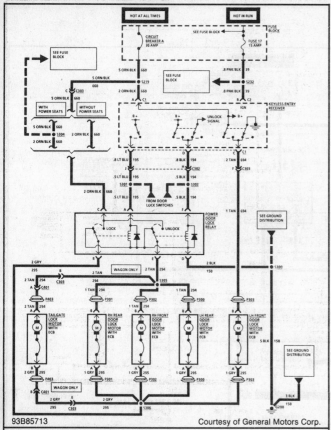

Fig. 15: Keyless Entry Wiring Diagram (Roadmaster – 1 Of 3)

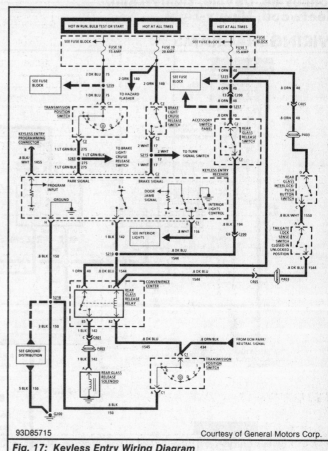

Fig. 17: Keyless Entry Wiring Diagram (Roadmaster – 3 Of 3)

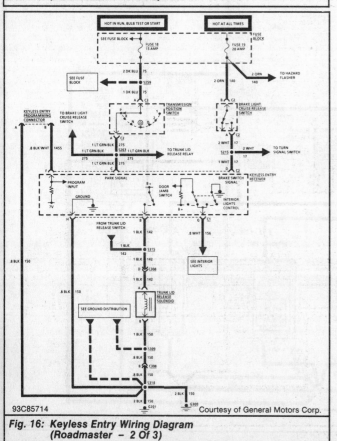

Fig. 16: Keyless Entry Wiring Diagram (Roadmaster – 2 Of 3)

GM
4-198

1993 ACCESSORIES & EQUIPMENT
Remote Keyless Entry System – All Others (Cont.)

**Bonneville, DeVille, Eighty-Eight,
Fleetwood, Ninety-Eight**

WIRING DIAGRAMS

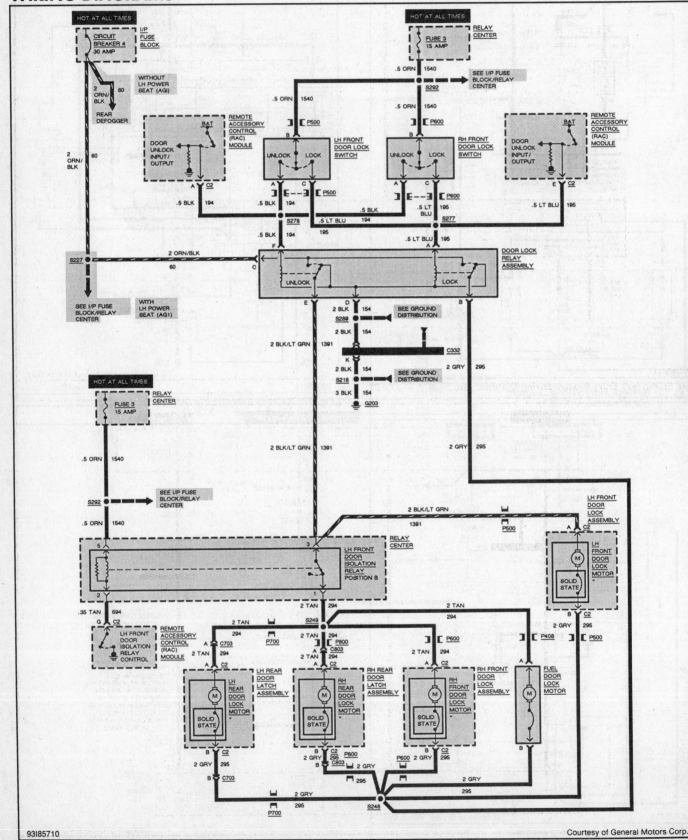

93I85710

Courtesy of General Motors Corp.

Fig. 4: Keyless Entry System Wiring Diagram (Bonneville – 1 Of 2)

1993 ACCESSORIES & EQUIPMENT
Remote Keyless Entry System — All Others (Cont.)

GM
4-199

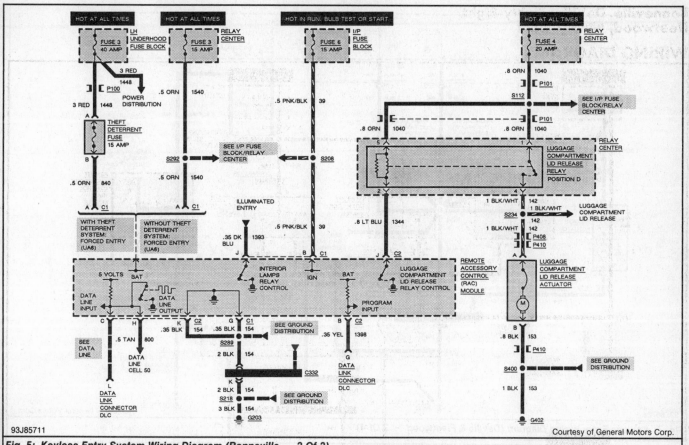

93J85711

Courtesy of General Motors Corp.

Fig. 5: Keyless Entry System Wiring Diagram (Bonneville – 2 Of 2)

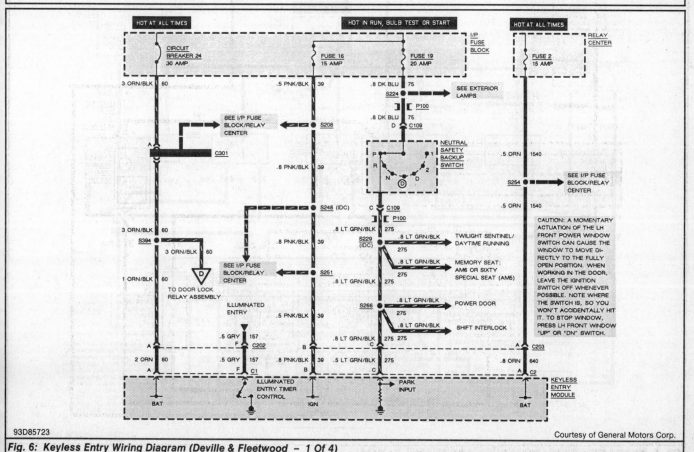

93D85723

Courtesy of General Motors Corp.

Fig. 6: Keyless Entry Wiring Diagram (Deville & Fleetwood – 1 Of 4)

GM
4-200

1993 ACCESSORIES & EQUIPMENT
Remote Keyless Entry System — All Others (Cont.)

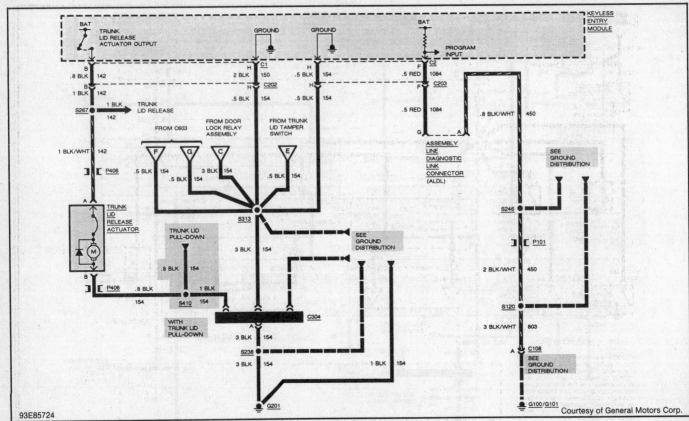

Fig. 7: Keyless Entry Wiring Diagram (Deville & Fleetwood – 2 Of 4)

93E85724

Courtesy of General Motors Corp.

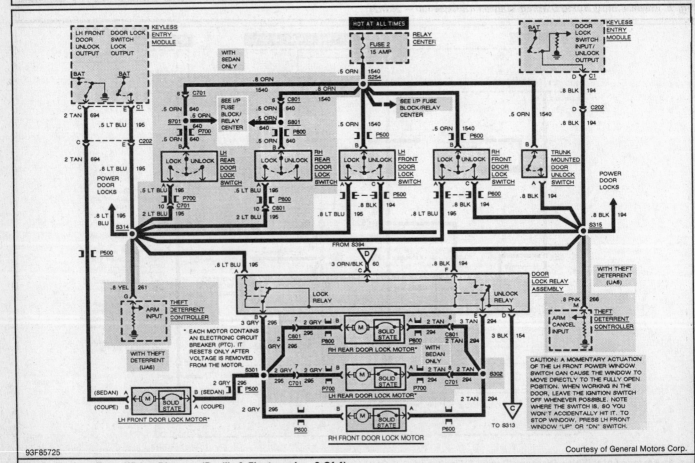

Fig. 8: Keyless Entry Wiring Diagram (Deville & Fleetwood – 3 Of 4)

93F85725

Courtesy of General Motors Corp.

1993 ACCESSORIES & EQUIPMENT
Remote Keyless Entry System – All Others (Cont.)

GM
4-201

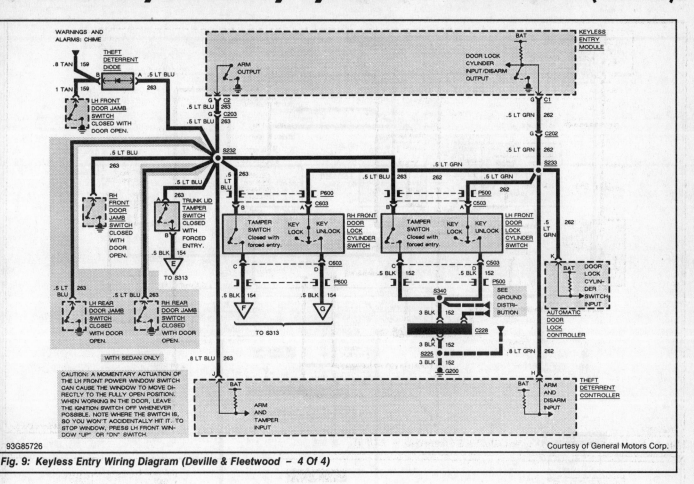

Fig. 9: Keyless Entry Wiring Diagram (Deville & Fleetwood – 4 Of 4)

93G85726

Courtesy of General Motors Corp.

GM
4-202

1993 ACCESSORIES & EQUIPMENT
Remote Keyless Entry System — All Others (Cont.)

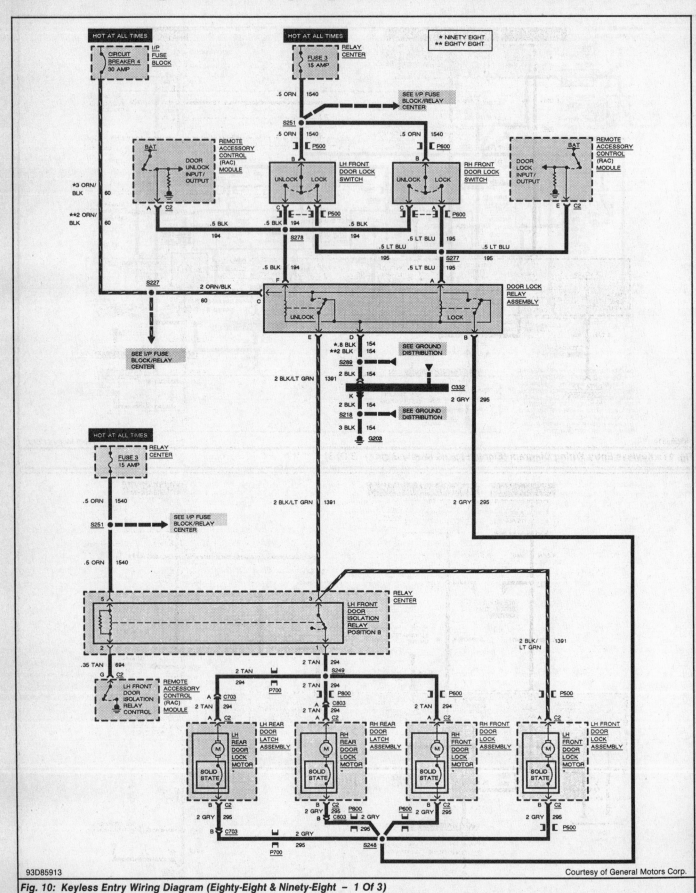

Fig. 10: Keyless Entry Wiring Diagram (Eighty-Eight & Ninety-Eight – 1 Of 3)

1993 ACCESSORIES & EQUIPMENT
Remote Keyless Entry System – All Others (Cont.)

GM
4-203

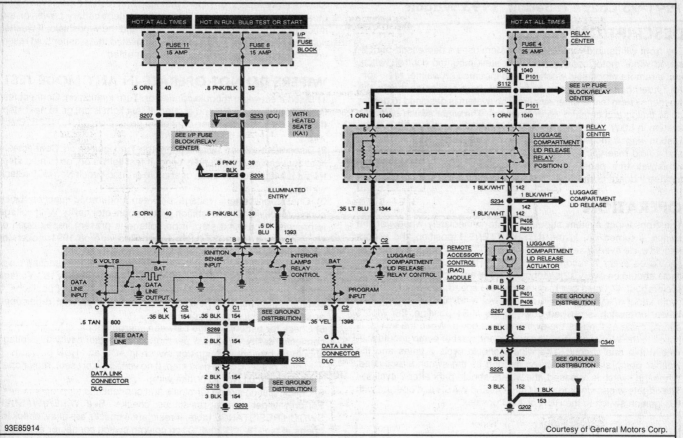

93E85914   Courtesy of General Motors Corp.

Fig. 11: Keyless Entry Wiring Diagram (Eighty-Eight & Ninety-Eight – 2 Of 3)

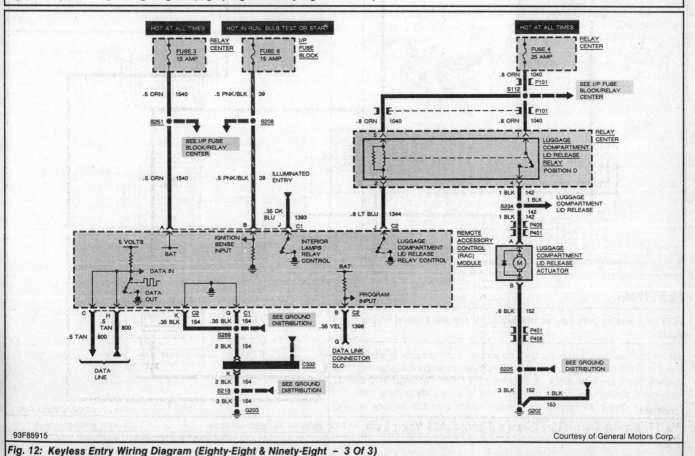

93F85915   Courtesy of General Motors Corp.

Fig. 12: Keyless Entry Wiring Diagram (Eighty-Eight & Ninety-Eight – 3 Of 3)

1991-93 Coupe & Sedan, 1993 Wagon

DESCRIPTION

The front windshield wiper/washer system uses a depressed park 2-speed wiper motor/control module, a stalk mounted control switch, and a remote windshield washer pump mounted on washer reservoir. An underhood junction box in the right front fender connects the washer system to the wiper system. The system is designed to deliver pulse timing and demand wash functions. The wiper switch operates system in LOW, HIGH, INTERMITTENT, MIST and WASHER modes. Station wagon models use a liftgate mounted wiper/washer module and a fluid reservoir with an electric pump mounted in the right rear wheelwell trim panel. Operation is controlled by a rotary switch located inboard of the stalk mounted windshield wiper switch.

OPERATION

The front wiper system should activate immediately whenever the switch is turned on. In the INTERMITTENT 1 position, the wipers should cycle every 2 seconds. In INTERMITTENT 2 position, the cycle should be every 7 seconds, and in INTERMITTENT 3 position, the cycle should be every 12 seconds. In LOW speed, the wipers should cycle about 47 times per minute. In HIGH speed, the wipers should cycle about 67 cycles per minute on a wet windshield.

When the switch is pushed down to the MIST position, the wipers should cycle as long as the switch is held down. When the switch is pulled to the WASH position, the wipers and washer pump should activate within one second. The wipers should cycle 2 times and the washer pump should remain on as long as the switch is activated. When the switch is released, the wipers should park after 2 cycles. The liftgate wiper functions are OFF, ON and WASH and operate with the ignition switch in the RUN or ACC position.

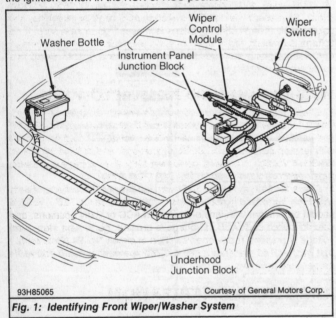

Fig. 1: Identifying Front Wiper/Washer System

93H85065   Courtesy of General Motors Corp.

TESTING

NOTE: No testing procedures are available for the liftgate wiper/washer.

Before performing any specific tests on a faulty wiper/washer system, check that the following fuses are okay. A 30-amp maxifuse is located in underhood junction block. A 25-amp mini fuse is located in the instrument panel fuse block. If either fuse is blown, determine the cause and repair as necessary. Always check that the battery is charged and terminals are clean and connected properly. Check that wiring connectors are securely connected and not corroded or broken.

Slow or jerky wipers, or wipers that stop and restart after several minutes are usually caused by low or intermittent battery power or too much friction between the wiper blades and the windshield. If washer fluid does not appear when WASH is activated, the washer fluid reservoir is empty or the fluid hose is disconnected.

WIPERS DO NOT OPERATE IN ANY MODE TEST

1) Disconnect wiper module connector. Turn ignition on. Connect test light between cavity "B" and ground. If test light is on, go to next step. If light is off, check for open or short in ground circuit No. 153R (Black wire).

2) Disconnect column switch connector. Turn ignition on. Connect test light between cavity "A" and ground. If test light is on, go to next step. If light is off, check for open or short in ground circuit No. 153F (Black wire).

3) Check for battery voltage between underhood junction block connector cavity "C" and ignition switch connector cavity "A". If voltage is present, go to next step. If no voltage is present, repair open or short in circuit No. 1932 (Light Green/Red wire on 1991 models or Red/White wire on 1992-93 models).

4) Check for battery voltage between instrument panel junction block connector cavity C8 and ignition switch connector cavity "B". Voltage should be present with ignition switch in ACC and RUN positions. If voltage is present, go to next step. If no voltage is present, repair open or short in circuit No. 4 (Brown wire).

5) Check for battery voltage between instrument panel junction block connector cavity "A7" and wiper module connector cavity "E". Voltage should be present with ignition switch in ACC and RUN positions. If voltage is present, go to next step. If no voltage is present, repair open or short in circuit No. 93 (White wire).

6) Check ignition switch terminals and connections for proper mating. Perform wiper switch resistance checks. See WIPER/WASHER SWITCH RESISTANCE table. If resistance checks are okay, check for opens at pins "A", "B" and "C" on column switch connector and repair as needed. If wiper switch checks are okay, go to next step. If wiper switch does not check okay, install new wiper switch and verify that wipers operate.

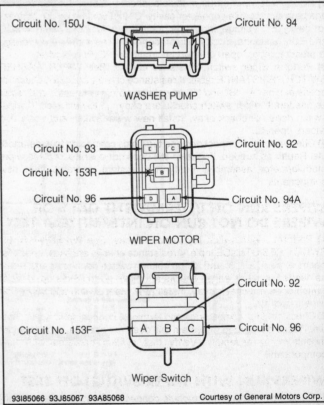

WASHER PUMP

WIPER MOTOR

Wiper Switch

93185066 93J85067 93A85068   Courtesy of General Motors Corp.

Fig. 2: Identifying Wiper/Washer System Connector Terminals

7) Check circuits, connections and terminals connected to wiper module. Repair as needed. If system still does not operate, replace wiper module/motor assembly. Verify that system operates with new components.

WIPER/WASHER SWITCH RESISTANCE

Switch Position	[1] Ohms
Between Terminals A & C	
OFF	0
LOW	300
HIGH	300
MIST	300
INT.1	2090
INT.2	990
INT.3	560
WASH	130
Between Terminals A & B	
HIGH	Less Than 1
All Others	Infinity

[1] – Plus or minus 10%.

WIPERS RUN AT HIGH SPEED ONLY TEST

1) Disconnect wiper motor module connector. Check for battery voltage between module connector cavity "D" and column switch connector cavity "C". Voltage should be present with ignition switch in ACC and RUN positions. If voltage is present, go to next step. If no voltage is present, repair open or short in circuit No. 96 (Brown wire).

2) Check ignition switch terminals and connections for proper mating. Check circuits, connections and terminals connected to wiper module. Repair as needed. If system still does not operate, replace wiper module/motor assembly. Verify that system operates with new components.

WIPERS RUN AT LOW SPEED ONLY TEST

1) Disconnect column switch connector. Turn ignition on. Connect test light between cavity "A" and ground. If test light is on, go to next step. If light is off, check for open or short in ground circuit No. 153F (Black wire). Reconnect connectors.

2) Disconnect wiper motor module connector. Check for battery voltage between module connector cavity "C" and column switch connector cavity "B". Voltage should be present with ignition switch in ACC and RUN positions. If voltage is present, go to next step. If no voltage is present, repair open or short in circuit No. 92 (Purple wire).

3) Perform wiper switch resistance checks. See WIPER/WASHER SWITCH RESISTANCE table. If resistance checks are okay, check for opens at pins "A", "B" and "C" on column switch connector and repair as needed. If wiper switch checks are okay, go to next step. If wiper switch does not check okay, install new wiper switch and verify that wipers operate.

4) Check circuits, connections and terminals connected to wiper module. Repair as needed. If system still does not operate, replace wiper module/motor assembly. Verify that system operates with new components.

WIPERS RUN ON INTERMITTENT ONLY OR WIPERS DO NOT RUN ON INTERMITTENT TEST

1) Perform wiper switch resistance checks. See WIPER/WASHER SWITCH RESISTANCE table. If resistance checks are okay, check for opens at pins "A", "B" and "C" on column switch connector and repair as needed. If wiper switch checks are okay, go to next step. If wiper switch does not check okay, install new wiper switch and verify that wipers operate.

2) Check circuits, connections and terminals connected to wiper module. Repair as needed. If system still does not operate, replace wiper module/motor assembly. Verify that system operates with new components.

WIPERS RUN WITH WIPER SWITCH OFF TEST

1) Disconnect wiper motor module connector. Check for battery voltage between module connector cavity "C" and column switch connector cavity "B". Voltage should be present with ignition switch in ACC and RUN positions. If voltage is present, go to next step. If no voltage is present, repair open or short in circuit No. 92 (Purple wire).

2) Check for battery voltage between module connector cavity "D" and column switch connector cavity "C". Voltage should be present with ignition switch in ACC and RUN positions. If voltage is present, go to next step. If no voltage is present, repair open or short in circuit No. 96 (Brown wire).

3) Perform wiper switch resistance checks. See WIPER/WASHER SWITCH RESISTANCE table. If resistance checks are okay, check for opens at pins "A", "B" and "C" on column switch connector and repair as needed. If problem is still not corrected, install new wiper switch and verify that wipers operate normally.

EXCESSIVE WIPER MOTOR NOISE TEST

Check that wiper module/motor mounting bolts are not overtightened, no more than 89 INCH lbs. (10 N.m). This will cause excessive friction on wiper blades. If okay, check circuits, connections and terminals connected to wiper module. Repair as needed. If noise still exists, replace wiper module/motor assembly. Verify that system operates quietly with new components.

WASHER PUMP DOES NOT OPERATE TEST

1) Connect test light between pump connector cavity "B" and ground. If test light is on, go to next step. If light is off, check for open or short in ground circuit No. 150J (Black wire).

2) Check for battery voltage between wiper module connector cavity "A" and junction block connector cavity "C8". Voltage should be present with ignition switch in ACC or RUN positions, and column switch on WASH. If voltage is present, go to next step. If no voltage is present, repair open or short in circuit No. 94A (Pink wire).

3) Check for battery voltage between washer pump connector cavity "A" (Pink wire) and junction block connector cavity "E6". Voltage should be present with ignition switch in ACC or RUN positions, and column switch on WASH. If voltage is present, go to next step. If no voltage is present, repair open or short in circuit No. 94 (Pink wire).

4) If washer pump still does not operate, replace washer pump and verify proper operation.

WASHER PUMP FLUID PRESSURE LOW TEST

1) Check that washer fluid hose is not kinked, clogged or leaking. Check for battery voltage between wiper module connector cavity "A" and junction block connector cavity "C8". Voltage should be present with ignition switch in ACC or RUN positions, and column switch on WASH. If voltage is present, go to next step. If no voltage is present, repair open or short in circuit No. 94A (Pink wire).

2) Check for battery voltage between washer pump connector cavity "A" (Pink wire) and junction block connector cavity "E6". Voltage should be present with ignition switch in ACC or RUN positions, and column switch on WASH. If voltage is present, go to next step. If no voltage is present, repair open or short in circuit No. 94 (Pink wire).

3) If washer fluid pressure is still low, replace washer pump and verify proper fluid pressure.

REMOVAL & INSTALLATION

CAUTION: When battery is disconnected, vehicle computer and memory systems may lose memory data. Driveability problems may exist until computer systems have completed a relearn cycle. See COMPUTER RELEARN PROCEDURES article in GENERAL INFORMATION before disconnecting battery.

FRONT WIPER MODULE/MOTOR

Removal – 1) Remove wiper arm finish cap and fastener. Lift wiper blade away from windshield and remove arm from pivot. Remove cowl trim fasteners at windshield edge of panel. Open hood and remove remaining cowl fasteners, then remove cowl trim panel.

2) Disconnect windshield washer hose (if equipped). Remove instrument panel top cover screw caps and screws. Lift top panel at rear edge to disengage clips and slide panel out of clips at windshield.

Remove screws and unsnap windshield defroster nozzle from mode valve assembly.

3) Remove defroster nozzle by rotating front of nozzle up and away from windshield. This will expose wiper module fasteners. Remove module fasteners. Partially remove module/motor and disconnect wiring. Remove module/motor. Remove crank arm nut and disconnect crank arm from motor shaft. Remove motor attaching screws and remove motor from module.

NOTE: *If replacing wiper module on 1991 and early 1992 vehicles, center fastening stud nuts must be removed from under instrument panel cover. To install a new module with studs already attached, the 9-mm holes in center cowl must be enlarged to 15 mm. If a new wiper motor is installed, remove wiper motor crank arm from new motor and discard.*

Installation – 1) Connect wiring to new motor and turn switch on. Turn off switch. This will place motor in PARK position. Place wiper motor onto control module. Position crank arm at 9 o'clock position and install on wiper motor shaft. Apply Loctite to crank arm attaching nut and tighten to 21 ft. lbs. (28 N.m)

2) Partially install wiper module in vehicle. Connect wiring to motor and module. Install motor/module assembly. Tighten to 89 INCH lbs. (10 N.m). Turn switch on momentarily, then turn off. Wiper arm should be in PARK position with crank arm at 9 o'clock position. Connect washer fluid hose (if equipped). Install cowl trim panel. Install wiper arms.

3) Rotate defroster nozzle into mode valve assembly and install screws. Ensure nozzle is attached on both sides of HVAC module. Install upper trim panel into clips at windshield. Install trim panel screws and screw caps. Test wiper operation.

FRONT WASHER PUMP MOTOR/RESERVOIR

Removal & Installation – Disconnect harness from pump motor. Remove reservoir attaching screws. Lift reservoir and release lower attaching tab. Disconnect fluid hose. Remove reservoir. Empty fluid from reservoir and remove pump from reservoir. To install, reverse removal procedure.

LIFTGATE WIPER ARM & MODULE

Removal & Installation – 1) Remove wiper arm cap and cap nut. Lift wiper arm away from glass and remove. Remove rear wiper pivot bushing. Raise liftgate. Remove wedge blocks from liftgate sides. Remove lower liftgate trim panel fasteners by pushing in center pin until it clicks, then remove fasteners.

2) Insert a screwdriver into hole in liftgate lower trim panel near rear wiper pivot, so that screwdriver sits on top of pivot. Lift up on screwdriver and disengage trim panel upper clips. Remove trim panel. Remove module attaching screws. Disconnect washer hose and connector. Remove module. To install, reverse removal procedure.

LIFTGATE WASHER PUMP/RESERVOIR

Removal & Installation – Remove rear quarter inner trim panel. Remove reservoir fasteners. Move reservoir away from body and disconnect connector. Disconnect fluid hose from pump. Drain contents of reservoir and remove pump from reservoir. To install, reverse removal procedure.

WIRING DIAGRAMS

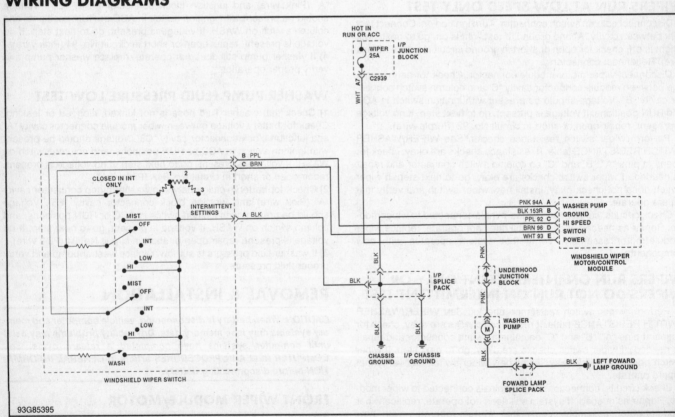

Fig. 3: Front Wiper/Washer Wiring Diagram (Saturn)

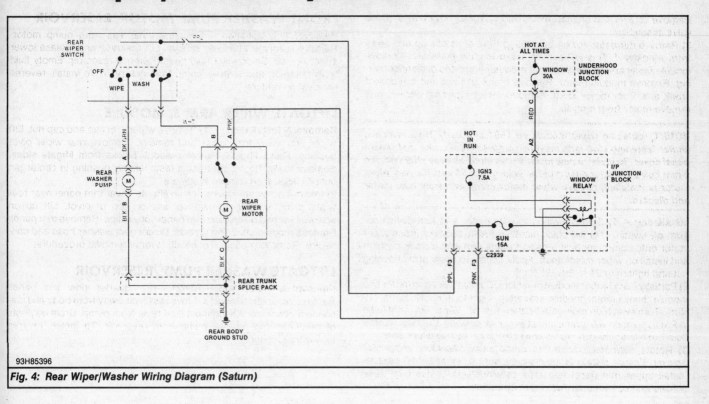

93H85396

Fig. 4: Rear Wiper/Washer Wiring Diagram (Saturn)